BIOLOGY
HOW
LIFE
WORKS
Preliminary Edition

James Morris
BRANDEIS UNIVERSITY

Daniel Hartl
HARVARD UNIVERSITY

Andrew Knoll
HARVARD UNIVERSITY

Robert Lue
HARVARD UNIVERSITY

**ANDREW BERRY, ANDREW BIEWENER,
BRIAN FARRELL, N. MICHELE HOLBROOK,
NAOMI PIERCE, ALAIN VIEL**
HARVARD UNIVERSITY

W. H.
FREEMAN

macmillan
HIGHER EDUCATION

PUBLISHER Susan Winslow
LEAD DEVELOPMENTAL EDITOR Lisa Samols
SENIOR DEVELOPMENTAL EDITOR Susan Moran
DEVELOPMENTAL EDITOR Erica Pantages Frost
EDITORIAL ASSISTANTS Yassamine Ebadat, Jane Taylor
REVIEW COORDINATOR Donna Brodman
PROJECT MANAGER Karen Misler
ART MANAGER Carolyn Deacy
EDITORIAL RESEARCH AND DEVELOPMENT Shannon Howard
MARKET DEVELOPMENT MANAGER Lindsey Veautour
ASSOCIATE DIRECTOR OF MARKETING Debbie Clare
ASSESSMENT TEAM LEADERS Melissa Michael, Mark Hens, John Merrill, Randall Phillis, Debra Pires

ART AND MEDIA DIRECTOR Robert Lue, Harvard
MANAGER OF DIGITAL DEVELOPMENT Amanda Dunning
SENIOR DEVELOPMENT EDITOR FOR TEACHING & LEARNING STRATEGIES Elaine Palucki
SENIOR MEDIA PRODUCER Keri Fowler
MEDIA PRODUCER Angelos Dosoulas
PROJECT EDITOR Robert Errera
MANUSCRIPT EDITOR Nancy Brooks
DESIGN MGMT. design
SENIOR ILLUSTRATION COORDINATOR Bill Page
ILLUSTRATIONS Imagineering
CREATIVE DIRECTOR Mark Mykytiuk, Imagineering
ART DIRECTOR Diana Blume
LAYOUT ARTIST Tom Carling, Carling Design Inc.
PHOTO EDITOR Christine Beuse
PHOTO RESEARCHER Jacquelin Wong
PRODUCTION MANAGER Paul Rohloff
COMPOSITION MPS Ltd.
PRINTING AND BINDING Quad Graphics–Versailles

Library of Congress Control Number: 2012940179
ISBN-13: 978-1-4641-2193-7
ISBN-10: 1-4641-2193-1

Printed in the United States of America

Second printing

Macmillan
W. H. Freeman and Company
41 Madison Avenue
New York, NY 10010
Houndmills, Basingstoke RG21 6XS, England
www.whfreeman.com

FROM THE AUTHORS

We wrote this book in recognition of recent and exciting changes in biology, education, and technology. There was a time when introductory biology could, over the course of a year, cover all of biology. That is no longer possible. The amount of scientific information has grown exponentially, necessitating that we, as teachers, rethink the role of introductory biology and the resources that support it. One goal remains paramount: to help students think like a biologist. To think like a biologist means to understand key concepts that span all of biology. It means being able to communicate in the shared language of biologists. It means recognizing the powerful ability of evolution to explain both the unity and diversity of life. It means thinking about how biological research can help solve some of the world's most pressing issues, from cancer to infectious diseases to biodiversity loss to climate change.

We have also noticed a change in the way biological problems are approached. We now have a "parts list" of genes and proteins for how life works, and many scientists today are focused on how the parts work together. As a result, we can no longer divide information into discrete, separate topics. To prepare students for science as it is currently practiced, we must integrate concepts from different areas of biology as well as other scientific disciplines.

What is particularly exciting for us as teachers is that the remarkable changes in the science of biology are paralleled by a new appreciation and understanding of how students learn. There is now good evidence that teaching students only by lecturing does not lead to mastery of the core concepts and scientific skills students need to become successful scientists and healthcare workers, or thoughtful, scientifically informed citizens. Students learn most effectively when they are actively involved in their learning and construct their own knowledge through a combination of lectures, problem-solving, hands-on experiences, and collaborative work.

At the same time, technology is transforming how and where students access information. The Internet provides all kinds of information at the click of a mouse. There is no need for a textbook to be a reference book. What, then, is the role of a textbook? A textbook needs to select from all of the information out there, help students see connections between seemingly disparate topics, and make the material engaging and relevant.

To support 21st-century student learning and instructor teaching, we feel that it is time to rethink what takes place both in and out of the introductory biology classroom, and to reimagine the resources that can best support these efforts. *Biology: How Life Works* provides an integrated set of resources to engage students, encourage critical thinking, help students make connections, and provide a framework for further studies.

—The How Life Works Author Team

BRIEF CONTENTS: Preliminary Edition

CONTENTS

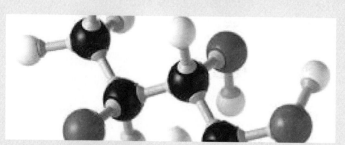

CHAPTER 3   **NUCLEIC ACIDS AND THE ENCODING OF BIOLOGICAL INFORMATION**   3-1

CHAPTER 4   **TRANSLATION AND PROTEIN STRUCTURE**   4-1

CHAPTER 5   ORGANIZING PRINCIPLES
Lipids, Membranes, and Cell Compartments   5-1

CHAPTER 6   MAKING LIFE WORK
Capturing and Using Energy   6-1

CHAPTER 7   **CELLULAR RESPIRATION**
Harvesting Energy from Carbohydrates and Other
Fuel Molecules   7-1

CHAPTER 8   **PHOTOSYNTHESIS**
Using Sunlight to Build Carbohydrates   8-1

CHAPTER 9 **CELL COMMUNICATION** 9-1

CHAPTER 10 **CELL FORM AND FUNCTION**
Cytoskeleton, Cellular Junctions, and
Extracellular Matrix 10-1

CHAPTER 17 **NON-MENDELIAN INHERITANCE**
Sex Chromosomes, Linkage, and Organelles 17-1

CHAPTER 18 **THE GENETIC AND ENVIRONMENTAL BASIS OF COMPLEX TRAITS** 18-1

CHAPTER 19 GENETIC AND EPIGENETIC REGULATION — 19-1

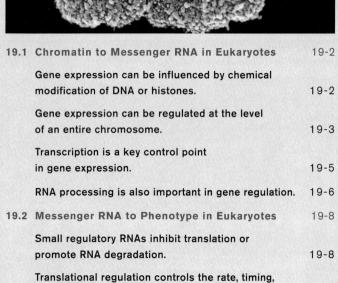

SCIENCEphotoLIBR

CHAPTER 20 GENES AND DEVELOPMENT — 20-1

CHAPTER 1

LIFE

Chemical, Cellular, and Evolutionary Foundations

Core Concepts

1.1 The scientific method is a deliberate way of asking and answering questions about the natural world.

1.2 Life works according to fundamental principles of chemistry and physics.

1.3 The fundamental unit of life is the cell.

1.4 Evolution explains the features that organisms share and those that set them apart.

1.5 Organisms interact with one another and with their physical environment, shaping ecological systems that sustain life.

1.6 In the 21st century, humans have become major agents in ecology and evolution.

Every day, remarkable things happen within and all around you. Strolling through a local market, you come across a bin full of crisp apples, pick one up, and take a bite. Underlying this unremarkable occurrence is a remarkable series of events. Your eyes sense the apple from a distance, and nerves carry that information to your brain, permitting identification. Biologists call this cognition, an area of biological study. Stimulated by the apple and recognizing it as ripe and tasty, your brain transmits impulses through nerves to your muscles. How we respond to external cues motivates behavior, another biological discipline. Grabbing the apple requires the coordinated activities of dozens of muscles that move your arm and hand to a precise spot. These movements are described by biomechanics, yet another area of biological research. And, as you bite down on the apple, glands in your mouth secrete saliva, starting to convert energy stored in the apple as sugar into energy that you will use to fuel your own activities. Physiology, like biomechanics, lies at the heart of biological function.

The study of cognition, behavior, biomechanics, and physiology are all ways of approaching **biology,** the science of how life works. **Biologists,** scientists who study life, have come to understand a great deal about these and other processes at levels that run from molecular mechanisms within the cell, through the integrated actions of many cells within an organ or body, to the interactions among different organisms in nature. We don't know everything about how life works—in fact, it seems as if every discovery raises new questions. But biology provides us with an organized way of understanding ourselves and the world around us.

Why study biology? The example of eating an apple, which we will follow through this chapter, was deliberately chosen because it is an everyday occurrence that we ordinarily wouldn't think twice about. The scope of modern biology, however, is vast, raising questions that can fire our imaginations, affect our health, and influence our future. How, for example, will our understanding of the human genome change the way that we fight cancer? How do bacteria in our digestive system help determine health and well-being? Will expected increases in the temperature and acidity of seawater doom coral reefs? Is there, or has there ever been, life on Mars? And, to echo the great storyteller Rudyard Kipling, why do leopards have spots, and tigers stripes?

We can describe six grand themes that connect and unite the many dimensions of life science, from molecules to the biosphere. These six themes are stated as Core Concepts and are introduced in the following sections. Throughout the book, these themes will be visited again and again. We view them as the keys to understanding the many details in subsequent chapters and relating them to one another. Our

FIG. 1.1   **A hummingbird visiting a flower.** This simple observation leads to questions: Why do hummingbirds pay so much attention to flowers? Why do they hover near red flowers?

Observation allows us to draw tentative explanations called hypotheses.

Observations allow us to ask focused questions about nature. Let's say you observe a hummingbird like the one pictured in **Fig. 1.1** hovering near a red flower, occasionally dipping its long beak into the bloom. What motivates this behavior? Is the bird feeding on some substance within the flower? Is it drawn to the flower by its vivid color? What benefit, if any, does the flower derive from this busy bird?

Observations such as these, and the questions they raise, allow us to propose tentative explanations, or **hypotheses.** We might, for example, hypothesize that the hummingbird is carrying pollen from one flower to the next, facilitating reproduction in the plant. Or we might hypothesize that nectar produced deep within the flower provides nutrition for the hummingbird—that the hummingbird's actions reflect the need to take in food. Both hypotheses provide a reasonable explanation of the behavior we observed, but they may or may not be correct. To find out, we have to test them.

hope is that by the time you finish this book, you will have an understanding of how life works, from the molecular machines inside cells and the metabolic pathways that cycle carbon through the biosphere to the process of evolution, which has shaped the living world that surrounds (and includes) us. You will, we hope, see the connections among these different ways of understanding life, and come away with a greater understanding of how scientists think about and ask questions about the natural world. How, in fact, do we know what we think we know about life? And we hope you will develop a basis for making informed decisions about your career and the actions you take as a citizen.

1.1 THE SCIENTIFIC METHOD

How do we go about trying to understand the vastness and complexity of nature? For most scientists, studies of the natural world involve the complementary processes of observation and experimentation. **Observation** is the act of viewing the world around us. **Experimentation** is a disciplined and controlled way of asking and answering questions about the world in an unbiased manner.

Piecing together individual observations to construct a working hypothesis is beautifully illustrated in Charles Darwin's classic book, *On the Origin of Species*, published in 1859. In his text, Darwin discussed a wide range of observations, from pigeon breeding to fossils and from embryology to the unusual animals and plants found on islands. Darwin noted the success of animal breeders in selecting specific individuals for reproduction and thereby generating new breeds for agriculture or show. He appreciated that selective breeding is successful only if specific features of the animals can be passed from one generation to the next by inheritance. Reading economic treatises by the English clergyman Thomas Malthus, he understood that limiting environmental resources could select among the variety of different individuals in populations in much the way that breeders do among cows or pigeons. Gathering all these seemingly disparate pieces of information, he argued that life has evolved over time by means of natural selection. Since its formulation, Darwin's initial hypothesis has been tested by experiments, many thousands of them. Our knowledge of many biological phenomena, ranging from biodiversity to the way the human brain is wired, depends on direct observation followed by careful inferences that lead to models of how things work.

A hypothesis makes predictions that can be tested by observation and experiments.

Not just any idea qualifies as a hypothesis. Two features set hypotheses apart from other ways of attacking problems. First, a good hypothesis makes **predictions** about observations not yet made or experiments not yet run. Second, because hypotheses make predictions, we can **test** them. That is, we can devise an experiment to see whether the predictions made by the hypothesis actually occur, or we can go into the field to try to make further observations predicted by the hypothesis. A hypothesis, then, is a statement about nature that can be tested by experiments or by new observations. Hypotheses are testable because even as they suggest an explanation for observations made previously, they make predictions about observations yet to be made.

Returning to the hummingbird and flower, we can test the hypothesis that the bird is transporting pollen from one flower to the next, enabling the plant to reproduce. Observation provides one type of test: If we catch and examine the bird just after it visits a flower, do we find pollen stuck to its beak or feathers? If so, our hypothesis survives the test. Note, however, that we haven't proved the case. Pollen might be stuck on the bird for a different reason—perhaps it provides food for the hummingbird. However, if the birds *didn't* carry pollen from flower to flower, we would reject the hypothesis that they facilitate pollination. In other words, a single observation or experiment can lead us to reject a hypothesis, or it can support the hypothesis, but it cannot prove that a hypothesis is correct. To move forward, then, we might make a second set of observations. Does pollen that adheres to the hummingbird rub off when the bird visits a second flower of the same species? If so, we have stronger support for our hypothesis.

We might also use observations to test a more general hypothesis about birds and flowers. Does red color generally attract birds and so facilitate pollination in a wide range of flowers? To answer this question, we might catalog the pollination of many red flowers and ask whether they are pollinated mainly by birds. Or we might go the opposite direction and catalog the flowers visited by many different birds—are they more likely to be red than chance alone might predict?

Finally, we can test the hypothesis that the birds visit the flowers primarily to obtain food, spreading pollen as a side effect of their feeding behavior. We can measure the amount of nectar in the flower before and after the bird visits and calculate how much energy has been assimilated by the bird during its visit. Continued observations over the course of the day will tell us whether the birds gain the nutrition they need by eating nectar, and whether the birds have other sources of food.

In many cases, experiments provide the most powerful tests of hypotheses because the scientist can ensure that conditions are tightly controlled. We might test whether hummingbirds facilitate pollination by surrounding the flowers with a mesh that allows small insects access to the plant but keeps hummingbirds away. Will the flowers be pollinated? Experimental or observational tests may support the initial hypothesis, in which case the hypothesis becomes less tentative and more certain, or the results might refute the hypothesis, in which case the scientist may discard it for another explanation or amend it to account for the new information.

→ **Quick Check 1** Mice that live in sand dunes commonly have light tan fur. Develop a hypothesis to explain this coloration. How can you test your hypothesis?

Using observations to generate a hypothesis and then making predictions based on that hypothesis that can be tested experimentally are the first two steps in the **scientific method,** which is outlined in **Fig. 1.2.** The scientific method is a deliberate and careful way of asking questions about the unknown. We make observations, collect field or laboratory samples, and design and carry out experiments to make sense of things we initially do not understand. The scientific method has proved to be spectacularly successful in helping us to understand the world around us.

FIG. 1.2   The scientific method.

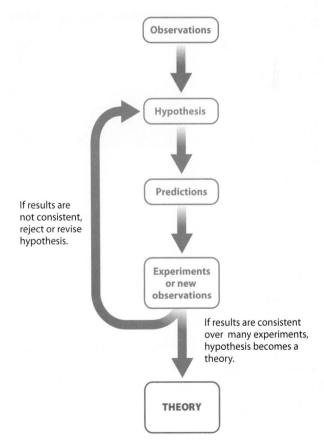

FIG. 1.3

What caused the extinction of the dinosaurs?

BACKGROUND Dinosaurs were diverse and ecologically important for nearly 150 million years, but became extinct about 65 million years ago.

OBSERVATION

Iridium, common in meteorites, was discovered in rock layers corresponding to the time of extinction.

HYPOTHESIS The impact of a large meteorite disrupted communities on land and in the sea, causing the extinction of the dinosaurs and many other species.

PREDICTIONS Independent evidence of a meteor impact should be found in rock layers corresponding to the time of the extinction, and be rare or absent in older and younger beds.

FURTHER OBSERVATIONS

Quartz crystals that form only at high temperature and pressure—conditions met by giant meteors as they crash into the Earth—occur abundantly in rock layers dated to the time of the extinction.

By 1990, geologists had located the "smoking gun"— a crater of just the right age and size in the Yucatán Peninsula of Mexico.

CONCLUSION A giant meteor struck the Earth 65 million years ago, causing the extinction of the dinosaurs and other species.

FOLLOW-UP WORK Researchers have documented additional episodes of mass extinction, but the event that eliminated the dinosaurs appears to be unique in its association with a meteorite impact.

SOURCE Alvarez, W. 1998. *T. rex and the Crater of Doom.* New York: Vintage Press.

To emphasize the power of the scientific method, we turn to a famous riddle drawn from the fossil record (**Fig. 1.3**). Since the nineteenth century, paleontologists have known that before mammals expanded to their current ecological importance, other large animals dominated Earth. Dinosaurs evolved about 210 million years ago and disappeared 65 million years ago, along with many other species of plants, animals, and microscopic organisms. In many cases, the skeletons and shells of these creatures were buried in sediment and became fossilized. Layers of sedimentary rock therefore record the history of Earth. Working in Italy, the American geologist Walter Alvarez collected samples from the precise point in the rock layers that corresponds to the time of the extinction 65 million years ago. Careful chemical analysis showed that rocks at this level are unusually enriched in the element iridium. Iridium is rare in most rocks on continents and the seafloor, but is relatively common in rocks that fall from space—that is, in meteorites. From these observations, Alvarez and his colleagues developed a remarkable hypothesis: 65 million years ago, a large (11-km diameter) meteor slammed into Earth, and in the resulting environmental havoc, dinosaurs and many other species became extinct. This hypothesis makes specific predictions, described in Fig. 1.3, which turned out to be supported by further observations. Thus, observational tests support the hypothesis that 150 million years of dinosaur evolution were undone in a moment.

→   **Quick Check 2** Devise a test for the hypothesis that cigarette smoke causes lung cancer.

General explanations of natural phenomena supported by many experiments and observations are called theories.

As already noted, a hypothesis may initially be tentative. Commonly, in fact, it will provide only one of several possible ways of explaining existing data. With repeated observation and experimentation, however, a good hypothesis gathers strength, and we have more and more confidence in it. When a number of related hypotheses survive repeated testing and so come to be accepted as good bases for explaining what we see in nature, scientists articulate a broader explanation that accounts for all of the hypotheses and the results of their tests. We call this statement a **theory,** a general explanation of the world supported by a large body of experiments and observations (see Fig. 1.2).

Note that scientists use the word "theory" in a very particular way. In general conversation, "theory" is often synonymous with "hypothesis," "idea," or "hunch"—"I've got a theory about that." But in a scientific context, the word "theory" has a specific meaning. Only if hypotheses have withstood testing to the point where they provide a general explanation for many observations and experimental results do scientists speak in terms of theories. Just as a good hypothesis makes testable predictions, a good theory both generates good hypotheses and predicts their outcomes. Thus, scientists talk about the theory of gravity—

a set of hypotheses you test every day by walking down the street or dropping a fork. Similarly, the theory of evolution is not one explanation among many for the unity and diversity of life. It is a set of hypotheses that has been tested for more than a century and shown to be an extraordinarily powerful means of explaining biological observations that range from amino acid sequences of proteins to the diversity of ants in a rain forest. In fact, as we discuss repeatedly in this book, evolution is the single most important theory in all of biology. It provides the most general and powerful explanation of how life works.

1.2 CHEMICAL AND PHYSICAL PRINCIPLES

We stated earlier that biology is the study of life. But what exactly *is* life? As simple as this question seems, it is frustratingly difficult to answer. We all recognize life when we see it, but coming up with a definition is harder than it first appears.

Living organisms are clearly different from nonliving things. But just how different is an organism from the rock shown in **Fig. 1.4**? On one level, the comparison is easy: The rock is much simpler than any living organism we can think of. It has far fewer

FIG. 1.4   **A climber scaling a rock.** Living organisms like this climber contain chemicals that are found in rocks, but only living organisms reproduce in a manner that allows for evolution over time.

components, and it is largely static, with no apparent response to environmental change on time scales that are readily tracked.

In contrast, even an organism as relatively simple as a bacterium contains many hundreds of different chemical compounds organized in a complex manner. The bacterium is also dynamic in that it changes continuously, especially in response to the environment. Organisms reproduce, which minerals do not. And organisms do something else that rocks and minerals don't: They evolve. Indeed, the molecular biologist Gerald Joyce has defined life as a chemical system capable of undergoing Darwinian evolution.

From these simple comparisons we can highlight four key characteristics of living organisms: (1) complexity, with precise spatial organization on several scales; (2) the ability to change in response to the environment; (3) the ability to reproduce; and (4) the capacity to evolve. Nevertheless, the living and nonliving worlds share an important attribute: Both are subject to the basic laws of chemistry and physics.

The living and nonliving worlds share the same chemical foundations and obey the same physical laws.

The chemical elements found in rocks and other nonliving things are no different from those found in living organisms. In other words, all the elements that make up living things can be found in the nonliving environment—there is nothing special about our chemical components when taken individually. That said, the *relative* abundances of elements in organisms differ greatly from those in the nonliving world. In the universe as a whole, hydrogen and helium make up more than 99% of known matter, while Earth's crust contains mostly oxygen and silicon, with significant amounts of aluminum, iron, and calcium (**Fig. 1.5a**). In organisms, by contrast, oxygen, carbon, and hydrogen are by far the most abundant elements (**Fig. 1.5b**). As discussed more fully in Chapter 2, carbon provides the backbone of life's chemistry. The particular properties of carbon make possible a wide diversity of molecules that, in turn, support a wide range of functions and activities within cells.

All living organisms are subject to the physical laws of the universe. Physics helps us to understand how animals move and why trees don't fall over; it explains how redwoods conduct water upward through their trunks and how oxygen gets into the cells that line your lungs. Indeed, two laws of thermodynamics, both of which describe how energy is transformed in any system, determine how living organisms are able to do work and maintain their spatial organization.

The **first law of thermodynamics** states that energy can neither be created nor destroyed; it can only be transformed from one form into another. In other words, the total energy in the universe is constant, but the form that energy takes can change. Living organisms are energy transformers. They acquire energy from the environment and transform it into a chemical form

FIG. 1.5 **Composition of (a) the Earth's crust and (b) the human body.** The Earth beneath our feet is made up of the same elements found in our feet, but in strikingly different proportions.

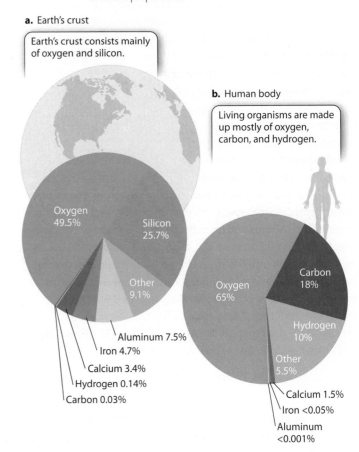

a. Earth's crust

Earth's crust consists mainly of oxygen and silicon.

b. Human body

Living organisms are made up mostly of oxygen, carbon, and hydrogen.

Oxygen 49.5%
Silicon 25.7%
Other 9.1%
Aluminum 7.5%
Iron 4.7%
Calcium 3.4%
Hydrogen 0.14%
Carbon 0.03%

Oxygen 65%
Carbon 18%
Hydrogen 10%
Other 5.5%
Calcium 1.5%
Iron <0.05%
Aluminum <0.001%

that cells can use. All organisms obtain energy from the sun or from chemical compounds. As they harness this energy, some is used to do work—such as moving, reproducing, and building cellular components—and the rest is dissipated as heat. The energy that is used to do work plus the heat that is generated is the total amount of energy, which is the same as the input energy (**Fig. 1.6**). In other words, the total amount of energy remains constant.

The **second law of thermodynamics** states that the degree of disorder in the universe tends to increase. To understand order and disorder in this context, think about a box full of marbles distributed more or less randomly; if you want to line up all the red ones or blue ones in a row, you have to do work. That is, you have to add energy. In this case, the addition of energy increases the order of the system, or, put another way, decreases its disorder. Physicists quantify the amount of disorder in a system, describing it as the **entropy** of the system.

Living organisms are highly organized. As with lining up marbles in a row, energy is needed to maintain this organization.

FIG. 1.6 **Energy transformation and the first law of thermodynamics.** The first law states that the total amount of energy in any system remains the same. Organisms transform energy from one form to another, but the total energy in any system is constant.

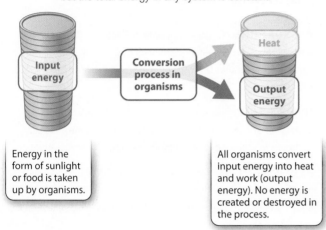

Energy in the form of sunlight or food is taken up by organisms.

All organisms convert input energy into heat and work (output energy). No energy is created or destroyed in the process.

FIG. 1.7 **Energy transformation and the second law of thermodynamics.** The second law states that the disorder in any system tends to increase. Entropy can decrease locally (inside a cell, for example) because the heat released increases disorder in the environment.

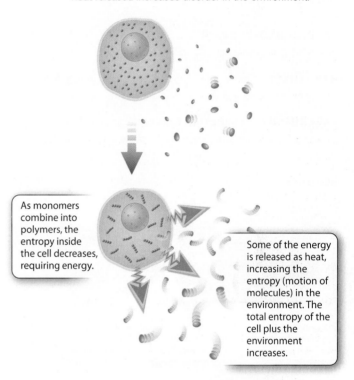

As monomers combine into polymers, the entropy inside the cell decreases, requiring energy.

Some of the energy is released as heat, increasing the entropy (motion of molecules) in the environment. The total entropy of the cell plus the environment increases.

Given the tendency toward greater disorder, the high level of organization of even a single cell would appear to violate the second law. But it does not. The key is that a cell is not an isolated system and therefore cannot be considered on its own; it exists in an environment. So we need to take into account the whole system, the cell plus the surrounding environment. As energy is harnessed by cells, only some is used to do work; the rest is dissipated as heat (Fig. 1.6). That is, conversions of energy from one form to another are never 100% efficient. Heat is a form of energy, so the total amount of energy is conserved, as dictated by the first law. In addition, heat corresponds to the motion of small molecules—the greater the heat, the greater the motion, and the greater the disorder. Therefore, the release of heat as organisms harness energy means that the total entropy for the combination of the cell and its surroundings increases, in keeping with the second law (**Fig. 1.7**).

The scientific method shows that living organisms come from other living organisms.

Life is made up of chemical components that also occur in the nonliving environment and obey the same laws of chemistry and physics. Can life spontaneously arise from these nonliving materials? We all know that living organisms come from other living organisms, but it is worth asking *how* we know this. Direct observation can be misleading here. For example, raw meat, if left out on a plate, will rot and become infested with maggots (fly larvae). It might seem as though the maggots appear spontaneously. In fact, the question of where maggots come from was a matter of vigorous debate for centuries, until application of the scientific method settled the issue. In the 1600s, the

Italian physician and naturalist Francesco Redi hypothesized that maggots (and hence flies) in rotting meat come only from other flies that laid their eggs in the meat.

To test his hypothesis, Redi set up an experiment in which he placed meat in three glass jars (**Fig. 1.8**). One jar was left open, a second was covered with gauze, and the third was sealed with a cap. The jars were left in a room with flies. Note that in this experiment, the three jars were subject to the same conditions—the only difference was the opening of the jar. The open jar allowed for the passage of flies and air; the jar with the gauze allowed for the passage of air but not flies; and the sealed jar did not allow air or flies to enter. Over time, Redi observed that maggots appeared only on the meat in the open jar. No maggots appeared in the other two jars, which did not allow access to the meat by flies. These observations supported Redi's hypothesis that flies come from other flies, and did not provide support for the alternative hypothesis that maggots and flies arise spontaneously from meat.

Redi demonstrated that living organisms come from other organisms, but some argued that his conclusion might apply only to larger organisms—microscopic life might be another matter entirely. It was not until the nineteenth century that the French

FIG. 1.8

Can living organisms arise from nonliving matter?

BACKGROUND Until the 1600s, many people believed that rotting meat spontaneously generates maggots (fly larvae).

HYPOTHESIS Francesco Redi hypothesized that maggots come only from flies and are not spontaneously generated.

EXPERIMENT Redi used three jars containing meat. One jar was left open; one was covered with gauze; one was sealed with a cap.

RESULTS

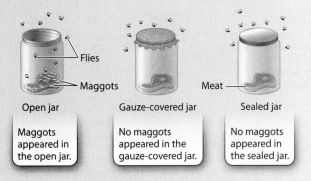

Flies

Maggots

Meat

Open jar	Gauze-covered jar	Sealed jar
Maggots appeared in the open jar.	No maggots appeared in the gauze-covered jar.	No maggots appeared in the sealed jar.

CONCLUSION The presence of maggots in the open jar and the absence of maggots in the gauze-covered and sealed jars supported the hypothesis that maggots come from flies, and allowed Redi to reject the hypothesis that maggots are spontaneously generated.

FOLLOW-UP WORK Redi's experiment argued against the idea of spontaneous generation for insects. However, it was unclear whether his results could be extended to microbes. Applying the scientific method, Louis Pasteur used a similar approach about 200 years later to investigate this question (see Fig. 1.9).

chemist and biologist Louis Pasteur tested the hypothesis that microorganisms can arise by spontaneous generation (**Fig. 1.9**).

Pasteur filled two glass flasks with heat-sterilized broth—one with a straight vertical neck and the other with a curved swan neck. As in Redi's experiments, there was only one variable, in this case the shape of the neck of the flask. The straight-neck flask allowed airborne dust particles carrying microbes to fall into the sterile broth, while the swan-neck flask prevented dust from getting inside. Over time, Pasteur observed that microbes grew in the broth inside the straight-neck flask but not in the

FIG. 1.9

Can microscopic life arise from nonliving matter?

BACKGROUND Educated people in Pasteur's time knew that microbes grow well in nutrient-rich liquids like broth. It was also known that boiling would sterilize the broth, killing the microbes.

HYPOTHESIS Pasteur hypothesized that if microbes were generated spontaneously from nonliving matter, they should reappear in sterilized broth without the addition of microbes.

EXPERIMENT Pasteur used two flasks, one with a straight neck and one with a swan neck. The straight-neck flask allowed dust particles with microbes to enter. The swan-neck flask did not.

swan-neck flask. From these observations, Pasteur rejected the hypothesis that microbes arise spontaneously from sterile broth. Instead, exposure to microbes carried on airborne dust particles is necessary for microbial growth.

Redi's and Pasteur's experiments demonstrated that living organisms come from other living organisms and are not generated spontaneously from chemical components. But this raises the question of how life arose in the first place. If life comes from life, where did the first living organisms come from? Although today all organisms are produced by parental organisms, early in Earth's history this was probably not the case. Scientists hypothesize that life initially emerged from chemical compounds about 4 billion years ago. That is, chemical systems capable of evolution arose from chemical reactions that took place on the early Earth. We'll return to the great question of the origin of life in Case 1: The First Cell and in Chapters 2 through 8.

1.3 THE CELL

To understand the universal features of life, we need to know what constitutes the minimal unit that can be considered alive. The **cell** is the simplest self-replicating entity that can exist as an independent unit of life. Every known living organism is either a single cell or an ensemble of many cells (**Fig. 1.10**). Most bacteria (like those in Pasteur's experiment), yeasts, and the tiny algae that float in oceans and ponds spend their lives as single cells. In contrast, multicellular plants and animals contain billions to trillions of cells that function in a coordinated fashion.

RESULTS

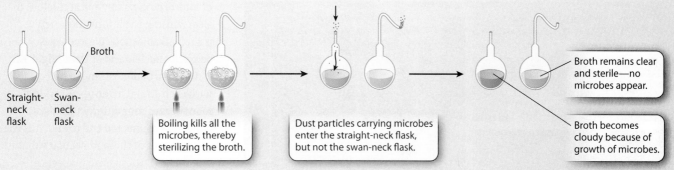

Straight-neck flask   Swan-neck flask   Broth

Boiling kills all the microbes, thereby sterilizing the broth.

Dust particles carrying microbes enter the straight-neck flask, but not the swan-neck flask.

Broth remains clear and sterile—no microbes appear.

Broth becomes cloudy because of growth of microbes.

CONCLUSION The presence of microbes in the straight-neck flask and the absence of microbes in the swan-neck flask supported the hypothesis that microbes come from other microbes and are not spontaneously generated.

DISCUSSION Redi's and Pasteur's research illustrate classic attributes of well-designed experiments. Multiple treatments are set up, and nearly all conditions are the same in them all—they are constant, and therefore cannot be the cause of different outcomes of the experiment. One key feature—the **variable**—is changed by the experimenter from one treatment to the next. This is a place to look for explanations of different experimental outcomes.

FIG. 1.10 Unicellular and multicellular organisms. All living organisms are made up of cells. (a) Bacteria; (b) brewer's yeast; (c) algae; (d) cheetahs; (e) humans

FIG. 1.11 **Cell diversity.** Cells vary greatly in size and shape. (a) Skin cells; (b) nerve cells; (c) ostrich egg.

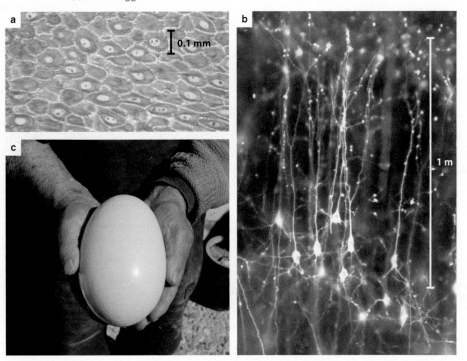

Most cells are tiny, their dimensions well below the threshold of detection by the naked eye **(Fig. 1.11)**. The cells that make up the layers of your skin (Fig. 1.11a) average about 100 microns or 0.1 mm in diameter, which means that about 10 would fit in a row across the period at the end of this sentence. Many bacteria are less than a micron long. Certain specialized cells, however, can be quite large. Some nerve cells in humans, like the ones pictured in Fig. 1.11b, extend slender projections known as axons for distances as great as a meter, and the cannonball-size egg of an ostrich in Fig. 1.11c is a single giant cell.

The types of cells just mentioned—bacteria, yeast, skin cells, nerve cells, and an egg—seem very different, but all are organized along broadly similar lines. In particular, they all contain a stable blueprint of information in molecular form; they have a discrete boundary that separates the interior of the cell from its external environment; and they have the ability to harness materials and energy from the environment.

Nucleic acids store and transmit information needed for growth, function, and reproduction.

The first essential feature of a cell is its ability to store and transmit information. To accomplish this, cells require a stable archive of information that encodes and helps determine their physical attributes. Just as the construction and maintenance of a house requires a blueprint that defines the walls, plumbing, and electrical wiring, organisms require an accessible and reliable archive of information that helps determine their structure and metabolic

activities. Another hallmark of life is the ability to reproduce. To reproduce, cells must be able to copy their archive of information rapidly and accurately. In all organisms, the information archive is a remarkable molecule known as deoxyribonucleic acid or **DNA** (**Fig. 1.12**).

DNA is a double-stranded helix, with each strand made up of varying sequences of four different kinds of molecules connected end to end. It is the arrangement of these molecular subunits that makes DNA special; in essence, they provide a four-letter alphabet that encodes cellular information. Notably, the information encoded in DNA directs the formation of **proteins,** the key structural and functional molecules that do the work of the cell. Virtually every aspect of the cell's existence—its internal architecture, its shape, its ability to move, and its various chemical reactions—depends on proteins.

How does the information stored in DNA direct the synthesis of proteins? First, existing proteins create a copy of the DNA's information in the form of a closely related molecule called ribonucleic acid, or **RNA.** The synthesis of RNA from a DNA template is called **transcription,** a term that describes the copying of information from one form into another. Specialized molecular structures within the cell then "read" the RNA molecule to determine what building blocks to use to create a protein. This process, called **translation,** converts information stored in the language of nucleic acids to information in the language of proteins.

The pathway from DNA to RNA (specifically to a form of RNA called messenger RNA, or mRNA) to protein is known as the **central dogma** of molecular biology (**Fig. 1.13**). The central dogma describes the basic flow of information in a cell and, while there are exceptions, it constitutes a fundamental principle in biology. As proteins are ultimately encoded by DNA, we can define specific stretches or segments of DNA according to the proteins that they encode. This is the simplest definition of a **gene:** the DNA sequence that corresponds to a specific protein product.

DNA has another remarkable feature. In addition to storing information, it is easily copied, or **replicated,** allowing genetic information to be passed from cell to cell or from one organism to its progeny. Each organism's DNA archive can be stably and reliably passed from generation to generation in large part because of its double-stranded helical structure. During replication, each strand of the double helix serves as a template for a new strand. Replication is necessarily precise and accurate because mistakes introduced into the cell's information archive

FIG. 1.12 **A molecule of DNA.** DNA is a double helix made up of varying sequences of four different subunits.

may be lethal to the cell. That said, errors in DNA can and do occur during the process of replication, and environmental insults can damage DNA. Such changes are known as **mutations;** they can spell death for the cell, or they can lead to the variations that underlie the diversity of life and the process of evolution.

→ **Quick Check 3** How does the central dogma help us to understand how mutations in DNA can result in disease?

Membranes define cells and spaces within cells.

The second essential feature of all cells is a **plasma membrane** that separates the living material within the cell from the nonliving environment around it (**Fig. 1.14**). This boundary between inside and outside does not mean that cells are closed systems independent of the environment. On the contrary, there is an active and dynamic interplay between cells and their surroundings that is mediated by the plasma membrane. All cells require

FIG. 1.13 **The central dogma of molecular biology, defining the flow of information in all living organisms from DNA to RNA to protein.**

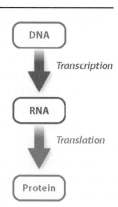

sustained contributions from their surroundings, both nutrients and the building blocks required to manufacture macromolecules. They also release waste products into the environment. As discussed more fully in Chapter 5, the plasma membrane controls the movement of materials into and out of the cell.

In addition to the plasma membrane, many cells have internal membranes that divide the cell into discrete compartments, each specialized for a particular function. A notable example is the **nucleus,** which houses the cell's DNA. Like the plasma membrane, the nuclear membrane selectively controls movement of molecules into and out of it. As a result, the nucleus occupies a discrete space within the cell, separate from the space outside of the nucleus, called the **cytoplasm.**

Not all cells have a nucleus. In fact, cells can be grouped into two broad classes depending on whether or not they have a nucleus. Cells without a nucleus are **prokaryotes,** and cells with a nucleus are **eukaryotes.**

The first cells were prokaryotes. They evolved about 4 billion years ago, and their descendants include familiar bacteria that are around today. They are found wherever life can persist. Some prokaryotes live in peaceful coexistence with humans, inhabiting our gut and aiding digestion. Others cause disease—salmonella, tuberculosis, and cholera are familiar examples. Their success depends in part on their small size, their ability to reproduce rapidly, and their ability to obtain energy and nutrients from diverse sources. Most prokaryotes live as single-celled organisms, but some have simple multicellular forms.

FIG. 1.14 **The plasma membrane.** The plasma membrane surrounds every cell and controls the exchange of material with the environment.

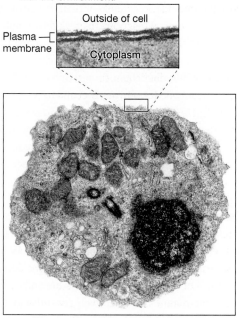

Scanning electron micrograph of a cell

Eukaryotes evolved much later, roughly 2 billion years ago, from one lineage among a diversity of prokaryotes that existed at the time. They include familiar groups such as animals, plants, and fungi, along with a wide diversity of single-celled microorganisms called protists. Eukaryotic organisms exist as single cells like yeast or as multicellular organisms like humans. In multicellular organisms, cells may specialize to perform different functions. For example, in humans, muscle cells contract; red blood cells carry oxygen to tissues; and skin cells provide an external barrier.

The terms "prokaryotes" and "eukaryotes" are useful in drawing attention to a fundamental distinction between these two groups of cells. However, today, biologists recognize three domains of life—**Bacteria, Archaea,** and **Eukarya** (Chapters 26 and 27). Bacteria and Archaea both lack a nucleus and are therefore prokaryotes, while Eukarya are eukaryotes. In spite of the similar cellular organization of Bacteria and Archaea, the Eukarya and Archaea are more closely related to each other than either is to Bacteria. Archaea are single-celled microorganisms, many of which flourish under seemingly hostile conditions, such as the hot springs of Yellowstone National Park.

Metabolism converts energy from the environment into a form that can be used by cells.

A third key feature of cells is the ability to harness energy from the environment. Let's go back to our example of eating an apple. The apple contains sugars, which store energy in their chemical bonds. By breaking down sugar, our cells harness this energy and convert it into a form that can be used to do the work of the cell. Energy from the food we eat allows us to grow, move, communicate, and do all the other things that we do.

Organisms acquire energy from just two sources—the sun and chemical compounds. Regardless of their source of energy, all organisms use chemical reactions to break down molecules, releasing energy in the process and storing it in a chemical form called **ATP** (adenosine triphosphate) that cells can use. The term **metabolism** describes chemical reactions that cells use to convert energy from one form to another and to build and break down molecules. These reactions are required to sustain life.

Many metabolic reactions are highly conserved between organisms, suggesting that they evolved early in the history of life and have been maintained for billions of years because of their fundamental importance to cellular biochemistry.

A virus is genetic material in need of a cell.

It's worth taking a moment to consider viruses. A virus is an agent that infects cells. It is smaller and simpler than cells. Why, then, aren't viruses the smallest unit of life? We just considered three essential features of cells—the capacity to store and transmit information, a membrane that selectively controls movement in and out, and the ability to harness energy from the environment. Viruses have a stable archive of genetic information, which can be RNA or DNA, and the genetic material of viruses is surrounded by a protein coat and sometimes a lipid envelope. But viruses cannot harness energy from the environment. Therefore, on their own viruses cannot read and use the information contained in their genetic material, nor can they regulate the passage of substances across their protein coats or lipid envelopes the way that cells do. To replicate, they require a cell.

A virus infects a cell by binding to the cell surface, inserting its genetic material into the cell, and, in most cases, using the cellular machinery to replicate its own genetic material, synthesize proteins, and produce more viruses. In this way, it is often said that a virus "hijacks" a cell. The infected cell may produce more viruses, sometimes by lysis, or breakage, of the cell, and the new viruses can then infect more cells. In some cases, the genetic material of the virus integrates into the DNA of the host cell.

We discuss viruses many times throughout the book, as they are interesting in themselves and infect all kinds of cells. Each species of Bacteria, Archaea, and Eukarya is susceptible to many types of virus that are specialized to attack its cells. Several hundred types of virus are known to infect humans, and the catalog is still incomplete. Useful tools in biological research, viruses have provided a model system for many problems in biology, including how genes are turned on and off and how cancer develops.

1.4 EVOLUTION

The themes introduced in the last two sections stress life's unity: Cells form the basic unit of all life; DNA, RNA, and proteins carry out the molecular functions of all cells; and metabolic reactions build and break down macromolecules. We need only look around us, however, to recognize that for all its unity, life displays a remarkable degree of diversity. We don't really know how many species share our planet, but reasonable estimates run to 10 million or more. Both the unity and the diversity of life are explained by the process of **evolution,** change over time.

Variation in populations provides the raw material for evolution, change over time.

Described in detail, evolution by **natural selection** calls on complex mathematical formulations, but at heart its main principles are simple, indeed unavoidable. When there is variation within a population of organisms, and when that variation can be inherited (that is, when it can be passed from one generation to the next), the variants best suited for growth and reproduction in a given environment will contribute disproportionately to the next generation. As Darwin recognized, farmers have used this principle for thousands of years to select for crops with high yield or improved resistance to drought and disease. It is how people around the world have developed breeds of dog ranging from terriers to huskies

FIG. 1.15 **Artificial selection.** Selection over many centuries has resulted in remarkable variations among dogs. Charles Darwin called this "selection under domestication" and noted that it resembles selection that occurs in nature.

(**Fig. 1.15**). And it is why antibiotic resistance is on the rise in many disease-causing microorganisms. Life has been shaped by evolution since its origin, and the capacity for Darwinian evolution may be life's most fundamental property.

The apples in the bin from which you made your choice didn't all look alike. Had you picked your apple in an orchard, you would have seen that different apples on the same tree looked different— some smaller, some greener, some misshapen, a few damaged by worms. Such variation is so commonplace that we scarcely pay attention to it. Variation is observed among individuals in virtually every species of organism. Variation that can be inherited provides the raw material on which evolution acts.

The causes of variation among individuals within a species are usually grouped into two broad categories. Variation among individuals is sometimes due to differences in the environment; this is called **environmental variation.** Among apples on the same tree, some may have good exposure to sunlight, some may be hidden in the shade, some were lucky enough to escape the female codling moth, whose egg develops into a caterpillar

that eats its way into the fruit. These are all examples of environmental variation.

The other main cause of variation among individuals is differences in the genes that are transmitted from parents to their offspring; this is known as **genetic variation.** Genes are composed of DNA and contain coded information that instructs the cell to produce specific types of RNA and protein. Differences among individuals' DNA lead to differences among the individuals' RNA and proteins, which affect the molecular functions of the cell and ultimately can lead to physical differences that we can observe. Genetic differences among apples produce varieties whose mature fruits differ in taste and color, such as the green Granny Smith, the yellow Golden Delicious, and the scarlet Red Delicious.

But even on a single tree, each apple contains seeds that are genetically distinct, because the apple tree is a sexual organism. Bees carry pollen from the flowers of one tree and deposit it in the flowers of another, enabling the sperm inside pollen grains to fertilize egg cells within that single flower. All the seeds on an apple tree contain shared genes from one parent, the tree on which they developed. But they contain distinct sets of genes contributed by sperm transported in pollen from other trees. In all sexual organisms, fertilization produces unique combinations of genes, which explains in part why sisters and brothers with the same parents can be so different from one another.

Genetic variation arises ultimately from mutations. A few mutations arise in each generation as a result of errors in DNA replication and environmental factors such as UV radiation. Most genetic variation, however, is due to mutations that occurred in previous generations. To put a human face on this, consider that lung cancer can reflect either environmental insult from cigarette smoking, for example, or an inherited genetic susceptibility.

In nature, most mutations that are harmful to growth and reproduction die out after a handful of generations. Those that are neither harmful nor beneficial can persist for hundreds or thousands of generations. And those that are beneficial to growth and reproduction can gradually become incorporated into the genetic makeup of every individual in the species. That is how evolution works: The genetic makeup of a population changes over time.

Evolution predicts a nested pattern of relatedness among species, depicted as a tree.

Evolutionary theory predicts that new species arise by the divergence of populations through time from a common ancestor. As a result, closely related species are likely to resemble each other more closely than they do more distantly related species. You know this to be true from common experience. All of us recognize the similarity between a chimpanzee's body and our own (**Fig. 1.16a**), and biologists have long known that we share more features with chimpanzees than we do with any other species.

FIG. 1.16 Phylogenetic relationships among primates. (a) Humans share many features with chimpanzees. (b) Humans and chimpanzees, in turn, share more features with gorillas than they do with other species, and so on down through the evolutionary tree of primates. Treelike patterns of nested similarities are the predicted result of evolution.

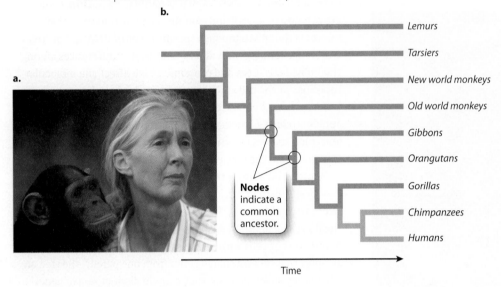

b.

Lemurs
Tarsiers
New world monkeys
Old world monkeys
Gibbons
Orangutans
Gorillas
Chimpanzees
Humans

Nodes indicate a common ancestor.

Time

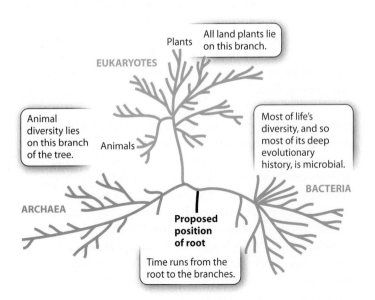

a.

Humans and chimpanzees, in turn, share more features with gorillas than they do with any other species. And humans, chimpanzees, and gorillas share more features with orangutans than they do with any other species. And so on. We can continue to include a widening diversity of species, successively adding monkeys, lemurs, and other primates, to construct a set of evolutionary relationships that can be depicted as a tree (**Fig. 1.16b**). In this tree, the tips or branches on the right represent different groups of organisms, nodes (where lines split) represent

the most recent common ancestor, and time runs from left to right.

Evolutionary theory predicts that primates show a nested pattern of similarity, and this is what morphological and molecular observations reveal. We can continue to add other mammals, and then other vertebrate animals, to our comparison, in the process generating a pattern of evolutionary relationships that forms a larger tree, with the primates confined to one limb. And using molecular comparisons among species, we can generate still larger trees, ones that include plants as well as animals and the full diversity of microscopic organisms. Biologists call the full set of evolutionary relationships among all organisms the **tree of life.** This tree, illustrated in **Fig. 1.17,** has three major branches representing the three domains mentioned earlier and is made up mostly of microorganisms. The last common ancestor of all living organisms, which form a root to the tree, is thought to lie between the branch leading to Bacteria and the branch leading to Archaea and Eukarya. The plants and animals so conspicuous in our daily existence make up only two branches on the eukaryotic limb of the tree.

The tree of life makes predictions for the order of appearance of different life-forms in the fossil record. For example, primates should show up before humans, and the first mammals should appear even earlier. The tree also predicts that all records of animal life should be preceded by a long interval of microbial evolution. As we will see in subsequent chapters, these predictions are met by the geologic record.

Shared features, then, sometimes imply inheritance from a common ancestor. In practice, molecular comparisons and fossils show that the close similarity between humans and chimpanzees reflects descent from a common ancestor that lived about 6 million years ago. Their differences reflect what Darwin called "descent with modification"—evolutionary changes that have accumulated over time since the two lineages split. For example, the flat face of humans, our small teeth, and our upright posture all evolved within our ancestors after they diverged from the ancestors of chimpanzees. As discussed in Chapter 24, fossils document the accumulation of uniquely human features over the past 6 million years. At a broader scale, the fundamental features of molecular function and cell organization that are shared by all organisms reflect inheritance from a common ancestor that lived billions of years ago. And the nested patterns of similarity and differences that characterize the many branches on the tree of life

FIG. 1.17 The tree of life.

EUKARYOTES

Plants

All land plants lie on this branch.

Animal diversity lies on this branch of the tree.

Animals

Most of life's diversity, and so most of its deep evolutionary history, is microbial.

BACTERIA

ARCHAEA

Proposed position of root

Time runs from the root to the branches.

have formed through the continuing action of evolution *since* the time of our earliest ancestors.

Nearly four decades ago, the geneticist Theodosius Dobzhansky wrote, "Nothing in biology makes sense except in the light of evolution." For this reason, evolution permeates discussions throughout this book, whether we are explaining the molecular biology of cells, how organisms function and reproduce, how species interact in nature, or the remarkable biological diversity of our planet.

Evolution can be studied by means of experiments. Both the patterns of similarity among living organisms and the succession of fossils in the geologic record fit the predictions of evolutionary theory. Can we actually capture evolutionary processes in action? One way to accomplish this is in the laboratory. Bacteria are ideal for these experiments because they reproduce rapidly and can form laboratory populations with millions of individuals. Large population size means that mutations will form in nearly every generation, even though the probability that any individual cell will acquire a mutation is small. (In contrast to bacteria, think about trying evolutionary experiments on elephants!)

One such experiment is illustrated in **Fig. 1.18.** The microbiologists Santiago Elena and Richard Lenski grew populations of the common intestinal bacterium *Escherichia coli* in a liquid medium, with the organic acid succinate as the only source of food. In general, *E. coli* cells can feed on succinate poorly

---

HOW DO WE KNOW?

FIG. 1.18

Can evolution be demonstrated in the laboratory?

BACKGROUND *Escherichia coli* is an intestinal bacterium commonly used in the laboratory. It grows poorly in liquid media where the only source of food is succinate. Santiago Elena and Richard Lenski wondered whether *E. coli* grown for 20,000 generations in succinate would evolve in ways that improved their ability to metabolize this compound.

HYPOTHESIS Any bacterium with a random mutation that happens to increase its ability to utilize succinate will reproduce at a faster rate than other bacteria in the population. Over time, such a mutant will increase in frequency relative to other types of bacteria, thereby demonstrating evolution in a bacterial population.

EXPERIMENT Cells of *E. coli* can be frozen in liquid nitrogen, which keeps them in a sort of suspended animation in which no biological processes take place, but the cells survive. At the beginning of the experiment, the researchers froze a large number of samples of the starting bacteria ("ancestral"). As the experiment progressed, they took samples of the bacterial populations at intervals ("later") and grew them together with a thawed sample of the starting bacteria in succinate. They then compared the rate of growth of the ancestral bacteria to that of the bacteria taken at later time points.

RESULTS At each time interval, the cells from later time points grew more rapidly than the ancestral cells when the two populations were grown together in succinate.

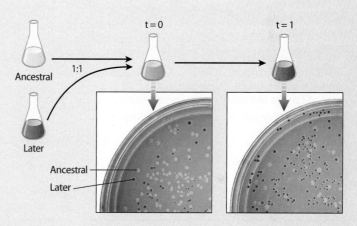

Over time, the bacteria grown in succinate showed more and more improvement in growth compared to the starting bacteria.

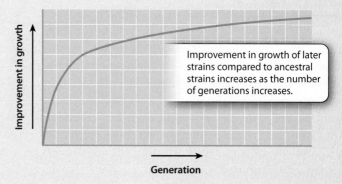

Improvement in growth of later strains compared to ancestral strains increases as the number of generations increases.

CONCLUSION Evolution occurred in the population: the bacteria evolved an improved ability to metabolize succinate.

FOLLOW-UP WORK Other experimental studies have shown that bacteria are able to evolve adaptations to a wide variety of environmental conditions.

SOURCE Elena, S. F., and R. E. Lenski. 2003. "Evolution Experiments with Microorganisms." *Nature Review Genetics* 4:457–469.

if at all, leading the researchers to hypothesize that any bacterium with a mutation that increased its ability to utilize succinate would reproduce at a faster rate than other bacteria in the population. The key questions were whether bacteria from later generations differed from those of earlier generations—that is, did evolution occur in the population?—and in particular whether the bacteria had evolved an improved ability to metabolize succinate.

In fact, the bacteria did evolve an improved ability to use succinate, which is demonstrated by the results shown in Fig. 1.18. This experiment illustrates several key points. It shows how experiments can be used to test hypotheses and, of course, it shows evolution in action. Not only did the experiments demonstrate evolutionary adaptation of *E. coli* populations to a specific laboratory environment, but follow-up studies of their DNA identified differences in genetic makeup that resulted in the observed changes. Many experiments of this general type have been carried out, applying the scientific method to demonstrate how bacteria adapt through mutation to any number of imposed environments.

Experiments in laboratory evolution help us to understand how life works, and they have an immensely important practical side as well. They allow biologists to develop new and beneficial strains of microorganisms that, for example, remove toxins from lakes and rivers and show how some of our worst pathogens develop resistance to drugs designed to eliminate them.

→ **Quick Check 4** How might the heavy-handed use of antibiotics result in the increase of antibiotic-resistant cells in bacterial populations?

1.5 ECOLOGICAL SYSTEMS

Watching a movie, we don't need a narrator to tell us whether the action is set in a tropical rain forest, the African savanna, or Arctic tundra. The plants in the scene tell us. Plants can be linked closely with environment—palm trees with the tropics, for example, or cacti with the desert—because the environmental distributions of different species reflect the sum of their biological features. Palms cannot tolerate freezing and so are confined to warmer environments; the cactus can store water in its tissues, enabling it to withstand prolonged drought. But the geographic ranges of palms and cacti reflect more than just their physical tolerances. They are also strongly influenced by interactions with other species, including other plants that compete for the limited resources available for growth, animals that feed on them or spread their pollen, and microorganisms that infest their tissues. **Ecology** is the study of how organisms interact with one another and with their physical environment in nature.

Basic features of anatomy, physiology, and behavior shape ecological systems.

Apple trees, we noted, reproduce sexually. How is this accomplished, given that the trees have no moving parts? The answer is that bees carry pollen from one flower to the next, enabling sperm carried within the pollen grain to fuse with an egg cell protected within the flower (**Fig. 1.19**). The process is much like the one discussed at the beginning of the chapter in which hummingbirds carry pollen from flower to flower. In both examples, the plants complete their life cycles by exploiting close interactions with animal species. Birds and bees visit flowers, attracted, as we are, by their color and odor. Neither visits flowers with the intent to pollinate; they come in expectation of a meal. As the birds and bees nestle into flowers to collect nutritious nectar, pollen rubs off on their bodies.

But if animals help apples to fertilize their eggs, how do apple trees disperse from one site to another? Again, the plants rely on animals—the apple's flesh attracts animals that eat the fruit, seeds and all, and spread the seeds through defecation. Humans tend to be finicky—we carefully eat only the sweet outer flesh, discarding the seedy core. Nonetheless, even as humans have selected apples for their quality of fruit, we have dispersed apple trees far beyond their natural range.

The many ways that organisms interact in nature reflect their basic functional requirements. If a plant is to grow and reproduce, for example, it must have access to light, carbon dioxide, water, and basic nutrients. All plants have these

FIG. 1.19 **Bee pollination.** Many plants reproduce sexually by exploiting the behavior of animals. Here a honey bee pollinates an apple flower.

FIG. 1.20 Ecological relationships. (a) The trees in a rain forest all require water and nutrients. Neighboring plants compete for the limited supplies of these materials. (b) Plants provide food for many animals. Leaf-cutter ants cut slices of leaves from tropical plants and transport them to their nests, where the leaves grow fungi that the ants eat.

requirements, so one plant's success in gathering nutrients may mean that fewer nutrients are available for its neighbor— the plants may compete for limited resources needed for growth (**Fig. 1.20a**). Animals in the same area require organic molecules for nutrition, and some of them may eat the plant's leaves or bark (**Fig. 1.20b**). Predation also benefits some organisms at the expense of others. In combination, the physical tolerances of organisms and the ways that organisms interact with one another determine the structure and diversity of communities.

In short, ecological relationships reflect the biomechanical, physiological, and behavioral traits of organisms in nature. Form and function, in turn, arise from molecular processes within cells, governed by the expression of genes.

Ecological interactions play an important role in evolution.

G. Evelyn Hutchinson, one of the founders of modern ecology, wrote a book called *The Ecological Theater and the Evolutionary Play* (1965). This wonderful title succinctly captures a key

feature of biological relationships. It suggests that ecological communities provide the "stage" on which the "play" of evolution takes place.

For example, plants often compete for resources. As a result, natural selection may favor plants that have more efficient uptake of nutrients or water. If animals eat plants, natural selection may favor animals with greater jaw strength or more efficient extraction of nutrients in the digestive system. In turn, plants that avoid predation by synthesizing toxic compounds in their leaves may gain the upper hand. In each case, interactions between organisms lead to the evolution of particular traits.

To take another example from mammal–plant interactions: Selection for fleshy fruits improved the dispersal of apples because it increased the attractiveness of these seed-bearing structures to hungry mammals. Tiny yeasts make a meal on sugary fruits as well, in the process producing alcohol that deters potential competitors for the food. Already in prehistoric times, humans had learned to harness this physiological capability of yeasts, and for this reason the total abundance and distribution of *Vitis vinifera*, the wine grape, has increased dramatically through time.

FIG. 1.21   Species that have benefited from human activity, including (a) corn, (b) rats, and (c) cockroaches.

1.6 THE HUMAN FOOTPRINT

The story of life has a cast of millions, with humans playing only one of many roles in an epic 4 billion years in the making. Our own species, *Homo sapiens*, has existed for only the most recent 1/200th of 1% of life's history, yet there are compelling reasons to pay special attention to ourselves. We want to understand how our own bodies work and how humans came to be: Curiosity about ourselves is after all a deeply human trait.

We also want to understand how biology can help us to conquer disease and improve human welfare. Epidemics have decimated human populations throughout history. The Black Death—bubonic plague caused by the bacterium *Yersinia pestis*—is estimated to have killed half the population of Europe in the fourteenth century. Casualties from the flu pandemic of 1918 exceeded those of World War I. Even King Tut, we now know, suffered from malaria in his Egyptian palace. Throughout this book, we discuss how basic biological principles are helping scientists to prevent and cure the great diseases that have

persisted since antiquity, as well as modern ones such as AIDS.

Furthermore, we need to understand the evolutionary and ecological consequences of a human population that has expanded to exceed 7 billion. All species affect the world around them, and we are no different in this regard. Indeed, in the 21st century human activities have taken on special importance because our numbers and technological abilities make our footprint on Earth's ecology so large. Human activities now emit more carbon dioxide than do volcanoes, through industrial processes we convert more atmospheric nitrogen to ammonia than nature does, and we commandeer, either directly or indirectly, as much as 25% of all photosynthetic production on land. To chart our environmental future, we need to understand our role in the Earth system as a whole.

And, as we have become major players in ecology, humans have become important agents of evolution. As our population has expanded, some species have expanded along with us. We've seen how agriculture has sharply increased the abundance and distribution of grapes, and the same is true for corn, cows, and apple trees. At the same time, we have inadvertently helped other species to expand—the crowded and not always clean environments of cities provide excellent habitats for cockroaches and rats (**Fig. 1.21**).

Other species, however, are in decline, their populations reduced by hunting and fishing, changes in land use, and other human activities. When Europeans first arrived on the Indian Ocean island of Mauritius, large flightless birds called dodos were plentiful (**Fig. 1.22**). Within a century, the dodo was gone. Early Europeans in midcontinental North America were greeted by vast populations of passenger pigeons, more than a million in a single flock. By the early 20th century, the species was extinct, a victim of hunting and habitat change through expanding agriculture. Other organisms both great (the Bali tiger) and small (the dusky seaside sparrow) have become extinct in recent decades. Still others are imperiled by human activities; the magnificent white rhinoceros of Africa evolved over millions of years, but today is threatened by both habitat destruction and poaching. Whether any rhinos will exist at the end of this century will depend almost entirely on decisions we make today.

FIG. 1.22   Extinct and endangered species. Humans have caused many organisms to become extinct, such as the (a) dodo, (b) passenger pigeon, (c) Bali tiger, and (d) dusky seaside sparrow. Burgeoning human populations have diminished the ranges of many others, including the (e) white rhinoceros.

Throughout this book, we return to the practical issues of life science. How can we use the principles of biology to improve human welfare, and how can we live our lives in ways that control our impact on the world around us? The answers to the questions critically depend on understanding biology in an *integrated* fashion. While it is tempting to consider molecules, cells, organisms, and ecosystems as separate entities, they are inseparable in nature. To tackle biological problems, whether building an artificial cell, stopping the spread of infectious diseases such as HIV or malaria, feeding a growing population, or preserving endangered habitats and species, we need an integrated perspective. In decisively important ways, our future welfare depends on improving our knowledge of how life works.

Core Concepts Summary

1.1 THE SCIENTIFIC METHOD IS A DELIBERATE WAY OF ASKING AND ANSWERING QUESTIONS ABOUT THE NATURAL WORLD.

Observations are used to generate a hypothesis, a tentative explanation that makes predictions that can be tested. page 1-2

On the basis of a hypothesis, scientists design experiments and make additional observations that test the hypothesis. page 1-3

If a hypothesis is supported through continued observation and experiments over long periods of time, it is elevated to a theory, a sound and broad explanation of some aspect of the world. page 1-5

1.2 LIFE WORKS ACCORDING TO FUNDAMENTAL PRINCIPLES OF CHEMISTRY AND PHYSICS.

Living organisms and nonliving objects are made up of the same chemicals and obey the same physical laws. page 1-6

Experiments by Redi in the 1600s and Pasteur in the 1800s demonstrated that organisms come from other organisms and are not spontaneously generated. page 1-7

Life originated on Earth about 4 billion years ago and most likely arose from nonliving matter. page 1-8

1.3 THE FUNDAMENTAL UNIT OF LIFE IS THE CELL.

The cell is the simplest biological entity that can exist independently. page 1-8

Information in a cell is stored in the form of the nucleic acid DNA. page 1-10

The central dogma describes the usual flow of information in a cell, from DNA to RNA to protein. page 1-10

The plasma membrane is the boundary that separates the cell from its environment. page 1-11

Cells with a nucleus are eukaryotes; cells without a nucleus are prokaryotes. page 1-11

Metabolism is the set of chemical reactions that are used by cells to build and break down macromolecules and to harness energy. page 1-12

1.4 BOTH THE FEATURES THAT ORGANISMS SHARE AND THOSE THAT SET THEM APART ARE EXPLAINED BY EVOLUTION.

When there is variation within a population of organisms, and when that variation can be inherited, the variants best able to grow and reproduce in a particular environment will contribute disproportionately to the next generation, leading to a change in the population over time, or evolution. page 1-12

Variation can be genetic or environmental. The ultimate source of genetic variation is mutation. page 1-12

Organisms show a nested pattern of similarity, with humans more similar to primates than other organisms, primates more similar to mammals, mammals more similar to vertebrates, and so on. page 1-13

Evolution can be demonstrated by laboratory experiments. page 1-15

1.5 ORGANISMS INTERACT WITH ONE ANOTHER AND WITH THEIR PHYSICAL ENVIRONMENT, SHAPING ECOLOGICAL SYSTEMS THAT SUSTAIN LIFE.

Ecology is the study of how organisms interact with one another and with their physical environment in nature. page 1-16

These interactions are driven in part by the anatomy, physiology, and behavior of organisms. page 1-16

1.6 IN THE 21ST CENTURY, HUMANS HAVE BECOME MAJOR AGENTS IN ECOLOGY AND EVOLUTION.

Humans have existed for only the most recent 1/200th of 1% of life's 4-billion-year history. page 1-18

In spite of our recent arrival, our growing numbers are leaving a large ecological and evolutionary footprint. page 1-18

Solving biological problems requires an integrated understanding of life, with contributions from all the fields of biology, including molecular biology, cell biology, genetics, organismal biology, and ecology, as well as from chemistry, physics, and engineering. page 1-19

Self-Assessment

1. Describe the steps in the scientific method.

2. Differentiate among a theory, a hypothesis, and a guess.

3. State the first and second laws of thermodynamics and describe how they relate to living organisms.

4. Describe what it means to say that a cell is life's functional unit.

5. Explain how we know that living organisms come from other living organisms.

6. Explain how evolution accounts for both the unity and diversity of life.

7. List features of organisms that shape ecological systems.

8. Name three ways that humans have affected life on Earth.

9. Take a step back and describe the six themes that are discussed in this chapter.

Do you understand the chapter's Core Concepts? Log into BIOPORTAL to check your answers to the Self-Assessment questions, then practice what you've learned and reinforce this chapter's concepts by working through the problems and multimedia tutorials provided there.

🛜 http://courses.bfwpub.com/yourbioportal/index.php

The First Cell

LIFE'S ORIGINS

Deep underground, in Mexico's Cueva de Villa Luz, the cave walls drip with slime. The rocky surfaces are teeming with colonies of mucus-producing bacteria. No sunlight reaches these organisms far beneath Earth's surface. Instead, the bacteria survive by capturing energy from hydrogen sulfide gas within the cave. As a by-product of that reaction, the microbes produce sulfuric acid. The stalactite-like slime formations oozing from the cave walls—dubbed "snottites" by researchers—are as corrosive as battery acid.

Snottites might be stomach turning, but they're intriguing, too. Called "extremophiles" because they live in places where humans and most other animals cannot survive, such microorganisms may tell us something about life when Earth was young.

From cave-dwelling bacteria to 100-ton blue whales, the diversity of life on Earth is astounding. Yet all of the planet's organisms, living and extinct, exist on branches of the same family tree. Snottites, swordfish, humans, hydrangeas—all evolved from one single common ancestor.

When, where, and how life originated are some of the biggest questions in biology. Chemical evidence from 3.5-billion-year-old rocks in Australia suggests that biologically driven carbon and sulfur cycles existed at the time those rocks were formed. In the eons since, the first primitive life-forms have evolved into the 100 million or so organisms thought to populate the planet today.

How did the first living cell arise? Before scientists can hope to tackle such a question, they must agree on a definition of life. That's not necessarily as straightforward as it sounds. In our modern world, the features that separate life from non-life are relatively easy to discern. But Earth's first organisms were almost certainly much less complicated than even the simplest bacteria alive today. And before those first truly living things appeared, molecular systems presumably existed that hovered somewhere between the domains of the living and the nonliving.

All cells require an archive of information, a membrane to maintain the inside of the cell different from the outside, and the ability to harness energy from the environment. In modern organisms, that archive is in the form of DNA, the double-stranded molecule that contains the instructions needed for cells to grow, differentiate, and reproduce. Without that molecular machinery, life as we know it would not exist.

DNA is critical, and it's also complex. Among the organisms alive today, the smallest known genome belongs to the bacterium *Carsonella rudii.* Even that relatively small genome contains nearly 160,000 DNA base pairs. How could such sophisticated molecular systems have arisen by chance?

The likely answer to that question is step by step. Laboratory experiments have shown how precursors to nucleic acids might have come together under the chemical conditions present on the young Earth. It's exceedingly unlikely that a molecule as complex as DNA was the first archive of information employed by the very first living cells. As you'll see in the chapters that follow, scientists have gathered evidence that hints at what the earliest nucleic acid molecules might have looked like.

While some kind of information archive was necessary for life to unfold, life requires more than a collection of nucleic acids replicating in a warm primordial pond. Living things must have some barrier that separates them from their

> All cells require an archive of information, a membrane to maintain the inside of the cell different from the outside, and the ability to harness energy from the environment.

Snottites deep underground in a Mexican cave. These stalactite-like slime formations are produced by bacteria that break down hydrogen sulfide gas as a source of energy.

environment. The cells of all living things, single-celled organisms or multicellular creatures, are each encased in a cell membrane.

Once again, scientists can only guess at how the first cell membranes came about. But research shows the molecules that make up modern membranes possess some interesting properties that may have led them to arise spontaneously. At first, the membranes were probably quite simple—straightforward (but leaky) barriers that kept the contents of early cells separated from the world at large. Over time, as chance variations arose, those membranes that provided a better barrier and that provided molecular gates were subject to an early example of the same natural selection process that is still happening today.

A third essential characteristic of living things is the ability to harness energy from the environment. Here, too, it's feasible that a series of natural chemical processes led to entities that could achieve this feat. Simple reactions may have produced molecular by-products that enabled more complex reactions down the road. Ultimately, that collection of reactions—combined with an archive of information and enclosed in some kind of primitive membrane—evolved into individual units that could breathe, grow, reproduce, and evolve.

Such a series of events may sound unlikely. However, some scientists argue that given the chemicals present on early Earth, it was likely—if not inevitable—that they would come together in such a way that life would emerge. Indeed, relatively simple, naturally occurring materials such as metal ions have been shown to play a role in key cellular reactions. Billions of years after the first cells arose, some of those metal ions—such as iron–sulfur minerals—still play a critical role in cells.

That's one reason researchers are so keen to study creatures like the sulfur-hungry snottites in the Cueva de Villa Luz. When life arose, the planet's atmosphere contained no oxygen—humans couldn't survive in such a world. By studying modern extremophiles—including bacteria that thrive in caves and near superheated hydrothermal vents at the bottom of the sea—scientists may uncover clues about how Earth's first cells came together and functioned.

Did life arise just once? Or could it have started up and died out several times before it finally got a foothold? If, given Earth's early chemistry, life here was inevitable, could it have arisen elsewhere in the universe? The study of life's origins involves many more questions than answers—and not just for biologists. The mystery of life spans the fields of biology, chemistry, physics, and planetary science. Though the questions are vast, our understanding of life's origins is likely to come about the same way life itself arose: step by step.

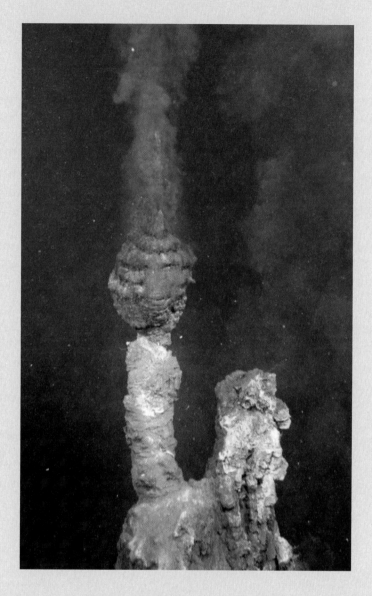

A hydrothermal vent. Some scientists think that this type of vent provided a favorable environment for chemical reactions that led to the origin of life.

? CASE 1 QUESTIONS

Answers to Case 1 questions can be found in Chapters 2-8.

1. How did the molecules of life form? *See page 2-17.*
2. What was the first nucleic acid molecule, and how did it arise? *See page 3-10.*
3. How did the genetic code originate? *See page 4-14.*
4. How did the first cell membranes form? *See page 5-3.*
5. What naturally occurring elements might have spurred the first reactions that led to life? *See page 6-15.*
6. What were the earliest energy-harnessing reactions? *See page 7-10.*
7. How did early cells meet their energy requirements? *See page 7-16 and page 8-15.*

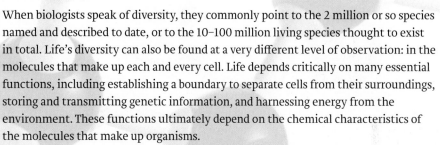

CHAPTER 2

THE MOLECULES OF LIFE

Core Concepts

2.1 The atom is the fundamental unit of matter.

2.2 Atoms can combine to form molecules linked by chemical bonds.

2.3 Water is abundant and essential for life.

2.4 Carbon is the backbone of organic molecules.

2.5 Organic molecules include proteins, nucleic acids, carbohydrates, and lipids, each of which is built from simpler units.

2.6 Life likely originated on Earth by a set of chemical reactions that gave rise to the molecules of life.

When biologists speak of diversity, they commonly point to the 2 million or so species named and described to date, or to the 10–100 million living species thought to exist in total. Life's diversity can also be found at a very different level of observation: in the molecules that make up each and every cell. Life depends critically on many essential functions, including establishing a boundary to separate cells from their surroundings, storing and transmitting genetic information, and harnessing energy from the environment. These functions ultimately depend on the chemical characteristics of the molecules that make up organisms.

In spite of the diversity of molecules and functions, the chemistry of life is based on just a few types of molecule, which in turn are made up of just a few elements. Of the 100 or so chemical elements, only about a dozen are found in more than trace amounts in living organisms. These elements interact with one another in only a limited number of ways. So, the question arises: How is diversity generated from a limited suite of chemicals and interactions? The answer lies in some basic features of chemistry.

2.1 PROPERTIES OF ATOMS

Since antiquity, it has been accepted that the materials of nature are made up of a small number of fundamental substances combined in various ways. Aristotle called these substances **elements**, and recognized four: earth, air, fire, and water. From the seventeenth century through the end of the nineteenth, elements were defined as pure substances that could not be broken down further by the methods of chemistry. In time, it was recognized that each element contains only one type of **atom**, the basic unit of matter. By 1850, about 60 elements were known, including such common ones as oxygen, copper, gold, and sodium. Today, 118 elements are known, of which 94 occur naturally and 24 have been created artificially in the laboratory. Elements are often indicated by a chemical symbol, which consists of a one- or two-letter abbreviation of the name of the element. For example, carbon is represented by C, hydrogen by H, and helium by He.

Atoms consist of protons, neutrons, and electrons.

Elements are composed of atoms. The atom contains a dense central **nucleus** made up of positively charged particles called **protons** and electrically neutral particles called **neutrons**. A third type of particle, the negatively charged **electron**, moves around the

FIG. 2.1 **A carbon atom.** Each carbon atom has six protons, six neutrons, and six electrons. The net charge of any atom is neutral because there are as many electrons as protons.

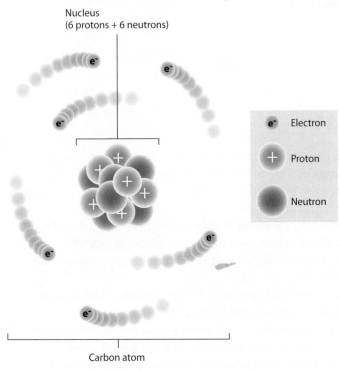

Nucleus
(6 protons + 6 neutrons)

e⁻ Electron
+ Proton
Neutron

Carbon atom

nucleus at some distance from it. Carbon, for example, typically has six protons, six neutrons, and six electrons (**Fig. 2.1**).

The number of protons, or the atomic number, specifies the atom as a particular element; an atom with one proton is hydrogen, for example, and an atom with six protons is carbon. The atomic number is sometimes indicated as a left subscript to the chemical symbol, for example $_6$C. Here, the "6" represents the number of protons in a carbon atom.

Together, the protons and neutrons determine the **atomic mass,** the mass of the atom. Each proton and neutron, by definition, has a mass of 1, whereas an electron has negligible mass. The number of neutrons in atoms of a particular element can vary, changing its mass. **Isotopes** are atoms of the same element that have different numbers of neutrons. For example, carbon has three isotopes: About 99% of carbon atoms have six neutrons and six protons, for an atomic mass of 12; about 1% has seven neutrons and six protons, for an atomic mass of 13; and only a very small fraction has eight neutrons and six protons, for an atomic mass of 14. The atomic mass is sometimes indicated as a left superscript to the chemical symbol. For instance, ^{12}C is the isotope of carbon with six neutrons and six protons.

Typically, an atom has the same number of protons and electrons. Because a carbon atom has six protons and six electrons, the positive and negative charges cancel each other out and the

FIG. 2.2 **Electron orbitals and energy levels (shells) for hydrogen and carbon.** The orbital of an electron can be visualized as a cloud of points that are more dense where the electron is more likely to be. The hydrogen atom contains a single orbital, in a single energy level (a and c). The carbon atom has five orbitals, one in the first energy level and four in the second energy level (b and c).

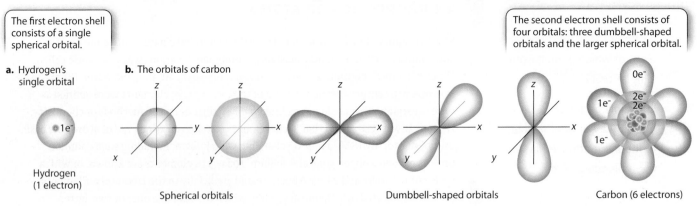

The first electron shell consists of a single spherical orbital.

The second electron shell consists of four orbitals: three dumbbell-shaped orbitals and the larger spherical orbital.

a. Hydrogen's single orbital

1e⁻

Hydrogen
(1 electron)

b. The orbitals of carbon

Spherical orbitals

Dumbbell-shaped orbitals

0e⁻
2e⁻
2e⁻
1e⁻
1e⁻

Carbon (6 electrons)

c. Energy levels of hydrogen and carbon

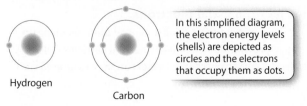

Hydrogen

Carbon

In this simplified diagram, the electron energy levels (shells) are depicted as circles and the electrons that occupy them as dots.

carbon atom is electrically neutral. Some chemical processes cause an atom to either gain or lose electrons. An atom that has lost an electron is positively charged, and one that has gained an electron is negatively charged. Electrically charged atoms are called **ions.** The charge of an ion is specified in the right superscript position next to the chemical symbol. Thus, H^+ indicates a hydrogen ion that has lost an electron and is positively charged.

Electrons occupy regions of space called orbitals.

Electrons move around the nucleus, but not in the simplified way shown in Fig. 2.1. The exact path that an electron takes is unknown, but it is possible to identify a region in space, called an **orbital,** where an electron is present most of the time. For example, **Fig. 2.2a** shows the orbital for hydrogen, which is simply a sphere occupied by a single electron. Most of the time, the electron is found within the space defined by the sphere, although its exact location at any instant is unpredictable.

Orbitals have certain properties. The maximum number of electrons in any orbital is two. Most atoms have more than two electrons and so have several orbitals positioned at different distances from the nucleus. These orbitals differ in size and shape. Electrons in orbitals close to the nucleus have less energy than do electrons in orbitals farther away, so electrons fill up orbitals close to the nucleus before occupying those farther away. Several orbitals can exist at a given energy level, or **shell.** The first shell consists of the spherical orbital shown in Fig. 2.2a.

Fig. 2.2b shows electron orbitals for carbon. Of carbon's six electrons, two occupy the small spherical orbital representing the lowest energy level. The remaining four are distributed among four possible orbitals at the next highest energy level: One of these four orbitals is a sphere (larger in diameter than that at the lowest energy level) and three are dumbbell-shaped. In carbon, the outermost spherical orbital has two electrons, two of the dumbbell-shaped orbitals have one electron each, and one of the dumbbell-shaped orbitals is empty. Because a full orbital contains two electrons, it would take a total of four additional electrons to completely fill all of the orbitals at this energy level. Therefore,

after the first shell, the maximum number of electrons per energy level is eight. **Fig. 2.2c** shows that the highest energy level, or shell, of carbon, represented by the outermost circle, contains four electrons, and that of hydrogen contains one electron.

→ **Quick Check 1** In the early 1900s, Ernest Rutherford produced a beam of very small negative particles and directed it at a thin piece of gold foil just a few atoms thick. Most of the particles passed through the foil without changing their path; very rarely, a particle was deflected. What conclusions can you draw from this experiment about the structure of an atom?

Elements have recurring, or periodic, chemical properties.

The chemical elements are often arranged in a tabular form known as the **periodic table of the elements**, shown in **Fig. 2.3** and generally credited to the nineteenth-century Russian chemist Dmitri Mendeleev. The table provides a way to organize all the chemical elements in terms of their chemical properties.

In the periodic table, the elements are indicated by their chemical symbols and arranged in order of increasing atomic number. For example, the second row of the periodic table begins with lithium (Li) with 3 protons and ends with neon (Ne) with 10 protons.

Elements in a given horizontal row all have the same number of shells, and so also have the same number and types of orbitals.

FIG. 2.3 **The periodic table of the elements.** Elements are arranged by increasing number of protons, the atomic number. The elements in any column share similar chemical properties.

Abundance in cells			
High	Low	Trace	None

1 H																	2 He
3 Li	4 Be											5 B	6 C	7 N	8 O	9 F	10 Ne
11 Na	12 Mg											13 Al	14 Si	15 P	16 S	17 Cl	18 Ar
19 K	20 Ca	21 Sc	22 Ti	23 V	24 Cr	25 Mn	26 Fe	27 Co	28 Ni	29 Cu	30 Zn	31 Ga	32 Ge	33 As	34 Se	35 Br	36 Kr
37 Rb	38 Sr	39 Y	40 Zr	41 Nb	42 Mo	43 Tc	44 Ru	45 Rh	46 Pd	47 Ag	48 Cd	49 In	50 Sn	51 Sb	52 Te	53 I	54 Xe
55 Cs	56 Ba	57-71 La-Lu	72 Hf	73 Ta	74 W	75 Re	76 Os	77 Ir	78 Pt	79 Au	80 Hg	81 Tl	82 Pb	83 Bi	84 Po	85 At	86 Rn
87 Fr	88 Ra	89-103 Ac-Lr	104 Rf	105 Db	106 Sg	107 Bh	108 Hs	109 Mt	110 Ds	111 Rg	112 Cn	113 Uut	114 Uuq	115 Uup	116 Uuh	117 Uus	118 Uuo

57 La	58 Ce	59 Pr	60 Nd	61 Pm	62 Sm	63 Eu	64 Gd	65 Tb	66 Dy	67 Ho	68 Er	69 Tm	70 Yb	71 Lu
89 Ac	90 Th	91 Pa	92 U	93 Np	94 Pu	95 Am	96 Cm	97 Bk	98 Cf	99 Es	100 Fm	101 Md	102 No	103 Lr

FIG. 2.4   **Energy levels (shells) of row 2 of the periodic table.** The complete complement of electrons in the outer shell of this row of elements is 8.

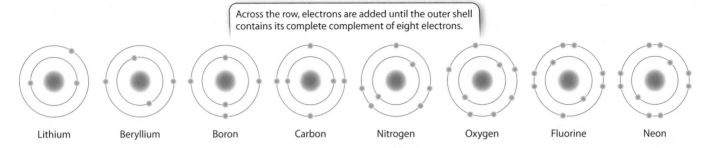

Across the row, electrons are added until the outer shell contains its complete complement of eight electrons.

| Lithium | Beryllium | Boron | Carbon | Nitrogen | Oxygen | Fluorine | Neon |

Across a row, therefore, electrons fill the shell until a full complement of electrons is reached on the right-hand side of the table. **Fig. 2.4** shows the filling of the shells for the second row of the periodic table. The elements in a vertical column are called a group or family. Members of a group all have the same number of electrons in their outermost orbital. For example, carbon (C) and lead (Pb) both have four electrons in their outermost orbital. The number of electrons in the outermost orbital determines in large part how elements behave and interact with other elements, as we will see in the next section.

2.2 MOLECULES AND CHEMICAL BONDS

Atoms can combine with other atoms to form **molecules,** which are substances made up of two or more atoms. When two atoms form a molecule, the individual atoms interact in what is called a **chemical bond,** a form of attraction between atoms that holds them together. The ability of atoms to form molecules in part explains why just a few types of element can make many different molecules and perform diverse functions in a cell. There

are many different ways in which atoms can interact with one another, and therefore many different types of chemical bond, as we describe in this section.

A covalent bond results when two atoms share electrons.

The ability of atoms to combine with other atoms is determined in large part by the electrons farthest from the nucleus—those in the outermost orbitals of an atom. These electrons are called **valence electrons,** and they are at the highest energy level. In many cases, when atoms combine with other atoms to form a molecule, the atoms share valence electrons with each other. Specifically, when the outermost orbitals of two atoms come into proximity, two atomic orbitals each containing one electron merge into a single orbital containing a full complement of two electrons. The merged orbital is called a **molecular orbital,** and each shared pair of electrons constitutes a **covalent bond** that holds the atoms together.

Hydrogen gas (H_2), illustrated in **Fig. 2.5,** is one of the simplest molecules. Note that the right subscript position is used to indicate the number of atoms in a molecule. Each hydrogen atom has a single electron in a spherical orbital. When the atoms join into a molecule, the two orbitals merge into a single molecular orbital containing two electrons that are shared by the hydrogen atoms. A covalent bond between atoms is denoted by a single line connecting the two chemical symbols for the atoms, as shown in the structural formula in Fig. 2.5.

→   **Quick Check 2** From their positions in the periodic table (see Fig. 2.3), can you predict how many lithium atoms and hydrogen atoms combine to form a molecule?

Molecules tend to be most stable when they share enough electrons to completely occupy the outermost energy level or shell. This simple rule of thumb is known as the octet rule and applies to many, but not all, elements. For example, as shown in **Fig. 2.6**, one carbon atom (C, with four valence electrons) combines with four hydrogen atoms (H, with one valence electron each) to form CH_4 (methane); nitrogen (N, with five valence electrons) combines with three H atoms to form NH_3

FIG. 2.5   **A covalent bond.** A covalent bond is formed when two atoms share a pair of electrons in a molecular orbital.

Chemical formula H_2
Structural formula $H-H$

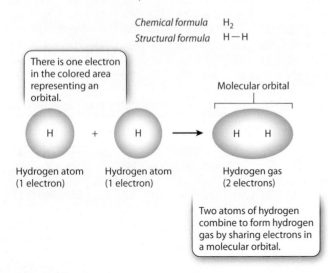

There is one electron in the colored area representing an orbital.

Molecular orbital

H   +   H   →   H   H

Hydrogen atom (1 electron)   Hydrogen atom (1 electron)   Hydrogen gas (2 electrons)

Two atoms of hydrogen combine to form hydrogen gas by sharing electrons in a molecular orbital.

FIG. 2.6 **Four molecules.** Atoms tend to combine in such a way as to complete the complement of electrons in the outer shell.

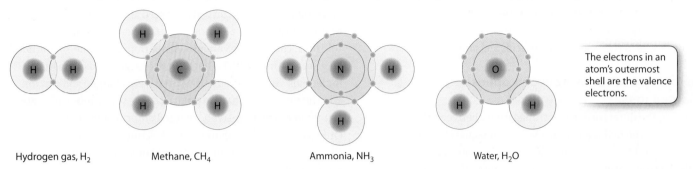

> The electrons in an atom's outermost shell are the valence electrons.

Hydrogen gas, H_2 Methane, CH_4 Ammonia, NH_3 Water, H_2O

(ammonia); and oxygen (O, with six valence electrons) combines with two H atoms to form H_2O (water). Interestingly, the elements of the same column in the next row behave similarly. This is just one example of the recurring, or periodic, behavior of the elements.

A polar covalent bond is characterized by unequal sharing of electrons.

In hydrogen gas, the electrons are shared equally by the two hydrogen atoms. In many bonds, however, the electrons are not shared equally by the two atoms. A notable example is provided by the bonds in a water molecule (H_2O), which consists of two hydrogen atoms each covalently bound to a single oxygen atom (**Fig. 2.7a**).

In a molecule of water, the electrons are not shared equally between the hydrogen and oxygen atoms; rather, the electrons are more likely to be located near the oxygen atom. Unequal sharing of electrons results from a difference in the ability of the atoms to attract electrons, a property known as **electronegativity.** Electronegativity tends to increase across a row in the periodic table; as the number of protons across a row increases, electrons are held more tightly to the nucleus.

Therefore, oxygen is more electronegative than hydrogen and attracts electrons more than does hydrogen. In a molecule of water, oxygen has a slight negative charge, while the two hydrogen atoms have a slight positive charge (**Fig. 2.7b**). When electrons are shared unequally between the two atoms, the resulting interaction is described as a **polar covalent bond.**

A hydrogen bond is an interaction of a hydrogen atom and an electronegative atom.

Because the oxygen and hydrogen atoms have slight charges, water molecules orient themselves to minimize the repulsion of like charges so that positive charges are near negative charges. A **hydrogen bond** results when a hydrogen atom covalently bound to an electronegative atom (such as oxygen or nitrogen) interacts with an electronegative atom of another molecule. In the case of water, a hydrogen atom covalently bound to an oxygen atom is attracted to and interacts with an oxygen atom of another water molecule. The result of many such interactions is a kind of molecular network stabilized by hydrogen bonds. Typically, a hydrogen bond is depicted by a dotted line, as in **Fig. 2.8.**

FIG. 2.7 **Polar covalent bond.** Polar covalent bonds do not share the electrons equally.

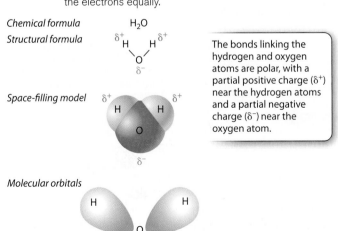

Chemical formula H_2O

Structural formula

Space-filling model

Molecular orbitals

> The bonds linking the hydrogen and oxygen atoms are polar, with a partial positive charge (δ^+) near the hydrogen atoms and a partial negative charge (δ^-) near the oxygen atom.

FIG. 2.8 **Hydrogen bonds in liquid water.** Because of thermal motion, hydrogen bonds in water are continually breaking and reforming between different pairs of molecules.

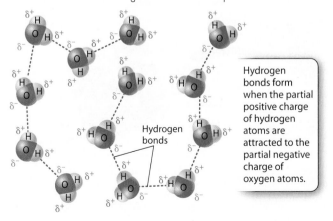

Hydrogen bonds

> Hydrogen bonds form when the partial positive charge of hydrogen atoms are attracted to the partial negative charge of oxygen atoms.

Hydrogen bonds are much weaker than covalent bonds, but it is hydrogen bonding that gives water many of its unusual properties, which are described in the next section. In addition, many weak hydrogen bonds can help stabilize biological molecules, as in the case of nucleic acids and proteins.

An ionic bond forms between oppositely charged ions.

In water, the difference in electronegativity between the oxygen and the hydrogen atoms leads to unequal sharing of electrons. In more extreme cases, when an atom of very high electronegativity is paired with an atom of very low electronegativity, the difference in electronegativity is so great that the electronegative atom "steals" the electron from its less electronegative partner. In this case, the atom with the extra electron has a negative charge and is a negative ion. The atom that has lost an electron has a positive charge and is a positive ion. The two ions are not covalently bound, but they associate with each other because of the attraction of opposite charges in what is called an **ionic bond.** An example of a compound formed by the attraction of a positive ion and a negative ion is table salt, or sodium chloride (NaCl) (**Fig. 2.9a**).

When sodium chloride is placed in water, the salt dissolves to form sodium ions (written as "Na$^+$") that have lost an electron and so are positively charged, and chloride ions (Cl$^-$) that have gained an electron and are negatively charged. In solution, the two ions are pulled apart and become surrounded by water molecules: The negatively charged ends of water molecules are attracted to the positively charged sodium ion and the positively charged ends of other water molecules are attracted to the negatively charged chloride ion (**Fig. 2.9b**). Only as the water evaporates do the concentrations of Na$^+$ and Cl$^-$ increase to the point where the ions join and precipitate as salt crystals.

A chemical reaction involves breaking and forming chemical bonds.

The chemical bonds that link atoms in molecules can change in a **chemical reaction,** a process by which given molecules, called **reactants,** are transformed into different molecules, called **products.** During a chemical reaction, atoms keep their identity but change their chemical bonds.

For example, two molecules of hydrogen gas ($2H_2$) and one molecule of oxygen (O_2) can react to form two molecules

FIG. 2.9   An ionic bond. (a) Sodium chloride (salt) is formed by the attraction of two ions. (b) In solution, the ions are surrounded by water molecules.

a.

In sodium chloride (salt), sodium loses an electron and becomes positively charged, and chlorine gains an electron and becomes negatively charged.

The two ions are attracted to each other.

Sodium atom (Na)

Chlorine atom (Cl)

Sodium ion (Na$^+$)

Chlorine ion (Cl$^-$)

Sodium chloride (NaCl)

b.

Sodium chloride (NaCl) dissolves in solution because the sodium (Na$^+$) ions and chloride (Cl$^-$) ions each become surrounded by water molecules.

NaCl

H$_2$O

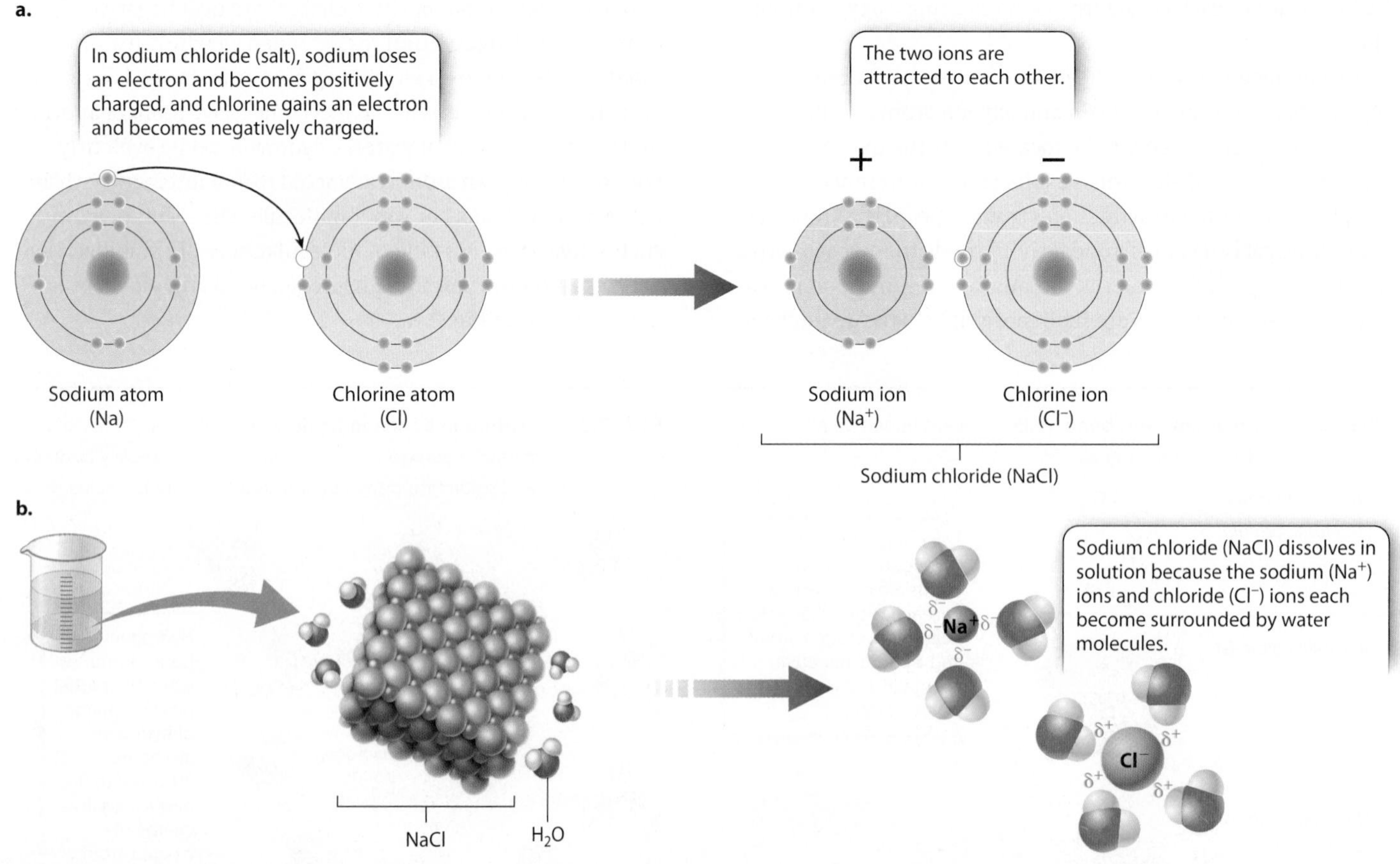

of water ($2H_2O$), as shown in **Fig. 2.10.** In this reaction, the numbers of each type of atom are conserved, but their arrangement is different in the reactants and the products. Specifically, the H–H bond in hydrogen gas and the $O=O$ bond in oxygen are broken. At the same time, each oxygen atom forms new covalent bonds with two hydrogen atoms, forming two molecules of water. In fact, this reaction is the origin of the name "hydrogen," which literally means "water former." The reaction releases a good deal of energy; it was used in the main engine of the Space Shuttle.

In biological systems, chemical reactions provide a way to build and break down molecules for use by the cell, as well as to harness energy, which can be stored in chemical bonds (Chapter 6).

2.3 WATER: THE MEDIUM OF LIFE

On Earth, all life depends on water. Indeed, life originated in water, and the availability of water strongly influences the environmental distributions of different species. Furthermore, water is the single most abundant molecule in all cells, so water is the medium in which the molecules of life interact. In the late 1990s, the National Aeronautic and Space Administration (NASA) announced that the search for extraterrestrial life would guide continuing exploration of the solar system and beyond. NASA's operational strategy was simple: Follow the water. NASA's logic was straightforward: Within our solar system, Earth stands out both for its abundance of water and the life it supports. What makes water so special as the medium of life?

Water is a polar molecule.

As we saw earlier, water molecules have polar covalent bonds, characterized by an uneven distribution of electrons. A molecule like water that has regions of positive and negative charge is called a **polar** molecule. Molecules, or even different regions of the same molecule, fall into two general classes, depending on how they interact with water: **hydrophilic** ("water loving") and **hydrophobic** ("water fearing").

Hydrophilic compounds, like water itself, are polar; they dissolve readily in water. That is, water is a good **solvent,** capable of dissolving many substances. Think of what happens when you stir a teaspoon of sugar into water: The sugar seems to disappear as the sugar dissolves. What is happening is that the sugar molecules are dispersing through the water and becoming separated from one another. Sugar is in solution in the watery, or **aqueous,** environment.

By contrast, hydrophobic compounds are nonpolar and arrange themselves to minimize their contact with water. For example, when oil and water are mixed, oil molecules organize themselves into droplets that limit the oil–water interface.

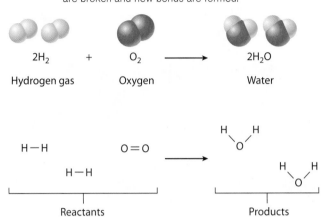

FIG. 2.10   A chemical reaction. During a chemical reaction, atoms retain their identity, but their connections change as bonds are broken and new bonds are formed.

2H₂ + O₂ ⟶ 2H₂O
Hydrogen gas   Oxygen   Water

H—H   O=O   ⟶   H,O,H / H,O,H
H—H
Reactants   Products

This **hydrophobic effect,** in which polar molecules like water exclude nonpolar ones, drives such biological processes as the formation of cell membranes (Chapter 3) and the folding of proteins (Chapter 5).

pH is a measure of the concentration of protons in solution.

A small proportion of the molecules in water exist as protons (H^+) and hydroxide ions (OH^-). The pH of a solution measures the proton concentration ($[H^+]$) by the following formula:

$$pH = -\log [H^+]$$

The pH of a solution can range from 0 to 14. Since the pH scale is logarithmic, a difference of one pH unit corresponds to a tenfold difference in hydrogen ion concentration. A solution is neutral (pH = 7) when the concentrations of protons (H^+) and hydroxide ions (OH^-) are equal. When the concentration of protons is higher than that of hydroxide ions, then the pH is lower than 7 and the solution is **acidic.** When the concentration of protons is lower than that of hydroxide ions, then the pH is higher than 7, and the solution is **basic.** An acid therefore is a molecule that releases a proton (H^+), and a base is a molecule that accepts a proton in aqueous solution.

Pure water has a pH of 7—that is, it is neutral, with an equal concentration of protons and hydroxide ions. The pH of most cells is approximately 7 and is tightly regulated, as most chemical reactions can be carried out only in a narrow pH range. Certain cellular compartments, however, have a much lower pH. The pH of blood is slightly basic, with a pH around 7.4. This value is sometimes referred to in medicine as physiological pH, as it can change in response to certain diseases. Freshwater lakes, ponds, and rivers tend to be slightly acidic because of dissolved carbon dioxide from the air, which forms carbonic acid in water.

FIG. 2.11   **Liquid water and ice.** Hydrogen bonds create a dense structure in water (a), and a highly ordered, less dense, crystalline structure in ice (b).

a. Liquid water   **b.** Ice

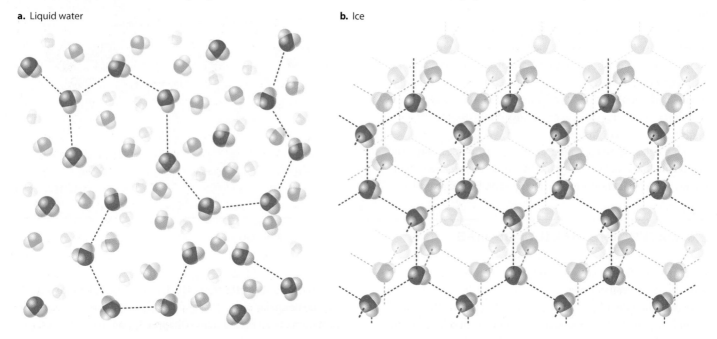

Hydrogen bonds give water many unusual properties.

Water is also characterized by extensive hydrogen bonding, as we have seen. Hydrogen bonds influence the structure of both liquid water (**Fig. 2.11a**) and ice (**Fig. 2.11b**). When water freezes, most water molecules become hydrogen bonded to four other water molecules, forming an open lattice-like, crystalline structure we call ice. As the temperature increases and the ice melts, some of the hydrogen bonds are destabilized. This allows the water molecules to pack more closely, and it is the reason why liquid water is more dense than solid water. As a result, ice floats on water, and ponds and lakes freeze from the top down, and therefore do not freeze completely. This special property allows fish and aquatic plants to survive winter in the cold water under the layer of ice.

→   **Quick Check 3** Why do containers of water, milk, soda, or other liquids sometimes burst when frozen?

Hydrogen bonds also make water molecules cohesive, meaning that they tend to stick to one another. A consequence of cohesion is high surface tension, a measure of the difficulty of breaking the surface of a liquid. Water cohesion and surface tension contribute to water movement in plants. As water evaporates from leaves, water is pulled upward, sometimes as high as 300 feet above the ground in giant sequoia and coast redwood trees, which are among the tallest trees on Earth.

The hydrogen bonds of water also influence how water responds to heating. Molecules are in constant motion, and this motion increases as the temperature increases. When water is heated, however, the increased motion first breaks hydrogen bonds, and only afterward leads to a temperature increase. The need to break hydrogen bonds first means that water resists temperature changes more than do other substances, a property that is important for living organisms on a variety of scales. In the cell, water resists temperature variations that would otherwise result from numerous biochemical reactions. On a global scale, the oceans minimize temperature fluctuations, stabilizing the temperature on Earth in a range compatible with life.

In short, water is clearly the medium of life on Earth, but is this because water is uniquely suited for life, or is it because life on Earth has adapted through time to a watery environment? We don't know the answer, but probably both explanations are partly true. Chemists have proposed that under conditions of high pressure and temperature, other small molecules, among them ammonia (NH_3) and some simple carbon-containing molecules, might display similar characteristics friendly to life. However, under the conditions of pressure and temperature that exist on Earth, water is the only molecule uniquely suited to life. Water is a truly remarkable substance, and life on Earth would not be possible without it. Leonardo da Vinci once wrote that water is the driving force of all nature. Without a doubt, water is the driving force of all biology.

2.4 CARBON: LIFE'S CHEMICAL BACKBONE

Hydrogen and helium are far and away the most abundant elements in the universe. In contrast, the solid Earth is dominated by silicon, oxygen, aluminum, iron, and calcium (Chapter 1). In other words, Earth is not a typical sample of the universe. Nor, as it turns out, is the cell a typical sample of the solid Earth. **Fig. 2.12** shows the relative abundance by mass of chemical elements present in human cells after all the water has been removed. Note that just four elements— carbon (C), oxygen (O), hydrogen (H), and nitrogen (N)— constitute 94% of the total dry mass, and that the most abundant is carbon. The elemental composition of human cells is typical of all cells. Human life, and all life as we know it, is based on carbon. Carbon molecules play such an important role in living organisms that carbon-containing molecules have a special name—they are called **organic molecules.** Their central role in life implies that there must be something very special about carbon, and there is. Carbon has the ability to combine with many other elements to form a wide variety of molecules, each specialized for the functions it carries out in the cell.

FIG. 2.12   Approximate proportions by dry mass of chemical elements found in human cells.

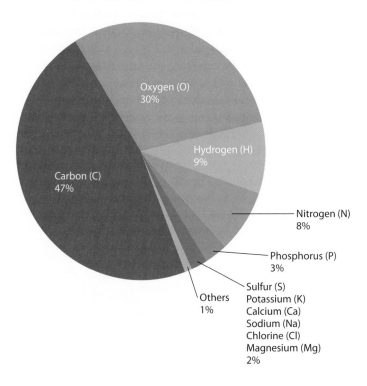

Carbon atoms form four covalent bonds.

One of the special properties of carbon is that, in forming molecular orbitals, a carbon atom behaves as if it had four unpaired electrons. This behavior occurs because one of the electrons in the outermost sphere moves into the empty dumbbell-shaped orbital. In this process, the single large spherical orbital and three dumbbell-shaped orbitals change shape, becoming four equivalent hybrid orbitals each with one electron.

Fig. 2.13 shows the molecular orbitals that result when one atom of carbon combines with four atoms of hydrogen to form the gas methane (CH_4). Each of the four valence electrons of carbon shares a new molecular orbital with the electron of one of the hydrogen atoms. These bonds can rotate freely about their axis. Furthermore, because of the shape of the orbitals, the carbon atom lies at the center of a three-dimensional structure called a tetrahedron, and the four molecular orbitals point toward the four corners of this structure. The ability of carbon to form four covalent bonds, the spatial orientation of these bonds in the form of a tetrahedron, and the ability of each bond to rotate freely all contribute importantly to the structural diversity of carbon-based molecules.

Carbon-based molecules are structurally and functionally diverse.

Carbon has other properties that contribute to its ability to form a diversity of molecules. For example, carbon atoms can link with each other by covalent bonds to form long chains. These chains can be branched, or two carbons at the ends of the chain or within the chain can link to form a ring structure.

FIG. 2.13   **A carbon atom with four covalent bonds.** One carbon atom combines with four hydrogen atoms to form methane.

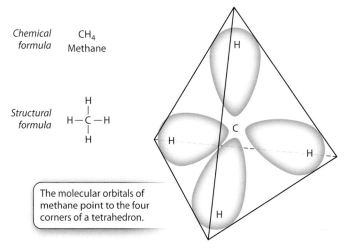

The molecular orbitals of methane point to the four corners of a tetrahedron.

FIG. 2.14 **Diverse carbon-containing molecules.** (a) The molecule ethane contains one C–C bond. (b) A linear chain of carbon atoms and a ring structure that also contains oxygen contain multiple C—C bonds.

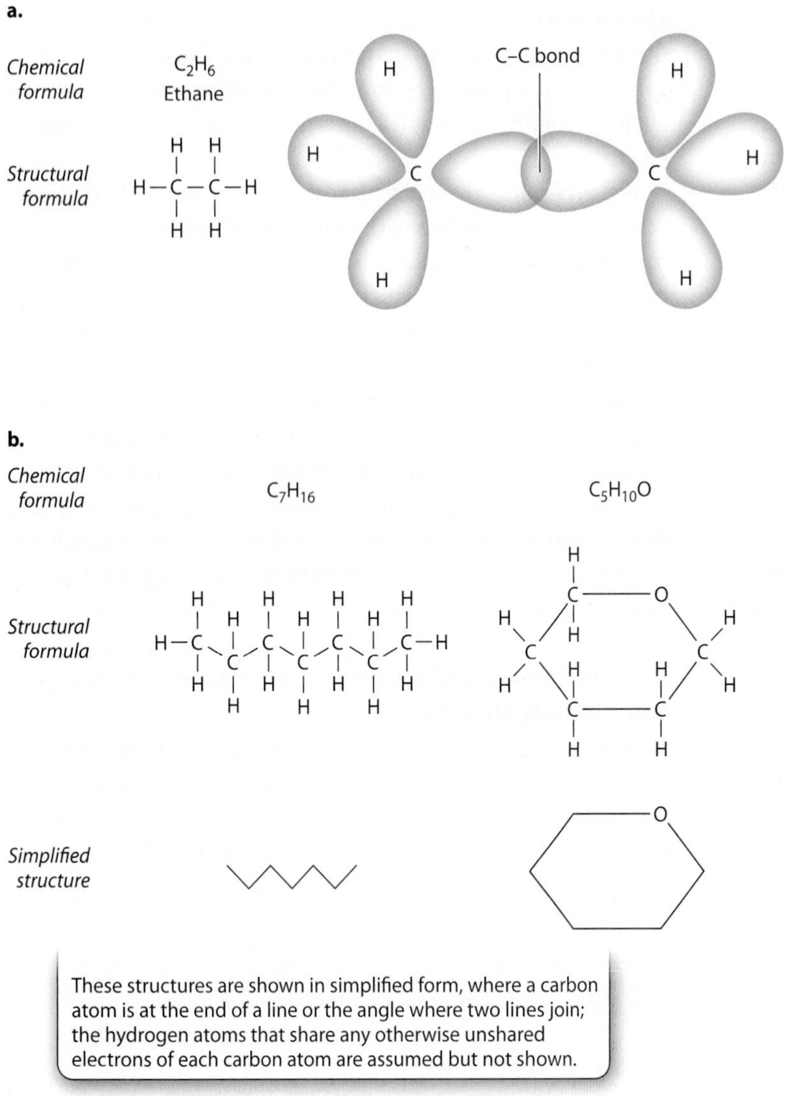

a.

Chemical formula C_2H_6 Ethane

Structural formula

C–C bond

b.

Chemical formula C_7H_{16} $C_5H_{10}O$

Structural formula

Simplified structure

These structures are shown in simplified form, where a carbon atom is at the end of a line or the angle where two lines join; the hydrogen atoms that share any otherwise unshared electrons of each carbon atom are assumed but not shown.

Among the simplest chains is ethane, shown in **Fig. 2.14a**, in which two carbon atoms become connected by a covalent bond. In this case, the orbitals of unpaired electrons in two carbon atoms merge to create the covalent bond. Some more complex examples of carbon-containing molecules, and an abbreviated form, are shown in **Fig. 2.14b.**

Two adjacent carbon atoms can also share two pairs of electrons, forming a **double bond,** as shown in **Fig. 2.15.** Note that each carbon atom has exactly four covalent bonds, but in this case two are shared between adjacent carbon atoms. The double bond is shorter than a single bond and is not free to rotate so that all of the covalent bonds in the carbon atoms connected by a double bond are in the same geometrical plane. As with single bonds, double bonds can be found in chains of atoms or cyclical structures. A double bond between atoms is represented by a double line connecting the two chemical symbols for the atoms.

While the types of atoms making up a molecule help characterize the molecule, the spatial arrangement of atoms is also important. For example, 6 carbon atoms, 13 hydrogen atoms, 2 oxygen atoms, and 1 nitrogen atom can join covalently in many different arrangements to produce molecules with different structures. Two of these many arrangements are shown in **Fig. 2.16.** Note that some of the connections between atoms are identical (black) and some are different (green), even though the chemical formulas are the same ($C_6H_{13}O_2N_1$). Molecules that have the same chemical formula but different structures are known as **isomers.**

We have seen that carbon-containing molecules can adopt a wide range of arrangements, a versatility

FIG. 2.15 **Molecules containing double bonds between carbon atoms.**

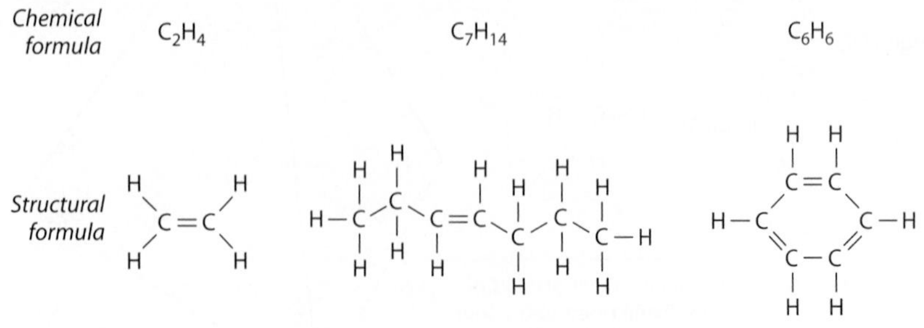

Chemical formula C_2H_4 C_7H_{14} C_6H_6

Structural formula

FIG. 2.16 **The isomers isoleucine and leucine.** Isoleucine and leucine are isomers: Their chemical formulas are the same, but their structures differ.

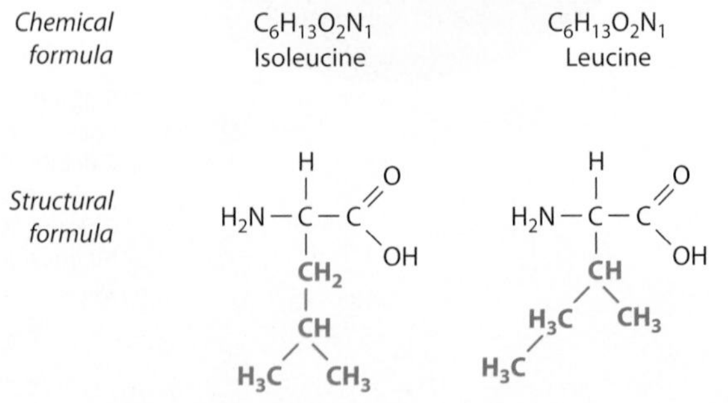

Chemical formula $C_6H_{13}O_2N_1$ Isoleucine $C_6H_{13}O_2N_1$ Leucine

Structural formula

that helps us to understand how a limited number of elements can create an astonishing variety of molecules. We might ask whether carbon is *uniquely* versatile. Put another way, if we ever discover life on a distant planet, will it be carbon based, like us? Silicon, just below carbon in the periodic table (see Fig. 2.3), is the one other element that is both reasonably abundant and characterized by four atomic orbitals with one electron each. Some scientists have speculated that silicon might provide an alternative to carbon as a chemical basis for life. However, silicon readily binds oxygen. On Earth, nearly all of the silicon atoms found in molecules are covalently bound to oxygen. Studies of Mars and of meteorites show that silicon is tightly bound to oxygen throughout our solar system, and that is likely to be true everywhere we might explore. There are about 1000 different silicate minerals on Earth, but this diversity pales before the millions of known carbon-based molecules. If we ever discover life beyond Earth, very likely its chemistry will be based on carbon.

2.5 ORGANIC MOLECULES

The chemistry of carbon creates diverse geometries, which in turn lead to molecules with different structures and functions. These molecules perform essential tasks of the cell, including the establishment of a boundary to separate the inside of the cell from the environment, the storage and transmission of genetic information, and the capture, storage, and utilization of energy from the environment. These processes depend on just a few classes of carbon-based molecules. **Proteins** provide structural support and act as catalysts that facilitate chemical reactions. **Nucleic acids** encode and transmit genetic information. **Carbohydrates** provide a source of energy and make up the cell wall in bacteria, plants, and algae. **Lipids** make up cell membranes, store energy, and act as signaling molecules.

These molecules are all relatively large, and most are **polymers,** complex molecules made up of repeated simpler units connected by covalent bonds. Proteins are polymers of **amino acids,** nucleic acids are made up of **nucleotides,** and carbohydrates such as starch are built from simple **sugars.** Lipids are a bit different, as we will see—they are defined by a property rather than by their chemical structure. The lipid membranes that define cell boundaries consist of **fatty acids** bonded to other organic molecules.

Building macromolecules from simple, repeating units provides a means of generating virtually limitless chemical diversity. Indeed, in macromolecules, the building blocks of polymers play a role much like that of the letters in words. In written language, a change in the content or order of letters changes the meaning of the word (or renders it meaningless). For example, by reordering the letters of the word "SILENT" you can write "LISTEN," a word with a different meaning. Similarly, rearranging the building blocks that make up macromolecules provides an important way to make a large number of diverse macromolecules.

In the following section, we focus on the building blocks of these four key molecules of life, reserving a discussion of the structure and function of the macromolecules for later chapters.

Proteins are composed of amino acids.

Proteins do much of the cell's work. Some function as catalysts that accelerate the rates of chemical reactions (in which case they are called **enzymes**), and some act as structural components necessary for cell shape and movement. Your body contains many thousands of proteins that perform a wide range of functions. Since proteins consist of amino acids linked covalently to form a chain, we need to examine the chemical features of amino acids to understand the diversity and versatility of proteins.

The general structure of an amino acid is shown in **Fig. 2.17a**. Each amino acid contains a central carbon atom, called the **α (alpha) carbon,** covalently linked to four groups: a **carboxyl group** (COOH; red), an **amino group** (NH_2; blue), a hydrogen atom (H), and an **R group,** or **side chain,** (green) that differs from one amino acid to the next. The identity of each amino acid is determined by the structure and composition of the side chain. The side chain of the amino acid glycine is simply H, for example, and that of alanine is CH_3. In most amino acids, the α-carbon is covalently linked to four different groups. Glycine is the exception, since its R group is a hydrogen atom.

Amino acids are linked in a chain to form a protein (**Fig. 2.17b**). The carbon atom in the carboxyl group of one amino acid is

FIG. 2.17 **Amino acids and peptide bonds** (a) An amino acid contains four groups attached to a central carbon. (b) Peptide bonds link amino acids to form a protein.

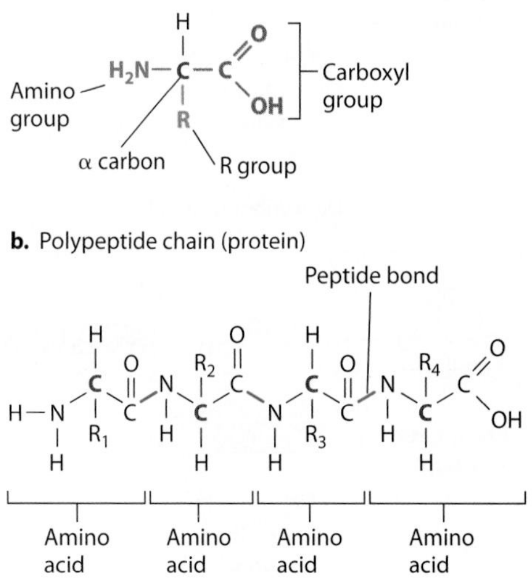

a. Amino acid

b. Polypeptide chain (protein)

joined to the nitrogen atom in the amino group of the next by a covalent linkage called a **peptide bond.** In Fig. 2.17b, the chain of amino acids includes four amino acids, and the peptide bonds are indicated in red. The formation of a peptide bond involves the loss of a water molecule since in order to form a C–N bond, the carbon atom must release an oxygen atom and the nitrogen must release two hydrogen atoms. These can then combine to form a water molecule (H_2O). The loss of a water molecule is a consistent feature in the linking of subunits to form polymers such as nucleic acids and complex carbohydrates.

Cellular proteins are composed of 20 amino acids, which can be classified according to the chemical properties of their side chains. The particular sequence, or order, in which amino acids are present in a protein determines how it folds into its three-dimensional structure. The three-dimensional structure, in turn, determines the protein's function. In Chapter 4, we will examine how the sequence of amino acids in a particular protein is specified and discuss how proteins fold into their three-dimensional configuration.

Nucleic acids encode genetic information in their nucleotide sequence.

Nucleic acids are examples of informational molecules—that is, they are large molecules that carry information in the sequence of nucleotides that make them up. This molecular information is much like the information carried by the letters in an alphabet, but in the case of nucleic acids, the information is in chemical form.

The nucleic acid **deoxyribonucleic acid (DNA)** is the genetic material in all organisms. It is transmitted from parents to offspring, and it contains the information needed to specify the amino acid sequence of all the proteins synthesized in an organism. The nucleic acid **ribonucleic acid (RNA)** has multiple functions; it is a key player in protein synthesis and the regulation of gene expression.

DNA and RNA are long molecules consisting of nucleotides bonded covalently one to the next. Nucleotides, in turn, are composed of three components: a 5-carbon sugar, a nitrogen-containing compound called a **base,** and one or more phosphate groups (**Fig. 2.18**). The sugar in RNA is ribose, and the sugar in DNA is deoxyribose. The sugars differ in that ribose has a hydroxyl (OH) group on the second carbon (designated the 2′ carbon), while deoxyribose has a hydrogen atom at this position (hence, *deoxy*ribose). (By convention, the carbons in the sugar are numbered with primes—1′, 2′, etc.—to distinguish them from carbons in the base—1, 2, etc.)

The bases are built from nitrogen-containing rings and are of two types. The **pyrimidine** bases (**Fig. 2.19a**) have a single ring and include **thymine (T), cytosine (C),** and **uracil (U).** The **purine** bases (**Fig. 2.19b**) have a double-ring structure and include **adenine (A)** and **guanine (G).** DNA contains the bases A, T, G, and C, and RNA contains the bases A, U, G, and C. Just as the order of amino acids provides the unique information carried in proteins, so, too, does the sequence of nucleotides determine the information in DNA and RNA molecules.

FIG. 2.18 A ribonucleotide and a deoxyribonucleotide, the units of RNA and DNA.

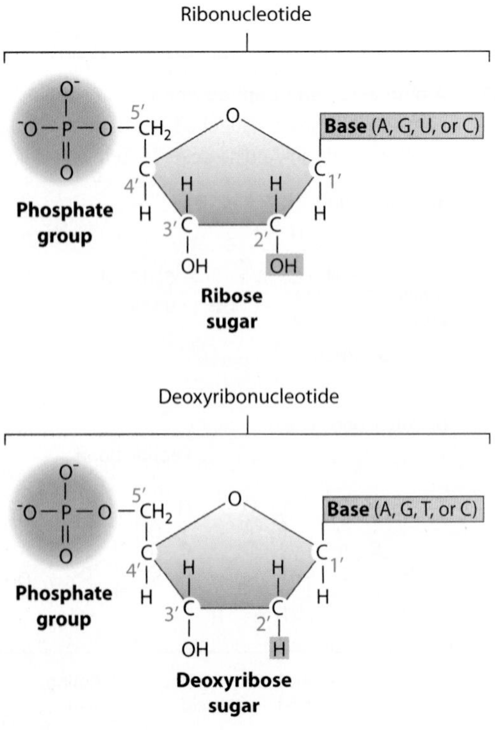

Ribonucleotide

Deoxyribonucleotide

FIG. 2.19 Pyrimidine bases (a) and purine bases (b). Pyrimidines have a single-ring structure, and purines have a double-ring structure.

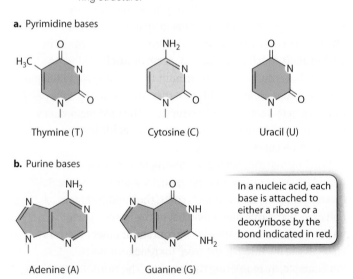

a. Pyrimidine bases

Thymine (T)   Cytosine (C)   Uracil (U)

b. Purine bases

Adenine (A)   Guanine (G)

In a nucleic acid, each base is attached to either a ribose or a deoxyribose by the bond indicated in red.

FIG. 2.20 **The phosphodiester bond.** Phosphodiester bonds link successive deoxyribonucleotides, forming the backbone of the DNA strand.

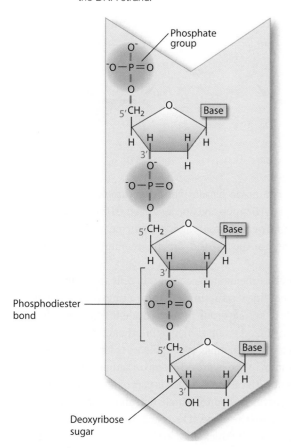

In DNA and RNA, each adjacent pair of nucleotides is connected by a **phosphodiester bond,** which forms when a phosphate group in one nucleotide is covalently joined to the sugar unit in another nucleotide (**Fig. 2.20**). As in the formation of a peptide bond, the formation of a phosphodiester bond involves the loss of a water molecule.

DNA in cells usually consists of two strands of nucleotides twisted around each other in the form of a **double helix** (**Fig. 2.21a**). The sugar–phosphate backbones of the strands wrap like a ribbon around the outside of the double helix, and the bases are pointed inward. The bases form specific purine–pyrimidine pairs that are said to be **complementary:** Where one strand carries an A, the other carries a T; and where one strand carries a G, the other carries a C (**Fig. 2.21b**). Base pairing results from hydrogen bonding between the bases (**Fig. 2.21c**).

Genetic information in DNA is contained in the sequence, or order, in which successive nucleotides

occur along the molecule. Successive nucleotides along a DNA strand can occur in *any* order, and hence a long molecule could contain any of an immense number of possible nucleotide sequences. This is one reason why DNA is an efficient carrier of genetic information. In Chapter 3, we consider the structure and function of DNA and RNA in greater detail.

Complex carbohydrates are made up of simple sugars.

Many of us, when we feel tired, reach for a candy bar for a quick energy boost. The quick energy in a candy bar comes from sugars, which are quickly broken down to release energy. Sugars belong to a class of molecules called **carbohydrates,** distinctive molecules composed of C, H, and O atoms, usually in the ratio 1:2:1. Carbohydrates provide a principal source of energy for metabolism.

The simplest carbohydrates are sugars (also called **saccharides**). Simple sugars are linear or, far more commonly, cyclic molecules containing five or six carbon atoms. All six-carbon sugars have the same chemical formula ($C_6H_{12}O_6$) and differ only in configuration. Glucose (the product of photosynthesis), galactose (found in dairy products), and fructose (a commercial sweetener) are examples; they share the same

FIG. 2.21 **The structure of DNA.** (a) DNA is most commonly in the form of a double helix, with the sugar and phosphate groups forming the backbone and the bases oriented inward. (b) The bases are complementary, with A pairing with T and G pairing with C. (c) Base pairing results from hydrogen bonds.

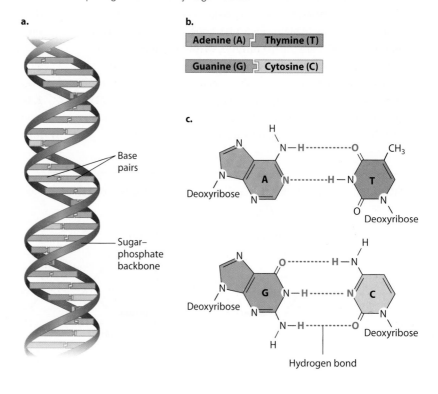

FIG. 2.22 Structural formulas for some 6-carbon aldoses and ketoses.

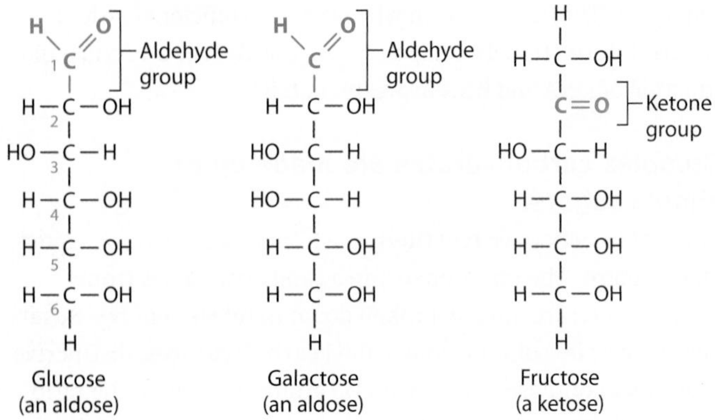

Glucose
(an aldose)

Galactose
(an aldose)

Fructose
(a ketose)

formula ($C_6H_{12}O_6$) but differ in the arrangement of their atoms (**Fig. 2.22**).

→ **Quick Check 4** Take a close look at Fig. 2.22. How is glucose different from galactose?

A simple sugar is also called a **monosaccharide** (*mono* means "one"), and two simple sugars linked together by a covalent bond is called a disaccharide (*di* means "two"). Sucrose ($C_{12}H_{22}O_{11}$), or table sugar, is a disaccharide that combines one molecule each of glucose and fructose. As noted above, nucleotides contain a 5-carbon sugar, either ribose (in RNA) or deoyxribose (in DNA). Simple sugars combine in many ways to form polymers called **polysaccharides** (*poly* means "many") that provide long-term energy storage (starch and glycogen) or structural support (cellulose in plant cell walls). Long, branched chains of monosaccharides are called **complex carbohydrates.**

Let's take a closer look at monosaccharides, the simplest sugars. Monosaccharides are unbranched carbon chains with either an aldehyde (HC═O) or a ketone (C═O) group (Fig. 2.22). Monosaccharides with an aldehyde group are called **aldoses** and those with a ketone group are known as **ketoses.** In

FIG. 2.23 Formation of the cyclic form of glucose.

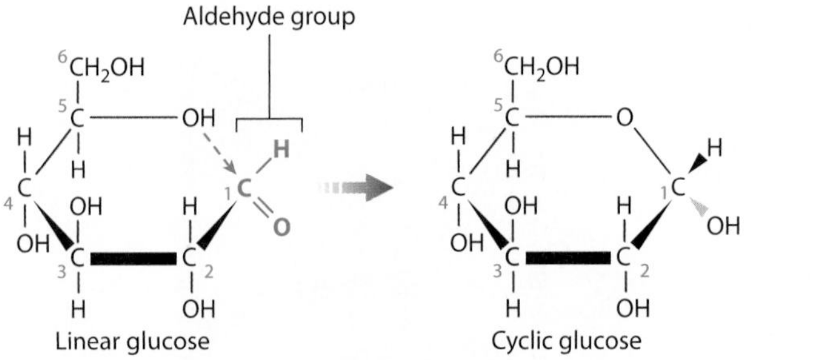

Linear glucose

Cyclic glucose

both types of monosaccharides, the other carbons each carry one hydroxyl (OH) group and one hydrogen (H) atom. When the linear structure of a monosaccharide is written with the aldehyde or ketone group at the top, the carbons are numbered from top to bottom.

Virtually all of the monosaccharides in cells are in ring form (**Fig. 2.23**), not linear structures. To form a ring, the carbon in the aldehyde or ketone group forms a covalent bond with the oxygen of a hydroxyl group carried by another carbon in the same molecule. For example, cyclic glucose is formed when the oxygen atom of the hydroxyl group on carbon 5 forms a covalent bond with carbon 1, which is part of an aldehyde group. The cyclic structure is approximately flat, and you can visualize it perpendicular to the plane of the paper with the covalent bonds indicated by the thick lines in the foreground. The groups attached to any carbon therefore project either above or below the ring. When the ring is formed, the aldehyde oxygen becomes a hydroxyl group.

Monosaccharides, especially 6-carbon sugars, are the building blocks of complex carbohydrates. Monosaccharides are attached to each other by covalent bonds called **glycosidic bonds** (**Fig. 2.24**). As with peptide bonds, the formation of glycosidic bonds involves the loss of a water molecule. A glycosidic bond is formed between carbon 1 of one monosaccharide and a hydroxyl

FIG. 2.24 **Glycosidic bonds.** Glycosidic bonds link glucose monomers together to form the polysaccharide starch.

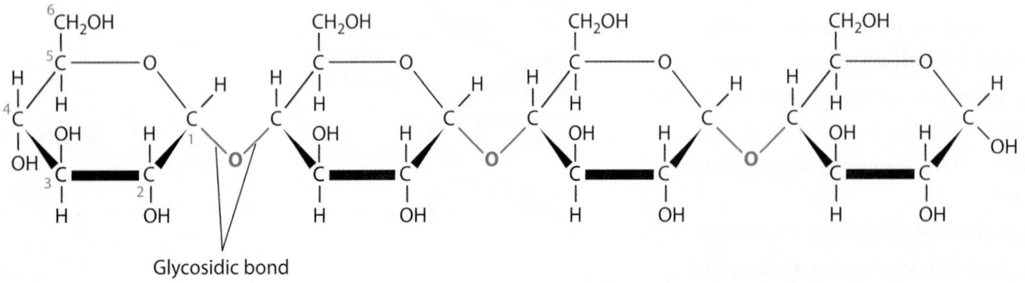

Glycosidic bond

group carried by a carbon atom in a different monosaccharide molecule.

Carbohydrate diversity stems in part from the monosaccharides that make them up, similar to the way that protein and nucleic acid diversity stems from the sequence of their subunits. Some complex carbohydrates are composed of a single type of monosaccharide, while others are a mix of different kinds of monosaccharide. Starch, for example, is a sugar storage molecule in plants composed completely of glucose molecules, whereas pectin, a component of the cell wall, contains up to five different monosaccharides.

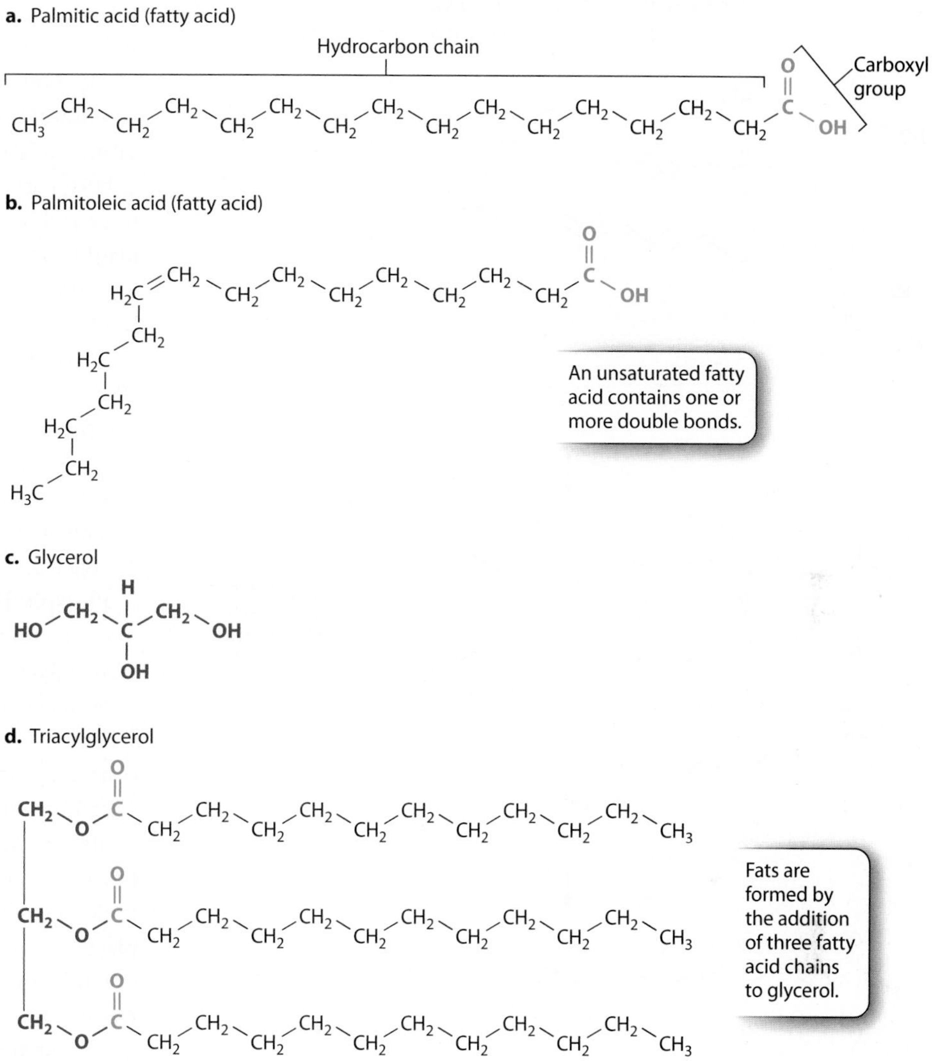

Lipids are hydrophobic molecules.

Proteins, nucleic acids, and carbohydrates all are polymers made up of smaller, repeating units with a defined structure. Lipids are different. Instead of being defined by a chemical structure, they share a particular property: Lipids are all hydrophobic. Because they share a property and not a structure, lipids are a chemically diverse group of molecules. They include familiar fats that make up part of our diet, components of cell membranes, and signaling molecules. Let's briefly consider each in turn.

Triacylglycerol is an example of a lipid that is used for energy storage. It is the major component of animal fat and vegetable oil. A triacylglycerol molecule is made up of three fatty acids joined to **glycerol** (**Fig. 2.25**). A fatty acid is a long chain of carbons attached to a carboxyl group (COOH) at one end (Figs. 2.25a and 2.25b). Glycerol is a 3-carbon molecule with OH groups attached to each carbon (Fig. 2.25c).

Fatty acids differ in the length (that is, in the number of carbons) of their hydrocarbon chain. Most fatty acids in cells contain an even number of carbons because they are synthesized by the stepwise addition of 2-carbon units. Some fatty acids have one or more carbon–carbon double bonds; these double bonds can differ in number and location. Fatty acids that do not contain double bonds are described as **saturated.** Because there are no double bonds, the maximum number of hydrogen atoms is attached to each carbon atom, so all of the carbons are

FIG. 2.25 Triacylglycerol and its components.

a. Palmitic acid (fatty acid)

b. Palmitoleic acid (fatty acid)

An unsaturated fatty acid contains one or more double bonds.

c. Glycerol

d. Triacylglycerol

Fats are formed by the addition of three fatty acid chains to glycerol.

said to be "saturated" with hydrogen atoms (Fig. 2.25a). Fatty acids that contain carbon–carbon double bonds are **unsaturated** (Fig. 2.25b). The chains of saturated fatty acids are straight, while the chains of unsaturated fatty acids have a kink at each double bond.

Triacylglycerols can contain different types of fatty acids attached to the glycerol backbone. They are all extremely hydrophobic and, therefore, triacylglycerols form oil droplets inside the cell. Triacylglycerols are an efficient form of energy storage because by excluding water molecules a large number can be packed into a small volume.

The hydrocarbon chains of fatty acids do not contain polar covalent bonds like those in a water molecule. Their electrons are distributed uniformly over the whole molecule and thus these molecules are uncharged. However, the constant motion

FIG. 2.26 **Van der Waals forces.** Transient asymmetry in the distribution of electrons along fatty acid chains leads to asymmetry in neighboring molecules, resulting in weak electrostatic attractions.

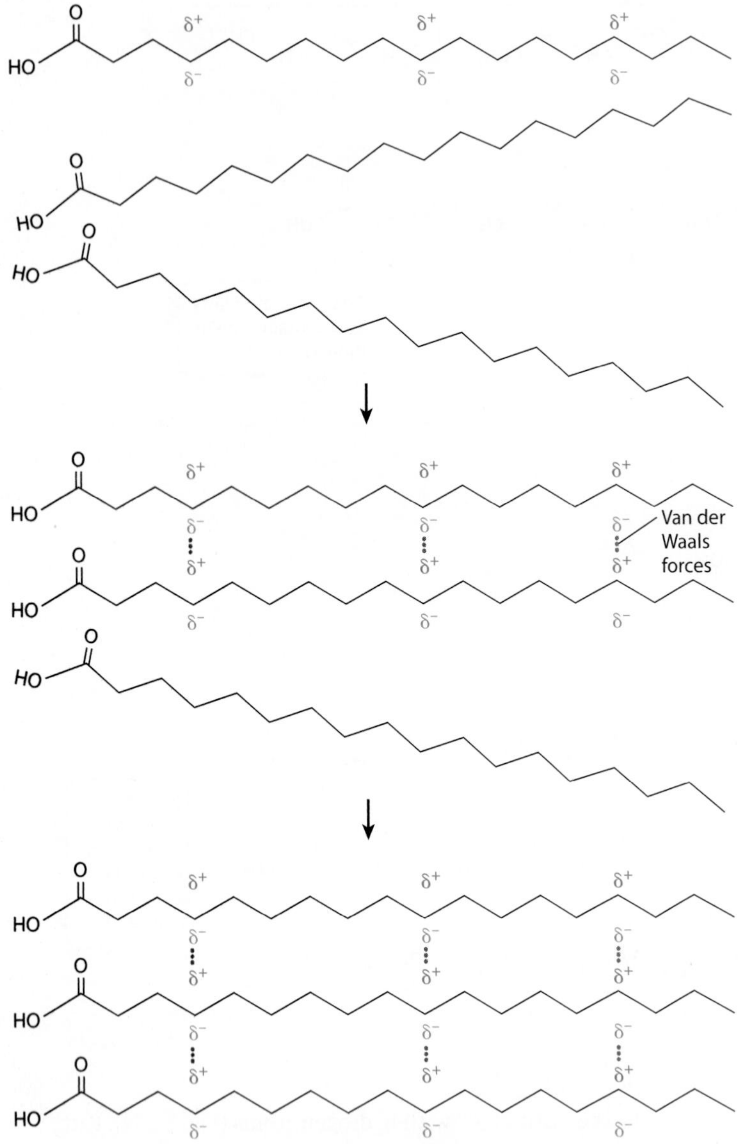

der Waals bonds between the chains also increases, and this in turn increases the melting temperature. Kinks introduced by double bonds reduce the tightness of the molecular packing and lead to fewer intermolecular interactions and a lower melting temperature. Therefore, an unsaturated fatty acid has a lower melting point than a saturated fatty acid of the same length. Animal fats such as butter are composed of triacylglycerols with saturated fatty acids and are solid at room temperature, whereas plant fats and fish oils are composed of triacylglycerols with unsaturated fatty acids and are liquid at room temperature.

Steroids such as cholesterol are a second type of lipid (**Fig. 2.27**). Like other steroids, cholesterol has a core composed of 20 carbon atoms bonded to form four fused rings, and it is hydrophobic. Cholesterol is a component of animal cell membranes (Chapter 5) and serves as a precursor for the synthesis of steroid hormones such as estrogen and testerone (Chapter 38).

Phospholipids are a third type of lipid and a major component of the cell membrane. Whereas triacylglycerol is made up of glycerol attached to three fatty acids, most phospholipids are made up of glycerol attached to two fatty acids and a third molecule that contains a phosphate group (**Fig. 2.28a**). The phosphate "head" group is hydrophilic, while the fatty acid "tails" are hydrophobic. As a result, phospholipids have hydrophobic and hydrophilic groups in the same molecule, giving them an interesting property when placed in water: They form a variety of structures all of which limit the exposure of the hydrophobic tails to water. One important structure is a **bilayer,** a two-layered structure with the hydrophilic heads pointing outward toward the aqueous environment and the hydrophobic tails oriented inward, away from water (**Fig. 2.28b**). The formation of lipid bilayers is discussed more fully in the next chapter.

of electrons leads to regions of slight positive and negative charges (**Fig. 2.26**). These charges in turn attract or repel electrons in neighboring molecules, setting up areas of positive and negative charge in those molecules as well. The temporarily polarized molecules weakly bind to one another because of the attraction of opposite charges. These interactions are known as **van der Waals forces.** The van der Waals forces are weaker than hydrogen bonds, but many of them acting together help to stabilize molecules.

Because of van der Waals forces, the melting points of fatty acids depend on their length and level of saturation. As the length of the hydrocarbon chains increases, the number of van

FIG. 2.27 **The chemical structure of cholesterol.**

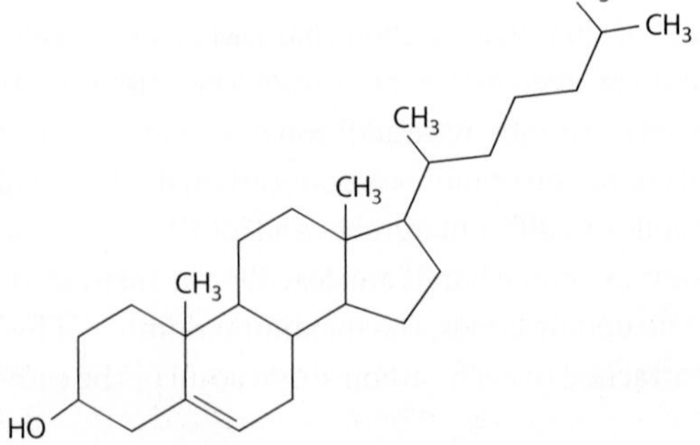

FIG. 2.28   Phospholipids. (a) Most phospholipids are made up of glycerol attached to two fatty acids and a phosphate-containing head group. (b) Phospholipids form a bilayer in aqueous solution.

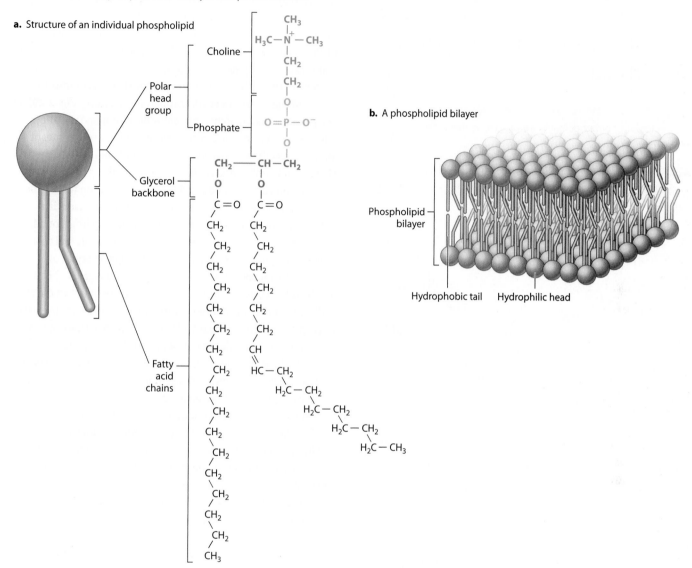

a. Structure of an individual phospholipid

b. A phospholipid bilayer

CASE 1 The First Cell: Life's Origins

2.6   HOW DID THE MOLECULES OF LIFE FORM?

In Chapter 1, we considered the similarities and differences between living and non-living things. Four billion years ago, however, the differences may not have been so pronounced. Scientists believe that life originated early in our planet's history by a set of chemical processes that, through time, produced organisms that could be distinguished from their non-living surroundings. How can we think scientifically about one of biology's deepest and most difficult problems? We can't reconstruct key events from the geological record—the study of fossils tells us that life already existed when

Earth's oldest surviving fossil-containing rocks were deposited. The alternative is to approach life's origins experimentally, asking whether chemical reactions likely to have taken place on the early Earth can generate the molecules of life. It is important to note that even the simplest living organisms living today are far more complicated than our earliest ancestors. No one suggests that cells as we know them emerged directly from primordial chemical reactions. Rather, the quest is to discover simple molecular systems able to replicate themselves, while subject to natural selection.

A key starting point is the observation, introduced earlier in this chapter, that the principal macromolecules found in organisms are themselves made of simpler molecules joined together. Thus, if we want to understand how proteins might have emerged on the early Earth, we should begin with the synthesis of amino acids, and if we are interested in nucleic acids, we should focus on nucleotides.

FIG. 2.29

Could the building blocks of organic molecules have been generated on the early Earth?

BACKGROUND In the 1950s, Earth's early atmosphere was widely believed to have been rich in water vapor, methane, ammonia, and hydrogen gas, with no free oxygen.

EXPERIMENT Stanley Miller built an apparatus, shown below, designed to simulate Earth's early atmosphere. Then he passed a spark through the mixture to simulate lightning.

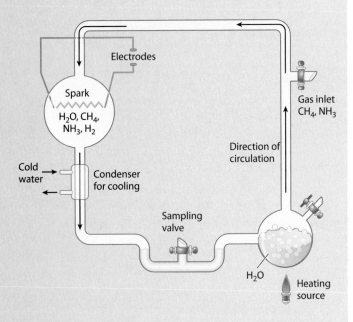

RESULTS As the experiment proceeded, reddish material accumulated on the walls of the flask. Analysis showed that the brown matter included a number of amino acids.

CONCLUSION Amino acids can be generated in conditions that mimic those of the early Earth.

FOLLOW-UP WORK Recent analysis of the original extracts, saved by Miller, shows that the experiment actually produced about 20 different amino acids, not all of them found in organisms.

SOURCE Miller, S. L. 1953. "Production of Amino Acids Under Possible Primitive Earth Conditions." *Science* 117:528–529.

The building blocks of life can be generated in the laboratory.

Research into the origins of life was catapulted into the experimental age in 1953, with an elegant experiment carried out by Stanley Miller, then a graduate student in the laboratory of Nobel laureate Harold Urey. Miller started with gases such as water vapor, methane, and hydrogen gas, all thought to have been present in the early atmosphere. He put these gases into a sealed flask and then passed a spark through the mixture (**Fig. 2.29**). On the primitive Earth, lightning might have supplied the energy needed to drive chemical reactions, and the spark was meant to simulate its effects. Analysis of the contents of the flask showed that a number of amino acids were generated.

Miller and others conducted many variations on his original experiment, all with similar results. Today, many scientists doubt that the early atmosphere had the composition found in Miller's experimental apparatus, but amino acids and other biologically important molecules can form in a variety of simulated atmospheric compositions. If oxygen gas (O_2) is absent and hydrogen is more common in the mixture than carbon, the addition of energy generates diverse amino acids. The absence of oxygen gas is critical, since Miller-Urey-type reactions cannot run to completion in modern air or seawater. Here, however, geology supports the experiments: Chemical analyses of Earth's oldest sedimentary rocks indicate that, for its first 2 billion years, Earth's surface contained little or no oxygen.

Later experiments have shown that other chemical reactions can generate simple sugars, the bases found in nucleotides, and the lipids needed to form primitive membranes. Independent evidence that simple chemistry can form the building blocks of life comes from certain meteorites, which provide samples of the early solar system and contain diverse amino acids, lipids, and other organic compounds.

Experiments show how life's building blocks can form macromolecules.

From the preceding discussion, we have seen that life's simple building blocks can be generated under conditions likely to have been present on the early Earth—but can these simple units be stitched together to form the polymeric molecules of life? Once again, careful experiments have shown how polymers could have formed in the conditions of the early Earth. Clay minerals that form from volcanic rocks can bind nucleotides on their surfaces (**Fig. 20.30a**). The clays provide a surface that places the nucleotides in proximity to one another, making it possible for them to join to form chains, or simple strands of nucleic acid.

In a classic experiment, biochemist Leslie Orgel placed a short nucleic acid sequence into a reaction vessel and then added individual chemically modified nucleotides. The nucleotides spontaneously joined into a polymer, forming the sequence complementary to the nucleic acid already present (**Fig. 20.30b**).

Such experiments show that nucleic acids can be synthesized experimentally from nucleotide building blocks, but until recently the synthesis of nucleotides themselves presented a formidable problem for research on the origins of life. Many tried to generate nucleotides from their sugar, base, and phosphate constituents, but no one succeeded until 2009. That year, John Sutherland and his colleagues showed that nucleotides can be synthesized under conditions thought to be like those on the young Earth. These chemists showed how simple organic molecules likely to have formed in abundance on the early Earth react in the presence of phosphate molecules, yielding the long-sought nucleotides.

Such humble beginnings eventually gave rise to the abundant diversity of life we see around us, described memorably by Charles Darwin in the final paragraph of *The Origin of Species:*

FIG. 2.30 **Spontaneous polymerization of nucleotides.** (a) Clays may have played an important role in the origin of life by providing surfaces for nucleotides to form nucleic acids. (b) Addition of a short RNA molecule, the template strand, to a flask containing modified nucleotides results in the formation of a complementary RNA strand.

a.

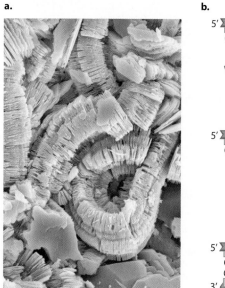

b.

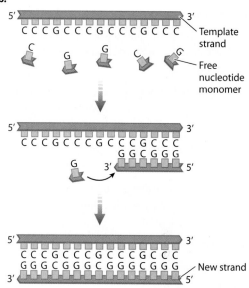

It is interesting to contemplate an entangled bank, clothed with many plants of many kinds, with birds singing on the bushes, with various insects flitting about, and with worms crawling through the damp earth, and to reflect that these elaborately constructed forms, so different from each other, and dependent on each other in so complex a manner, have all been produced by laws acting around us. . . . There is grandeur in this view of life . . . from so simple a beginning endless forms most beautiful and most wonderful have been, and are being, evolved.

Core Concepts Summary

2.1 THE ATOM IS THE FUNDAMENTAL UNIT OF MATTER.

Atoms consist of positively charged protons and electrically neutral neutrons in the nucleus, and negatively charged electrons darting around the nucleus. page 2-1

The number of protons determines the identity of an atom. page 2-2

Protons and neutrons together determine the mass of an atom. page 2-2

Protons and electrons determine the charge of an atom. page 2-3

Negatively charged electrons travel around the nucleus in regions called orbitals. page 2-3

The periodic table of the elements reflects a regular and repeating pattern in the chemical behavior of elements. page 2-3

2.2 ATOMS CAN COMBINE TO FORM MOLECULES LINKED BY CHEMICAL BONDS.

Electrons that occupy the outermost energy level (shell) of an atom (valence electrons) determine its ability to combine with other atoms to form molecules. page 2-4

A covalent bond results from the sharing of electrons between atoms to form molecular orbitals. page 2-4

A polar covalent bond results when two atoms do not share electrons equally as a result of a difference in the ability of the atoms to attract electrons, a property called electronegativity. page 2-5

A hydrogen bond results when a hydrogen atom covalently bonded to an electronegative atom interacts with an electronegative atom of another molecule. page 2-5

An ionic bond results from the attraction of oppositely charged ions. page 2-6

2.3 WATER IS ABUNDANT AND ESSENTIAL FOR LIFE.

Water is a polar molecule because shared electrons are distributed asymmetrically between the oxygen and hydrogen atoms. page 2-7

Hydrophilic molecules dissolve readily in water, while hydrophobic molecules in water tend to associate with one another, minimizing their contact with water. page 2-7

The pH of an aqueous solution is a measure of the acidity of the solution. page 2-7

Water forms hydrogen bonds, which help explain its high cohesion, surface tension, and resistance to rapid temperature change. page 2-8

2.4 CARBON IS THE BACKBONE OF ORGANIC MOLECULES.

A carbon atom can form up to four covalent bonds with other atoms. page 2-9

The geometry of these covalent bonds helps explain the structural and functional diversity of organic molecules. page 2-9

2.5 ORGANIC MOLECULES INCLUDE PROTEINS, NUCLEIC ACIDS, CARBOHYDRATES, AND LIPIDS, EACH OF WHICH IS BUILT FROM SIMPLER UNITS.

Amino acids are linked by covalent bonds to form proteins. page 2-11

An amino acid consists of a carbon atom (the α-carbon) attached to a carboxyl group, an amino group, a hydrogen atom, and a side chain. page 2-11

The side chain determines the properties of each amino acid. page 2-11

Nucleotides assemble to form nucleic acids, which store and transmit genetic information. page 2-12

Nucleotides are composed of a 5-carbon sugar, a nitrogen-containing base, and a phosphate group. page 2-12

Nucleotides in DNA incorporate the sugar ribose, and nucleotides in RNA incorporate the sugar deoxyribose. page 2-12

The bases are pyrimidines (thymine, cytosine, and uracil) and purines (adenine and guanine). page 2-12

Sugars are carbohydrates, distinctive molecules composed of C, H, and O atoms, usually in the ratio 1:2:1, that are a source of energy. page 2-13

Monosaccharides assemble to form disaccharides or longer polymers called complex carbohydrates. page 2-14

Lipids are hydrophobic. page 2-15

Triacylglycerols store energy and are made up of glycerol and fatty acids. page 2-15

Fatty acids consist of a linear hydrocarbon chain of variable length with a carboxyl group at one end. page 2-15

Fatty acids are either saturated (no carbon–carbon double bonds) or unsaturated (one or more carbon–carbon double bonds). page 2-15

The tight packing of fatty acids in lipids is the result of van der Waals forces, a type of weak, noncovalent bond. page 2-16

2.6 LIFE LIKELY ORIGINATED ON EARTH BY A SET OF CHEMICAL REACTIONS THAT GAVE RISE TO THE MOLECULES OF LIFE.

In 1953, Stanley Miller and Harold Urey demonstrated that amino acids can be generated in the laboratory in conditions that mimic those of the early Earth. page 2-18

Other experiments have shown that sugars, bases, and lipids can be generated in a similar way. page 2-18

Once the building blocks were synthesized, they could join together in the presence of clay minerals to form polymers. page 2-18

Self-Assessment

1. Name and describe the components of an atom.

2. Explain how the periodic table of the elements is organized.

3. Differentiate among covalent, polar covalent, hydrogen, and ionic bonds.

4. List three features of water that make it conducive to life.

5. Name the four most common elements in organic molecules.

6. List features of carbon that allow it to form diverse structures.

7. List essential functions of proteins, nucleic acids, carbohydrates, and lipids.

8. Describe how diversity is achieved in polymers.

9. Sketch the basic structures of amino acids, nucleotides, monosaccharides, and fatty acids.

10. State and defend current hypotheses about how life originated on Earth.

Do you understand the chapter's Core Concepts? Log into BIO*PORTAL* to check your answers to the Self-Assessment questions, then practice what you've learned and reinforce this chapter's concepts by working through the problems and multimedia tutorials provided there.

🛜 http://courses.bfwpub.com/yourbioportal/index.php

CHAPTER 3

NUCLEIC ACIDS AND THE ENCODING OF BIOLOGICAL INFORMATION

Core Concepts

3.1 Deoxyribonucleic acid (DNA) stores and transmits genetic information.

3.2 DNA is a polymer of nucleotides and forms a double helix.

3.3 Transcription is the process by which RNA is synthesized from a DNA template.

3.4 The primary transcript is processed to become messenger RNA (mRNA).

So much in biology depends on shape. Take your hand, for example. You can pick up a pin, text on a cellphone, and touch your pinky to your thumb. These activities are made possible by the coordinated movement of dozens of bones, muscles, nerves, and blood vessels that give shape to your hand. The functional abilities of your hand emerge from its structure. A causal connection between structure and function exists in many molecules, too. Proteins are a good example. Composed of linear strings of 20 amino acids, each protein folds into a specific three-dimensional shape due to chemical interactions between the amino acids along the chain. The three-dimensional structure of the protein determines its functional properties, such as what other molecules it can bind with, and enables the protein to carry out its job in the cell.

Another notable example is the macromolecule **deoxyribonucleic acid (DNA)**, a linear polymer of four subunits. DNA molecules from all cells and organisms have a very similar three-dimensional structure, reflecting their shared ancestry. This structure, called a **double helix,** is composed of two strands coiled around each other to form a sort of spiral staircase. The banisters of the spiral staircase are formed by the linear backbone of the paired strands, and the steps are formed by the pairing of the subunits at the same level in each strand.

The spiral-staircase structure is common to all cellular DNA molecules, and its structure gave immediate clues to its function. First, DNA *stores* information. Some of the information in DNA encodes for proteins that provide structure and do much of the work of the cell. Information in DNA is called **genetic information,** and it is organized in the form of **genes,** as textual information is organized in the form of words. Genes can differ from one individual to the next, even within a single species. Differences in genes can affect the shape of the hand, for example, yielding long or short fingers or extra or missing fingers. As we will see, it is the order of individual subunits (bases) of DNA that accounts for differences in genes.

Second, DNA plays a special role in *transmitting* genetic information from one generation to the next. The transmission of genetic information from parents to their offspring enables species of organisms to maintain their identity through time. The genetic information in DNA guides the development of the offspring, ensuring that parental apple trees give rise to apple seedlings and parental geese give rise to goslings. As we will see, determining the double-helical structure of DNA provided one of the first hints of how genetic information could be faithfully copied from cell to cell, and from one generation to the next.

In this chapter, we examine the structure of DNA in more detail and show how its structure is well suited to its biological function as the carrier and transmitter of genetic information.

3.1 MAJOR BIOLOGICAL FUNCTIONS OF DNA

DNA is the molecule by which hereditary information is transmitted from generation to generation. Today the role of DNA is well known, but at one time hardly any biologist would have bet on it. Any poll of biologists before about 1950 would have shown overwhelming support for proteins as life's information molecule. Compared to the seemingly monotonous, featureless structure of DNA, the three-dimensional structures of proteins are highly diverse. Proteins carry out most of the essential activities in the life of a cell, and so it seemed logical to assume that they would play a key role in heredity, too. But while proteins do play a role in heredity, they play a supporting role in looking after the DNA—rather like the way worker bees are essential in maintaining the queen bee, who alone is able to reproduce.

DNA can transfer biological characteristics from one organism to another.

The first experiments to demonstrate that molecules can transfer genetic information from one organism to another were carried out in 1928 by Frederick Griffith, working with the bacterium *Streptococcus pneumoniae*. This organism causes a variety of infections in humans and a deadly form of pneumonia in mice. In the original experiments, illustrated in **Fig. 3.1,**

HOW DO WE KNOW?

FIG. 3.1

What is the nature of the genetic material?

BACKGROUND In the 1920s, it was not clear what biological molecule carries genetic information. Fred Neufeld, a German microbiologist, identified several strains of the bacterium *Streptococcus pneumoniae*, one of which was virulent and caused death when injected into mice (Fig. 3.1a), and another which was nonvirulent and did not cause illness when injected into mice (Fig. 3.1b).

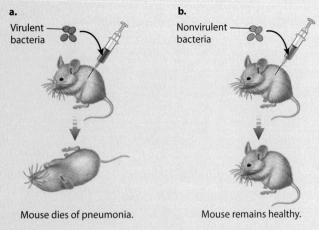

a. Virulent bacteria

Mouse dies of pneumonia.

b. Nonvirulent bacteria

Mouse remains healthy.

EXPERIMENT Frederick Griffith was also a microbiologist interested in bacterial virulence. He made a puzzling observation. He noted that nonvirulent bacteria do not cause mice to get sick (Fig. 3.1b) and killed virulent bacteria do not cause mice to get sick (Fig. 3.1c), but when the two were mixed, the injected mice got sick and died (Fig. 3.1d). Furthermore, when he isolated bacteria from the dead mice, they had the appearance of the virulent strain, even though he had injected nonvirulent bacteria.

RESULTS

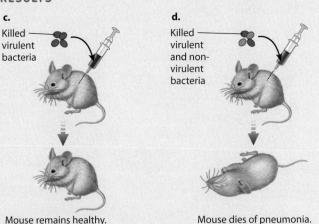

c. Killed virulent bacteria

Mouse remains healthy.

d. Killed virulent and nonvirulent bacteria

Mouse dies of pneumonia.

CONCLUSION One strain of bacteria (nonvirulent) can be transformed into another (virulent) by an unknown molecule from the virulent cells. In other words, the unknown molecule carries information that causes virulence.

FOLLOW-UP WORK Griffith's experiments were followed up by many researchers, most notably Oswald Avery, Colin MacLeod, and Maclyn McCarty, who identified DNA as the molecule responsible for transforming bacteria from one strain to the other (see Fig. 3.2). In addition, the process in which DNA is taken up by cells, called transformation, is now a common technique used in molecular biology.

SOURCE: Griffith, F. 1928. "The Significance of Pneumococcal Types." *Journal of Hygiene* 27:113–159.

Griffith studied two strains of the bacterium, one a virulent strain that caused pneumonia and death in injected mice and the other a mutant, nonvirulent strain that allowed injected mice to survive. When the debris of dead virulent cells was mixed with nonvirulent cells, some of the nonvirulent cells became virulent. Griffith concluded that some type of molecule in the debris carried the genetic information for virulence, but he did not identify the molecule.

Experiments carried out in 1944 by Oswald Avery, Colin MacLeod, and Maclyn McCarty showed that the molecule responsible for the conversion, or **transformation,** of nonvirulent cells into virulent cells is DNA (**Fig. 3.2**). These collaborators made a highly purified preparation from the debris of virulent cells, and they found that the preparation could carry out transformation. When enzymes were used to destroy any trace of protein or RNA in the preparation, the transforming ability of the preparation remained. But when an enzyme that destroys DNA was used, the transforming ability was lost.

These experiments, along with others, established that DNA is the genetic material. Today, transformation is widely used in biological research and in the genetic modification of agricultural plants and animals (Chapter 12).

DNA molecules are copied in the process of replication.
DNA can serve as the genetic material because it is unique among cellular molecules in being able to specify exact copies of itself. This copying process, known as **replication,** allows the genetic information from one DNA molecule to be copied into that of another DNA molecule. Faithful replication is critical in that it allows DNA to pass genetic information from cell to cell and from parent to offspring. The copying must reproduce the sequence of subunits almost exactly because most changes that occur are harmful to the cell or organism.

A rare error that can take place in DNA replication is known as a **mutation,** which is a change in the genetic information in DNA. A mutation in DNA causes the genetic difference between virulent and nonvirulent *Streptococcus pneumoniae*. While most mutations are harmful, rare favorable mutations are essential in the process of evolution because they allow populations of organisms to change through time and adapt to their environment.

Genetic information flows from DNA to RNA to protein.
Biologists often say that genetic information in DNA directs the activities in a cell or guides the development of an organism, but these effects of DNA are indirect. Most of the key molecules in cells and development are proteins, including the enzymes that convert energy into usable forms and the proteins that provide structural support for the cell. DNA acts indirectly by specifying the sequence of amino acid subunits of which each protein is

FIG. 3.2

What is the nature of the genetic material?

BACKGROUND Oswald Avery, Colin MacLeod, and Maclyn McCarty also studied virulence in pneumococcal bacteria. They recognized the significance of Griffith's experiments (see Fig. 3.1) and wanted to identify the molecule responsible for transforming nonvirulent bacteria into virulent ones.

EXPERIMENT Avery, MacLeod, and McCarty extracted DNA from virulent bacteria, which allowed them to perform a series of tests and control variables. To identify what caused transformation, they treated the extract, which contained DNA as well as trace amounts of RNA and protein, with enzymes that destroyed one of the three molecules. Their hypothesis was that transformation would not occur if they destroyed the molecule responsible for it.

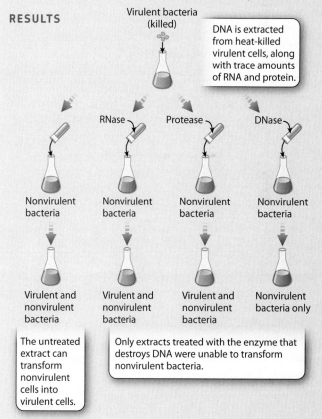

RESULTS

Virulent bacteria (killed)

DNA is extracted from heat-killed virulent cells, along with trace amounts of RNA and protein.

RNase   Protease   DNase

Nonvirulent bacteria | Nonvirulent bacteria | Nonvirulent bacteria | Nonvirulent bacteria

Virulent and nonvirulent bacteria | Virulent and nonvirulent bacteria | Virulent and nonvirulent bacteria | Nonvirulent bacteria only

The untreated extract can transform nonvirulent cells into virulent cells.

Only extracts treated with the enzyme that destroys DNA were unable to transform nonvirulent bacteria.

CONCLUSION DNA is the molecule responsible for transforming nonvirulent bacteria into virulent bacteria. This experiment provided a key piece of evidence that DNA is the genetic material.

FOLLOW-UP WORK These experiments were followed up by Alfred Hershey and Martha Chase, who used a different system to confirm that DNA is the genetic material.

SOURCE: Avery, O., C. MacLeod, and M. McCarty. 1944. "Studies on the Chemical Nature of the Substance Inducing Transformation of Pneumococcal Types." *Journal of Experimental Medicine.* 79:137–158.

composed, and this sequence in turn determines the three-dimensional structure of the protein, its chemical properties, and its biological activities.

In specifying the amino acid sequence of proteins, DNA acts through an intermediary molecule known as **ribonucleic acid (RNA),** another type of linear polymer. As we saw in Chapter 1, the flow of information from DNA to RNA to protein has come to be known as the **central dogma** of molecular biology (**Fig. 3.3).** The central dogma states that genetic information can be transferred from DNA to RNA to protein. Through the years, some exceptions to this "dogma" have been discovered, including the transfer of genetic information from RNA to DNA (as in HIV, which causes AIDS), from RNA to RNA (as in replication of the genetic material of influenza virus), and even from protein to protein (in the unusual case of prions). Nevertheless, the central dogma still conveys the basic idea that in most cases the flow of information is from DNA to RNA to protein.

The first step in this process is **transcription,** in which the genetic information in a molecule of DNA is used as a **template,** or pattern, to generate a molecule of RNA. The term "transcription" is used because it emphasizes that both molecules use the same language of nucleic acids. Transcription is the first step in **gene expression,** which is the production of a functional gene product. The second step in the readout of genetic information is **translation,** in which a molecule of RNA is used as a code for the sequence of amino acids in a protein. The term "translation" is used to indicate a change of languages, from nucleotides that make up nucleic acids to amino acids that make up proteins.

The processes of transcription and translation are regulated, meaning that they do not occur at all times in all cells. Genes are expressed, or turned "on," only at certain times and places, and not expressed, or turned "off," at other times and places. In multicellular organisms, for instance, cells are specialized for certain functions, and these different functions depend on which genes are on and which genes are off in specific cells. Muscle cells express genes that encode for proteins involved in muscle contraction, but these genes are not expressed in skin cells or liver cells, for example. Similarly, during development of a multicellular organism, genes may be required at certain times, but not at others. In this case, the timing of expression is carefully controlled.

In prokaryotes, transcription and translation occur in the cytoplasm, but in eukaryotes, the two processes are separated from each other, with transcription occurring in the nucleus and translation in the cytoplasm. The separation of transcription and translation in time and space in eukaryotic cells allows for additional levels of gene regulation that are not possible in prokaryotic cells. In spite of this and other differences in the details of transcription and translation between prokaryotes and eukaryotes, the processes are sufficiently similar that they must have evolved early in the history of life.

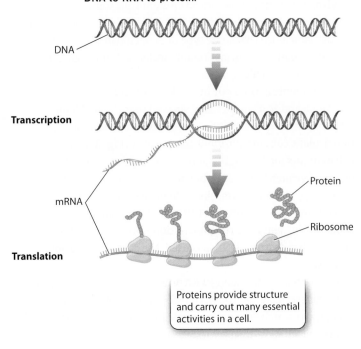

FIG. 3.3 The central dogma of molecular biology, which defines the usual flow of information in a cell from DNA to RNA to protein.

DNA

Transcription

mRNA

Translation

Protein

Ribosome

Proteins provide structure and carry out many essential activities in a cell.

3.2 CHEMICAL COMPOSITION AND STRUCTURE OF DNA

By about 1950, some biologists were convinced by the work of Griffith, Avery, and others that DNA is the genetic material. To serve as the genetic material, DNA would have to be able to replicate itself, undergo rare mutations, replicate mutant forms as faithfully as the original forms, and direct the synthesis of other macromolecules in the cell. How could one molecule do all this? Part of the answer emerged in 1953, when James D. Watson and Francis H. C. Crick announced a description of the three-dimensional structure of DNA. This discovery marked a turning point in modern biology. The discovery of the structure of DNA opened the door to understanding how genetic information is stored, faithfully replicated, and altered by rare mutations.

A DNA strand consists of subunits called nucleotides. In the 50 years since the publication of Watson and Crick's paper, we have all become familiar with the iconic double helix of DNA. The elegant shape of the twisting strands relies on the structure of DNA's subunits, called **nucleotides.** As we saw in Chapter 2, nucleotides consist of three components: a 5-carbon **sugar,** a **base,** and one or more **phosphate groups (Fig. 3.4).** Each component plays an important role in DNA structure. The 5-carbon sugars and phosphate groups form the backbone of the molecule, with each sugar linked to the phosphate group of the

FIG. 3.4   Nucleotide structure.

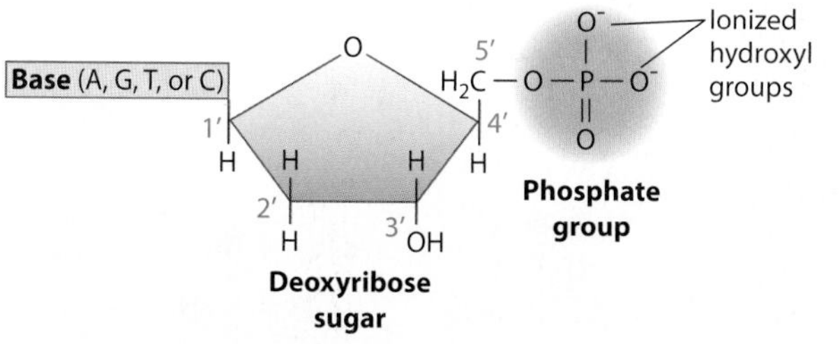

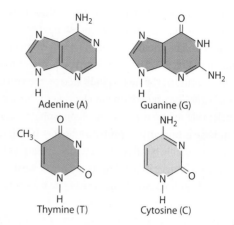

FIG. 3.5   Bases normally found in DNA.

neighboring nucleotide. The bases sticking out from the sugar give each nucleotide its chemical identity. Each strand of DNA consists of an enormous number of nucleotides linked one to the next.

DNA had been discovered 85 years before its three-dimensional structure was determined, and in the meantime a great deal had been learned about its chemistry, specifically the chemistry of nucleotides. Fig. 3.4 illustrates a nucleotide. In the figure, the 5-carbon sugar is indicated by the pentagon, in which each vertex represents the position of a carbon atom. By convention the carbon atoms of the sugar ring are numbered with primes (1′, 2′, and so forth, read as "one prime," "two prime" and so forth). Technically, the sugar in DNA is 2′-deoxyribose because the chemical group projecting downward from the 2′ carbon is a hydrogen atom (–H) rather than a hydroxyl group (–OH), but for our purposes the term **deoxyribose** will suffice.

Note in Fig. 3.4 that the phosphate group attached to the 5′ carbon has negative charges on two of its oxygen atoms. These charges are present because at cellular pH (around 7), the free hydroxyl groups attached to the phosphorus atom are ionized by the loss of a proton, and hence are negatively charged. It is these negative charges that make DNA a mild acid, which you will recall from Chapter 2 is a molecule that tends to lose protons to the aqueous environment.

Each base is attached to the 1′ carbon of the sugar and projects above the sugar ring. A nucleotide normally contains one of four kinds of bases, denoted A, G, T, and C **(Fig. 3.5).** Two of the bases are double-ring structures known as **purines;** these are the bases **adenine (A)** and **guanine (G),** shown across the top of the figure. The other two bases are single-ring structures known as **pyrimidines;** these are the bases **thymine (T)** and **cytosine (C),** shown across the bottom.

The combination of sugar and base is known as a **nucleoside,** which is shown in simplified form in **Fig. 3.6**. A nucleoside with one or more phosphate groups constitutes a nucleotide. When a nucleoside has one phosphate group attached to the 5′ carbon, it is called a nucleoside 5′-monophosphate, in which the 5′ indicates where a phosphate group is attached to the ring. The nucleotide shown in Fig. 3.4 is therefore a nucleoside 5′-monophosphate. When one of the free hydroxyl

groups attached to the phosphorus atom is in turn attached to another phosphate group, the nucleotide becomes a nucleoside 5′-diphosphate, and if yet another phosphate group is attached to the second, it becomes a nucleoside 5′-triphosphate (Fig. 3.6). The nucleoside triphosphates are particularly important because, as we will see later in this chapter, they are the molecules that are used to form nucleotide polymers, such as DNA and RNA. In addition, nucleoside triphosphates have other functions in the cell, notably as carriers of chemical energy in the form of ATP and GTP.

FIG. 3.6   **Nucleoside and nucleoside phosphates.** A nucleoside is a sugar attached to a base, and nucleotides are nucleosides with one, two, or three phosphate groups.

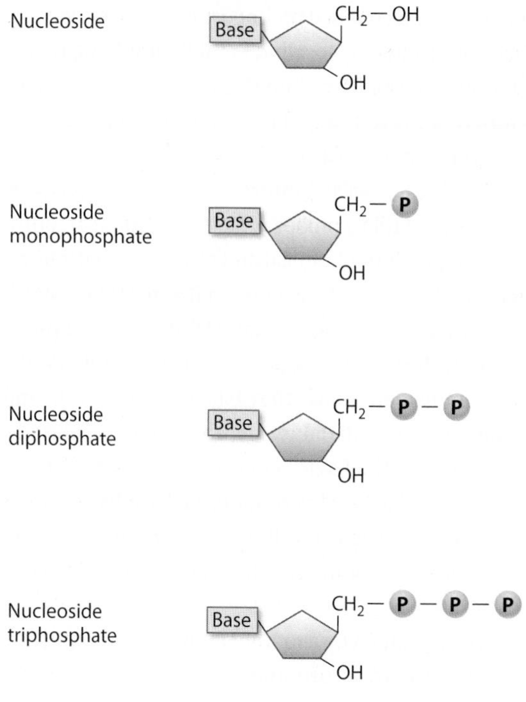

Nucleoside

Nucleoside monophosphate

Nucleoside diphosphate

Nucleoside triphosphate

DNA is a linear polymer of nucleotides linked by phosphodiester bonds.

Not only were the nucleotide building blocks of DNA known before the structure was discovered, it was also known how they were linked into a polymer. The chemical linkages between nucleotides in DNA are shown in **Fig. 3.7.** The characteristic covalent bond that connects one nucleotide to the next is indicated by the vertical red lines that connect the 3′ carbon of one nucleotide to the 5′ carbon of the next nucleotide in line through the 5′-phosphate group. This C–O–P–O–C linkage is known as a **phosphodiester bond,** which in DNA is a relatively stable bond that can withstand stress like heat and substantial changes in pH that would break weaker bonds. The succession of phosphodiester bonds traces the backbone of the DNA strand.

The phosphodiester linkages in a DNA strand give it **polarity,** which means that one end differs from the other. In Fig. 3.7, the nucleotide at the top has a free 5′ phosphate, and is known as the **5′ end** of the molecule. The nucleotide at the bottom has a free 3′ hydroxyl and is known as the **3′ end**. The DNA strand in Fig. 3.7 has the sequence of bases AGCT from top to bottom, but because of strand polarity we need to specify which end is which. For this strand of DNA, we could say that the base sequence is 5′-AGCT-3′ or equivalently 3′-TCGA-5′. When a base sequence is stated without specifying the 5′ end, by convention the end at the left is the 5′ end. Hence, we could say the sequence in Fig. 3.7 is AGCT, which means 5′-AGCT-3′.

Cellular DNA molecules take the form of a double helix.

To the knowledge of the chemical makeup of the nucleotides and their linkages in a DNA strand, Watson and Crick added results from earlier physical studies indicating that DNA is a long molecule. They also relied on important information from X-ray diffraction studies by Rosalind Franklin implying that DNA molecules form a helix with a simple repeating structure. Analysis of the pattern of X-rays diffracted from a crystal of a molecule can indicate the arrangement of atoms in the molecules.

With these critical pieces of information in hand, Watson and Crick set out to build a model of DNA that could account for the results of all previous chemical and physical experiments, using sheet metal cutouts of the bases and wire ties for the sugar–phosphate backbone. After many false starts and much disappointment, they finally found a structure that worked. They realized immediately that they had made one of the most important discoveries in all of biology, and that day, February 28, 1953, they lunched at the Eagle, a pub across the street from their laboratory, where Crick loudly pronounced, "We have discovered the secret of life." The Eagle is still there in Cambridge, England, and sports on its wall a commemorative plaque marking the table where the two ate.

Why all the fuss (and why the Nobel Prize 9 years later)? First, let's look at the structure, and you will see that the

FIG. 3.7 Nucleotides linked by phosphodiester bonds to form a DNA strand.

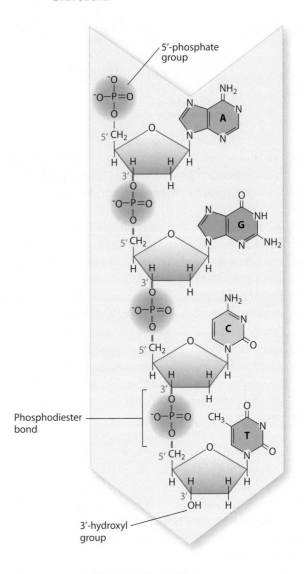

structure itself tells you how DNA carries and transmits genetic information. The Watson-Crick structure, now often called the double helix, is shown in **Fig. 3.8.** Fig. 3.8a is a space-filling model, in which each atom is represented as a color-coded sphere. The big surprise of the structure is that it consists of two DNA strands like that in Fig. 3.7, each wrapped around the other in the form of a helix coiling to the right, with the sugar–phosphate backbones winding around the outside of the molecule and the bases pointing inward. In the double helix, there are 10 base pairs per complete turn, and the diameter of the molecule is 2 nm, a measurement that is hard to relate to everyday objects, but it might help to know that the cross section of a bundle of 100,000 DNA molecules would be about the size of the period at the end of this sentence. The outside contours of the twisted strands form an uneven pair of grooves, called the **major groove** and the

minor groove. These grooves are important because proteins that interact with DNA often recognize a particular sequence of bases by making contact with the bases via the major or minor groove or both.

Importantly, the individual DNA strands in the double helix are **antiparallel,** which means that they run in opposite directions. That is, the 3′ end of one strand is opposite the 5′ end of the other. In Fig. 3.8a, the strand that starts at the bottom left and coils upward begins with the 3′ end and terminates at the top with the 5′ end, whereas its partner strand begins with its 5′ end at the bottom and terminates with the 3′ end at the top.

Fig. 3.8b shows a different depiction of double-stranded DNA, called a ribbon model, which clearly shows the sugar–phosphate backbones winding around the outside with the bases paired between the strands. The ribbon model of the structure closely resembles a spiral staircase, with the backbones forming the banisters and the base pairs the steps. If the amount of DNA in

the human genome (3 billion base pairs) were scaled to the size of a real spiral staircase, it would reach from Earth to the moon.

Note that, as shown in Fig. 3.8b, an A in one strand pairs only with a T in the other, and G pairs only with C. Each base pair contains a purine and a pyrimidine. This precise pairing maintains the structure of the double helix, since pairing two purines would cause the backbones to bulge, and pairing two pyrimidines would cause them to narrow. The pairing of one purine with one pyrimidine preserves the distance between the backbones along the length of the entire molecule.

Because they form specific pairs, the bases A and T are said to be **complementary,** as are the bases G and C. Why is it that A pairs only with T, and G only with C? **Fig. 3.9** illustrates the answer. The specificity of base pairing is brought about by hydrogen bonds that form between A and T (two hydrogen bonds) and between G and C (three hydrogen bonds). A hydrogen bond in DNA is formed when an electronegative atom (O or N) in one

---

FIG. 3.8 **Structure of DNA.** The DNA double helix can be shown with (a) the atoms as solid spheres or (b) the backbones as ribbons.

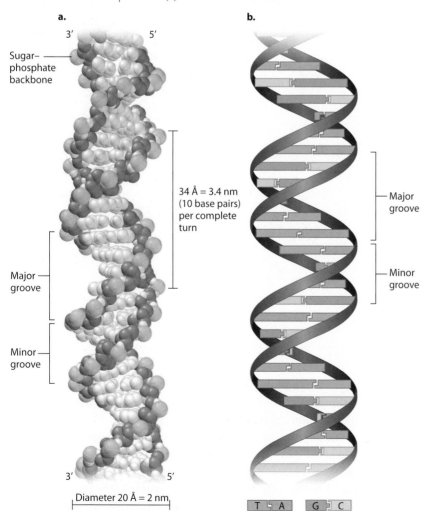

a.

Sugar–phosphate backbone

34 Å = 3.4 nm (10 base pairs) per complete turn

Major groove

Minor groove

3′   5′

Diameter 20 Å = 2 nm

b.

Major groove

Minor groove

T A   G C

FIG. 3.9 **Base pairing.** Adenine pairs with thymine, and guanine pairs with cytosine. These base pairs differ in the number of hydrogen bonds.

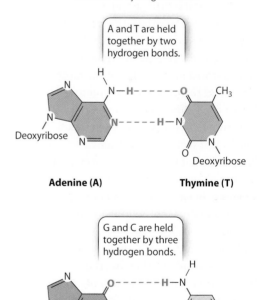

A and T are held together by two hydrogen bonds.

Deoxyribose

Adenine (A)   **Thymine (T)**

G and C are held together by three hydrogen bonds.

Deoxyribose

Guanine (G)   **Cytosine (C)**

base shares a proton (H) with another electronegative atom in the base across the way. Hydrogen bonds are relatively weak bonds, typically 5% to 10% of the strength of covalent bonds, and can be disrupted by high pH or heat. However, in total they contribute to the stability of the DNA double helix.

An almost equally important factor contributing to the stability of the double helix is the interactions between bases in the same strand (**Fig. 3.10**). This stabilizing force is known as **base stacking,** and it occurs because the nonpolar, flat surfaces of the bases tend to group together away from water molecules, and hence stack on top of one another as tightly as possible.

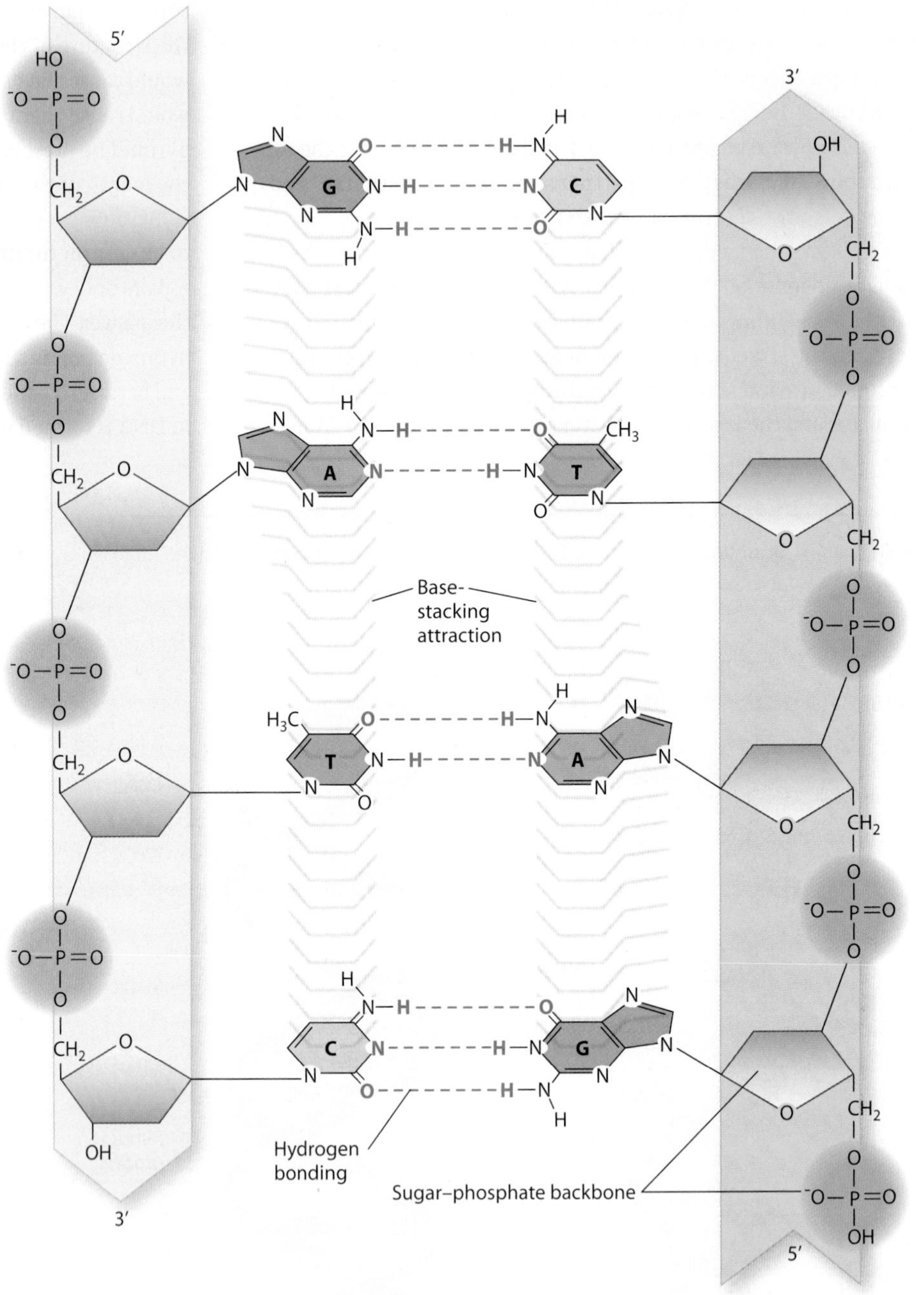

The three-dimensional structure of DNA gave important clues about its functions.

The double helix is a good example of how chemical structure and biological function come together. The structure of the molecule itself immediately suggested how genetic information can be stored in DNA. One of the most important features of DNA structure is that there is no restriction on the sequence of bases along a DNA strand. The lack of sequence constraint suggested that the genetic information in DNA could be encoded in the sequence of bases along the DNA, much as textual information in a book is stored in a sequence of letters of the alphabet. With any of four possible bases at each nucleotide site, the information-carrying capacity of a DNA molecule is unimaginable. The number of possible base sequences of a DNA molecule only 133 nucleotides in length is equal to the estimated number of electrons, protons, and neutrons in the entire universe! This is the secret of how DNA can carry the genetic information for so many different types of organisms, and how variation in DNA sequence even within a single species can underlie genetic differences among individuals.

Watson and Crick's model still left many questions unanswered in regard to how the information is read out

FIG. 3.10   **Interactions stabilizing the double helix.** Hydrogen bonds between the bases in opposite strands and base stacking of bases within a strand contribute to the stability of the DNA double helix.

and what it does, but in the years following it became clear that the major processes in the readout of genetic information were transcription and translation (see Fig. 3.3).

The sequence of bases along either strand completely determines that of the other because wherever one strand carries an A, the other must carry a T, and wherever one carries a G, the other must carry a C. The complementary base sequences of the strands means that, in any double-stranded DNA molecule, the total number of A bases must equal that of T, and the total number of G bases must equal that of C. These equalities are often written in terms of the percent (%) of each base in double-stranded DNA. In these terms, the base-pairing rules imply that %A = %T and %G = %C. Interestingly, these equalities were known and described by the American biochemist Erwin Chargaff before the double helix was discovered, and they provided important clues to the structure of DNA. It was the double helix that finally showed why they are observed.

→ **Quick Check 1** The letter R is conventionally used to represent any purine base (A or G) and Y to represent any pyrimidine base (T or C). In double-stranded DNA, what is the relation between %R and %Y?

The complementary, double-stranded nature of the double helix also suggested a mechanism by which DNA replication could take place. In fact, in their 1953 paper describing the structure of DNA, Watson and Crick wrote, "It has not escaped our notice that the specific pairing we have postulated immediately suggests a possible copying mechanism for the genetic material."

A simplified outline of DNA replication is shown in **Fig. 3.11.** In brief, the two strands of a parental double helix unwind, and as they do each of the parental strands serves as a pattern, or template, for the synthesis of a complementary daughter strand. When the process is complete, there are two molecules, each of which is identical in sequence to the original molecule, except possibly for rare errors (mutations) that cause one base pair to be replaced with another. Although the process of replication as depicted in Fig. 3.11 looks exceedingly simple and straightforward, there are technical details that make the actual process more complex. These are discussed in Chapter 12.

Cellular DNA is coiled and packaged with proteins.

The DNA molecules inside cells are highly convoluted. They have to be because DNA molecules in cells have a length far

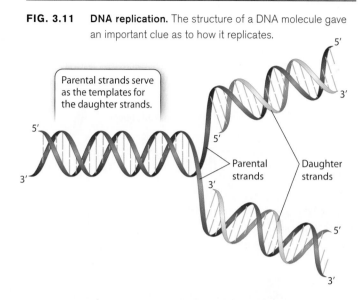

FIG. 3.11 **DNA replication.** The structure of a DNA molecule gave an important clue as to how it replicates.

Parental strands serve as the templates for the daughter strands.

Parental strands

Daughter strands

greater than the diameter of the cell itself. The DNA of a bacterium known as *Mycoplasma*, for example, if stretched to its full linear extent, would be about 1000 times longer than the diameter of the bacterial cell. Many of the double-stranded DNA molecules in prokaryotic cells are circular and form **supercoils** in which the circular molecule coils upon itself, much like what happens to a rubber band when you twist it between your thumb and forefinger (**Fig. 3.12**). Supercoiling is caused by enzymes called **topoisomerases** that cleave, partially unwind, and reattach a DNA strand, which puts strain on the DNA double helix. Supercoils then relieve the strain and help to preserve the 10 base pairs per turn in the double helix.

In eukaryotic cells, most DNA molecules in the nucleus are linear, and each individual molecule forms one **chromosome.** There is a packaging problem here, too, which you can appreciate by considering that the length of the DNA molecule contained in a single human chromosome is roughly 6000 times greater than the average diameter of the cell nucleus

FIG. 3.12 **Supercoils.** A highly twisted rubber band forms coils of coils (supercoils), much as a circular DNA molecule does when it contains too many base pairs per helical turn.

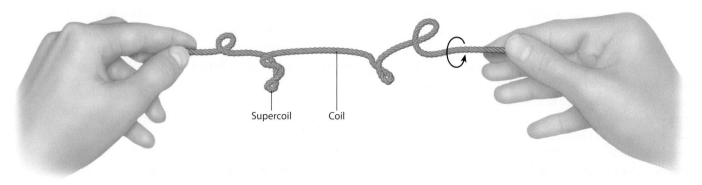

Supercoil   Coil

FIG. 3.13   **Chromatin.** (a) Double-stranded DNA is usually packaged with histone proteins into nucleosomes forming a chromatin fiber. The diameter of the fiber differs according to how closely the nucleosomes are packaged. (b) A nucleosome consists of a segment of DNA wrapped around eight histone proteins.

a.

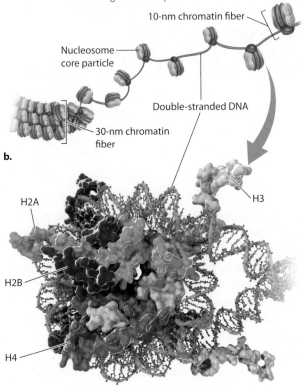

10-nm chromatin fiber

Nucleosome core particle

Double-stranded DNA

30-nm chromatin fiber

b.

H2A

H2B

H4

H3

(**Fig. 3.13**). Double-stranded DNA molecules in eukaryotes are usually packaged with proteins called histones into a **30-nm chromatin fiber** (Fig. 3.13a). In regions of the nucleus in which transcription is actively taking place, the 30-nm fiber is usually relaxed into a **10-nm chromatin fiber** (Fig. 3.13a), which is about 5 times the diameter of the double helix. Chromatin fibers of either dimension are often referred to simply as **chromatin.**

The 10-nm chromatin fiber is composed of a beadlike repeating unit known as a **nucleosome** (Fig. 3.13b). The core particle of each nucleosome is a flattened sphere consisting of approximately 150 base pairs of double-stranded DNA wrapped around a cluster of two molecules each of the histones H2A, H2B, H3, and H4. Each of these **histone** proteins is rich in the positively charged amino acids lysine and arginine, which enables them to form ionic bonds with the negatively charged sugar–phosphate backbone of DNA. The DNA double helix is wrapped twice around the core particle.

Histone proteins are found in all eukaryotes, and they interact with double-stranded DNA without regard to sequence. In addition, histone proteins from any organism can form

nucleosomes with the DNA of any other organism. The reason for this ability is that these proteins are **evolutionarily conserved,** which means that they are very similar in sequence from one organism to the next. Conserved DNA, RNA, or protein sequences indicate that they serve an essential function and therefore have not changed very much over long stretches of evolutionary time. The more distantly related two organisms are that share conserved sequences, the more highly conserved the sequence is. Among the histone proteins, histones H3 and H4 are the most conserved; for example, 98% of the amino acids in histone H4 are identical in organisms as diverse as domesticated cattle and the garden pea. Histones are very highly conserved, reflecting their key role in packaging DNA.

3.3 RETRIEVAL OF GENETIC INFORMATION STORED IN DNA: TRANSCRIPTION

Although the three-dimensional structure of DNA gave important clues about how DNA stores and transmits information, it left open many questions about how the genetic information in DNA is read out to control cellular processes. In 1953, when the double helix was discovered, virtually nothing was known about these processes. Within a few years, however, evidence was already accumulating that DNA carries the genetic information for proteins, and that proteins are synthesized on particles in the cytoplasm called **ribosomes.** But ribosomes contain no DNA! There must therefore be an intermediary molecule by which the genetic information is transferred from the DNA to the ribosome, and some researchers began to suspect that this intermediary was another type of nucleic acid called ribonucleic acid (RNA).

This hypothesis was supported by a clever experiment carried out in 1961 by Sydney Brenner, François Jacob, and Matthew Meselson. They used the virus T2, which infects cells of the bacterium *Escherichia coli* and hijacks the cellular machinery to produce viral proteins. The researchers showed that, shortly after infection and before viral proteins are made, the infected cells produce a burst of RNA molecules that correspond to the viral DNA. This finding and others suggested that RNA is used to retrieve the genetic information stored in DNA for use in protein synthesis. The transfer of genetic information from DNA to RNA constitutes the key step of transcription in the central dogma of molecular biology (see Fig. 3.2). In this section, we examine RNA and the process of transcription.

? CASE 1 The First Cell: Life's Origins
What was the first nucleic acid molecule, and how did it arise?

RNA is a remarkable molecule. Like DNA, it is able to store information in its sequence of nucleotides. In addition, some

RNA molecules can actually act as enzymes that facilitate chemical reactions. Because RNA has properties of both DNA (information storage) and proteins (enzymes), many scientists think that RNA, not DNA, was the original information-storage molecule in the earliest forms of life on Earth. This idea, sometimes called the **RNA world hypothesis,** is supported by other evidence as well. Notably, as we will see, RNA is used in key cellular processes, including DNA replication, transcription, and translation. Many scientists believe that this involvement is a remnant of a time when RNA played a more central role in life's fundamental processes.

In addition, ingenious experiments show how RNA could have evolved the ability to catalyze a simple reaction. A strand of RNA was synthesized in the laboratory and then replicated many times to produce a large population of identical RNA molecules. Next, the RNA was exposed to a chemical that induced random changes in the identity of some of the nucleotides in these molecules. These random changes were mutations that created a population of diverse RNA molecules, much in the way that mutation builds genetic variation in cells.

Next, all of these RNA molecules were placed into a container, and those RNA variants that successfully catalyzed a simple reaction—cleaving a strand of RNA, for example, or joining two strands together—were isolated, and the cycle was repeated. In each round of the experiment, the RNA molecules that functioned best were retained, replicated, subjected to treatments that induced additional mutations, and then tested for the ability to catalyze the same reaction. With each generation, the RNA catalyzed the reaction more efficiently, and after only a few dozen rounds of the procedure, very efficient RNA catalysts had evolved. Experiments such as this one suggest that RNA molecules can evolve over time and act as catalysts. Therefore, many scientists believe that RNA, with its dual functions of information storage and catalysis, was a key molecule in the very first forms of life.

If RNA played a key role in the origin of life, why do cells now use DNA for information storage and proteins to carry out other cellular processes? RNA is much less stable than DNA, and proteins are more versatile, so a plausible explanation is that life evolved from an RNA-based world to one in which DNA, RNA, and proteins are specialized for different functions.

RNA is a polymer of nucleotides linked by phosphodiester bonds, similar to those in DNA (see Fig. 3.7). Each RNA strand therefore has a polarity determined by which end of the chain carries the 3′ hydroxyl (–OH) and which end carries the 5′ phosphate. There are a number of important differences that distinguish RNA from DNA, however (**Fig. 3.14**). First, the sugar in RNA is **ribose,** which carries a hydroxyl group on the 2′ carbon (Fig. 3.14a). Hydroxyls are reactive functional groups, so the additional hydroxyl group on ribose in part explains why RNA is a less stable molecule than DNA. Second, the base **uracil** found

in RNA replaces thymine found in DNA (Fig. 3.14b). The groups that participate in hydrogen bonding (highlighted in pink in Fig. 3.14b) are identical so that uracil pairs with adenine (U–A) just as thymine pairs with adenine (T–A). Third, while the 5′ end of a DNA strand is typically a monophosphate, the 5′ end of an RNA molecule is typically a triphosphate.

Two other features that distinguish RNA from DNA are physical rather than chemical. One is that RNA molecules are usually much shorter than DNA molecules. A typical RNA molecule used in protein synthesis consists of a few thousand nucleotides, whereas a typical DNA molecule consists of millions or tens of millions of nucleotides. The other major distinction is that most RNA molecules in the cell are single stranded, whereas DNA molecules, as we saw, are double stranded. Single-stranded RNA molecules often form complex three-dimensional structures by folding back upon themselves, which enhances their stability.

In transcription, DNA is used as a template to make complementary RNA.

Conceptually, the process of transcription is straightforward. As a region of the DNA duplex unwinds, one strand is used as a template, or pattern, for the synthesis of an **RNA transcript** that is complementary in sequence to the template according to the

---

FIG. 3.14   RNA. RNA differs from DNA in that (a) RNA contains the sugar ribose rather than deoxyribose and (b) the base uracil rather than thymine.

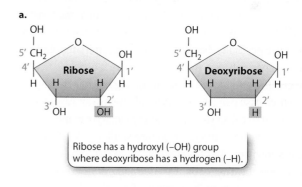

base-pairing rules, except that the transcript contains U (uracil) where the template has an A (**Fig. 3.15**). The transcript is produced by polymerization of ribonucleoside triphosphates. The enzyme that carries out the polymerization is known as **RNA polymerase,** which acts by adding successive nucleotides to the 3′ end of the growing transcript (Fig. 3.15). Only the template strand of DNA is transcribed. Its partner, called the **nontemplate strand,** is not transcribed.

It is important to keep in mind the direction of growth of the RNA transcript and the direction that the DNA template is read. All nucleic acids are synthesized by addition of nucleotides to the 3′ end. That is, they grow in a 5′-to-3′ direction, also described simply as the 3′ direction. Because of the antiparallel nature of the DNA–RNA duplex, the DNA template that is being transcribed runs in the opposite direction, from 3′ to 5′ (Fig. 3.15).

→   **Quick Check 2** A segment of one strand of a double-stranded DNA molecule has the sequence 5′-ACTTTCAGCGAT-3′. What is the sequence of an RNA molecule synthesized from this DNA template?

Transcription starts at a promoter and ends at a terminator.

A long DNA molecule typically contains thousands of genes, most of them coding for proteins or RNA molecules with specialized functions, and hence thousands of different transcripts are produced. For example, the DNA molecule in the bacterium *E. coli* has about 4 million base pairs and produces about 4000 transcripts, most of which code for proteins. A typical map of a small part of a long DNA molecule is shown in **Fig. 3.16**. Each green segment indicates the position where a transcription is initiated, and each purple segment indicates the position where it ends.

The green segments are **promoters,** regions of typically a few hundred base pairs where RNA polymerase and associated proteins bind to the DNA duplex. Many eukaryotic and archaeal promoters contain a sequence similar to 5′-TATAAA-3′, which is known as a **TATA box** because the TATA sequence is usually present. The first nucleotide to be transcribed is usually positioned about 25 base pairs from the TATA box, and transcription takes place as the RNA polymerase moves along the template strand in the 3′-to-5′ direction.

Transcription continues until the RNA polymerase encounters a sequence known as a **terminator** (shown in purple in Fig. 3.16). Transcription stops at the terminator, and the transcript is released. Transcripts from a DNA duplex may be produced from either strand, depending on the orientation of the promoter. As shown in Fig. 3.16, promoters oriented in one direction result in transcription from right to left (top strand), whereas those

FIG. 3.15   **Template and nontemplate strands.** When the DNA double helix unwinds for transcription, usually only one strand is transcribed.

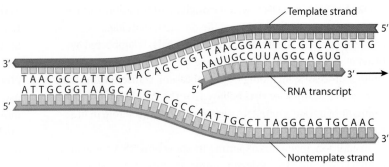

oriented in the reverse direction result in transcription from left to right (bottom strand). Orientation matters, as noted earlier, because transcription can proceed only by successive addition of nucleotides to the 3′ end of the transcript.

Transcription does not take place indiscriminately from promoters but is a regulated process. For genes called **housekeeping genes,** whose products are needed at all times in all cells, transcription takes place continually. But most genes are transcribed only at certain times, under certain conditions, or in certain cell types. In *E. coli*, for example, the genes that encode proteins needed to utilize the sugar lactose (milk sugar) are transcribed only when lactose is present in the environment. For such genes, regulation of transcription often depends on whether the RNA polymerase and associated proteins are able to bind with the promoter.

In bacteria, promoter recognition is mediated by a protein called **sigma factor,** which associates with RNA polymerase

FIG. 3.16   **Transcription along a stretch of DNA.** A DNA molecule usually contains many genes that are transcribed individually and at different times, often from opposite strands.

Transcription is initiated at a promoter sequence and ends at a terminator sequence. The transcript is synthesized in a 5′-to-3′ direction.

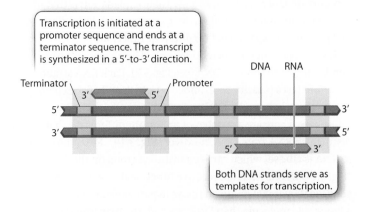

Both DNA strands serve as templates for transcription.

and facilitates its binding to specific promoters. One primary sigma factor is used for transcription of housekeeping genes and many others, but there are other sigma factors for genes whose expression is needed under special environmental conditions such as lack of nutrients or excess heat.

Promoter recognition in eukaryotes is considerably more complicated. Transcription requires the combined action of at least six proteins known as **general transcription factors** that assemble at the promoter of a gene. The general transcription factors attract, or recruit, the RNA polymerase and its associated proteins to the site (**Fig. 3.17**). Cells have several different types of RNA polymerase enzymes, but in both prokaryotes and eukaryotes all protein-coding genes are transcribed by just one of them. In eukaryotes, the RNA polymerase complex responsible for transcription of protein-coding genes is called **Pol II.**

Assembly of the general transcription factors with the RNA polymerase complex is necessary for transcription to occur, but not sufficient. Also needed is the presence of one or more types of **transcriptional activator protein,** each of which binds to a specific DNA sequence known as an **enhancer** (Fig. 3.17). The transcriptional activator proteins recruit a **mediator complex** of proteins, which in turn interacts with the Pol II complex, and transcription begins. The initiation of transcription of any gene therefore depends on the availability of the transcriptional activator proteins that bind with the enhancers controlling the expression of the gene.

RNA polymerase adds successive nucleotides to the 3′ end of the transcript.

Transcription actually takes place in a sort of bubble in which the strands of the DNA duplex are separated and the growing end of

---

FIG. 3.17 The eukaryotic transcription complex composed of many different proteins.

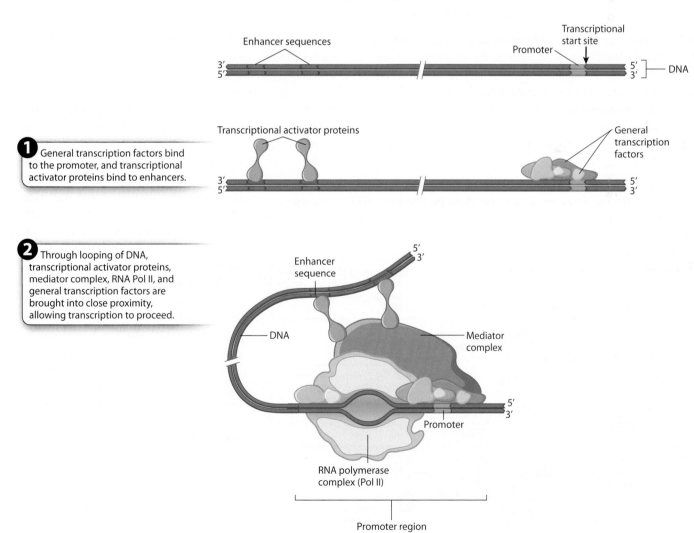

1. General transcription factors bind to the promoter, and transcriptional activator proteins bind to enhancers.

2. Through looping of DNA, transcriptional activator proteins, mediator complex, RNA Pol II, and general transcription factors are brought into close proximity, allowing transcription to proceed.

FIG. 3.18   **Transcription bubble.** Within the polymerase, the two strands of DNA separate and the growing RNA strand forms a duplex with the DNA template.

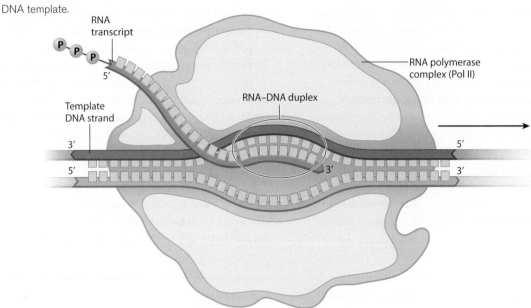

the RNA transcript is paired with the template strand, creating an RNA–DNA duplex (**Fig. 3.18**). In bacteria, the total length of the transcription bubble is about 14 base pairs, and the length of the RNA–DNA duplex in the bubble is about 8 base pairs.

Details of the polymerization reaction are shown in **Fig. 3.19.** The incoming ribonucleoside triphosphate, shown at the bottom right, is accepted by the RNA polymerase only if it undergoes proper base pairing with the base in the template DNA strand. In Fig. 3.19, there is a proper match because U pairs with A. At this point, the RNA polymerase orients the oxygen in the hydroxyl group at the 3' end of the growing strand into a position from which it can attack the innermost phosphate of the triphosphate, competing for the covalent bond. The bond connecting the innermost phosphate to the next is a **high-energy phosphate bond,** which when cleaved provides the energy to drive the reaction that creates the phosphodiester bond attaching the incoming nucleotide to the 3' end of growing chain. The term "high-energy" here refers to the amount of energy released when the phosphate bond is broken that can be used to drive other chemical reactions.

The polymerization reaction releases a phosphate–phosphate group (pyrophosphate), shown at the lower right in Fig. 3.19, which also has a high-energy phosphate bond that is cleaved by another enzyme. Cleavage of the pyrophosphate molecule makes the polymerization reaction irreversible, and the next ribonucleoside triphosphate that complements the template is brought into line.

FIG. 3.19   **The polymerization reaction that allows the RNA transcript to be elongated.**

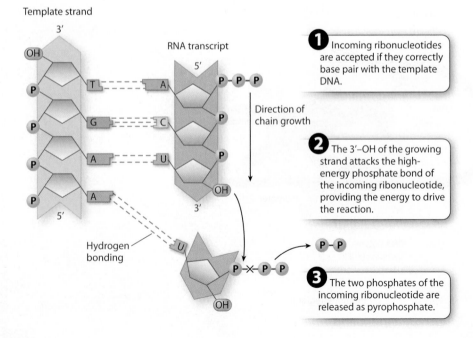

① Incoming ribonucleotides are accepted if they correctly base pair with the template DNA.

② The 3'–OH of the growing strand attacks the high-energy phosphate bond of the incoming ribonucleotide, providing the energy to drive the reaction.

③ The two phosphates of the incoming ribonucleotide are released as pyrophosphate.

→ **Quick Check 3** What is the consequence in terms of elongation for a growing RNA transcript after incorporating an abnormal nucleotide with a 3' H rather than a 3' OH? How about a 2' H rather than a 2' OH?

The RNA polymerase complex is a molecular machine that opens, transcribes, and closes duplex DNA. Transcription does not take place spontaneously. It requires template DNA, a supply of ribonucleoside triphosphates, and RNA polymerase, a large multiprotein complex in which transcription occurs. To illustrate RNA polymerase in action, we consider here bacterial RNA polymerase because of its relative simplicity.

The transcription bubble forms and transcription takes place in the polymerase (**Fig. 3.20**). RNA polymerase contains structural features that separate the DNA strands, allow an RNA–DNA duplex to form, elongate the transcript nucleotide by nucleotide, release the finished transcript, and restore the original DNA double helix. Fig. 3.20 shows how structure and function come together in the bacterial RNA polymerase.

DNA enters the polymerase through a channel and is threaded out another channel via a structure that splits the strands apart, forming a bubble, so that ribonucleotides can assemble on the template strand. Another part of the enzyme forces the growing RNA out a different channel. As the DNA travels through the RNA polymerase, the RNA transcript is elongated at the active site of the enzyme as successive ribonucleotides are added to its 3′ end.

RNA polymerase is a remarkable molecular machine capable of adding thousands of nucleotides to a transcript before dissociating from the template. It is also very accurate, with only about 1 incorrect nucleotide incorporated per 10,000 nucleotides.

3.4 FATE OF THE RNA PRIMARY TRANSCRIPT

The RNA transcript that comes off the template DNA strand is known as the **primary transcript,** and it contains the genetic information of the gene that was transcribed. For protein-coding genes, this means that the primary transcript includes the information needed to direct the ribosome to produce the protein corresponding to the gene (Chapter 4). The RNA molecule that combines with the ribosome to direct protein synthesis is known as the **messenger RNA (mRNA)** because it serves to carry the genetic "message" (information) from the DNA to the ribosome. As we will see in this section, there is a major difference between prokaryotes and eukaryotes in the manner in which the primary transcript relates to the mRNA. We will also see that some genes do not code for proteins, but for RNA molecules that have functions of their own.

Messenger RNA carries information for the synthesis of a specific protein.

In prokaryotes, the relation between the primary transcript and the mRNA is as simple as can be: The primary transcript *is* the mRNA. Even as the 3′ end of the primary transcript is still being synthesized, ribosomes bind with special sequences near its 5′ end and begin the process of protein synthesis (**Fig. 3.21**). This intimate connection between transcription and translation can take place because prokaryotes have no nuclear envelope to spatially separate transcription from translation; the two processes are coupled, which means that they are connected in space and time.

FIG. 3.20   The RNA polymerase complex in prokaryotes. This molecular machine has channels for DNA input and output, nucleotide input and RNA output, and features that disrupt the DNA double helix, stabilize the RNA–DNA duplex, and allow the DNA double helix to re-form.

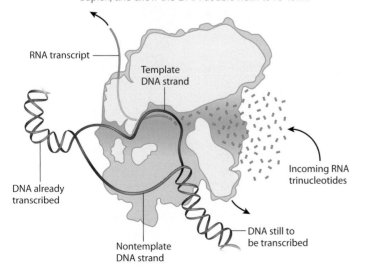

RNA transcript
Template DNA strand
Incoming RNA trinucleotides
DNA already transcribed
DNA still to be transcribed
Nontemplate DNA strand

FIG. 3.21   Fate of the primary transcript for protein-coding genes in prokaryotes.

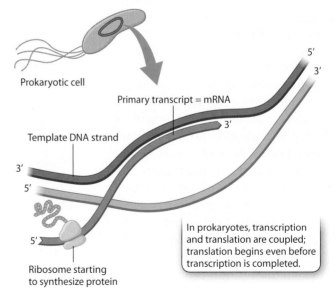

Prokaryotic cell
Primary transcript = mRNA
5′
3′
3′
Template DNA strand
3′
5′
5′
Ribosome starting to synthesize protein

In prokaryotes, transcription and translation are coupled; translation begins even before transcription is completed.

Primary transcripts for protein-coding genes in prokaryotes have another feature not shared with those in eukaryotes: They often contain the genetic information for the synthesis of two or more different proteins, usually proteins that code for successive steps in the biochemical reactions that produce small molecules needed for growth, or successive steps needed to break down a small molecule used for nutrients or energy. Molecules of mRNA that code for multiple proteins are known as **polycistronic mRNA** because the term "cistron" was once widely used to refer to a protein-coding sequence in a gene.

Primary transcripts in eukaryotes undergo several types of chemical modification.

In eukaryotes, the nuclear envelope is a barrier between the processes of transcription and translation. Transcription takes place in the nucleus, and translation in the cytoplasm. The separation allows for a complex chemical modification of the primary transcript, known as **RNA processing,** which converts the primary transcript into the finished mRNA, which can then be translated by the ribosome.

RNA processing consists of three principal types of chemical modification, illustrated in **Fig. 3.22**. First, the 5′ end of the primary transcript is modified by the addition of a special nucleotide attached in an unusual linkage. This addition is called the **5′ cap,** and it consists of a modified nucleotide called 7-methylguanosine. An enzyme attaches the cap to the 5′ end of the primary transcript essentially backwards: in a normal linkage between two nucleotides, the phosphodiester bridge forms between the 5′ carbon of one and the 3′-OH group of the next, but here the cap is linked to the RNA transcript by a triphosphate bridge between the 5′ carbons of both ribose sugars (**Fig. 3.23**). The 5′ cap is essential for translation because in eukaryotes the ribosome recognizes an mRNA by its 5′ cap. Without the cap, the ribosome would not attach the mRNA and translation would not occur.

The second major modification of eukaryotic primary transcripts is **polyadenylation,** the addition of a string of about 250 consecutive A-bearing ribonucleotides to the 3′ end, forming a **poly(A) tail** (see Fig. 3.22). Polyadenylation plays an important role in transcription termination as well as in the export of the mRNA to the cytoplasm of the cell. In addition, both the 5′ cap and poly(A) tail help to stabilize the RNA transcript. Single-stranded nucleic

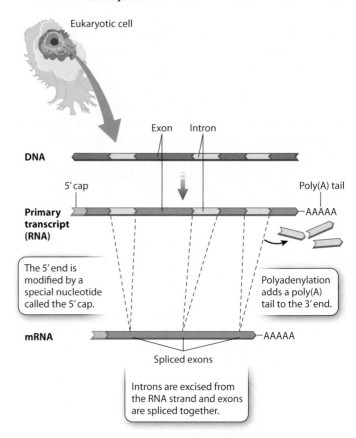

FIG. 3.22 Fate of the primary transcript for protein-coding genes in eukaryotes.

Eukaryotic cell

Exon   Intron

DNA

5′ cap   Poly(A) tail

Primary transcript (RNA)   —AAAAA

The 5′ end is modified by a special nucleotide called the 5′ cap.

Polyadenylation adds a poly(A) tail to the 3′ end.

mRNA   —AAAAA

Spliced exons

Introns are excised from the RNA strand and exons are spliced together.

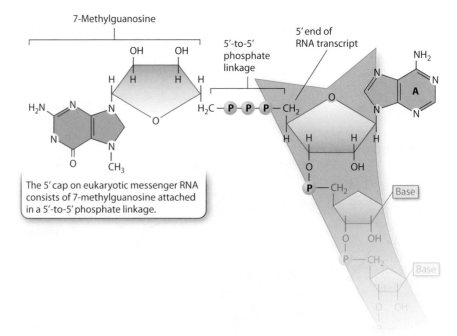

FIG. 3.23 Structure of the 5′ cap on eukaryotic messenger RNA.

7-Methylguanosine

5′-to-5′ phosphate linkage

5′ end of RNA transcript

The 5′ cap on eukaryotic messenger RNA consists of 7-methylguanosine attached in a 5′-to-5′ phosphate linkage.

Base

Base

acids can be unstable and are even susceptible to enzymes that break them down. In eukaryotes, the 5′ cap and poly(A) tail protect the two ends of the transcript and increase the stability of the RNA transcript until it is translated in the cytoplasm.

A third modification of the primary transcript is the excision of certain sequences, which are known as **introns,** from the transcript (see Fig. 3.22). What's left intact are sequences known as **exons.** The process of intron removal is known as **RNA splicing,** which is catalyzed by a complex of RNA and protein known as the **spliceosome.** The mechanism of splicing is outlined in **Fig. 3.24.** In the first step, specific sequences near the ends of the intron (Fig. 3.24a) undergo base pairing with RNA molecules in the spliceosome and are brought into close proximity (Fig. 3.24b). The spliceosome enables a reaction that cuts one end of the intron and connects it to a nucleotide

near the other, forming a loop and tail called a **lariat** (Fig. 3.24c). In the next step, the exon on one end of the intron is brought close to the exon at the other end (Fig. 3.24c). These exons are joined and the introns are released (Fig. 3.24d). The lariat making up the intron is quickly broken down into its constituent nucleotides.

About 90% of all human genes contain at least one intron. Although most genes contain 6 to 9 introns, the largest number is 147, found in a muscle gene. Most introns are just a few thousand nucleotides in length, but about 10% are longer than 10,000 nucleotides. The presence of multiple introns in most genes allows for a process known as **alternative splicing,** in which primary transcripts from the same gene can be spliced in different ways to yield different mRNAs and therefore different protein products (**Fig. 3.25**). More than 80% of human genes are alternatively spliced. In most cases, the alternatively spliced forms differ in whether a particular exon is or is not removed from the primary transcript along with its flanking introns.

→ **Quick Check 4** When a region of DNA that contains the genetic information for a protein is isolated from a bacterial cell and inserted into a eukaryotic cell in a proper position between a promoter and a terminator, the resulting cell usually produces the correct protein. But when the experiment is done in the reverse direction (eukaryotic DNA into a bacterial cell), the correct protein is often not produced. Can you suggest an explanation?

FIG. 3.24   RNA splicing.

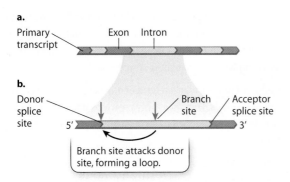

a.

Primary transcript   Exon   Intron

b.

Donor splice site   Branch site   Acceptor splice site

5′   3′

Branch site attacks donor site, forming a loop.

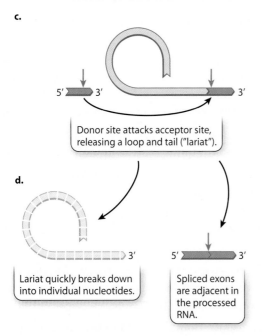

c.

5′   3′   3′

Donor site attacks acceptor site, releasing a loop and tail ("lariat").

d.

3′   5′   3′

Lariat quickly breaks down into individual nucleotides.

Spliced exons are adjacent in the processed RNA.

FIG. 3.25   **Alternative splicing.** A single primary transcript can be spliced in different ways .

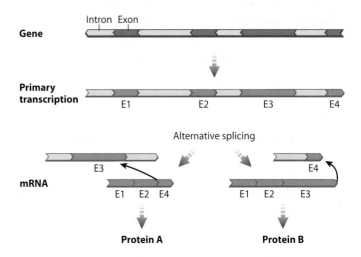

Intron Exon

Gene

Primary transcription   E1   E2   E3   E4

Alternative splicing

mRNA   E3   E4

E1 E2 E4   E1 E2 E3

Protein A   **Protein B**

Some RNA transcripts are processed differently from protein-coding transcripts and have functions of their own.

Not all primary transcripts are processed into mRNA because not all genes code for proteins. Some RNA transcripts have functions of their own, and many of these transcripts are produced by RNA polymerases other than Pol II. These primary transcripts undergo different types of RNA processing, and their processed forms include such important noncoding RNA types as:

- **Ribosomal RNA** (**rRNA**), found in all ribosomes that aid in translation.

- **Transfer RNA** (**tRNA**) that carries individual amino acids for use in translation.

- **Small nuclear RNA** (**snRNA**), found in eukaryotes and involved in splicing, polyadenylation, and other processes in the nucleus.

- Small, regulatory RNA molecules that can inhibit translation (**microRNA** or **miRNA**) or cause destruction of an RNA transcript (**small interfering RNA** or **siRNA**).

By far, the most abundant transcripts in mammalian cells are those for ribosomal RNA and transfer RNA. In a typical mammalian cell, about 80% of all of the RNA consists of ribosomal RNA, and another approximately 10% consists of transfer RNA. Why are these types of RNA so abundant? The answer is that they are needed in large amounts to synthesize the proteins encoded in the messenger RNA. The roles of mRNA, tRNA, and rRNA in protein synthesis are discussed in the next chapter.

Core Concepts Summary

3.1 DEOXYRIBONUCLEIC ACID (DNA) STORES AND TRANSMITS GENETIC INFORMATION.

Experiments carried out by Griffith in 1928 demonstrated that bacteria can transmit genetic information from one strain to another. page 3-2

Experiments performed by Avery, MacLeod, and McCarty in 1944 showed that DNA is the molecule that transmits genetic information. page 3-3

DNA is copied in the process of replication. page 3-3

Ribonucleic acid (RNA) is synthesized from a DNA template. page 3-4

The central dogma of molecular biology states that the usual flow of genetic information is from DNA to RNA to protein. DNA is transcribed to RNA, and RNA is translated to protein. page 3-4

3.2 DNA IS A POLYMER OF NUCLEOTIDES AND FORMS A DOUBLE HELIX.

A nucleotide consists of a 5-carbon sugar, a phosphate group, and a base. page 3-4

The four bases of DNA are adenine, guanine, cytosine, and thymine. page 3-5

Successive nucleotides are linked by phosphodiester bonds to form a linear DNA molecule. page 3-6

DNA strands have polarity, with a 5′-phosphate group at one end and a 3′-hydroxyl group at the other end. page 3-6

Cellular DNA molecules consist of a helical spiral of two paired, antiparallel strands called a double helix. page 3-6

In a DNA double helix, A pairs with T, and G pairs with C. page 3-7

The structure of DNA relates to its function. Information is coded in the sequence of bases, and the structure suggests a mechanism for replication, in which each parental strand serves as a template for a daughter strand. page 3-8

Cellular DNA is packaged with evolutionary conserved proteins called histones. Histones form a nucleosome core particle around which DNA is wrapped to form a 10-nm and a 30-nm chromatin fiber. page 3-9

3.3 TRANSCRIPTION IS THE PROCESS BY WHICH RNA IS SYNTHESIZED FROM A DNA TEMPLATE.

RNA, like DNA, is a polymer of nucleotides linked by phosphodiester bonds. page 3-10

Some types of RNA can store genetic information and other types can catalyze chemical reactions. These characteristics have led to the RNA world hypothesis, the idea that RNA played a critical role in the early evolution of life on Earth. page 3-11

Unlike DNA, RNA incorporates the sugar ribose instead of deoxyribose, and the base uracil instead of thymine. page 3-11

RNA is synthesized from one of the two strands of DNA, called the template strand. page 3-11

RNA is synthesized by RNA polymerase in a 5′-to-3′ direction, starting at a promoter and ending at a terminator in the DNA template. page 3-12

RNA polymerase separates the two DNA strands, allows an RNA–DNA duplex to form, elongates the transcript, releases the transcript, and restores the DNA duplex. page 3-13

3.4 THE PRIMARY TRANSCRIPT IS PROCESSED TO BECOME MESSENGER RNA (mRNA).

In prokaryotes, the primary transcript is immediately translated into protein. page 3-15

In eukaryotes, transcription and translation are separated in time and space, with transcription first occurring in the nucleus and then translation in the cytoplasm. page 3-16

In eukaryotes, there are three major types of modification to the primary transcript—the addition of a 5′ cap, polyadenylation, and splicing. page 3-16

The 5′ cap is a 7-methylguanosine added to the 5′ end of the transcript. page 3-16

The poly(A) tail is a stretch of adenines added to the 3′ end of the transcript. page 3-16

Splicing is the excision of introns from the transcript, bringing exons together. page 3-16

Alternative splicing is a process in which primary transcripts from the same gene are spliced in different ways to yield different protein products. page 3-17

Some RNAs, called noncoding RNAs, do not code for proteins, but instead have functions of their own. page 3-18

Self-Assessment

1. Explain how the function of DNA is attributable to and dependent on its structural features.

2. Describe how DNA molecules are replicated.

3. Explain how the sequence of just four nucleotide monomers found in DNA can encode the enormous amount of genetic information stored in the chromosomes of living organisms.

4. Draw a nucleosome, indicating the positions of DNA and proteins.

5. Describe the usual flow of genetic information in a cell.

6. Name two differences between the structure of DNA and RNA.

7. Describe how a molecule of RNA is synthesized using a DNA molecule as a template.

8. Explain the relationship between RNA structure and function.

9. Name and describe three mechanisms of RNA processing in eukaryotes, and explain their importance to the cell.

10. List three types of noncoding RNA and describe their functions.

Do you understand the chapter's Core Concepts? Log into BIO **PORTAL** to check your answers to the Self-Assessment questions, then practice what you've learned and reinforce this chapter's concepts by working through the problems and multimedia tutorials provided there.

🛜 http://courses.bfwpub.com/yourbioportal/index.php

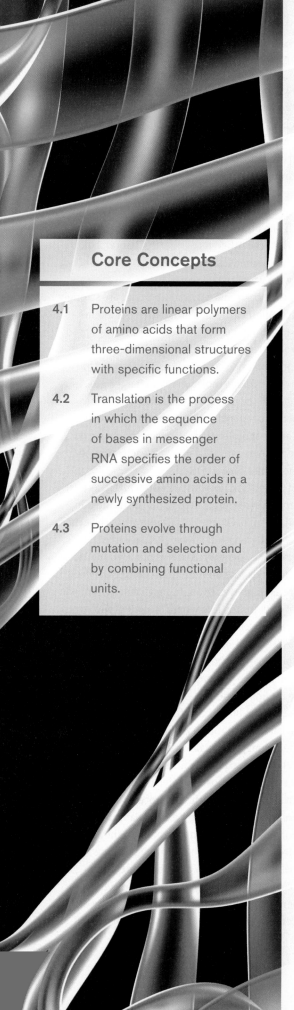

CHAPTER 4

TRANSLATION AND PROTEIN STRUCTURE

Core Concepts

4.1 Proteins are linear polymers of amino acids that form three-dimensional structures with specific functions.

4.2 Translation is the process in which the sequence of bases in messenger RNA specifies the order of successive amino acids in a newly synthesized protein.

4.3 Proteins evolve through mutation and selection and by combining functional units.

Hardly anything happens in the life of a cell that does not require proteins. They are the most versatile of macromolecules, each with its own inbuilt ability to carry out a cellular function. Some proteins aggregate to form relatively stiff filaments that help define the cell's shape and hold organelles in position. Others span the cell membrane and form channels or pores through which ions and small molecules can move. Many others are enzymes that catalyze the thousands of chemical reactions needed to maintain life. Still others are signaling proteins that enable cells to coordinate their internal activities or to communicate with other cells.

Want to see some proteins? Look at the white of an egg. Apart from the 90% or so that is water, most of what you see is protein. The predominant type of protein is ovalbumin. Easy to obtain in large quantities, ovalbumin was one of the first proteins studied by the scientific method (Chapter 1). In the 1830s, ovalbumin was shown to consist largely of carbon, hydrogen, nitrogen, and oxygen. Each molecule of ovalbumin was estimated to contain at least 400 carbon atoms. Leading chemists of the time scoffed at this number, believing that no organic molecule could possibly be so large. Little did they know: The number of carbon atoms in ovalbumin is actually closer to 2000 than to 400!

The reason that proteins can be such large organic molecules began to become clear only about 100 years ago, when scientists hypothesized that proteins are polymers (large molecules made up of repeated subunits). Now we know that proteins are linear polymers of any combination of 20 amino acids, each of which differs from the others in its chemical characteristics. In size, ovalbumin is actually an average protein, consisting of a chain of 385 amino acids.

In Chapter 3, we discussed how genetic information flows from the sequence of bases of DNA into the sequence of bases in a transcript of RNA. For protein-coding genes, the transcript is processed into messenger RNA (mRNA). In this chapter, we examine how protein polymers are assembled by ribosomes by means of a template of messenger RNA and transfer RNAs. We also discuss how the amino acid sequences of proteins help determine their three-dimensional structures and diverse chemical activities, as well as how proteins change through evolutionary time.

4.1 MOLECULAR STRUCTURE OF PROTEINS

If you think of a protein as analogous to a word in the English language, then the amino acids are like letters. The comparison is not altogether fanciful, as there are about as many amino acids in proteins as letters in the alphabet, and the order of both amino acids and letters is important. For example, the word PROTEIN has the same letters as POINTER, but the two words have completely different meanings. Similarly, the exact order of amino acids in a protein makes a big difference because that order determines the protein's shape and function.

FIG. 4.1   **Structure of an amino acid.** The central carbon atom is attached to an amino group, a carboxyl group, an R group or side chain, and a hydrogen atom.

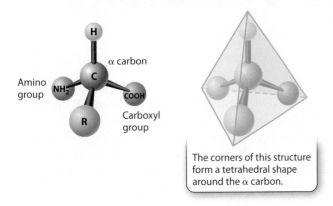

The corners of this structure form a tetrahedral shape around the α carbon.

Amino acids differ in their side chains.

The general structure of an amino acid was discussed in Chapter 2 and is shown again in **Fig. 4.1.** It consists of a central carbon atom, called the **α (alpha) carbon,** connected by covalent bonds to four different chemical groups: an **amino group** (–NH$_2$ shown in dark blue), a **carboxyl group** (–COOH shown in brown), a hydrogen atom (–H shown in light blue), and a **side chain** or **R group** (shown in green). The four covalent bonds from the α carbon are at equal angles. As a result, an amino acid forms a tetrahedron, a sort of pyramid with four triangular faces (Fig. 4.1).

The R groups of the amino acids are also known as side chains, and they differ from one amino acid to the next. They are what make the "letters" of the amino acid "alphabet" distinct from one another. Just as letters differ in their shapes and sounds—vowels like E, I, and O and hard consonants like B, P, and T—amino acids differ in their chemical and physical properties.

The chemical structures of the 20 amino acids commonly found in proteins are shown in **Fig. 4.2.** The side chains (shown in green) are chemically diverse and are grouped according to their properties, with a particular emphasis on whether they are hydrophobic or hydrophilic, or have special characteristics that might affect a protein's structure. Within these broad categories are additional groupings based on whether they are nonpolar or polar, basic or acidic. These properties strongly influence how a polypeptide folds, and hence the three-dimensional shape of the protein.

For example, as we saw in Chapter 2, hydrophobic molecules do not readily interact with water and do not easily form hydrogen bonds. Water molecules in the cell therefore tend to form hydrogen bonds with each other instead of with hydrophobic side chains. The aggregation of hydrophobic side chains is also stabilized by weak van der Waals forces (Chapter 2), in which asymmetries in electron distribution create temporary

charges in the interacting molecules, which are then attracted to each other. The tendency for hydrophilic water molecules to interact with each other and for hydrophobic molecules to interact with each other is the very same tendency that leads to the formation of oil droplets in water. This is also the reason why most hydrophobic amino acids tend to be buried in the interior of folded proteins, where they are kept away from water.

Amino acids with polar side chains have a permanent charge separation, in which one end of the side chain is slightly more negatively charged than the other. As we saw in Chapter 2, polar molecules are hydrophilic, and they tend to form hydrogen bonds with each other or with water molecules.

The side groups of the basic and acidic amino acids are strongly polar and are also hydrophilic. The side groups of basic amino acids tend to be positively charged at intracellular pH, and those of the acidic amino acids tend to be negatively charged. For this reason, basic and acidic side chains are usually located on the outside surface of the folded molecule. The charged groups can also form ionic bonds (negative with positive) with each other and with other charged molecules in the environment. This ability to bind another molecule of opposite charge is one important way that proteins can associate with each other or with other macromolecules such as DNA.

The properties of several amino acids are noteworthy because of their effect on protein structure. These amino acids include glycine, proline, and cysteine. Glycine is different from the other amino acids because its R group is hydrogen, exactly like the hydrogen on the other side, and therefore it is not asymmetric. All of the other amino acids have four different groups attached to the α carbon and are asymmetric. In addition, glycine is nonpolar and small enough to tuck into spaces where other R groups would not fit. The small size of glycine's R group also allows for freer rotation around the C–N bond since its R group does not get in the way of the R groups of neighboring amino acids. Thus, glycine increases the flexibility of the polypeptide backbone, which can be important in the folding of the protein.

Proline is also distinctive, but for a different reason. Note how its R group is linked back to the amino group. This linkage creates a kink or bend in the polypeptide chain and restricts rotation of the C–N bond, thereby imposing constraints on protein folding in its vicinity, an effect the very opposite of glycine's.

Cysteine makes a special contribution to protein folding through its –SH group. When two cysteine side chains in the same or different polypeptides come into proximity, they can react to form an S–S disulfide bond, which covalently joins the side chains. Such disulfide bonds form cross-bridges that can connect different parts of the same protein or even different proteins. This property contributes to the overall structure of single proteins or combinations of proteins.

FIG. 4.2   Structures of the 20 amino acids commonly found in proteins.

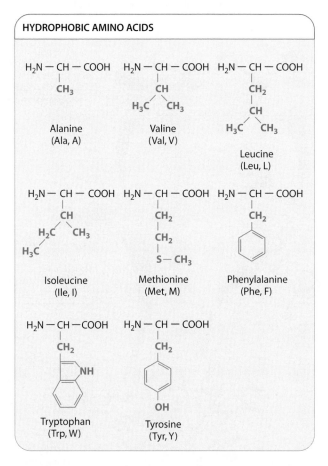

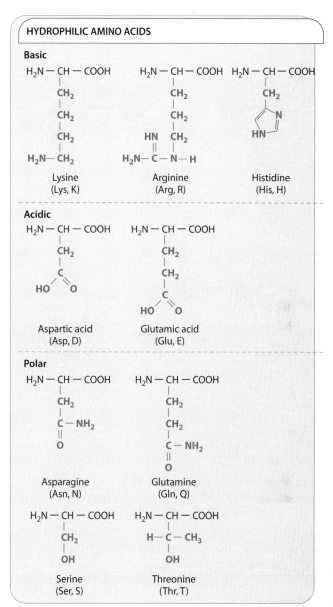

Successive amino acids in proteins are connected by peptide bonds.

Amino acids are linked together to form proteins. **Fig. 4.3** shows how amino acids in a protein are bonded together. The bond formed between the two amino acids is a **peptide bond,** shown in red in Fig. 4.3. In forming the peptide bond, the carboxyl group of one amino acid reacts with the amino group of the next amino acid in line, and a molecule of water is released. Note that in the resulting molecule, the R groups of each amino acid point in different directions.

The C=O group in the peptide bond is known as a carbonyl group, and the N–H group is an amide group. Note in Fig. 4.3 that these two groups are on either side of the peptide bond. This arrangement results in the delocalization of electrons, with the effect that the peptide bond has some of the characteristics of a double bond. The peptide bond is shorter than a single bond, for example, and it is not free to rotate like a single bond. The other bonds are free to rotate around their central axes.

Polymers of amino acids ranging from as few as two to many hundreds share a chemical feature common to individual amino

FIG. 4.3 **Formation of a peptide bond.** A peptide bond forms between the carboxyl group of one amino acid and the amino group of another.

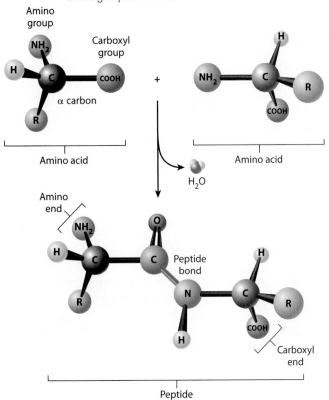

FIG. 4.4 **Levels of protein structure.** The primary structure of an amino acid determines its shape and function.

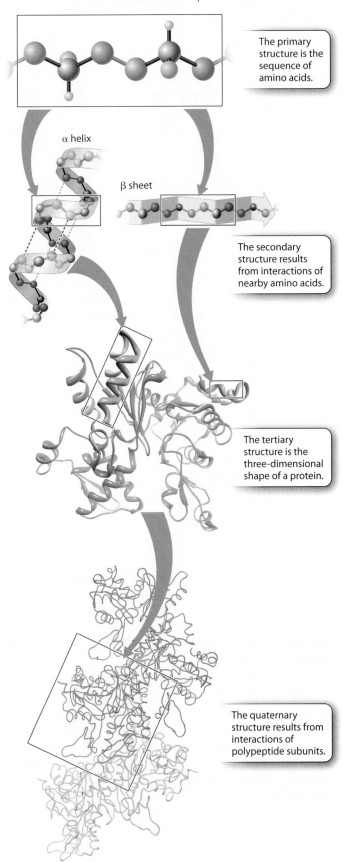

The primary structure is the sequence of amino acids.

The secondary structure results from interactions of nearby amino acids.

The tertiary structure is the three-dimensional shape of a protein.

The quaternary structure results from interactions of polypeptide subunits.

acids: namely, that the ends are chemically distinct from each other. One end, shown at the left in Fig. 4.3, has a free amino group; this is the **amino end** of the peptide. The other end has a free carboxyl group, which constitutes the **carboxyl end** of the molecule. More generally, a polymer of amino acids connected by peptide bonds is known as a **polypeptide.** Typical polypeptides produced in cells consist of a few hundred amino acids. In human cells, the shortest polypeptides are about 100 amino acids in length; the longest is the muscle protein titin, with 34,350 amino acids. The term **protein** is often used as a synonym for polypeptide, especially when the polypeptide chain has folded into a stable, three-dimensional conformation. Amino acids that are incorporated into a protein are often referred to as amino acid **residues.**

The sequence of amino acids dictates protein folding, which determines function.

Up to this point, we have considered the sequence of amino acids that make up a protein. This is the first of several levels of protein structure, illustrated in **Fig. 4.4.** The sequence of amino acids in a protein is its **primary structure.** The sequence of amino acids ultimately determines how a protein folds. Interactions between stretches of amino acids in a protein form local **secondary structures.** Longer-range interactions between these secondary structures in turn support the overall three-dimensional shape of the protein, which is its **tertiary structure.** Finally, some proteins are made up of several individual polypeptides that interact with each other, and the resulting ensemble is the **quaternary structure.**

Proteins have a remarkably wide range of functions in the cell, from serving as structural elements to communicating with the external environment to accelerating the rate of chemical reactions. No matter what the function of a protein is, the ability to carry out this function depends on the three-dimensional shape of the protein. When fully folded, some proteins contain pockets with positively or negatively charged side chains at just the right positions to trap small molecules; others have surfaces that can bind another protein or a sequence of nucleotides in DNA or RNA; some form rigid rods for structural support; and still others keep their hydrophobic side chains away from water molecules by inserting into the cell membrane.

The sequence of amino acids in a protein (its primary structure) is usually represented by a series of three-letter or one-letter abbreviations for the amino acids (abbreviations for the 20 common amino acids are given in Fig. 4.2). By convention, the amino acids in a protein are listed in order from left to right, starting at the amino end and proceeding to the carboxyl end. The amino and the carboxyl ends are different, so the order matters. Just as TIPS is not the same word as

SPIT, the sequence Thr–Ile–Pro–Ser is not the same peptide as Ser–Pro–Ile–Thr.

→ **Quick Check 1** A mutation leads to a change in one amino acid in a protein. The result is that the protein no longer functions properly. How is this possible?

Secondary structures result from hydrogen bonding in the polypeptide backbone.

Hydrogen bonds can form between the carbonyl group in one peptide bond and the amide group in another, thus allowing localized regions of the polypeptide chain to fold. This localized folding is a major contributor to the secondary structure of the protein. In the early 1950s, American structural biologists Linus Pauling and Robert Corey used a technique known as X-ray crystallography to study the structure of proteins. This technique was pioneered by British biochemists Dorothy Crowfoot Hodgkin, Max Perutz, and John Kendrew, among others (**Fig. 4.5**).Pauling and Corey studied crystals of highly purified proteins and discovered that two types of secondary structure are found in many different proteins. These are the **α helix** and the **β (beta) sheet.** Both these secondary structures are stabilized by hydrogen bonding along the peptide backbone.

HOW DO WE KNOW?

FIG. 4.5

What are the shapes of proteins?

BACKGROUND The three-dimensional shapes of proteins can be determined by X-ray crystallography. One of the pioneers in this field was Dorothy Crowfoot Hodgkin, who used this technique to define the structures of cholesterol, vitamin B_{12}, penicillin, and insulin. She was awarded the Nobel Prize in Chemistry in 1964 for her early work. Max Perutz and John Kendrew shared the Nobel Prize in Chemistry in 1962 for defining the structures of myoglobin and hemoglobin using this method.

METHOD X-ray crystallography can be used to determine the shape of proteins, as well as other types of molecules. The first step, which can be challenging, is to make a crystal of the protein. Then X-rays are aimed at the crystal while it is rotated. Some X-rays pass through the crystal, while others are scattered in different directions. A film or other detector records the pattern as a series of spots, which is known as a diffraction pattern. The locations and intensities of these spots can be used to infer the position and arrangement of the atoms in the molecule.

RESULTS The X-ray diffraction pattern for hemoglobin looks like this:

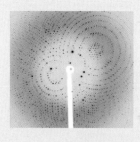

From this two-dimensional pattern, researchers can use mathematical methods to determine the three-dimensional shape of the protein.

FOLLOW-UP WORK Linus Pauling and Robert Corey used X-ray crystallography to determine two types of secondary structures commonly found in proteins—the α helix and the β sheet. Today, this technique is a common method for determining the shape of proteins.

SOURCES Crowfoot, D. 1935. "X-Ray Single Crystal Photographs of Insulin." *Nature* 135:591–592. Kendrew, J.C., G. Bodo, H. M. Dintzis, et al. 1958. "A Three-Dimensional Model of the Myoglobin Molecule Obtained by X-Ray Analysis." *Nature* 181:662–666.

FIG. 4.6 **An α helix.** Hydrogen bonding between carbonyl and amide groups in the backbone stabilize the helix.

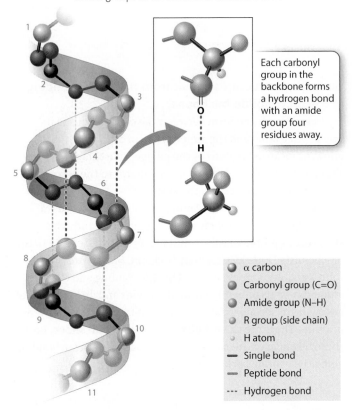

Each carbonyl group in the backbone forms a hydrogen bond with an amide group four residues away.

- α carbon
- Carbonyl group (C=O)
- Amide group (N–H)
- R group (side chain)
- H atom
- — Single bond
- — Peptide bond
- --- Hydrogen bond

In the α helix shown in **Fig. 4.6**, the polypeptide backbone is twisted tightly in a right-handed coil with 3.6 amino acids per complete turn. The helix is stabilized by hydrogen bonds that form between each amino acid's carbonyl group and the amide group four residues ahead in the sequence, as indicated by the dashed lines in Fig. 4.6. Note that the side chains project outward from the α helix. The chemical properties of the projecting side chains largely determine where the α helix is positioned in the folded protein, and how it might interact with other molecules.

The other secondary structure that Pauling and Corey found is the β sheet, depicted in **Fig. 4.7.** In a β sheet, the polypeptide folds back and forth on itself, forming a pleated sheet that is stabilized by hydrogen bonds between carbonyl groups in one chain and amide groups in the other chain across the way (dashed lines). The side chains (shown in green) project alternately above and below the plane of the β sheet. β sheets typically consist of 4 to 10 polypeptide chains aligned side by side, with the amides in each chain hydrogen-bonded to the carbonyls on either side (except for those at the edges).

β sheets are typically denoted by broad arrows, where the direction of the arrow runs from the amino end of the polypeptide segment to the carboxyl end. In Fig. 4.7, the arrows run in opposite directions, and the polypeptide chains are said to be antiparallel. β sheets can also be formed by hydrogen bonding between polypeptide chains that are parallel (pointing in the same direction). However, the antiparallel configuration is more stable because the carbonyl and amide groups are more favorably aligned for hydrogen bonding.

Tertiary structures result from interactions between amino acid side chains.

The **tertiary structure** of a protein is the three-dimensional conformation of a single polypeptide chain, usually made up of several secondary structure elements. The shape of a protein is defined largely by interactions between the amino acid side chains. By contrast, the formation of secondary structures

FIG. 4.7 **A β sheet.** Hydrogen bonds between neighboring strands stabilize the structure.

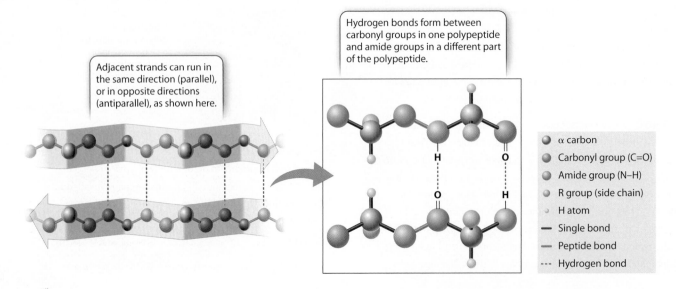

Adjacent strands can run in the same direction (parallel), or in opposite directions (antiparallel), as shown here.

Hydrogen bonds form between carbonyl groups in one polypeptide and amide groups in a different part of the polypeptide.

- α carbon
- Carbonyl group (C=O)
- Amide group (N–H)
- R group (side chain)
- H atom
- — Single bond
- — Peptide bond
- --- Hydrogen bond

FIG. 4.8 **Three ways of showing the structure of the protein hemoglobin:** (a) ball-and-stick model; (b) ribbon model; (c) space-filling model.

a.

b.

c.

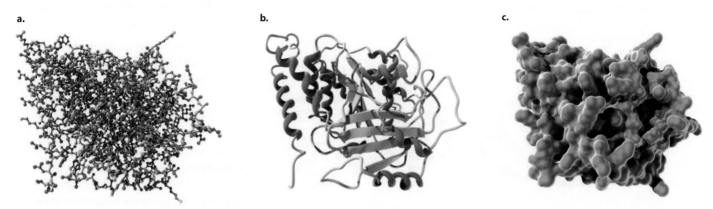

discussed earlier relies on interactions in the polypeptide backbone and is relatively independent of the side chains. Tertiary structure is determined by the spatial distribution of hydrophilic and hydrophobic side chains along the molecule, as well as by different types of chemical bonds and interactions (ionic, hydrogen, and van der Waals) that form between various side chains. The amino acids whose side chains form bonds with each other may be far apart in the polypeptide chain, but can end up near each other in the folded protein. Hence, the tertiary structure usually includes loops or turns in the backbone that allow these side chains to sit near each other in space and for bonds to form.

The three-dimensional shapes of proteins can be illustrated in different ways, as shown in **Fig. 4.8.** A ball-and-stick model (Fig. 4.8a) draws attention to the atoms in the amino acid chain. A ribbon model (Fig. 4.8b) emphasizes secondary structures, with α helices depicted as twisted ribbons and β sheets as broad arrows. Finally, a space-filling model (Fig. 4.8c) shows the overall shape and contour of the folded protein.

Remember that the folding of a polypeptide chain is determined by the sequence of amino acids. The primary structure determines the secondary and tertiary structures. Furthermore, tertiary structure determines function because it is the three-dimensional shape of the molecule—the contours and distribution of charges on the outside of the molecule and the presence of pockets that might bind with smaller molecules on the inside—that enables the protein to serve as structural support, membrane channel, enzyme, or signaling molecule. **Fig. 4.9** shows the tertiary structure of a bacterial protein that contains a pocket in the center in which certain side groups can form hydrogen bonds with a specific small molecule and hold it in place.

The principle that structure determines function can be demonstrated by many observations. For example, most proteins can be unfolded, or **denatured,** by chemical treatment or high temperature, and under these conditions they lose their functional activity; but when the chemicals are removed or the

temperature reduced, the proteins refold and their functional activity returns. Similarly, mutant proteins containing an amino acid that prevents proper folding are often devoid of their functional activity.

Polypeptide subunits can come together to form quaternary structures.

Although many proteins are complete and fully functional as a single polypeptide chain with a tertiary structure, there are many other proteins that are composed of two or more polypeptide chains or subunits, each of which has a tertiary structure, and that also come together to form a higher-order quaternary structure. In the case of a multi-subunit protein, the activity of the complex depends on the quaternary structure formed by the combination of the various tertiary structures.

FIG. 4.9 **Tertiary structure determines function.** This bacterial protein has a cavity that can bind with a small molecule (shown as a ball-and-stick model in the center).

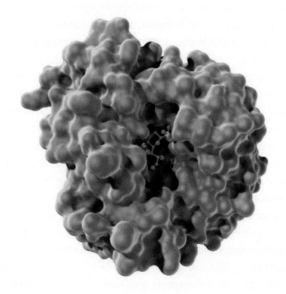

FIG. 4.10 **Quaternary structure.** Polypeptide units of proteins may be identical, as in an enzyme from HIV (a), or different, as in hemoglobin (b).

a.

b.

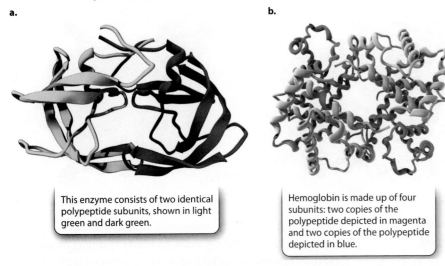

This enzyme consists of two identical polypeptide subunits, shown in light green and dark green.

Hemoglobin is made up of four subunits: two copies of the polypeptide depicted in magenta and two copies of the polypeptide depicted in blue.

The polypeptide subunits may be identical or different (**Fig. 4.10**). Fig. 4.10a shows an example of a protein produced by HIV that consists of two identical polypeptide subunits. By contrast, many proteins, such as hemoglobin shown in Fig. 410b, are composed of different subunits. In either case, the subunits can influence each other in subtle ways and influence their function. For example, the hemoglobin in red blood cells that carries oxygen has four subunits. When one of these binds oxygen, a slight change in its structure is transmitted to the other subunits, making it easier for them to take up oxygen. In this way, oxygen transport from the lungs to the tissues is improved.

Chaperones help some proteins fold properly.

The amino acid sequence (primary structure) of a protein determines how it forms its secondary, tertiary, and quaternary structures. For about 75% of proteins, the folding process takes place within milliseconds as the molecule is synthesized. Some proteins fold more slowly, however, and for these molecules folding is a dangerous business. The longer these polypeptides remain in a denatured (unfolded) state, the longer their hydrophobic groups are exposed to other macromolecules in the crowded cytoplasm. The hydrophobic effect, along with van der Waals interactions, tends to bring the exposed hydrophobic groups together, and their inappropriate aggregation may prevent proper folding. Correctly folded proteins can sometimes unfold because of elevated temperature, for example, and in the denatured state they are subject to the same risks of aggregation.

Cells have evolved proteins called **chaperones** that help protect slow-folding or denatured proteins until they can attain their proper three-dimensional structure. Chaperones bind with hydrophobic groups and nonpolar side chains to shield them from inappropriate aggregation, and in repeated cycles of binding and release they give the polypeptide time to find its correct shape.

4.2 TRANSLATION: HOW PROTEINS ARE SYNTHESIZED

The three-dimensional structure of a protein determines what it can do and how it works, and the immense diversity in the tertiary and quaternary structures among proteins explains their wide range of functions in cellular processes. Yet it is the sequence of amino acids along a polypeptide chain—its primary structure—that governs how the molecule folds into a stable three-dimensional configuration. How is the sequence of amino acids specified? It is specified by the sequence of nucleotides in the DNA, in coded form. The decoding of the information takes place according to the central dogma of molecular biology, which defines information flow in a cell from DNA to RNA to protein (**Fig. 4.11**). The key steps are known as **transcription** and **translation.** In transcription, the sequence of bases along part of a DNA strand is used as a template in the synthesis of a complementary sequence of bases in a molecule of RNA, as described in Chapter 3. In translation, the sequence of bases in an RNA molecule known as **messenger RNA** (**mRNA**) is used to specify the order in which successive amino acids are added to a newly synthesized polypeptide chain.

Translation uses many molecules found in all cells.
Translation requires many components. Well over 100 genes encode components needed for translation, some of which are

FIG. 4.11 **The central dogma, showing how information flows from DNA to RNA to protein.** Note the large number of cellular components required for translation.

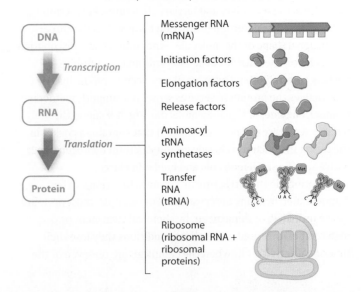

DNA

Transcription

RNA

Translation

Protein

Messenger RNA (mRNA)

Initiation factors

Elongation factors

Release factors

Aminoacyl tRNA synthetases

Transfer RNA (tRNA)

Ribosome (ribosomal RNA + ribosomal proteins)

shown in Fig. 4.11. What are these needed components? First, the cell needs **ribosomes,** which are complex structures of RNA and protein. Ribosomes bind with mRNA, and it is on ribosomes that translation takes place. In prokaryotes, translation occurs as soon as the mRNA comes off the DNA template. In eukaryotes, the processes of transcription and translation are physically separated: Transcription takes place in the nucleus, and translation takes place on ribosomes in the cytoplasm.

In both eukaryotes and prokaryotes, the ribosome consists of a small subunit and a large subunit, each composed of both RNA and protein. The sizes of the subunits are given in Svedberg units (S), a measure of size and shape. Eukaryotic ribosomes are larger than prokaryotic ribosomes. As indicated in **Fig. 4.12**, the large subunit of the ribosome includes three binding sites for molecules of **transfer RNA (tRNA),** which are called the **A (aminoacyl)** site, the **P (peptidyl)** site, and the **E (exit) site.**

A major role of the ribosome is to ensure that, when the mRNA is in place on the ribosome, the sequence in the mRNA coding for amino acids is read in successive, non-overlapping groups of three nucleotides, much as you would read the sentence

THEBIGBOYSAWTHEBADMANRUN

Each non-overlapping group of three adjacent nucleotides (like THE or BIG or BOY, for example) constitutes a **codon,** and each codon in the mRNA codes for a single amino acid in the polypeptide chain.

In the example above, it is clear that the sentence begins with THE. However, in a long linear mRNA molecule, the ribosome could begin at any of three possible positions. These are known as **reading frames.** As an analogy, if the letters THE were the start codon for reading text, then we would know immediately how to read

ZWTHEBIGBOYSAWTHEBADMANRUN

However, without knowing the first codon of this string of

letters, we could find three ways to break the sentence into three-letter words:

ZWT HEB IGB OYS AWT HEB ADM ANR UN
Z WTH EBI GBO YSA WTH EBA DMA NRU N
ZW THE BIG BOY SAW THE BAD MAN RUN

Obviously, only one of these frames is correct. The same is true for mRNAs.

While the ribosome establishes the correct reading frame for the codons, the actual translation of each codon in the mRNA into one amino acid in the polypeptide is carried out by means of transfer RNA (tRNA). Transfer RNAs are small RNA molecules of 70 to 90 nucleotides (**Fig. 4.13**). Each has a characteristic

FIG. 4.13 Transfer RNA structure depicted in (a) a cloverleaf configuration and (b) a more realistic three-dimensional structure.

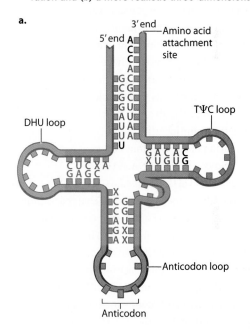

FIG. 4.12 Composition and simplified structure of ribosomes in prokaryotes and eukaryotes.

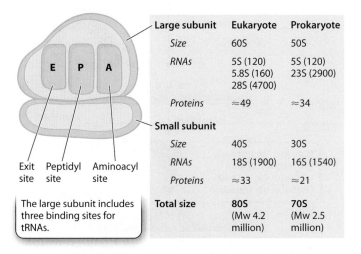

Large subunit	Eukaryote	Prokaryote
Size	60S	50S
RNAs	5S (120) 5.8S (160) 28S (4700)	5S (120) 23S (2900)
Proteins	≈49	≈34
Small subunit		
Size	40S	30S
RNAs	18S (1900)	16S (1540)
Proteins	≈33	≈21
Total size	**80S** (Mw 4.2 million)	**70S** (Mw 2.5 million)

The large subunit includes three binding sites for tRNAs.

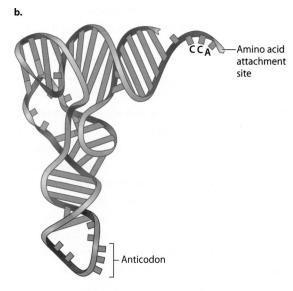

self-pairing structure that can be drawn as a cloverleaf, as shown in Fig. 4.13a, but the actual structure is more like that in Fig. 4.13b. In Fig. 4.13a, the bases found in all tRNA molecules are indicated by the letters; the Greek letter Ψ (psi) stands for pseudouracil, a slightly modified form of uracil. Three bases in the anticodon loop make up the anticodon; these are the three nucleotides that undergo base pairing with the corresponding codon.

Each tRNA has the nucleotide sequence CCA at its 3′ end (Fig. 4.13), and the 3′ hydroxyl of the A is the attachment site for the amino acid corresponding to the anticodon. Enzymes called **aminoacyl tRNA synthetases** connect specific amino acids to specific tRNA molecules (**Fig. 4.14**). Therefore, they are directly responsible for actually translating the codon sequence in a nucleic acid to a specific amino acid in a polypeptide chain. Most organisms have one aminoacyl tRNA synthetase for each amino acid. The enzyme binds to multiple sites on any tRNA that has an anticodon corresponding to the amino acid, and it catalyzes formation of the covalent bond between the amino acid and tRNA. A tRNA that has no amino acid attached is said to be uncharged, and one with its amino acid attached is said to be charged. Amino acid tRNA synthetases are very accurate and attach the wrong amino acid far less often than 1 time in 10,000. This accuracy is greater than that of subsequent steps in translation.

Although the specificity for attaching an amino acid to the correct tRNA is a property of aminoacyl tRNA synthetase, the specificity of DNA–RNA and codon–anticodon interactions result from base pairing. **Fig. 4.15** shows the relationships for one codon in double-stranded DNA, in the corresponding mRNA, and in the codon–anticodon pairing between the mRNA and the tRNA. Note that the first (5′) base in the codon in mRNA pairs with the last (3′) base in the anticodon because, as noted in Chapter 3, nucleic acid strands that undergo base pairing must be antiparallel.

The genetic code shows the correspondence between codons and amino acids.

Fig. 4.15 shows how the codon AUG specifies the amino acid methionine (Met) by base pairing with the anticodon of a charged tRNA, denoted tRNA^Met. Most codons specify an amino acid according to a **genetic code.** This code is sometimes called the "standard" genetic code because, while it is used by almost all cells, some minor differences are found in a few organisms as well as in mitochondria.

The codon that initiates the process of translation is AUG, which specifies Met. The polypeptide is synthesized from the

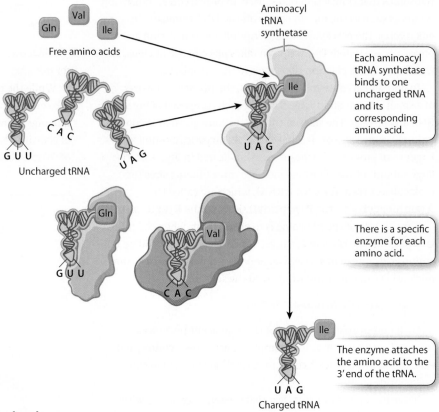

FIG. 4.14   Function of aminoacyl tRNA synthetase enzymes. Aminoacyl tRNA synthetases attach specific amino acids to tRNAs and are therefore responsible for translating the codon sequence into an amino acid sequence in a protein.

Each aminoacyl tRNA synthetase binds to one uncharged tRNA and its corresponding amino acid.

There is a specific enzyme for each amino acid.

The enzyme attaches the amino acid to the 3′ end of the tRNA.

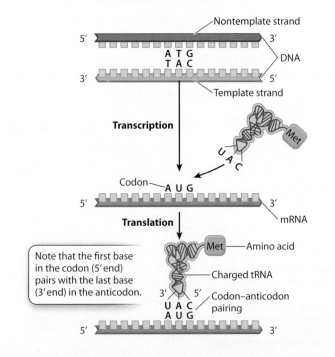

FIG. 4.15   Role of base pairing. Base pairing determines the relationship between a three-base triplet in double-stranded DNA to a codon in mRNA, and between a codon in mRNA to an anticodon in tRNA.

Note that the first base in the codon (5′ end) pairs with the last base (3′ end) in the anticodon.

amino end to the carboxyl end, and so Met forms the amino end of any polypeptide being synthesized; however, in many cases the Met is cleaved off by an enzyme after synthesis is complete. The AUG codon is also used to specify the incorporation of Met at internal sites within the polypeptide chain.

As is apparent in Fig. 4.15, the AUG codon that initiated translation is preceded by a region in the mRNA that is not translated. The position of the initiator AUG codon in the mRNA establishes the reading frame that determines how the downstream codons (those following the AUG) are to be read.

Once the initial Met creates the amino end of a new polypeptide chain, the downstream codons are read one by one in non-overlapping groups of three bases. At each step,

the ribosome binds to a tRNA with an anticodon that can base pair with the codon, and the amino acid on that tRNA is attached to the growing chain to become the new carboxyl end of the polypeptide chain. This process continues until one of three "stop" codons is encountered: UAA, UAG, or UGA. (The stop codons are also called termination codons or sometimes nonsense codons.) At this point, the polypeptide is finished and released into the cytosol.

The standard genetic code was deciphered in the 1960s by a combination of techniques, but among the most ingenious was the development by American biochemist Har Gobind Khorana and his colleagues of chemical methods for making synthetic RNAs of known sequence. This experiment is illustrated in **Fig. 4.16**.

HOW DO WE KNOW?

FIG. 4.16

How was the genetic code deciphered?

BACKGROUND The genetic code is the correspondence between three-letter nucleotide codons in RNA and amino acids in a protein. American biochemist Har Gobind Khorana performed key experiments that helped to crack the code.

METHOD Khorana and his group made RNAs of known sequence. They then added these synthetic RNAs to a solution containing all of the other components needed for translation. By adjusting the concentration of magnesium and other factors, the researchers could get the ribosome to initiate synthesis with any codon, even if not AUG.

EXPERIMENT 1 AND RESULTS When a synthetic poly(U) was used as the mRNA, the resulting polypeptide was polyphenylalanine (Phe–Phe–Phe…):

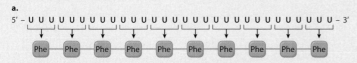

CONCLUSION The codon UUU corresponds to Phe. The poly(U) mRNA can be translated in three possible reading frames, depending on which U is the 5′ end of the start codon, but in each of them, all the codons are UUU.

EXPERIMENT 2 AND RESULTS When a synthetic mRNA with alternating U and C was used, the resulting polypeptide had alternating serine (Ser) and leucine (Leu):

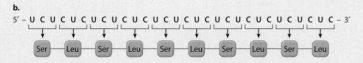

CONCLUSION Here again there are three reading frames, but each of them has alternating UCU and CUC codons. The researchers could not deduce from this result whether UCU corresponds to Ser and CUC to Leu or the other way around; the correct assignment came from experiments using other synthetic mRNA molecules.

EXPERIMENT 3 AND RESULTS When a synthetic mRNA with repeating UCA was used, three different polypeptides were produced—polyserine (Ser), polyhistidine (His), and polyisoleucine (Ile).

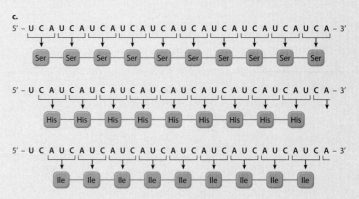

CONCLUSION The results do not reveal which of the three reading frames corresponds to which amino acid, but this was sorted out by studies of other synthetic polymers.

SOURCE Khorana, H. G. 1972. "Nucleic Acid Synthesis in the Study of the Genetic Code." In *Nobel Lectures, Physiology or Medicine 1963–1970*. Amsterdam: Elsevier.

The standard genetic code shown in **Table 4.1** has 20 amino acids specified by 64 codons. Many amino acids are therefore specified by more than one codon, and hence the genetic code is redundant, or degenerate. The redundancy has strong patterns, however:

- The redundancy results almost exclusively from the third codon position.

- When an amino acid is specified by two codons, they differ either in whether the third position is a U or a C (both pyrimidine bases), or in whether the third position is an A or a G (both purine bases).

- When an amino acid is specified by four codons, the identity of the third codon position does not matter; it could be U, C, A, or G.

The chemical basis of these patterns results from two features of translation. First, in many tRNA anticodons the 5′ base that pairs with the 3′ (third) base in the codon is chemically modified into a form that can pair with two or more bases at the third position in the codon. Second, in the ribosome, there is less-than-perfect alignment between the third position of the codon and the base that pairs with it in the anticodon, so the requirements for base pairing are somewhat relaxed; this feature of the codon–anticodon interaction is referred to as wobble.

→   **Quick Check 2** What polypeptide sequences would you expect to result from a synthetic mRNA with the repeating sequence 5′-UUUGGGUUUGGGUUUGGG-3′?

Translation consists of initiation, elongation, and termination.

Translation is usually divided into three separate processes. The first is **initiation,** in which the initiator AUG codon is recognized and Met is established as the first amino acid in the new polypeptide chain. The second process is **elongation,** in which successive amino acids are added one by one to the growing chain. And the third process is **termination,** in which the addition of amino acids stops and the completed polypeptide chain is released from the ribosome.

Initiation of translation (**Fig. 4.17**) requires a number of protein **initiation factors** that bind to the mRNA. In eukaryotes, one group of initiation factors binds to the 5′ cap that is added to the mRNA during processing (Fig. 4.17a). These recruit a small subunit of the ribosome, and other initiation factors bring up a transfer RNA charged with methionine (Met). The initiation complex then moves along the mRNA until it encounters the first AUG triplet. The position of this AUG establishes the translational reading frame.

When the first AUG codon is encountered, a large ribosomal subunit joins the complex, the initiation factors are released, and the next tRNA is ready to join the ribosome (Fig. 4.17b). Note in Fig. 4.17b that the tRNA^{Met} binds with the P (peptidyl) site in the ribosome and that the next tRNA in line comes in at the A (aminoacyl) site. Once the new tRNA is in place, a coupled reaction takes place in which the bond connecting the Met to its tRNA is transferred to the amino group of the next amino acid in line as the first peptide bond is formed (Fig. 4.17c). The new peptide is now attached to the tRNA in the A site. Formation of the peptide bond requires multiple proteins in the large subunit, but an RNA in the large subunit is the actual catalyst. The ribosome then shifts one codon to the right (Fig. 4.17d), which moves the uncharged tRNA^{Met} to the E site and the peptide-bearing tRNA to the P site, freeing the A site for the next charged tRNA in line to come in.

Once translation has been initiated, it proceeds step by step through the

---

TABLE 4.1   The standard genetic code.

First position (5′end)	Second position				Third position (3′end)
	U	C	A	G	
U	UUU Phe ⎤ F UUC Phe ⎦ UUA Leu ⎤ L UUG Leu ⎦	UCU Ser ⎤ UCC Ser ⎥ S UCA Ser ⎥ UCG Ser ⎦	UAU Tyr ⎤ Y UAC Tyr ⎦ UAA Stop UAG Stop	UGU Cys ⎤ C UGC Cys ⎦ UGA Stop UGG Trp W	U C A G
C	CUU Leu ⎤ CUC Leu ⎥ L CUA Leu ⎥ CUG Leu ⎦	CCU Pro ⎤ CCC Pro ⎥ P CCA Pro ⎥ CCG Pro ⎦	CAU His ⎤ H CAC His ⎦ CAA Gln ⎤ Q CAG Gln ⎦	CGU Arg ⎤ CGC Arg ⎥ R CGA Arg ⎥ CGG Arg ⎦	U C A G
A	AUU Ile ⎤ AUC Ile ⎥ L AUA Ile ⎦ AUG Met M	ACU Thr ⎤ ACC Thr ⎥ T ACA Thr ⎥ ACG Thr ⎦	AAU Asn ⎤ N AAC Asn ⎦ AAA Lys ⎤ K AAG Lys ⎦	AGU Ser ⎤ S AGC Ser ⎦ AGA Arg ⎤ R AGG Arg ⎦	U C A G
G	GUU Val ⎤ GUC Val ⎥ V GUA Val ⎥ GUG Val ⎦	GCU Ala ⎤ GCC Ala ⎥ A GCA Ala ⎥ GCG Ala ⎦	GAU Asp ⎤ D GAC Asp ⎦ GAA Glu ⎤ E GAG Glu ⎦	GGU Gly ⎤ GGC Gly ⎥ G GGA Gly ⎥ GGG Gly ⎦	U C A G

■ Nonpolar   ■ Polar   ■ Basic   ■ Acidic   ■ Stop codon

FIG. 4.17 **Initiation of translation.** Initiation factors bind the small subunit of the ribosome, which scans until it reaches an AUG codon, where the large subunit of the ribosome joins the complex.

a.

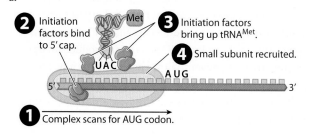

b.

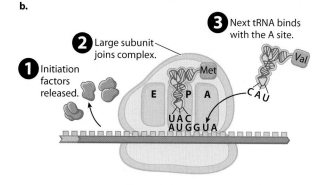

c.

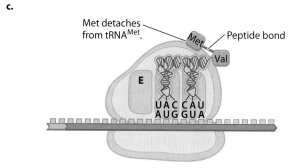

d.

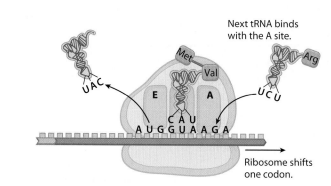

FIG. 4.18 **Elongation of the polypeptide chain.** Note that the growing polypeptide chain remains attached to a tRNA throughout the process.

a.

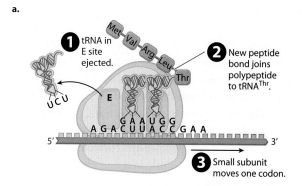

b.

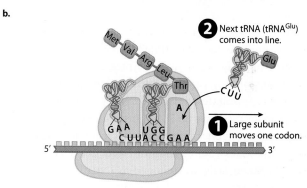

c.

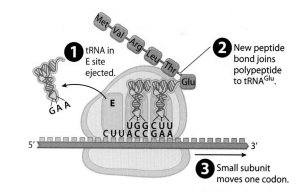

ribosomal subunit has moved one codon farther along the mRNA, and the tRNA in the E (exit) site is being ejected. Fig. 4.18b shows the situation an instant later, when the large ribosomal subunit has moved downstream one codon, emptying the A site by shifting the tRNA^Thr to the P site in the middle and the tRNA^Leu to the E site. Note that, while there are three tRNA binding sites on the ribosome, only two of them are occupied at any one time. Fig. 4.18c shows the situation slightly later; it is almost identical to that in Fig. 4.18a, except that the polypeptide is one amino acid longer and the ribosome has moved one codon farther to the

process of elongation (**Fig. 4.18**). Fig. 4.18a shows the situation immediately after the formation of a new peptide bond that attaches the growing polypeptide chain to the amino acid linked to the tRNA in the A site (in this case tRNA^Thr); the small

right. Ribosome movement along the mRNA and formation of the peptide bonds require energy, which is obtained by breaking the high-energy bonds of the molecule GTP bound with proteins called **elongation factors.**

The elongation process shown in Fig. 4.18 continues until one of the stop codons (UAA, UAG, or UGA) is encountered; these codons signal termination of polypeptide synthesis. Termination takes place because the stop codons do not have corresponding tRNA molecules. Rather, when a stop codon is encountered, a protein **release factor** binds to the A site of the ribosome. The release factor causes the bond connecting the polypeptide to the tRNA to break, which creates the carboxyl terminus of the polypeptide and completes the chain. Once the finished polypeptide is released, the small and large ribosomal subunits disassociate from the mRNA and from each other.

Although elongation and termination are very similar in prokaryotes and in eukaryotes, translation initiation differs between the two (**Fig. 4.19**). In eukaryotes, the initiation complex forms at the 5′ cap and scans along the mRNA until the first AUG is encountered (Fig. 4.19a). In prokaryotes, the mRNA molecules have no 5′ cap. Instead, the initiation complex is formed at one or more internal sequences present in the mRNA known as a Shine–Dalgarno sequence (Figure 4.19b). In *E. coli*, the Shine–Dalgarno sequence is 5′-AGGAGGU-3′, and it is followed by an AUG codon eight nucleotides farther downstream that serves as an initiation codon for translation. The ability to initiate translation internally allows prokaryotic mRNAs to contain open reading frames for more than one protein. Such an mRNA is known as a **polycistronic mRNA.** In Fig. 4.19b, the polycistronic mRNA codes for three different polypeptide chains, each with its own AUG initiation codon preceded eight nucleotides upstream by its own Shine–Dalgarno sequence. Each Shine–Dalgarno sequence can serve as an initiation site for translation, and so all three polypeptides can be translated.

A polycistronic mRNA results from transcription of a group of functionally related genes located in tandem along the DNA and transcribed as a single unit from one promoter. This type of gene organization is known as an **operon.** Prokaryotes have many of their genes organized into operons because the production of a polycistronic mRNA allows all the protein products to be expressed together whenever they are needed. Typically, the genes organized into operons are those whose products are needed either for successive steps in the synthesis of an essential small molecule, such as an amino acid, or else for successive steps in the breakdown of a source of energy, such as a complex carbohydrate.

→ **Quick Check 3** Bacterial DNA containing an operon encoding three enzymes is introduced into chromosomal DNA in yeast (a eukaryote) in such a way that it is properly flanked by a promoter and a transcriptional terminator. The bacterial DNA is transcribed and the RNA correctly processed, but only the protein nearest the promoter is produced. Can you suggest why?

? CASE 1 The First Cell: Life's Origins
How did the genetic code originate?

During transcription and translation, proteins and nucleic acids work together to convert the information stored in DNA into proteins. If we think about how such a system might have originated, however, we immediately confront a chicken-and-egg problem: Cells need nucleic acids to make proteins, but proteins are required to make nucleic acids. Which came first? In Chapter 2, we discussed the special features that make RNA an attractive candidate for both information storage and catalysis in early life. Early in evolutionary history, then, proteins had to be added to the mix. No one fully understands

FIG. 4.19   Initiation in eukaryotes and in prokaryotes. (a) In eukaryotes, translation is initiated only at the 5′ cap. (b) In prokaryotes, initiation takes place at any Shine–Dalgarno sequence; this mechanism allows a single mRNA to include coding sequences for multiple polypeptides.

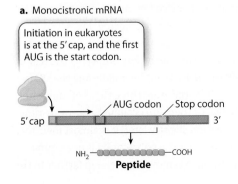
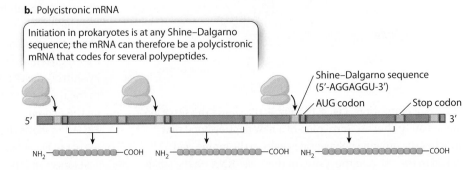

how they were incorporated, but researchers are looking closely at tRNA, the molecule that completes the "translating" step of translation.

In modern cells, tRNA shuttles amino acids to the ribosome, but an innovative hypothesis suggests that in early life tRNA-like molecules might have served a different function. This proposal holds that the early precursors of the ribosome were RNA molecules that facilitated the replication of other RNAs, not proteins. In this version of an RNA world, precursors to tRNA would have shuttled nucleotides to growing RNA strands. Researchers hypothesize that tRNAs bound to amino acids may have acted as simple catalysts, facilitating more accurate RNA synthesis. Through time, amino acids brought into close proximity in the process of building RNA molecules might have polymerized to form peptide chains. From there, natural selection would favor the formation of peptides that enhanced replication of RNA molecules, bringing proteins into the chemistry of life.

All of the steps in gene expression, including transcription and translation, are summarized in **Fig. 4.20** on the next page.

4.3 PROTEIN EVOLUTION AND THE ORIGIN OF NEW PROTEINS

The amino acid sequences of more than a million proteins are known, and the particular three-dimensional structure has been determined for each of more than 10,000 proteins. While few of the sequences and structures are identical, many are sufficiently similar that the proteins can be grouped into about 25,000 **protein families** that are structurally and functionally related. Why are there not more types of proteins? The number of possible sequences is unimaginably large. For example, for a polypeptide of only 62 amino acids, there are 20^{62} possible sequences (because each of the 62 positions could be occupied by any of the 20 amino acids). The number 20^{62} equals approximately 10^{80}; this number is also the estimated total number of electrons,

protons, and neutrons in the entire universe! So why are there so few protein families? The most likely answer is that the chance that any random sequence of amino acids would fold into a stable configuration and carry out some useful function in the cell is very close to zero.

Most proteins are composed of modular folding domains.
If functional proteins are so unlikely, how could life have evolved? The answer is that the earliest proteins were probably much shorter than modern proteins and needed only a trace of function. Only as proteins evolved through billions of years did they become progressively longer and more specialized in their functions. Many protein families that exist today exhibit small regions of three-dimensional structure in which the protein folding is similar. These regions range in length from 25 to 100 or more amino acids. A region of a protein that folds in a similar way relatively independently of the rest of the protein is known as a **folding domain.**

Several examples of folding domains are illustrated in **Fig. 4.21.** Many folding domains are functional units in themselves. The folding domain in Fig. 4.21a is a globin fold composed of multiple α helices that have a hydrophobic core and a hydrophilic exterior. The globin fold is characteristic of hemoglobin and other oxygen-carrying proteins. Fig. 4.21b is a Rossman fold, which in many enzymes binds a nicotinamide adenine dinucleotide (NAD) used in oxidation reactions. The TIM barrel (Fig. 4.21c) is named after the enzyme triose phosphate isomerase in which it is a prominent feature. The TIM barrel consists of alternating α helices and parallel β sheets connected by loops. In many enzymes with a TIM barrel, the active site is formed by the loops at the carboxyl ends of the sheets. Finally, Fig. 4.21d is a β barrel formed from antiparallel β sheets. β barrel structures occur in proteins in some types of bacteria, usually in proteins that span the cell membrane, where the β barrel provides a channel that binds hydrophobic molecules.

The number of known folding domains is only about 2500, which is far fewer than the number of protein families. The

---

FIG. 4.21 **Examples of folding domains:** (a) globin fold; (b) Rossman fold; (c) TIM barrel; (d) β barrel.

a.
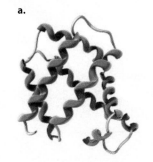

b.
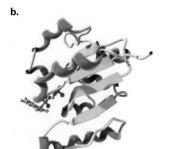

c.
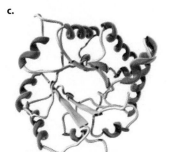

d.
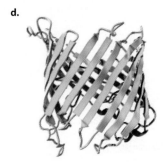

Gene Expression

FIG. 4.20

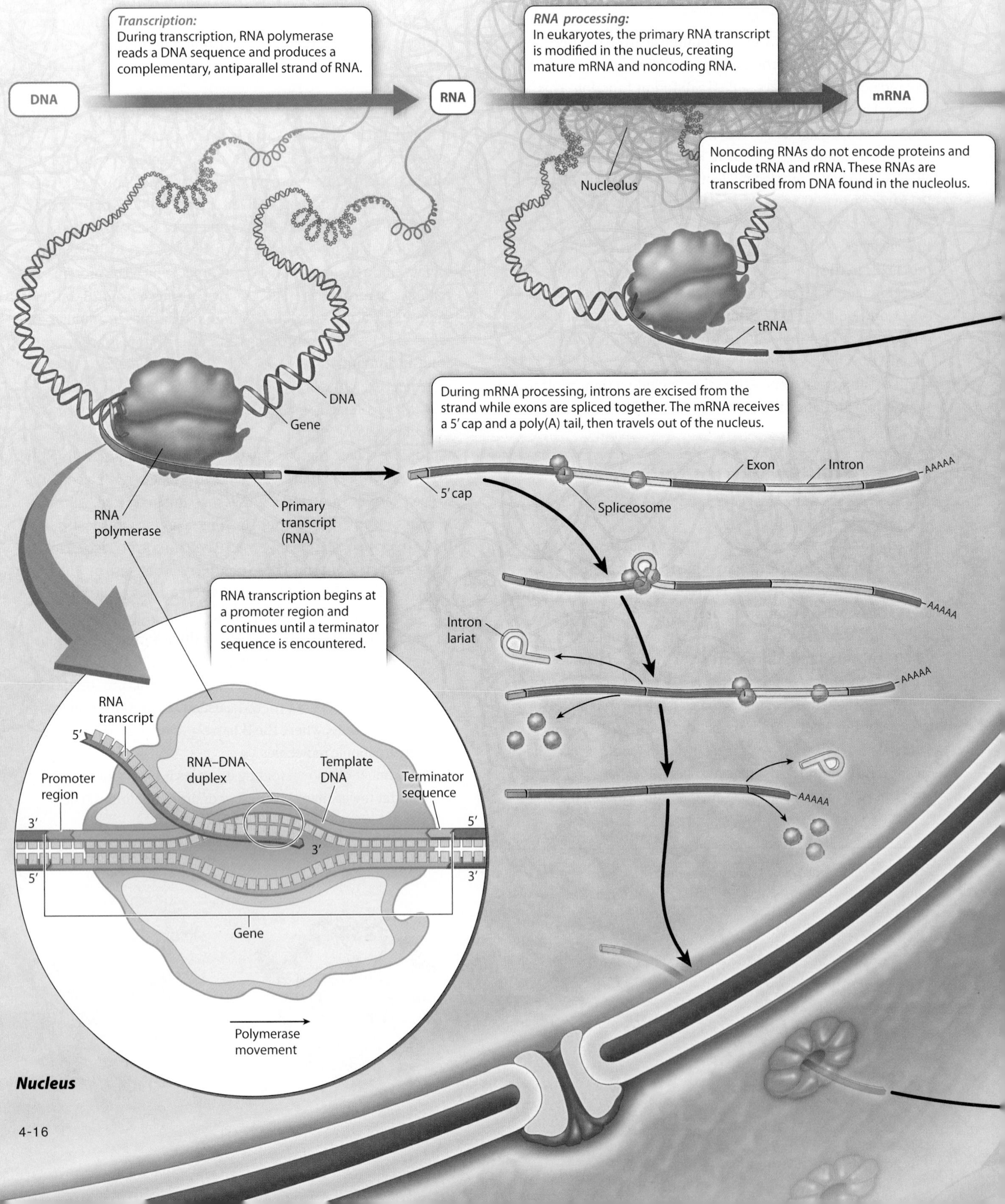

Transcription:
During transcription, RNA polymerase reads a DNA sequence and produces a complementary, antiparallel strand of RNA.

RNA processing:
In eukaryotes, the primary RNA transcript is modified in the nucleus, creating mature mRNA and noncoding RNA.

DNA

RNA

mRNA

Noncoding RNAs do not encode proteins and include tRNA and rRNA. These RNAs are transcribed from DNA found in the nucleolus.

Nucleolus

tRNA

DNA

Gene

During mRNA processing, introns are excised from the strand while exons are spliced together. The mRNA receives a 5' cap and a poly(A) tail, then travels out of the nucleus.

RNA polymerase

Primary transcript (RNA)

5' cap

Exon

Intron

AAAAA

Spliceosome

AAAAA

RNA transcription begins at a promoter region and continues until a terminator sequence is encountered.

Intron lariat

AAAAA

RNA transcript

5'

Promoter region

RNA–DNA duplex

Template DNA

Terminator sequence

3'

5'

3'

5'

3'

Gene

AAAAA

Polymerase movement

Nucleus

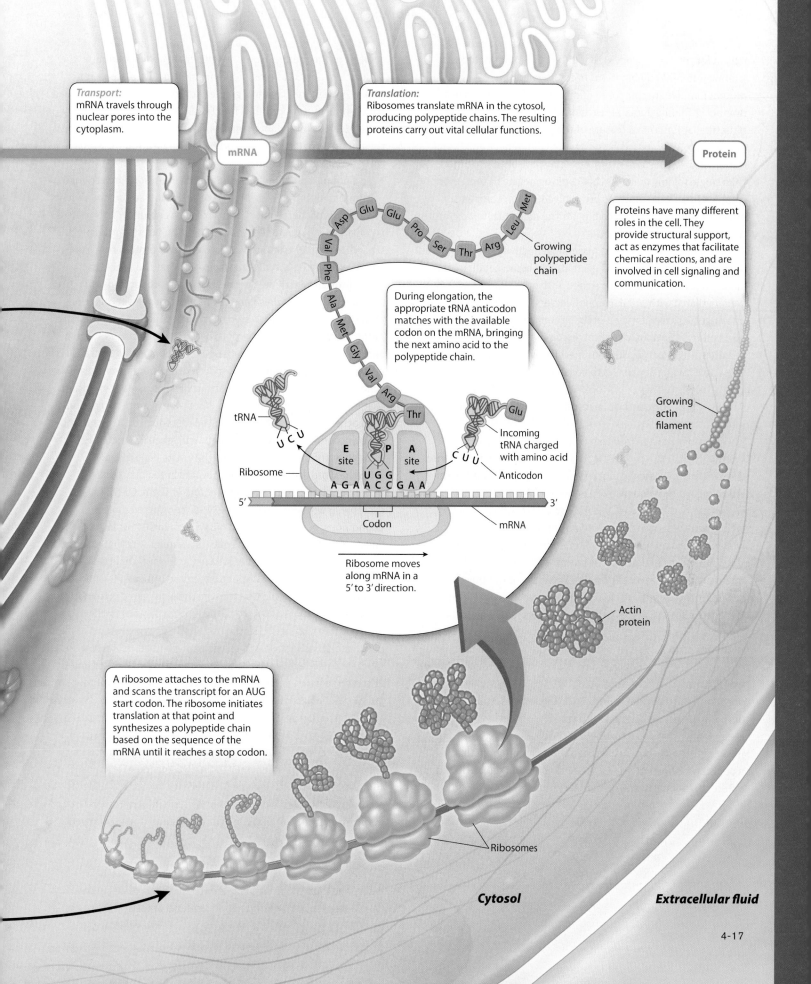

Translation:
Ribosomes translate mRNA in the cytosol, producing polypeptide chains. The resulting proteins carry out vital cellular functions.

mRNA

Protein

Proteins have many different roles in the cell. They provide structural support, act as enzymes that facilitate chemical reactions, and are involved in cell signaling and communication.

Growing polypeptide chain

Asp
Glu
Glu
Pro
Ser
Thr
Arg
Leu
Met

Val
Phe
Ala
Met
Gly
Val
Arg
Thr

During elongation, the appropriate tRNA anticodon matches with the available codon on the mRNA, bringing the next amino acid to the polypeptide chain.

Growing actin filament

tRNA

E site
P site
A site

Glu

Incoming tRNA charged with amino acid

Ribosome

UGG
AGAACCGAA

Anticodon

UCU

CUU

5'

Codon

3'

mRNA

Ribosome moves along mRNA in a 5' to 3' direction.

Actin protein

A ribosome attaches to the mRNA and scans the transcript for an AUG start codon. The ribosome initiates translation at that point and synthesizes a polypeptide chain based on the sequence of the mRNA until it reaches a stop codon.

Ribosomes

Cytosol

Extracellular fluid

reason for the discrepancy is that different protein families contain different combinations of folding domains. Modern protein families are composed of different combinations of a number of folding domains, each of which contributes some structural or functional feature of the protein. Different types of protein folds occur again and again in different contexts and combinations. The earliest proteins may have been little more than single folding domains that could aggregate to form more complex functional units. As life evolved, the proteins became longer by joining the DNA coding for the individual folding units together into a single molecule.

For example, human tissue plasminogen activator, a protein that is used in treating strokes and heart attacks because it dissolves blood clots, contains domains shared with cell-surface receptors, a domain shared with cellular growth factors, and a domain that folds into large loops facilitating protein–protein interactions. Hence, novel proteins do not always evolve from random combinations of amino acids; instead, they often evolve by combining already functional folding domains into novel combinations.

Amino acid sequences evolve through mutation and selection.

Another important reason that complex proteins can evolve seemingly against long odds is that evolution proceeds stepwise through the processes of mutation and selection. A **mutation** is a change in the sequence of a gene. The process of mutation is discussed in Chapter 14, but for now all you need to know is that mutations affecting proteins occur at random in regard to their effects on protein function. In protein-coding genes, some mutations may affect the amino acid sequence; others might change the level of protein expression or the time in development or type of cell in which the protein is produced. Here, we will consider only those mutations that change the amino acid sequence.

By way of analogy, we can use a word game that we call change-one-letter. The object of the game is to change an ordinary English word into another meaningful English word by changing exactly one letter. Consider the word GONE. To illustrate "mutations" of the word that are random with respect to function (that is, random with respect to whether the change will yield a meaningful new word), we wrote a computer program that would choose one letter in GONE at random and replace it with a different random letter. The first 26 "mutants" of GONE are:

UONE	GNNE	GONJ	GOZE
GONH	GOLE	GFNE	XONE
NONE	GKNE	GJNE	DONE
GCNE	GONB	GOIE	GGNE
GONI	GFNE	GPNE	GENE
BONE	GOWE	OONE	GYNE

Most of the mutant words are gibberish, corresponding to the biological reality that most random amino acid replacements impair protein function to a greater or lesser extent. On the other hand, some mutant proteins function just as well as the original, and a precious few change function. In the word-game analogy, the mutants that can persist correspond to meaningful words, those words shown in red.

In a population of organisms, random mutations are retained or eliminated through the process of **selection** among individuals on the basis of their ability to survive and reproduce. This process is considered in greater detail in Chapter 21, but the principle is straightforward. Most mutations that impair protein function will be eliminated because, to the extent that the function of the protein contributes to survival and reproduction, the individuals carrying these mutations will leave fewer offspring than others. Mutations that do not impair function may remain in the population for long periods because their carriers survive and reproduce in normal numbers; a mutation of this type has no tendency to either increase or decrease in frequency over time. In contrast, individuals that carry the occasional mutation that improves protein function will reproduce more successfully than others. Because of the enhanced reproduction, the mutant gene encoding the improved protein will gradually increase in frequency and spread throughout the entire population.

In the word game, any of the mutants in red may persist in the population, but suppose that one of them, GENE for example, is actually superior to GONE (considered more euphonious, perhaps). Then GENE will gradually displace GONE, and eventually GONE will be gone. In a similar way that one meaningful word may replace another, one amino acid sequence may be replaced with a different one in the course of evolution.

A real-world example that mirrors the word game is found in the evolution of resistance of the malaria parasite to the drug pyrimethamine. This drug inhibits an enzyme known as dihydrofolate reductase, which the parasite needs to survive and reproduce inside red blood cells. Resistance to pyrimethamine is known to have evolved through a stepwise sequence of four amino acid replacements. In the first replacement, serine (S) at the 108th amino acid in the polypeptide sequence (position 108) was replaced with asparagine (N); then cysteine (C) at position 59 was replaced with arginine (R); asparagine (N) at position 51 was then replaced with isoleucine (I); finally isoleucine (I) at position 164 was replaced with leucine (L). If we list the amino acids according to their single-letter abbreviation in the order of their occurrence in the protein, the evolution of resistance followed this pathway:

NCSI → NCNI → NRNI → IRNI → IRNL

where the mutant amino acids are shown in red. Each successive amino acid replacement increased the level of resistance, so that a greater concentration of drug was needed to treat the disease. The quadruple mutant IRNL is resistant to such high levels that the drug is no longer useful.

Depicted according to stepwise amino acid replacements, the analogy between the evolution of pyrimethamine resistance and the change-one-letter game is clear. It should also be clear from our earlier discussion that hundreds of other mutations causing amino acid replacements in the enzyme must have

occurred in the parasite during the course of evolution, but only these amino acid changes occurring in this order persisted and increased in frequency because they conferred greater survival and reproduction of the parasite under treatment with the drug.

→ **Quick Check 4** What do you think happened to the mutations that decreased survival or reproduction of the mosquitoes?

Core Concepts Summary

4.1 PROTEINS ARE LINEAR POLYMERS OF AMINO ACIDS THAT FORM THREE-DIMENSIONAL STRUCTURES WITH SPECIFIC FUNCTIONS.

An amino acid consists of an α carbon connected by covalent bonds to an amino group, a carboxyl group, a hydrogen atom, and a side chain or R group. page 4-2

There are 20 common amino acids that differ in their side chains. page 4-2

Amino acids are connected by peptide bonds to form proteins. page 4-3

The primary structure of a protein is its amino acid sequence. The primary structure determines how a protein folds, which in turn determines how it functions. page 4-4

The secondary structure of a protein results from the interactions of nearby amino acids. Examples include the α helix and β sheet. page 4-5

The tertiary structure of a protein is its three-dimensional shape, which results from long-range interactions of amino acid side chains. page 4-6

Some proteins are made up of several polypeptide subunits; this group of subunits is the protein's quaternary structure. page 4-7

Chaperones help some proteins fold properly. page 4-8

4.2 TRANSLATION IS THE PROCESS BY WHICH THE SEQUENCE OF BASES IN MESSENGER RNA SPECIFIES THE ORDER OF SUCCESSIVE AMINO ACIDS IN A NEWLY SYNTHESIZED PROTEIN.

Translation requires many cellular components, including ribosomes, tRNAs, and proteins. page 4-8

mRNAs have three possible reading frames comprised of three-nucleotide codons. page 4-9

tRNAs have an anticodon that base pairs with the codon in the mRNA and carries a specific amino acid. page 4-10

Aminoacyl tRNA synthetases attach specific amino acids to tRNAs. page 4-10

The genetic code defines the relationship between the three-letter codons of nucleic acids and their corresponding amino acids. It was deciphered using synthetic RNA molecules. page 4-10

The genetic code is redundant in that many amino acids are specified by more than one codon. page 4-12

Translation consists of three steps: initiation, elongation, and termination. page 4-12

4.3 PROTEINS EVOLVE THROUGH MUTATION AND SELECTION AND BY COMBINING FUNCTIONAL UNITS.

Protein families are groups of proteins that are structurally and functionally related. page 4-15

There are far fewer protein families than the total number of possible proteins because the probability that a random sequence of amino acids will fold properly to carry out a specific function is very small. page 4-15

A region of a protein that folds in a particular way and that carries out a specific function is called a folding domain. page 4-15

Proteins evolve by combining different folding domains. page 4-18

Proteins also evolve by changes in amino acid sequence, which occurs by mutation and selection. page 4-18

Self-Assessment

1. Draw one of the 20 amino acids and label the amino group, the carboxyl group, the side chain (R group), and the α carbon.

2. Name four major groups of amino acids, categorized by the properties of their side chains. Explain how the chemical properties of each group affect protein shape.

3. Describe the importance to proteins of peptide bonds, hydrogen bonds, ionic bonds, disulfide bridges, and noncovalent interactions.

4. Explain how the order of amino acids determines the way in which a protein folds.

5. Explain the relationship between protein folding and protein function.

6. Describe the relationship between codons of mRNA, anticodons of tRNA, and amino acids.

7. Describe the process by which ribosomes synthesize polypeptides.

8. Name and describe two ways that proteins can acquire new functions in the course of evolution.

Do you understand the chapter's Core Concepts? Log into BIO**P⊕RTAL** to check your answers to the Self-Assessment questions, then practice what you've learned and reinforce this chapter's concepts by working through the problems and multimedia tutorials provided there.

📶 **http://courses.bfwpub.com/yourbioportal/index.php**

CHAPTER 5

ORGANIZING PRINCIPLES: LIPIDS, MEMBRANES, AND CELL COMPARTMENTS

Core Concepts

5.1 Cell membranes are composed of lipids, proteins, and carbohydrates.

5.2 The plasma membrane is a selective barrier that controls the movement of molecules between the inside and outside of the cell.

5.3 Cells can be classified as prokaryotes or eukaryotes; these differ in the degree of internal compartmentalization.

5.4 The endomembrane system is an interconnected system of membranes that includes the nuclear envelope, endoplasmic reticulum, Golgi apparatus, lysosomes, vesicles, and plasma membrane.

5.5 Mitochondria and chloroplasts are organelles involved in harnessing energy, and likely evolved from free-living prokaryotes.

"With the discovery of the cell, biologists found their atom." So stated François Jacob, the French biologist who shared the Nobel Prize in Physiology or Medicine in 1965. Just as the atom is the smallest, most basic unit of matter, the cell is the smallest, most basic unit of living organisms. All organisms, from single-celled algae to complex multicellular organisms like humans, are made up of cells. Therefore, essential properties of life, including growth, reproduction, and metabolism, must be understood in terms of cell structure and function.

Cells were first seen sometime around 1665, when the English scientist Robert Hooke built a microscope that he used to observe thin sections of dried cork tissue derived from plants. In these sections, Hooke observed arrays of small cavities and named them "cells" (**Fig. 5.1**). Although Hooke was probably looking at empty cell walls that make up the plant vascular system rather than at living cells, his observations nevertheless led to the concept that cells are the fundamental units of life. Later in the seventeenth century, the Dutch microbiologist Anton van Leeuwenhoek greatly improved the magnifying power of microscope lenses, enabling him to see and describe unicellular organisms, including bacteria, protozoa, and algae. Today, modern microscopy is providing unprecedented detail and a deeper understanding of the inner architecture of cells.

Cells differ in size and shape, but they share many features. This similarity in the microscopic organization of all living organisms led to the development, in the middle of the nineteenth century, of one of the pillars of modern biology: the **cell theory**. Based on the work and ideas of Matthias Schlieden, Theodor Schwann, Rudolf Virchow, and others, the cell theory states that all organisms are made up of cells, that the cell is the fundamental unit of life, and that cells come from preexisting cells. There is no life without cells, and the cell is the smallest unit of life.

This chapter focuses on cells and their internal organization. We pay particular attention to the key role that membranes play in separating a cell from the external environment and defining structural and functional spaces within cells.

5.1 STRUCTURE OF CELL MEMBRANES

Cells are defined by membranes. After all, membranes physically separate cells from their external environment. In addition, membranes define spaces within many cells that allow them to carry out their diverse functions. Lipids are the main component of cell membranes. Proteins are often embedded in or associated with the membrane. Carbohydrates can also be found in cell membranes, usually attached to lipids (glycolipids) and proteins (glycoproteins).

FIG. 5.1   The first observation of cells. Robert Hooke used a simple microscope to observe small chambers in a sample of cork tissue that he described as "cells."

Drawing by Hooke

Cork tissue

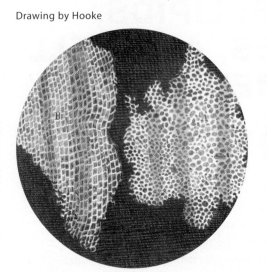
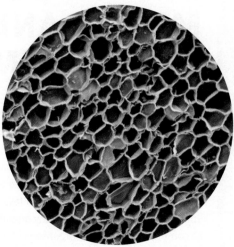

Cell membranes are composed of two layers of lipids.

The major types of lipid found in cell membranes are phospholipids, introduced in Chapter 2. Phospholipids have both hydrophilic ("water-loving") and hydrophobic ("water-fearing") regions in a single molecule (**Fig. 5.2**). The phosphate "head" group is hydrophilic because it is polar, enabling it to form hydrogen bonds with water. By contrast, the two long fatty acid "tails" are hydrophobic because they are nonpolar and do not form hydrogen bonds with water. Molecules with both hydrophilic and hydrophobic regions are termed **amphipathic**.

In an aqueous environment, amphipathic molecules such as phospholipids behave in an interesting way. They spontaneously arrange themselves into various structures that have the polar head groups on the outside interacting with water and the nonpolar tail groups grouped together on the inside away from water. This arrangement results from the tendency of polar molecules like water to exclude nonpolar molecules or nonpolar groups within molecules. The shape of the structure is determined

by the bulkiness of the head group relative to that of the hydrophobic tails. For example, lipids with bulky heads and a single hydrophobic fatty acid tail are wedge-shaped and pack into spherical structures called **micelles** (**Fig. 5.3a**). By contrast, lipids with less bulky head groups and two hydrophobic tails form a **bilayer** (**Fig. 5.3b**). A lipid bilayer is a two-layered structure organized in such a way that the hydrophilic portion of the lipid faces out toward the aqueous environment and the hydrophobic portion faces in toward the hydrophobic portions of other lipids and away from the aqueous environment.

The resulting bilayers form closed structures with an inner space since free edges would expose the hydrophobic chains to the aqueous environment. This organization in part explains why bilayers are effective cell membranes. It also explains why

FIG. 5.2   Phospholipid structure. Phospholipids, the major component of cell membranes, are termed amphipathic because they have both hydrophilic and hydrophobic domains.

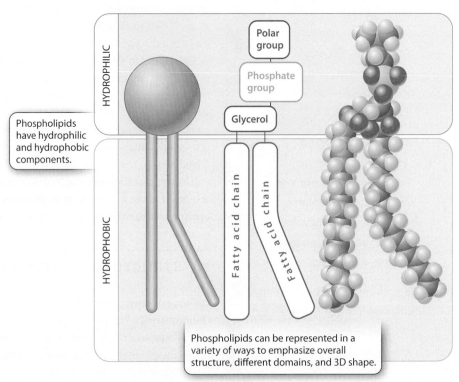

HYDROPHILIC

HYDROPHOBIC

Polar group

Phosphate group

Glycerol

Fatty acid chain

Fatty acid chain

Phospholipids have hydrophilic and hydrophobic components.

Phospholipids can be represented in a variety of ways to emphasize overall structure, different domains, and 3D shape.

FIG. 5.3 **Lipid structures.** Lipids can form micelles (a), bilayers (b), or liposomes (c) when placed in water.

a. Micelle

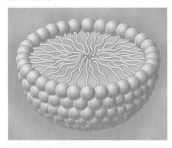

b. Bilayer

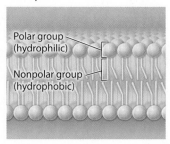

Polar group (hydrophilic)

Nonpolar group (hydrophobic)

c. Liposome

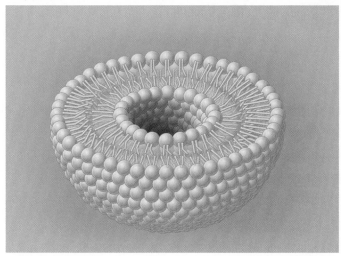

membranes are "self-healing." Small tears in a membrane are rapidly sealed by a spontaneous rearrangement of the lipids surrounding the damaged region, due to the tendency of water to exclude nonpolar molecules.

? CASE 1 The First Cell: Life's Origins
How did the first cell membranes form?
We have seen that the phospholipid bilayer forms spontaneously in water, arranged in such a way that the hydrophobic fatty acids do not interact with water and the polar head groups do interact with water. The bilayer structure forms spontaneously as long as the concentration of free phospholipids is high enough and the pH of the solution is similar to that of a cell. The pH is important because it ensures that the head groups are in their ionized (charged) form and thus suitably hydrophilic. Thus, if phospholipids are added to a test tube of water at neutral pH, they spontaneously form enclosed bilayer structures called **liposomes** (**Fig. 5.3c**). An enzyme is not required to catalyze

any chemical reaction. The membrane enclosure forms by a process of self-assembly that depends only on the chemical properties of the lipids. As the liposomes form, they may capture macromolecules present in solution.

Such a process may have been at work in the early evolution of life on Earth. Experiments show that liposomes can form and re-form in environments like tidal flats where wetting and drying occur repeatedly. The liposomes can even grow, incorporating more and more lipids from the environment. In addition, the liposomes can incorporate nucleic acids and other molecules into their interiors. Depending on their chemical composition, early membranes might have been either leaky or almost impervious to the molecules of life. Over time, they evolved in such a way as to allow at least limited molecular traffic between the environment and cell interior. At some point, new lipids no longer had to be incorporated from the environment. Instead, proteins guided lipid synthesis within the cell, although how this switch to synthesis happened remains uncertain.

All evidence suggests that membranes formed originally by straightforward physical processes, but that their composition and function evolved over time. François Jacob once said that evolution works more like a tinkerer than an engineer, modifying already existing materials rather than designing systems from scratch. It seems that the evolution of membranes is no exception to this pattern.

Cell membranes are dynamic.
Lipids freely associate with one another because of extensive van der Waals forces between their fatty acid tails (Chapter 2). These weak interactions are easily broken and re-formed, so lipid molecules are able to move within the plane of the membrane. For example, a single phospholipid can move across the entire length of a bacterial cell in less than a second. Lipids can also rapidly rotate around their vertical axis, and individual fatty acid chains are able to flex, or bend. As a result, membranes are dynamic, forming and re-forming continually during the lifetime of a cell.

Because membrane lipids are able to move in the plane of the membrane, the membrane is said to be **fluid.** The degree of membrane fluidity depends on which types of lipid make up the membrane. In a single layer of the lipid bilayer, most of the van der Waals and hydrophobic interactions occur between the hydrophobic tails of lipids. The strength of these interactions depends on the length of the fatty acid tails and the presence of double bonds between neighboring carbon atoms. The longer the fatty acid tails, the more surface is available to participate in van der Waals interactions. The tighter packing that results tends to reduce lipid mobility. Likewise, saturated fatty acid tails, which have no double bonds, are straight and tightly packed—again reducing

FIG. 5.4   **Saturated and unsaturated fatty acids in phospholipids.** The composition of cell membranes affects the tightness of packing.

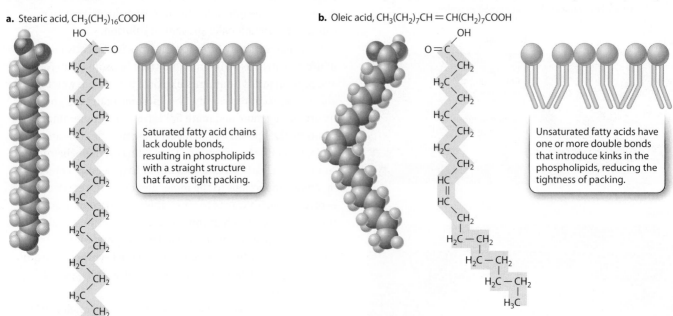

a. Stearic acid, $CH_3(CH_2)_{16}COOH$

Saturated fatty acid chains lack double bonds, resulting in phospholipids with a straight structure that favors tight packing.

b. Oleic acid, $CH_3(CH_2)_7CH=CH(CH_2)_7COOH$

Unsaturated fatty acids have one or more double bonds that introduce kinks in the phospholipids, reducing the tightness of packing.

mobility (**Fig. 5.4a**). The double bonds in unsaturated fatty acids introduce kinks in the fatty acid tails, reducing the tightness of packing and enhancing lipid mobility in the membrane (**Fig. 5.4b**).

→   **Quick Check 1** Animal fats tend to be solid at room temperature, whereas plant and fish oils tend to be liquid. Both contain fatty acids. Can you predict which type of fat contains saturated fatty acids, and which type contains unsaturated fatty acids?

In addition to phospholipids, cell membranes often contain other types of lipid, and these can also influence membrane fluidity. For example, **cholesterol** is a major component of animal cell membranes, representing about 30% by mass of the membrane lipids. Like phospholipids, cholesterol is amphipathic, with both hydrophilic and hydrophobic groups in the same molecule. In the case of cholesterol, the hydrophilic region is simply a hydroxyl group (OH) and the hydrophobic region consists of four interconnected carbon rings with an attached hydrocarbon chain (**Fig. 5.5**). This structure allows cholesterol to insert into the lipid bilayer. Specifically, the hydrophilic head group of cholesterol interacts with the hydrophilic head group of phospholipids, while the ring structure participates in van der Waals interactions with the fatty acid chains.

Cholesterol increases or decreases membrane fluidity depending on temperature. At normal temperatures typically found in a cell, the interaction of the rigid ring structure of cholesterol with the phospholipid fatty acid tails reduces the mobility of the phospholipids and hence the fluidity of the membrane. However, at low temperatures, cholesterol prevents phospholipids from packing tightly with other phospholipids and therefore increases membrane fluidity. Thus, cholesterol helps maintain a consistent state of membrane fluidity by preventing dramatic transitions from a fluid to solid state.

For many decades, it was thought that the various types of lipid found in the membrane were randomly distributed throughout the bilayer. However, more recent studies show that specific types of lipid sometimes assemble into defined patches called **lipid rafts.** For example, sphingolipids (a type of lipid) cluster in discrete patches in the membrane. Furthermore, cholesterol and other membrane components such as proteins appear to accumulate in some of these regions. Thus, membranes are not always a uniform fluid bilayer, but instead contain regions with discrete components.

Although lipids are free to move in the plane of the membrane, the spontaneous transfer of a lipid between layers of the bilayer, known as lipid flip-flop, is very rare. This is not surprising, since flip-flop requires the hydrophilic head group to pass through the hydrophobic interior of the membrane. As a result, there is little exchange of components between

FIG. 5.5   **Cholesterol in the lipid bilayer.** Cholesterol molecules embedded in the lipid bilayer affect the fluidity of the membrane.

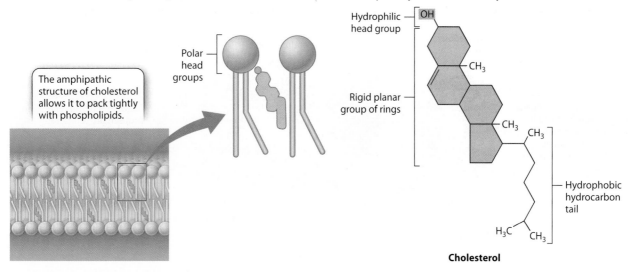

Cholesterol

the two layers of the membrane, which in turn allows the two layers to differ in composition. In fact, in many membranes, different types of lipid are present primarily in one layer or the other.

Proteins associate with cell membranes in different ways.

Most membranes contain proteins as well as lipids. For example, the cell membrane of a red blood cell contains a large variety of proteins, representing as much as 50% of the membrane by mass. These membrane proteins serve different functions (**Fig. 5.6**). Some act as **transporters,** moving ions or other molecules across the membrane. Transporters include **channels** that allow movement of molecules through them, and **carriers** that facilitate movement. Other membrane proteins act as **receptors** that allow the cell to receive signals from the environment. Still others are **enzymes** that catalyze chemical reactions or **anchors** that attach to other proteins that help to maintain cell structure and shape.

These various kinds of membrane protein can be classified into two groups depending on how they associate with the

FIG. 5.6   Functions of membrane proteins.

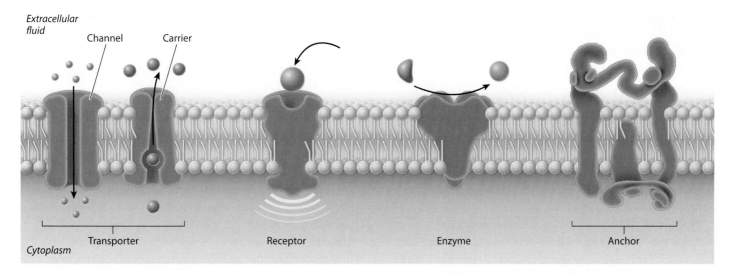

FIG. 5.7   **Integral and peripheral membrane proteins.** Integral membrane proteins are permanently associated with the membrane. Peripheral membrane proteins are temporarily associated with one of the two lipid bilayers or with an integral membrane protein.

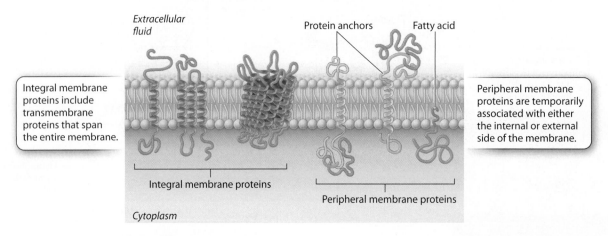

membrane (**Fig. 5.7**). **Integral membrane proteins** are permanently associated with cell membranes and cannot be separated from the membrane experimentally without destroying the membrane itself. **Peripheral membrane proteins** are temporarily associated with the lipid bilayer or with integral membrane proteins through weak noncovalent interactions. They are easily separated from the membrane by simple experimental procedures that leave the structure of the membrane intact.

Most integral membrane proteins are **transmembrane proteins** that span the entire lipid bilayer, as shown in Fig. 5.7. These proteins are composed of three regions: two hydrophilic regions, one protruding from each face of the membrane, and a connecting hydrophobic region that spans the membrane. The hydrophilic region on the internal side of the membrane often interacts with other proteins in the cytoplasm of the cell, whereas the hydrophilic region on the external side can interact with signaling molecules.

Peripheral membrane proteins may be associated with either the internal or external side of the membrane (Fig. 5.7). These proteins interact either with the polar heads of lipids or with integral membrane proteins via weak noncovalent interactions such as hydrogen bonds. Peripheral membrane proteins are only transiently associated with the membrane and can play a role in transmitting information received from external signals. Other peripheral membrane proteins limit the ability of transmembrane proteins to move within the membrane and assist proteins to cluster in lipid rafts.

Proteins, like lipids, are free to move in the membrane. How do we know this? The mobility of proteins in the cell membrane can be demonstrated using an elegant experimental technique called fluorescence recovery after photobleaching, or FRAP (**Fig. 5.8**).

In this technique, proteins embedded in the cell membrane are labeled with fluorescent dye molecules. Labeling an entire membrane creates a fluorescent cell that can be visualized using a fluorescent microscope. A laser is then used to bleach the fluorescent dye molecules in a small area of the cell membrane, leaving a nonfluorescent spot on the surface of the cell. If proteins in the cell membrane were not capable of movement, the bleached area would remain nonfluorescent. However, over time fluorescence appears in the bleached area, telling us that fluorescent proteins that were not bleached moved into the bleached area.

The idea that lipids and proteins coexist in the membrane, and that both are able to move in the plane of the membrane, led American biologists S. Jonathan Singer and Garth Nicolson to propose the **fluid mosaic model** in 1972. According to this model, the lipid bilayer is a fluid structure that allows molecules to move laterally within the membrane, and is a mosaic (a mixture) of two types of molecules, lipids and proteins.

5.2 THE PLASMA MEMBRANE AND CELL WALL

All cells are enclosed by a **plasma membrane,** also called the cell membrane. The plasma membrane is a fundamental, defining feature of all cells. It is the boundary that defines the space of the cell, separating its internal contents from the surrounding environment. But the plasma membrane is not simply a passive boundary or wall. Instead, it serves an active and important function. The environment outside the cell is changing all the time. In contrast, the internal environment of a cell operates within a persistent and narrow window of conditions, such as pH

FIG. 5.8

Do proteins move in the plane of the membrane?

BACKGROUND Fluorescent recovery after photobleaching (FRAP) is a technique used to measure mobility of molecules in the plane of the membrane. A fluorescent dye is attached to proteins embedded in the cell membrane in a process called labeling. A laser is then used to bleach a small area of the membrane.

HYPOTHESIS If membrane components such as proteins move in the plane of the membrane, the bleached spot should become fluorescent over time as unbleached fluorescent molecules move into the bleached area. If membrane components do not move, the bleached spot should remain intact.

EXPERIMENT AND RESULTS

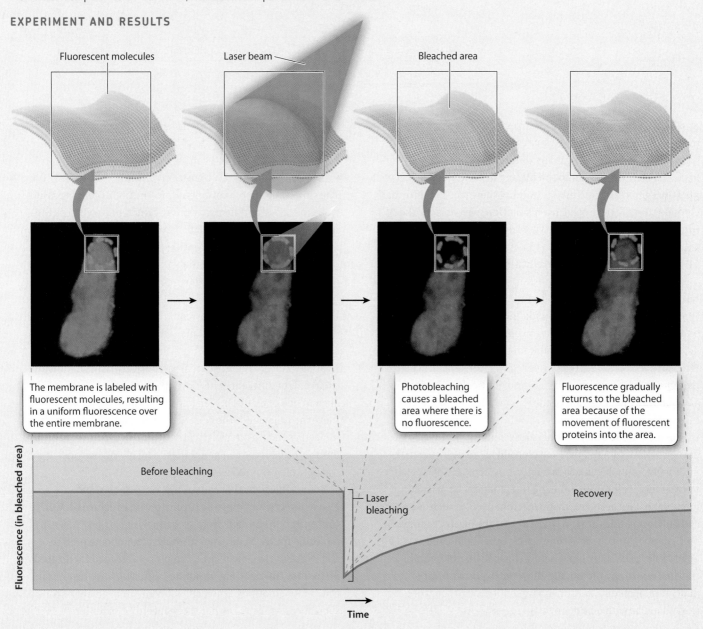

Fluorescent molecules

Laser beam

Bleached area

The membrane is labeled with fluorescent molecules, resulting in a uniform fluorescence over the entire membrane.

Photobleaching causes a bleached area where there is no fluorescence.

Fluorescence gradually returns to the bleached area because of the movement of fluorescent proteins into the area.

Fluorescence (in bleached area)

Before bleaching

Laser bleaching

Recovery

Time

CONCLUSION The gradual recovery of fluorescence in the bleached area indicates that proteins move in the plane of the membrane.

SOURCE Peters, R., J. Peters, K.H. Tews, and W. Bähr. 1974. "A Microfluorimetric Study of Translational Diffusion in Erythrocyte Membranes." *Biochim Biophys Acta* 367:282–294.

FIG. 5.9   **Diffusion, the movement of molecules due to random motion.** Net movement of molecules only results when there are concentration differences.

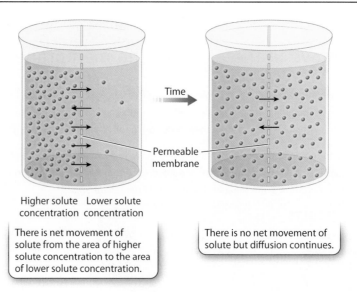

Higher solute   Lower solute
concentration   concentration

There is net movement of solute from the area of higher solute concentration to the area of lower solute concentration.

Time

Permeable membrane

There is no net movement of solute but diffusion continues.

or salt concentration. It is the plasma membrane that actively maintains intracellular conditions compatible with life.

In addition, the cells of many different groups of organisms have a **cell wall** external to the plasma membrane. The cell wall plays an important role in maintaining the shape and internal composition of these cells. In this section, we consider the functions performed by these two key structures.

The plasma membrane maintains homeostasis.

The active maintenance of a constant environment is known as **homeostasis,** and it is a critical attribute of cells and of life itself. Chemical reactions and protein folding, for example, are carried out efficiently only within a narrow range of conditions. How does the plasma membrane maintain homeostasis? The answer is that it acts as a **selective barrier.** This means that the plasma membrane lets some molecules in and out freely; it lets others in and out only under certain conditions; and it prevents still other molecules from passing through at all.

The membrane's ability to act as a selective barrier is the result of the combination of lipids and embedded proteins that make it up. The hydrophobic lipid bilayer prevents ions as well as charged or polar molecules from diffusing freely across the plasma membrane. Furthermore, many macromolecules such as proteins and polysaccharides are too large to cross the plasma membrane on their own. At the same time, gases, other lipids, and small polar molecules freely move across the lipid bilayer. Protein transporters in the membrane allow the export and import of molecules, including certain ions and nutrients, that cannot cross the cell membrane on their own.

The identity and abundance of these membrane-associated proteins vary among cell types, reflecting the specific functions of different cells. For example, cells in your gut contain membrane transporters that specialize in the uptake of glucose, while nerve

cells have different types of ion channel that are involved in electrical signaling.

Passive transport involves diffusion.

The simplest form of movement into and out of cells is passive transport. Passive transport works by **diffusion,** which is the random movement of molecules. When there is a concentration difference (that is, a concentration gradient) in the distribution of a molecule, with areas of higher and lower concentrations, diffusion results in net movement of the molecule from an area of higher concentration to an area of lower concentration (**Fig. 5.9**). However, diffusion occurs even in the absence of concentration differences, due to the random motion of molecules, but in this case there is no net movement of the substance.

Some molecules diffuse freely across the plasma membrane as a result of differences in concentrations between the inside and outside of a cell. Oxygen and carbon dioxide, for example, move into and out of the cell in this way. Certain hydrophobic molecules, such as triacylglycerols (Chapter 2), are also able to diffuse through the cell membrane, which is not surprising since the lipid bilayer is likewise hydrophobic.

Some molecules that cannot move across the lipid bilayer directly can move passively toward a region of lower concentration through protein channels or carriers. When a molecule moves by diffusion through a membrane protein and bypasses the lipid bilayer, the process is called **facilitated diffusion.** Diffusion and facilitated diffusion both result from the random motion of molecules, and net movement of the substance occurs when there are concentration differences (**Fig. 5.10**). In the case of facilitated diffusion, the molecule moves through a membrane protein channel or carrier, whereas in the case of simple diffusion, the molecule moves directly through the lipid bilayer.

FIG. 5.10 **Simple diffusion and facilitated diffusion through the cell membrane.**

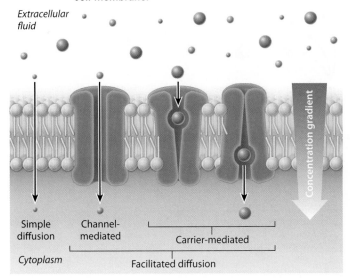

Extracellular fluid

Simple diffusion

Channel-mediated

Carrier-mediated

Facilitated diffusion

Cytoplasm

Concentration gradient

Although some membrane proteins provide a channel or opening between the inside and outside of the cell, most are carriers selective for specific molecules or are even "gated," opening and closing only in response to the binding of specific molecules or some other signal. These membrane proteins exist in two shapes or conformations, one that is open to one side of the cell, and another that is open to the other side of the cell. Binding of the transported molecule induces a conformational change in the membrane protein, allowing the molecule to be transported across the lipid bilayer, as shown on the right in Fig. 5.10.

Up to this point, we have focused our attention on the movement of molecules (solutes) in water (solvent). We can take a different perspective and focus instead on water movement. Water itself also moves into and out of cells by passive transport.

Although the plasma membrane is hydrophobic, water molecules are small enough to move passively through the membrane to a limited extent by simple diffusion. In addition, many cells have specific protein channels, known as **aquaporins,** which allow water to flow through the plasma membrane more readily by facilitated diffusion.

The diffusion of water is known as **osmosis.** As in any form of diffusion, water moves from regions of higher *water* concentration to regions of lower *water* concentration (**Fig. 5.11**). Because water is a solvent within which nutrients such as glucose or ions such as sodium or potassium are dissolved, water concentration drops as solute concentration rises. Therefore, it is sometimes easier to think about water moving from regions of lower *solute* concentration to regions of higher *solute* concentration. Either way, the direction of water movement is the same.

→ **Quick Check 2** A container is divided into two compartments by a membrane that is fully permeable to water and small ions. Water is added to one side of the membrane (side A), and a 5% solution of sodium chloride (NaCl) is added to the other (side B). In which direction will water molecules move? In which direction will sodium and chloride ions move? When the concentration is equal on both sides, will diffusion stop?

Primary active transport uses the energy of ATP.

Passive transport works to the cell's advantage only if the concentration gradient is in the right direction, from higher on the outside to lower on the inside for nutrients that the cell needs to take in, and from higher on the inside and lower on the outside for wastes that the cell needs to export. However, many of the molecules that cells require are in low concentration in the environment. Although some of these molecules can be synthesized by the cell, others need to be taken up from the environment and concentrated inside the cell. In other

FIG. 5.11 **Osmosis.** Osmosis is the diffusion of water across a semipermeable membrane from an area of lower solute concentration to an area of higher solute concentration.

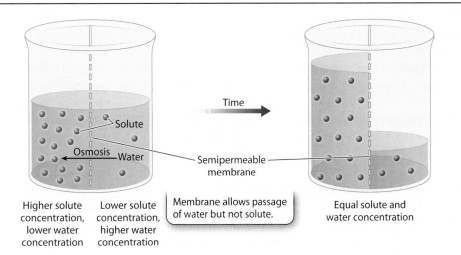

Time

Solute

Osmosis — Water

Semipermeable membrane

Membrane allows passage of water but not solute.

Higher solute concentration, lower water concentration

Lower solute concentration, higher water concentration

Equal solute and water concentration

FIG. 5.12 **Primary active transport.** The sodium-potassium pump is a membrane protein that uses the energy stored in ATP to move sodium and potassium ions against their concentration gradients.

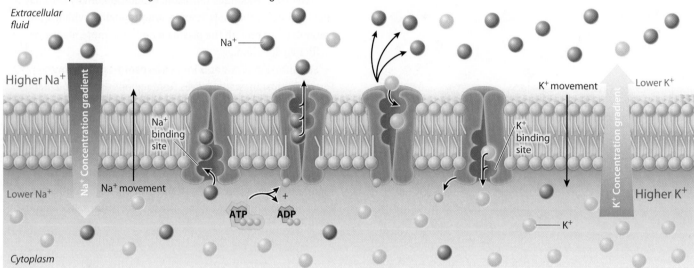

words, cells have to move these substances from areas of lower concentration to areas of higher concentration. The "uphill" movement of substances against a concentration gradient, called **active transport,** requires energy. The transport of many kinds of molecules across membranes requires energy, either directly or indirectly. In fact, most of the energy used by a cell goes into keeping the inside of the cell different from the outside, a function carried out by proteins in the plasma membrane.

During active transport, cells move substances through transport proteins embedded in the cell membrane. Some of these proteins act as pumps, using energy directly to move a substance into or out of a cell. A good example is the sodium-potassium pump (**Fig. 5.12**). Within cells, sodium is kept at concentrations much lower than in the exterior environment; the opposite is true of potassium. Therefore, both sodium and potassium have to be moved against a concentration gradient. The sodium-potassium pump actively moves sodium out of the cell and potassium into the cell. This movement of ions takes energy, which comes from the chemical energy stored in ATP. Active transport that uses energy directly in this manner is called **primary active transport.** Note that the sodium and potassium ions move in opposite directions. Protein transporters that work in this way are sometimes referred to as antiporters. Other transporters move two molecules in the same direction. These transport proteins are referred to as symporters or cotransporters.

Secondary active transport is driven by an electrochemical gradient.

Active transport can also work in another way. Because small ions cannot cross the lipid bilayer, many cells use a transport protein

to build up the concentration of a small ion on one side of the membrane. The resulting concentration gradient stores energy that can be harnessed to drive the movement of other substances across the membrane against their concentration gradient.

For example, some cells actively pump protons (H⁺) across the cell membrane using ATP (**Fig. 5.13a**). As a result, the concentration of protons is higher on one side of the membrane and lower on the other side. In other words, the pump generates a concentration gradient, also called a chemical gradient because the entity forming the gradient is a chemical (**Fig. 5.13b**). We have already seen that concentration differences favor the movement of protons back to the other side of the membrane. However, the lipid bilayer blocks the movement of protons to the other side and therefore stores energy, just like a dam or battery.

In addition to the chemical gradient, another force favors the movement of protons back across the membrane: a difference in charge. Because protons carry a positive charge, the side of the membrane with more protons is more positive than the other side. This difference in charge is called an electrical gradient. Protons (and other ions) move from areas of like charge to areas of unlike charge, driven by an electrical gradient. Together, the charge and chemical gradients are known as an **electrochemical gradient** (Fig. 5.13b).

If protons are then allowed to pass through the cell membrane by a transport protein, they will move down their electrochemical gradient toward the region of lower proton concentration. These transport proteins can use the movement of protons to drive the movement of other molecules against their concentration gradient (**Fig. 5.13c**). The movement of protons is always from regions of higher to lower concentration, while the movement of the coupled molecule is from regions of lower to higher

FIG. 5.13 **Secondary active transport.** Protons are pumped across a membrane by primary active transport (a), resulting in an electrochemical gradient (b), which drives the movement of another molecule against its concentration gradient (c).

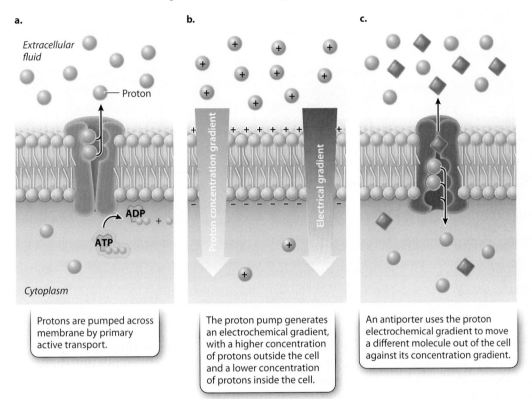

a.

Extracellular fluid

Proton

ADP

ATP

Cytoplasm

Protons are pumped across membrane by primary active transport.

b.

Proton concentration gradient

Electrical gradient

The proton pump generates an electrochemical gradient, with a higher concentration of protons outside the cell and a lower concentration of protons inside the cell.

c.

An antiporter uses the proton electrochemical gradient to move a different molecule out of the cell against its concentration gradient.

hypotonic solution (one with a lower solute concentration than that inside the cell), water moves into the cell by osmosis and the cell lyses, or bursts. Animal cells solve the problem of water movement in part by maintaining the intracellular fluid isotonic (that is, at the same solute concentration) as the extracellular fluid. Cells use the active transport of ions to maintain equal concentrations inside and out, and the sodium-potassium pump plays an important role in keeping the inside of the cell isotonic with the extracellular fluid.

→ **Quick Check 3** In the absence of the sodium-potassium pump, the extracellular solution becomes hypotonic relative to the inside of the cell. Poisons such as the snake venom ouabain can interfere with the action of the sodium-potassium pump. What are the consequences for the cell?

concentration. Because the movement of the coupled molecule is driven by the movement of protons and not by ATP directly, this form of transport is called **secondary active transport.** Secondary active transport uses the energy of an electrochemical gradient to drive the movement of molecules; by contrast, primary active transport uses the energy of ATP directly.

The use of an electrochemical gradient as a temporary energy source is a common cellular strategy. For example, cells use the sodium electrochemical gradient generated by the sodium-potassium pump to transport glucose and amino acids into cells. In addition, cells use the proton electrochemical gradient to move other molecules and, as we discuss below and in Chapter 7, to synthesize ATP.

Many cells maintain size and composition using active transport.

Many cells use active transport to maintain their size and composition. Consider human red blood cells placed in a variety of different solutions (**Fig. 5.14**). If a red blood cell is placed in a hypertonic solution (one with a higher solute concentration than that inside the cell), water leaves the cell by osmosis and the cell shrinks. By contrast, if a red blood cell is placed in a

Human red blood cells avoid shrinking or bursting by maintaining an intracellular environment isotonic with the extracellular environment, the blood. But what about a single-celled organism, like *Paramecium*, swimming in a freshwater lake? In this case, the extracellular environment is hypotonic

FIG. 5.14 **Changes in red blood cell shape due to osmosis.** Red blood cells shrink, swell, or burst because of net water movement (osmosis) driven by differences in solute concentration between the inside and the outside of the cell.

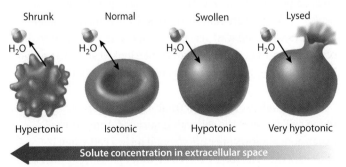

Shrunk

H_2O

Hypertonic

Normal

H_2O

Isotonic

Swollen

H_2O

Hypotonic

Lysed

H_2O

Very hypotonic

Solute concentration in extracellular space

FIG. 5.15   **The plant cell wall and vacuoles.** The plant cell wall is a rigid structure that maintains the shape of the cell. The pressure exerted by water absorbed by vacuoles also provides support.

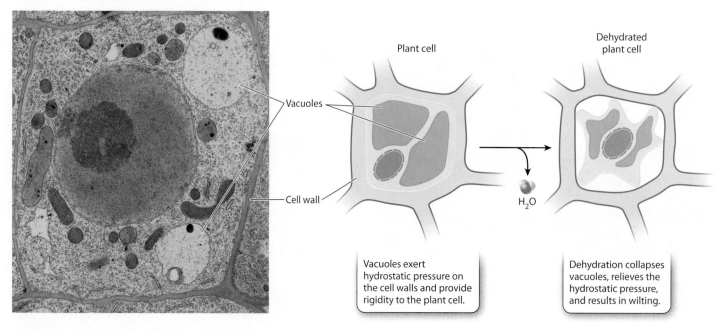

Vacuoles exert hydrostatic pressure on the cell walls and provide rigidity to the plant cell.

Dehydration collapses vacuoles, relieves the hydrostatic pressure, and results in wilting.

compared to the concentration in the cell's interior. As a result, *Paracemium* faces the risk of bursting caused by water moving in by osmosis. *Paramecium* and some other single-celled organisms contain **contractile vacuoles** that solve this problem. Contractile vacuoles are compartments that take up excess water from inside the cell and then, by contraction, expel it into the external environment. The mechanism by which water moves into the contractile vacuole differs depending on the organism. The contractile vacuole of some organisms takes in water through aquaporins, while other organisms have proton pumps that first move protons into the contractile vacuole, with water following by osmosis.

The cell wall provides another means of maintaining cell shape.

Most organisms do not contain contractile vacuoles. How do organisms such as plants, fungi, and bacteria maintain cell size and composition? A key feature of these organisms is the cell wall, a rigid structure that surrounds the plasma membrane (**Fig. 5.15**). The cell wall plays a critical role in the maintenance of cell shape and volume. When Hooke looked at cork through his microscope, what he saw was not living cells but the remains of cell walls.

The cell wall provides structural support and protection to the cell. Because the cell wall is fairly rigid and resists expansion, it allows pressure to build up in a cell when it absorbs water. The force exerted by water pressing against an object results in hydrostatic pressure, or **turgor pressure.** The pressure exerted by water provides structural support for many organisms that is similar in function to the support provided by the skeletons or shells of animals. In addition, many plant cells have another structure, called the **vacuole** (distinct from the contractile vacuole), that also absorbs water and contributes to turgor pressure (Fig. 5.15). It is therefore easy to understand why plants wilt when dehydrated—the loss of water from the vacuoles reduces turgor pressure and the tissue can no longer maintain rigidity.

The cell wall is made up of many different components, including carbohydrates and proteins. The specific components differ depending on the organism. The plant cell wall is composed of polysaccharides, one of the best known of which is cellulose, a polymer of the sugar glucose. Cellulose is the most abundant biological material in nature. Many types of algae have cell walls made up of cellulose, as in plants. Fungi have cell walls made of chitin, another polymer based on sugars. In bacteria, the cell wall is made up primarily of peptidoglycan, a mixture of amino acids and sugars. Animal cells do not have walls.

5.3 THE INTERNAL ORGANIZATION OF CELLS

In addition to the plasma membrane, many cells contain membrane-bound regions within which specific functions are carried out. Such a cell can be compared to a large factory with many rooms and different departments. Each department has a specific function and internal organization that contribute to the overall "life" of the factory. In this section, we give an overview of two broad classes of cells that can be distinguished by the presence or absence of these membrane-enclosed compartments.

Eukaryotes and prokaryotes differ in internal organization.

All cells have a plasma membrane and contain genetic material. In some cells, the genetic material is housed in a membrane-bound space called the **nucleus.** Cells can be divided into two classes based on the presence or absence of a nucleus (Chapter 1). **Prokaryotes,** including bacteria and archaea, lack a nucleus; **eukaryotes**, including plants, animals, fungi, and protists, have a nucleus (**Fig. 5.16**).

Although the two groups are defined by the presence or absence of a nucleus, they differ in many other aspects as well. For example, we saw in Chapter 3 that promoter recognition during transcription is different in prokaryotes and in eukaryotes. In addition, there are differences in the specific types of lipid that make up their cell membranes. In mammals,

as we have seen, cholesterol is present in cell membranes. Cholesterol belongs to a group of chemical compounds known as sterols, which are molecules containing a hydroxyl group attached to a four-ringed structure. In eukaryotes other than mammals, diverse sterols are synthesized and present in cell membranes. Most prokaryotes do not synthesize sterols, but some synthesize compounds called hopanoids. These five-ringed structures are thought to serve a function similar to that of cholesterol in mammalian cell membranes. Additional differences between prokaryotes and eukaryotes are discussed below.

Prokaryotic cells lack a nucleus and extensive internal compartmentalization.

Prokaryotes do not have a nucleus—that is, there is no physical barrier separating the genetic material from the rest of the cell. Instead, the DNA is concentrated in a discrete region of the cell interior known as the **nucleoid.** Bacteria often contain additional small circular molecules of DNA known as **plasmids** that carry a small number of genes. Plasmids are commonly transferred between bacteria through threadlike, hollow structures known as **pili** (singular, pilus), which extend from one cell to another. Genes for antibiotic resistance are commonly transferred in this way, which accounts for the quick spread of antibiotic resistance among bacterial populations.

Although the absence of a nucleus is a defining feature of prokaryotes, other features also stand out. For example, prokaryotes are small, just 1–2 micrometers (1/1000 of a meter) in diameter or smaller. By contrast, eukaryotic cells are commonly much larger, on the order of 10 times larger in diameter and 1000 times larger in volume. The small size of prokaryotic cells means that they have a relatively high ratio of surface area to volume, which makes sense for an organism that absorbs nutrients from the environment. In other words, there is a large amount of membrane surface area for absorption relative to the volume of the cell that it serves. In addition, most prokaryotes lack the extensive internal organization characteristic of eukaryotes.

Eukaryotic cells have a nucleus and specialized internal structures.

Eukaryotes are defined by the presence of a nucleus, which houses the vast majority of the cell's DNA. The nuclear membrane allows for more complex regulation of gene expression than is possible in prokaryotic cells. In eukaryotes, DNA is transcribed to RNA inside the nucleus, but the RNA molecules carrying the genetic message travel from inside to outside the nucleus, where they instruct the synthesis of proteins.

Eukaryotes have a remarkable internal array of membranes. These membranes define compartments, called **organelles,** that divide the cell contents into smaller spaces specialized

---

FIG. 5.16 **Prokaryotic and eukaryotic cells.** Prokaryotic cells lack a nucleus and extensive internal compartmentalization. Eukaryotic cells have a nucleus and extensive internal compartmentalization.

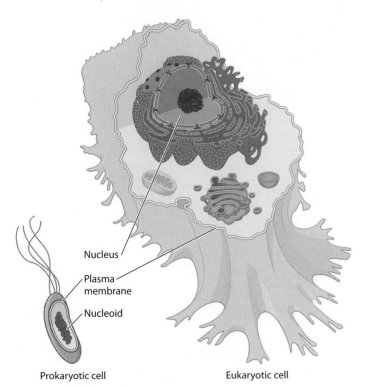

Nucleus

Plasma membrane

Nucleoid

Prokaryotic cell   Eukaryotic cell

for different functions. **Fig. 5.17a** shows a typical animal cell (a macrophage) with various organelles. The **endoplasmic reticulum (ER)** is involved in the synthesis of proteins and lipids. The **Golgi apparatus** modifies proteins and lipids produced by the ER and acts as a sorting station as they move to their final destinations. **Lysosomes** contain enzymes that break down macromolecules such as proteins, nucleic acids, lipids, and complex carbohydrates. **Mitochondria** (singular, mitochondrion) are specialized organelles that harness energy for the cell. Many

cell membranes that define these organelles are also associated with a protein scaffold called the **cytoskeleton** that helps cells to maintain their shape and serves as a network of tracks for the movement of substances within cells. Some cells even move with the help of the cytoskeleton.

Fig. 5.17b shows a typical plant cell. In addition to the organelles described above, plant cells have a cell wall outside the plasma membrane, vacuoles specialized for water uptake, and **chloroplasts** that convert energy of sunlight into chemical energy.

FIG. 5.17   An animal cell and a plant cell. Animal and plant cells have many cell components in common.

a. Typical features of an animal cell

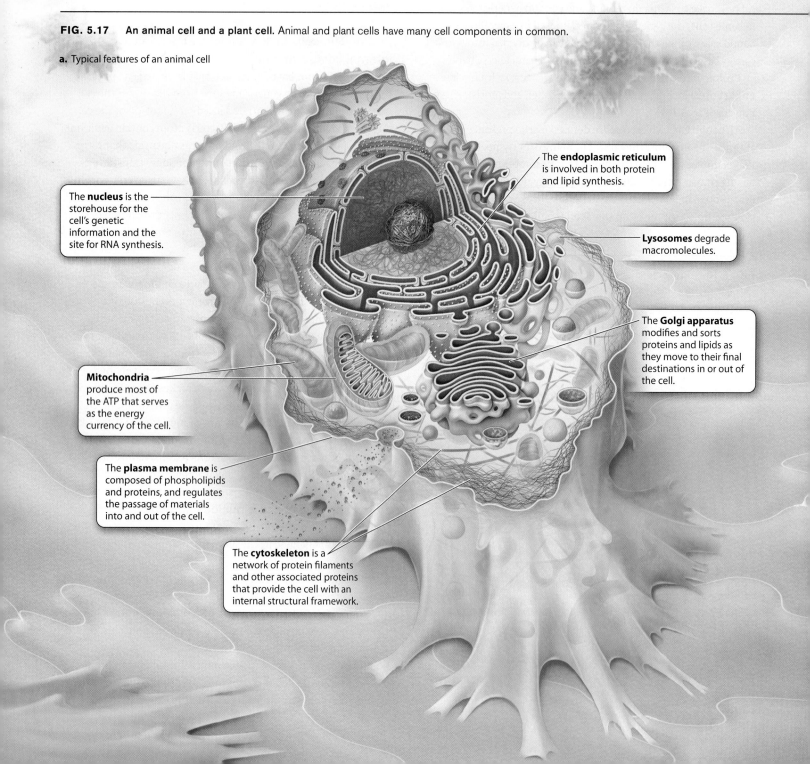

The **endoplasmic reticulum** is involved in both protein and lipid synthesis.

The **nucleus** is the storehouse for the cell's genetic information and the site for RNA synthesis.

Lysosomes degrade macromolecules.

The **Golgi apparatus** modifies and sorts proteins and lipids as they move to their final destinations in or out of the cell.

Mitochondria produce most of the ATP that serves as the energy currency of the cell.

The **plasma membrane** is composed of phospholipids and proteins, and regulates the passage of materials into and out of the cell.

The **cytoskeleton** is a network of protein filaments and other associated proteins that provide the cell with an internal structural framework.

The entire contents of a cell other than the nucleus make up the **cytoplasm.** The region of the cell inside the plasma membrane but outside the organelles is referred to as the **cytosol.** This is the jelly-like internal environment surrounding the organelles.

In the next two sections, we consider these organelles in more detail, focusing on the role of membranes in forming distinct compartments within the cell. The cytoskeleton is discussed in Chapter 10.

5.4 THE ENDOMEMBRANE SYSTEM

In eukaryotes, the total surface area of intracellular membranes is about tenfold greater than that of the plasma membrane. This high ratio of internal membrane area to plasma membrane area underscores the significant degree to which a eukaryotic cell is divided into internal compartments. Many of the organelles inside cells are not distinct, isolated entities,

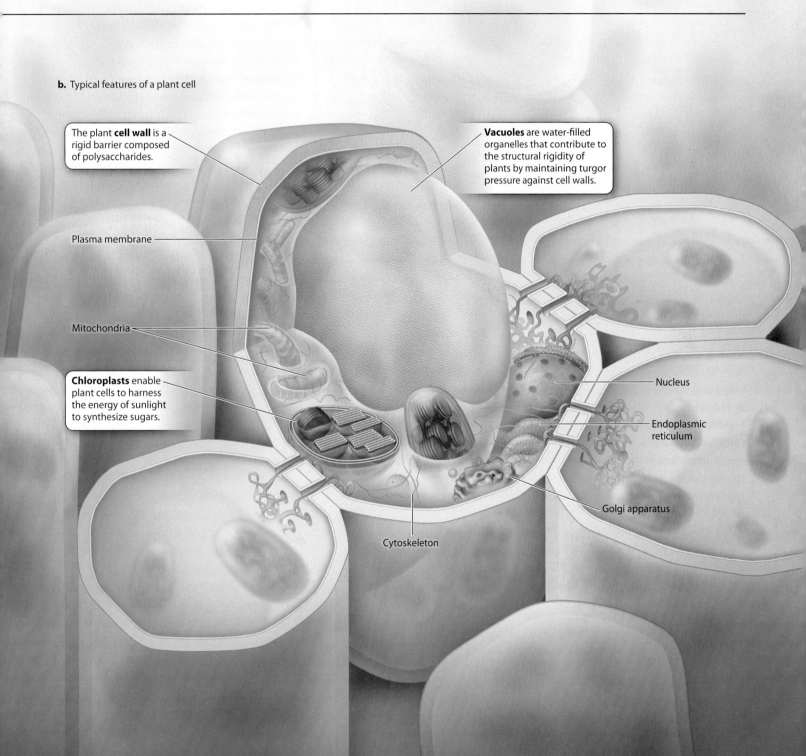

b. Typical features of a plant cell

The plant **cell wall** is a rigid barrier composed of polysaccharides.

Vacuoles are water-filled organelles that contribute to the structural rigidity of plants by maintaining turgor pressure against cell walls.

Plasma membrane

Mitochondria

Chloroplasts enable plant cells to harness the energy of sunlight to synthesize sugars.

Nucleus

Endoplasmic reticulum

Golgi apparatus

Cytoskeleton

FIG. 5.18 **The endomembrane system.** The endomembrane system is a series of membrane-bound internal compartments in eukaryotic cells.

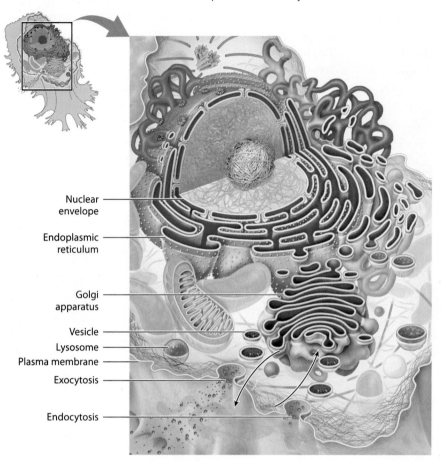

Nuclear envelope

Endoplasmic reticulum

Golgi apparatus

Vesicle

Lysosome

Plasma membrane

Exocytosis

Endocytosis

fusing of a vesicle between these organelles. Similarly, a molecule associated with the ER membrane can move to the Golgi membrane or the plasma membrane by vesicle transport. However, molecules in the cytosol are in a different physical space, separated by membranes of the endomembrane system. This physical separation allows specific functions to take place within the spaces defined by the membranes and also within the membrane itself.

In spite of forming a continuous and interconnected system, the various compartments have unique properties and maintain distinct identities determined by which lipids and proteins are present in their membranes. Recall that membranes are not fixed but dynamic, able to change their lipid and protein composition over time.

As we have seen, vesicles can bud off and fuse with components of the endomembrane system, creating a set of interconnected spaces. They can even fuse with the plasma membrane. This process, called **exocytosis,** provides a way for a vesicle to empty its contents to the extracellular space or to deliver proteins embedded in the vesicle membrane to the plasma membrane (Fig. 5.18). The process also works in reverse: A vesicle can bud off

but instead communicate with one another. In fact, the membranes of these organelles are either physically connected by membrane "bridges" or communicate by the budding off and fusing of **vesicles,** small membrane-enclosed sacs that transport substances. In total, these membranes make up the **endomembrane system.** The endomembrane system includes the nuclear envelope, endoplasmic reticulum, Golgi apparatus, lysosomes, the plasma membrane, and the vesicles that move between them (**Fig. 5.18**).

Extensive internal membranes are not common in prokaryotic cells. However, photosynthetic bacteria do have internal membranes that are specialized for harnessing light energy (Chapters 8 and 26).

The endomembrane system compartmentalizes the cell.
Because of the selective permeability of cell membranes, the endomembrane divides the interior of a cell into two distinct "worlds," one inside the spaces defined by these membranes and one outside these spaces. Note that a molecule within the interior space of the ER can stay in the ER or end up within the Golgi apparatus or even outside the cell by the budding off and

FIG. 5.19 **A surface view of the nuclear envelope.** The nucleus is surrounded by a double membrane and houses the cell's DNA.

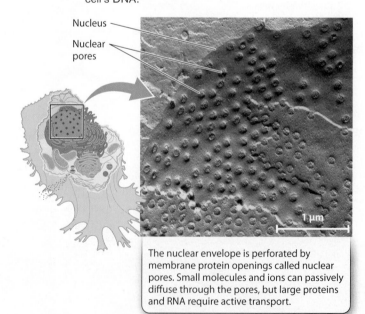

Nucleus

Nuclear pores

1 μm

The nuclear envelope is perforated by membrane protein openings called nuclear pores. Small molecules and ions can passively diffuse through the pores, but large proteins and RNA require active transport.

from the plasma membrane, bringing material from outside the cell into a vesicle, which can then fuse with other organelles. This process is called **endocytosis.** Together, exocytosis and endocytosis provide a way to move material into and out of cells without passing through the cell membrane.

The nucleus houses the genome and is the site of RNA synthesis.

The **nucleus** stores DNA, the genetic material that encodes the information necessary for all the activities and structures of the cell. The **nuclear envelope** defines the boundary of the nucleus (**Fig. 5.19**). It consists of two membranes, the inner and outer membranes, and each is a lipid bilayer with associated proteins.

These two membranes are continuous with each other at protein openings called **nuclear pores.** These pores act as gateways that allow molecules to move into and out of the nucleus, and thus are essential for the nucleus to communicate with the rest of the cell. In fact, the transfer of information

encoded by DNA depends on the movement of RNA molecules out of the nucleus, while the control of how and when this information is expressed depends on the movement of proteins into the nucleus. The nuclear envelope with its associated protein pores regulates which molecules move into and out of the nucleus.

The endoplasmic reticulum is involved in protein and lipid synthesis.

The outer membrane of the nuclear envelope is physically continuous with the endoplasmic reticulum (ER), an organelle bounded by a single membrane (**Fig. 5.20**). The ER is a conspicuous feature of many eukaryotic cells, accounting in some cases for as much as half of the total amount of membrane. The ER produces and transports many of the lipids and proteins used inside and outside the cell. It is the site of production of most of the lipids that make up the various cell membranes. In addition, transmembrane proteins and proteins destined for the Golgi apparatus, lysosomes, or export out of the cell are synthesized in the ER.

FIG. 5.20   The endoplasmic reticulum (ER). The ER is a major site for lipid and protein synthesis. (Proteins are also synthesized in the cytoplasm.)

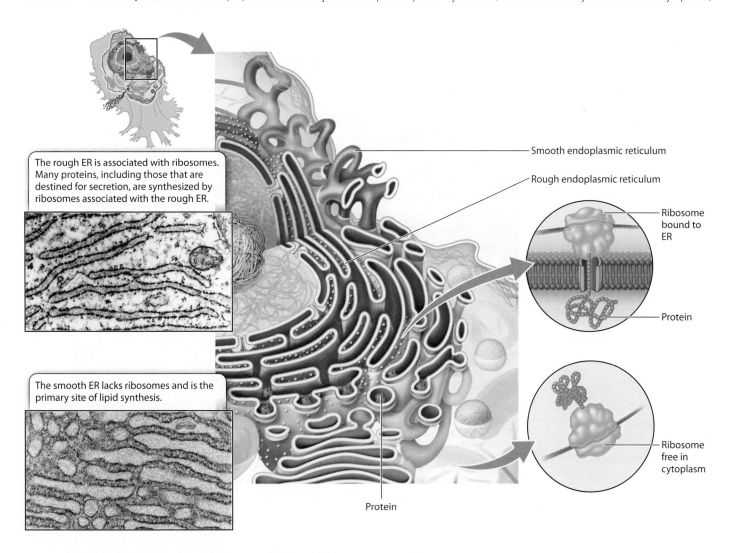

The rough ER is associated with ribosomes. Many proteins, including those that are destined for secretion, are synthesized by ribosomes associated with the rough ER.

The smooth ER lacks ribosomes and is the primary site of lipid synthesis.

Smooth endoplasmic reticulum

Rough endoplasmic reticulum

Ribosome bound to ER

Protein

Ribosome free in cytoplasm

Protein

Unlike the nucleus, which is a single rounded structure in the cell, the ER consists of a complex network of interconnected tubules and flattened sacs. The interior of the ER is continuous throughout and is called the **lumen.** As shown in Fig. 5.20, the ER has an almost mazelike appearance when sliced and viewed in cross section. The ER membrane is extensively convoluted, allowing a large amount of membrane surface area to fit within the cell. The amount of ER membrane in a cell varies among cells of different functions. For example, mucus-producing cells of the gut synthesize a large amount of protein for export and thus have an extensive ER, as do the cells of the pancreas that produce the protein insulin. In cells that do not secrete large quantities of protein, the ER can be quite small.

When viewed through an electron microscope, ER membranes have two different appearances (Fig. 5.20). In most cells, the majority of ER membranes have small, rounded particles associated with them that are exposed to the cytosol. This portion of the ER is referred to as **rough endoplasmic reticulum (RER).** The particles bound to the cytosolic face of the RER are **ribosomes.** Ribosomes are the sites of protein synthesis, in which amino acids are assembled into polypeptides guided by the information stored in mRNA (Chapter 4). Ribosomes can be free in the cytosol or associated with the ER membrane.

In most cells, there is a small amount of ER membrane that lacks ribosomes and is consequently called **smooth endoplasmic reticulum (SER)** (Fig. 5.20). Portions of the smooth ER membrane actively bud off to produce vesicles that are free to move in the cytosol. Since each vesicle is formed from a patch of ER membrane and encloses a portion of the ER lumen, vesicles are an effective means of moving proteins that are either embedded in the ER membrane or free floating inside.

SER is also the site of fatty acid and phospholipid biosynthesis. Thus, this type of ER predominates in cells specialized for the production of lipids. For example, cells that synthesize steroid hormones have a well-developed SER that produces large quantities of cholesterol and contains enzymes that convert cholesterol into steroid hormones.

The Golgi apparatus modifies and sorts proteins and lipids.

Although it is not physically continuous with the ER, the Golgi apparatus is often the next stop for vesicles that bud off the ER. These vesicles carry lipids and proteins that are either located in the vesicle interior or embedded in their membranes. The movement of these vesicles from the ER to the Golgi apparatus and then to the rest of the cell is part of a biosynthetic pathway in which lipids and proteins are successively modified and delivered to their final destinations. The Golgi apparatus has three primary roles: (1) It further modifies proteins and lipids produced by the ER; (2) it acts as a sorting station as they move to their final destinations; and (3) it is the site where most of the cell's carbohydrates are synthesized.

Under the microscope, the Golgi apparatus looks like a series of flattened membrane sacs, which are called **cisternae** (**Fig. 5.21**). The cisternae, which are stacked, are surrounded by many small vesicles. These vesicles transport proteins from the ER to the Golgi apparatus, between the various cisternae, and between the Golgi apparatus and the plasma membrane or other organelles. Vesicles are therefore the primary means

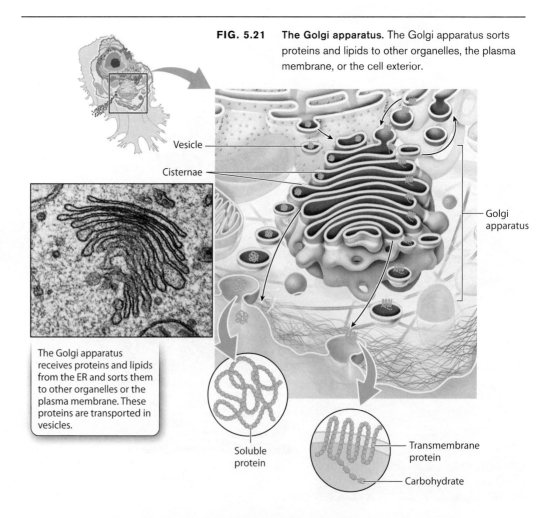

FIG. 5.21 **The Golgi apparatus.** The Golgi apparatus sorts proteins and lipids to other organelles, the plasma membrane, or the cell exterior.

Vesicle

Cisternae

Golgi apparatus

The Golgi apparatus receives proteins and lipids from the ER and sorts them to other organelles or the plasma membrane. These proteins are transported in vesicles.

Soluble protein

Transmembrane protein

Carbohydrate

by which proteins and lipids move through the Golgi apparatus to their final destinations.

Enzymes within the Golgi apparatus chemically modify proteins and lipids as they pass through it. These modifications are sequential since each region of the Golgi apparatus contains a different set of enzymes that catalyze specific reactions. As a result, there is a general movement of vesicles from the ER through the Golgi apparatus and then to their final destinations.

An example of a chemical modification that occurs predominantly in the Golgi apparatus is glycosylation, in which sugars are covalently linked to lipids or specific amino acids of proteins. As these lipids and proteins move through the Golgi apparatus, sugars are added and trimmed in a sequential fashion. Glycoproteins are important components of the eukaryotic cell surface because their attached sugars can protect the protein from enzyme digestion by blocking access to the peptide chain. As a result, glycoproteins form a relatively flexible and protective coating over the plasma membrane. The distinctive shapes that sugars contribute to glycoproteins and glycolipids also allow cell surface components to be recognized specifically by other cells and molecules in the external environment. For example, human blood types (A, B, AB, and O) are distinguished by the particular sugars that are linked to proteins and lipids on the surface of red blood cells.

While traffic usually travels from the ER to the Golgi apparatus, there is also a small amount of traffic moving in the reverse direction, from the Golgi apparatus to the ER. This reverse pathway is important to retrieve ER or Golgi resident proteins that are accidentally moved forward, and to recycle membrane components.

Lysosomes degrade macromolecules.

The ability of the Golgi apparatus to sort and dispatch proteins to particular destinations is dramatically illustrated by lysosomes. **Lysosomes** are specialized vesicles derived from the Golgi apparatus that degrade damaged or unneeded macromolecules. They contain a variety of enzymes that break down macromolecules such as proteins, nucleic acids, lipids, and complex carbohydrates (**Fig. 5.22**). Macromolecules destined for degradation are packaged by the Golgi apparatus into vesicles. The vesicles then fuse with lysosomes, delivering their contents to the lysosome interior.

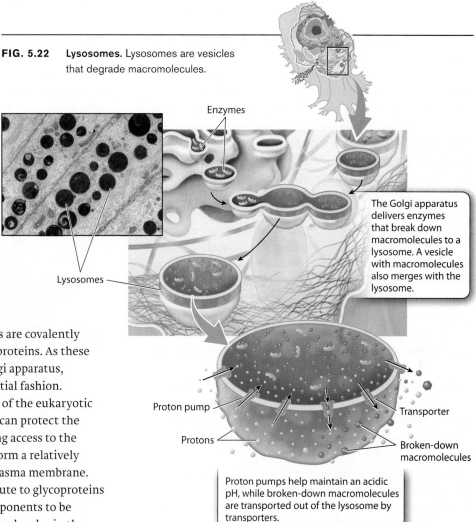

FIG. 5.22   Lysosomes. Lysosomes are vesicles that degrade macromolecules.

Enzymes

Lysosomes

The Golgi apparatus delivers enzymes that break down macromolecules to a lysosome. A vesicle with macromolecules also merges with the lysosome.

Proton pump

Protons

Transporter

Broken-down macromolecules

Proton pumps help maintain an acidic pH, while broken-down macromolecules are transported out of the lysosome by transporters.

The formation of lysosomes also illustrates the ability of the Golgi apparatus to sort key proteins. The enzymes inside of lysosomes are synthesized in the RER, sorted in the Golgi apparatus, and then packaged into lysosomes. In addition, the Golgi apparatus sorts and delivers specialized proteins that become embedded in lysosome cell membranes. These include proton pumps that keep the internal environment at an acidic pH of around 5, the optimum pH for the activity of the enzymes inside. Other proteins in the lysosomal membranes transport the breakdown products of macromolecules, such as amino acids and simple sugars, across the membrane to the cytosol for use by the cell.

The function of lysosomes underscores the importance of having separate compartments within the cell bounded by selectively permeable membranes. Many of a cell's enzymes and proteins would unfold and degrade if the entire cell were at a pH of 5, and lysosomal enzymes cannot function in the normal cellular environment, which has a pH of about 7. By restricting the activity of these enzymes to the lysosome, proteins and organelles in the cytosol are protected from degradation.

Protein sorting directs proteins to their proper location in or out of the cell.

As we have seen, eukaryotic cells have many compartments, and different proteins function in different places, such as enzymes that act in lysosomes or transmembrane proteins embedded in the plasma membrane. **Protein sorting** is the process by which proteins end up where they need to be to perform their function. Protein sorting directs proteins to the cytosol, the lumen of organelles, the membranes of the endomembrane system, or even out of the cell entirely. Let's consider in more detail how proteins produced from free ribosomes and those produced from membrane-bound ribosomes on the RER are sorted to their final destinations in the cell.

Proteins produced on free ribosomes start off in the cytosol and are sorted to their final destination after translation. These proteins are often directed to their proper cellular compartments by means of particular amino acid sequences called **signal sequences.** As shown in **Fig. 5.23,** there are several types of signal sequences that direct proteins to different cellular compartments. Proteins with no signal sequence remain in the cytosol (Fig. 5.23a). Most proteins with a signal sequence at their amino ends are targeted to mitochondria or chloroplasts (Fig. 5.23b). Proteins targeted to the nucleus usually have signal sequences located internally (Fig. 5.23c). The signal sequence for the nucleus, also called a **nuclear localization signal,** enables proteins to move through pores in the nuclear envelope.

Proteins produced by ribosomes on the RER end up within the lumen of the endomembrane system or embedded in its membrane, or they may be secreted out of the cell. These proteins are sorted as they are translated: Proteins destined for the lumen or for secretion are fed into the ER lumen as they are synthesized,

whereas the proteins destined for membranes are inserted in the ER membrane as they are synthesized (**Fig. 5.24**).

The polypeptide chains of proteins can move into the lumen or membrane because of the presence of an amino-terminal signal sequence shown in **Fig. 5.25**. This signal sequence is recognized

---

FIG. 5.23 Signal sequences on proteins synthesized by free ribosomes. Most proteins with no signal peptide remain in the cytosol (a). Other signal sequences direct proteins to mitochondria and chloroplasts (b) or to the nucleus (c).

a. No signal peptide

To cytosol

b. Amino-terminal signal

To chloroplast
To mitochondrion

c. Internal signal

To nucleus

FIG. 5.24 Pathways for proteins destined to be secreted (left) or transported to the plasma membrane (right).

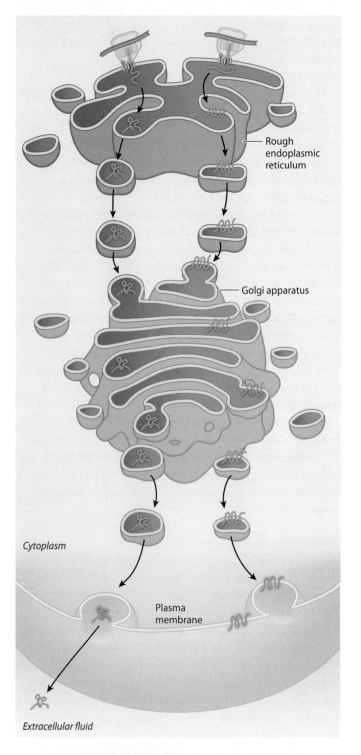

Rough endoplasmic reticulum

Golgi apparatus

Cytoplasm

Plasma membrane

Extracellular fluid

FIG. 5.25   Interaction of a signal sequence, signal recognition particle (SRP), and SRP receptor. Binding of a signal sequence with a signal recognition particle (SRP) halts translation, followed by docking of the ribosome on the ER membrane, release of the SRP, and continuation of translation.

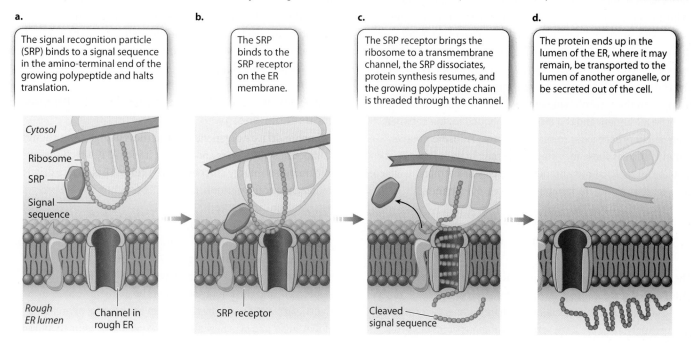

a. The signal recognition particle (SRP) binds to a signal sequence in the amino-terminal end of the growing polypeptide and halts translation.

b. The SRP binds to the SRP receptor on the ER membrane.

c. The SRP receptor brings the ribosome to a transmembrane channel, the SRP dissociates, protein synthesis resumes, and the growing polypeptide chain is threaded through the channel.

d. The protein ends up in the lumen of the ER, where it may remain, be transported to the lumen of another organelle, or be secreted out of the cell.

Cytosol

Ribosome

SRP

Signal sequence

Rough ER lumen — Channel in rough ER

SRP receptor

Cleaved signal sequence

almost immediately after synthesis by an RNA–protein complex known as a **signal-recognition particle (SRP).** The SRP binds to both the signal sequence and the ribosome and brings about a pause in translation (Fig. 5.25a). The SRP then binds with a receptor on the RER (Fig. 5.25b). The SRP dissociates and translation continues. The SRP receptor brings the ribosome to a channel through the hydrophobic membrane of the RER. Each growing polypeptide chain is threaded through the channel (Fig. 5.25c). A specific protease cleaves the signal sequence as it emerges in the lumen of the ER. The finished protein ends up in the lumen of the RER (Fig. 5.25d).

Whether the polypeptide chain ends up in the membrane or in the lumen depends on whether or not the polypeptide chain has a signal-anchor sequence in its interior. Proteins destined for the lumen of the ER, the Golgi apparatus, a lysosome, or the exterior of the cell have no signal-anchor sequence. These chains are fed completely through the channel into the lumen. Then, chaperone proteins assist with protein folding. Some proteins are retained in the ER, while others are transported in

vesicles to the Golgi apparatus. Some of these proteins end up being secreted by exocytosis, as shown on the left in Fig. 5.24.

Proteins destined to be embedded in membranes (shown on the right in Fig. 5.24) do contain signal-anchor sequences (**Fig. 5.26**). The growing polypeptide chain is transported across the

FIG. 5.26   Targeting of a transmembrane protein by means of a hydrophobic signal-anchor sequence. Proteins with a signal-anchor sequence end up embedded in the membrane.

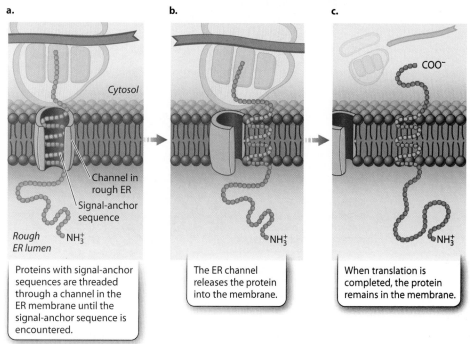

a.

Cytosol

Channel in rough ER

Signal-anchor sequence

Rough ER lumen NH_3^+

Proteins with signal-anchor sequences are threaded through a channel in the ER membrane until the signal-anchor sequence is encountered.

b.

NH_3^+

The ER channel releases the protein into the membrane.

c.

COO^-

NH_3^+

When translation is completed, the protein remains in the membrane.

channel in the ER membrane until the signal-anchor sequence is encountered (Fig. 5.26a). In the case of transmembrane proteins, the signal-anchor sequence is hydrophobic and can become so intimately associated with the membrane that it exits the channel and diffuses laterally in the lipid bilayer (Fig. 5.26b). At this point, the ribosome disassociates from the channel while translation continues (Fig. 5.26c). When translation is completed and the polypeptide is released, the carboxyl end of the chain remains on the cytosolic side of the ER membrane, the amino end is in the ER lumen, and the membrane-bound region between them anchors both sides to the membrane. Transmembrane proteins such as these may stay in the membrane of the ER or end up in other internal membranes or the plasma membrane, where they serve as channels, pumps, receptors, or enzymes.

5.5 MITOCHONDRIA AND CHLOROPLASTS

The membranes of two organelles, **mitochondria** and **chloroplasts,** are not part of the endomembrane system. Both of these organelles are specialized to harness energy for the cell. Interestingly, they are both semi-autonomous organelles that grow and multiply independently of the other membrane-bound compartments, and they contain their own genomes. As we discuss in Chapter 27, the similarities between mitochondrial and chloroplast DNA and the DNA of certain bacteria have led scientists to conclude that these organelles originated as bacteria that were captured by a eukaryotic cell and, over time, evolved to their current function.

Mitochondria provide the eukaryotic cell with most of its useable energy.

Mitochondria are organelles that harness energy from chemical compounds like sugars and convert it into ATP, which serves as the universal energy currency of the cell. ATP is able to drive the many chemical reactions in the cell. Mitochondria are present in nearly all eukaryotic cells.

Mitochondria are rod-shaped organelles with an outer membrane and a highly convoluted inner membrane whose folds project into the interior (**Fig. 5.27**). The inner mitochondrial membrane is where a proton electrochemical gradient is generated, and the energy stored in the gradient is used to synthesize ATP for use by the cell. In the process of breaking down sugar and synthesizing ATP, oxygen is consumed and carbon

FIG. 5.27   Mitochondria. Mitochondria synthesize most of the ATP required to meet the cell's energy needs.

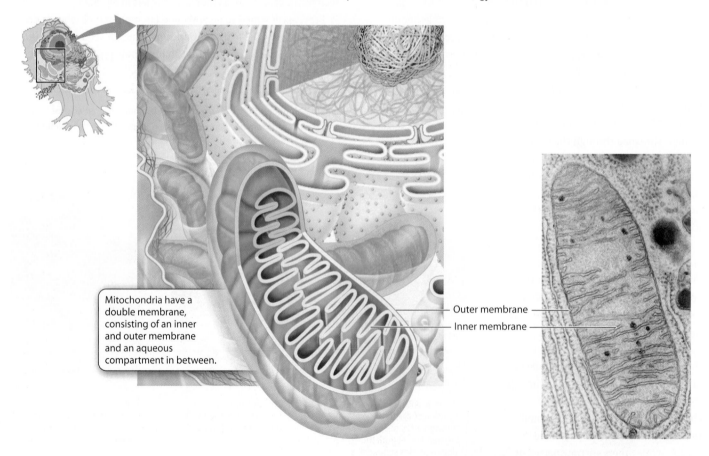

Mitochondria have a double membrane, consisting of an inner and outer membrane and an aqueous compartment in between.

Outer membrane
Inner membrane

FIG. 5.28 **Chloroplasts.** Chloroplasts capture energy from sunlight and use it to synthesize sugars.

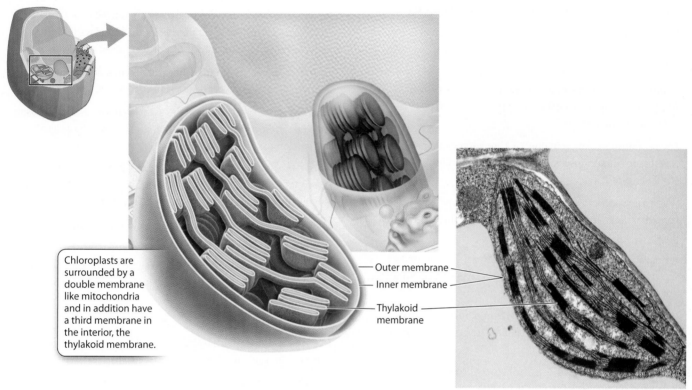

Chloroplasts are surrounded by a double membrane like mitochondria and in addition have a third membrane in the interior, the thylakoid membrane.

Outer membrane

Inner membrane

Thylakoid membrane

dioxide is released. Does this process sound familiar? It also describes your own breathing, or respiration. Mitochondria are the site of cellular respiration, and the oxygen that you take in with each breath is used by mitochondria to produce ATP. Cellular respiration is discussed in greater detail in Chapter 7.

Chloroplasts capture energy from sunlight.

Both animal and plant cells have mitochondria to provide them with life-sustaining ATP. In addition, plant cells and green algae have organelles called chloroplasts that capture the energy of sunlight to synthesize simple sugars (**Fig. 5.28**). This process, called **photosynthesis,** results in the release of oxygen as a

waste product. Like the nucleus and mitochondria, chloroplasts are surrounded by a double membrane. They also have a separate internal membrane-bound compartment called the **thylakoid.** The thylakoid membrane contains specialized light-collecting molecules called pigments, of which **chlorophyll** is the most common.

Chlorophyll plays a key role in the organelle's ability to capture energy from sunlight. The green color of chlorophyll explains why so many plants have green leaves. Using the light energy collected by pigments, enzymes present in the cytoplasm use carbon dioxide as a carbon source to produce carbohydrates. Photosynthesis is discussed in greater detail in Chapter 8.

Core Concepts Summary

5.1 CELL MEMBRANES ARE COMPOSED OF LIPIDS, PROTEINS, AND CARBOHYDRATES.

Phospholipids have both hydrophilic and hydrophobic regions. As a result, they spontaneously form structures such as micelles and bilayers when placed in an aqueous environment. page 5-2

Membranes are fluid, meaning that membrane components are able to move laterally in the plane of the membrane. page 5-3

Membrane fluidity is influenced by length of fatty acid chains, presence of carbon–carbon double bonds in fatty acid chains, and amount of cholesterol. page 5-4

Many membranes also contain proteins that span the membrane (transmembrane proteins) or are temporarily associated with one layer of the lipid bilayer (peripheral proteins). page 5-6

5.2 THE PLASMA MEMBRANE IS A SELECTIVE BARRIER THAT CONTROLS THE MOVEMENT OF MOLECULES BETWEEN THE INSIDE AND OUTSIDE OF THE CELL.

Selective permeability results from the combination of lipids and proteins that make up cell membranes. page 5-8

Passive transport works by diffusion, the random movement of molecules. Net movement of molecules occurs from regions of higher concentration to regions of lower concentration. page 5-8

Passive transport can occur directly through the plasma membrane (simple diffusion) or be aided by protein channels (facilitated diffusion). page 5-8

Active transport moves molecules from regions of lower concentration to regions of higher concentration and requires energy. page 5-10

Primary active transport uses energy stored in ATP; secondary active transport uses the energy stored in an electrochemical gradient. page 5-10

Cells maintain size and composition by protein pumps that actively move ions in and out of the cell, contractile vacuoles, and the cell wall. page 5-11

5.3 CELLS CAN BE CLASSIFIED AS PROKARYOTES OR EUKARYOTES; THESE DIFFER IN THE DEGREE OF INTERNAL COMPARTMENTALIZATION.

Prokaryotic cells lack a nucleus and other internal membrane-enclosed compartments. page 5-13

Prokaryotic cells include bacteria and archaea and are much smaller than eukaryotes. page 5-13

Eukaryotic cells have a nucleus and other internal compartments called organelles. page 5-13

Eukaryotes include animals, plants, fungi, and protists. page 5-13

5.4 THE ENDOMEMBRANE SYSTEM IS AN INTERCONNECTED SYSTEM OF MEMBRANES THAT INCLUDES THE NUCLEAR ENVELOPE, ENDOPLASMIC RETICULUM, GOLGI APPARATUS, LYSOSOMES, VESICLES, AND PLASMA MEMBRANE.

The nucleus, which is enclosed by a double membrane called the nuclear envelope, houses the genome. page 5-17

The endoplasmic reticulum is continuous with the outer nuclear envelope and manufactures proteins and lipids for use by the cell or for export out of the cell. page 5-17

The Golgi apparatus communicates with the ER via transport vesicles. It receives proteins and lipids from the endoplasmic reticulum and directs them to their final destinations. page 5-18

Lysosomes break down macromolecules like proteins to simpler compounds that can be used by the cell. page 5-19

Protein sorting directs proteins to their final destinations in or out of the cell. page 5-20

Proteins synthesized on free ribosomes are sorted after translation and proteins synthesized on ribosomes associated with the endoplasmic reticulum are sorted during translation. page 5-20

Proteins synthesized on free ribososomes are sorted by means of an amino acid sequence known as a signal sequence. page 5-21

Proteins synthesized on ribosomes associated with the endoplasmic reticulum have a signal sequence that is recognized by a signal recognition particle (SRP). page 5-21

5.5 MITOCHONDRIA AND CHLOROPLASTS ARE ORGANELLES INVOLVED IN HARNESSING ENERGY; THEY ARE LIKELY EVOLVED FROM FREE-LIVING PROKARYOTES.

Mitochondria harness energy from chemical compounds for use by both animal and plant cells. page 5-22

Chloroplasts harness the energy of sunlight to build sugars. page 5-23

Self-Assessment

1. Describe how lipids with hydrophilic and hydrophobic regions behave in an aqueous environment.

2. Describe two ways in which proteins associate with membranes.

3. Describe an experiment that demonstrates that proteins move in membranes.

4. Name three parameters that need to be stably maintained inside a cell.

5. Explain the role of lipids and proteins in maintaining the selective permeability of membranes.

6. Distinguish between passive and active transport mechanisms across cell membranes.

7. Describe three different ways in which cells maintain size and composition.

8. Compare the organization, degree of compartmentalization, and size of prokaryotic and eukaryotic cells.

9. Name the major organelles in eukaryotic cells and describe their functions.

10. Explain how a protein ends up in the cytosol, in the plasma membrane, or secreted from the cell.

Do you understand the chapter's Core Concepts? Log into BIOPORTAL to check your answers to the Self-Assessment questions, then practice what you've learned and reinforce this chapter's concepts by working through the problems and multimedia tutorials provided there.

🛜 http://courses.bfwpub.com/yourbioportal/index.php

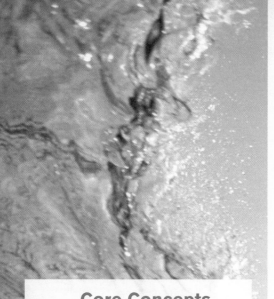

CHAPTER 6

MAKING LIFE WORK:

Capturing and Using Energy

Core Concepts

6.1 Metabolism is the set of biochemical reactions that transforms biomolecules and transfers energy.

6.2 The energy of a system is its capacity to do work.

6.3 The laws of thermo-dynamics govern energy flow in biological systems.

6.4 Chemical reactions are subject to the laws of thermodynamics.

6.5 The rate of biochemical reactions is controlled by protein catalysts called enzymes.

We have seen that cells require a way to encode and transmit information and a membrane to separate inside from out. The third requirement of a cell is energy, which cells need to do work. Among other things, they must grow and divide, move, change shape, pump ions in and out of the cell, transport vesicles, and synthesize macromolecules such as DNA, RNA, proteins, and complex carbohydrates. All these activities are considered work, and they require energy.

We are all familiar with different forms of energy—the sun and wind provide a source of energy, as do fossil fuels such as oil and natural gas. We have learned to harness the energy from these sources and convert it into other forms, such as electricity, to provide needed power to our homes and cities.

Cells are faced with similar challenges. They must harness energy from the environment and convert it to a form that allows them to do work necessary to sustain life. Cells harness energy from the sun and from chemical compounds, including carbohydrates, lipids, and proteins. Although the source of energy may differ among cells, all cells convert energy to a form that can be easily used for cellular processes. All cells use energy in the form of a molecule called **adenosine triphosphate,** or **ATP.**

ATP is often called the universal "currency" of cellular energy to indicate that ATP provides energy in a form that all cells can readily use to perform the work of the cell. Although the term "currency" is a useful shorthand, keep in mind an important distinction between actual currency, such as a dollar bill, and ATP. A dollar bill *represents* a certain value but does not in fact have any value in itself. By contrast, ATP does not represent energy; it actually contains energy in its chemical bonds. Nevertheless, the analogy is useful because ATP, like a dollar bill, engages in a broad range of energy "transactions" in the cell, as we discuss below.

In this chapter, we consider energy in the context of cells. What exactly is energy? What principles govern its flow in biological systems? And how do cells make use of it?

6.1 AN OVERVIEW OF METABOLISM

When considering a cell's use of energy, it is also useful to consider the cell's sources of carbon, because carbon is the backbone of the organic molecules that make up cells and because cells often use carbon-based compounds as a source of energy to carry out their functions. How organisms obtain the energy and carbon needed for growth and other vital functions is so fundamental that it is sometimes used to provide a metabolic classification of life (**Fig. 6.1**). Simply put, organisms have two ways of harvesting energy from their environment and two sources of carbon. Together, this means that there are four principal ways in which organisms acquire the energy and materials needed to grow, function, and reproduce.

FIG. 6.1   **A metabolic classification of organisms.** Organisms can be classified according to their energy and carbon sources.

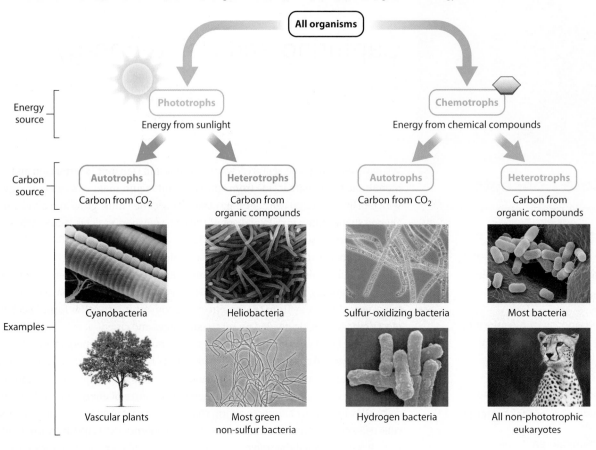

Organisms can be classified according to their energy and carbon sources.

Organisms have two ways of harvesting energy from their environment: They can obtain energy either from the sun or from chemical compounds (Fig. 6.1). Organisms that capture energy from sunlight are called **phototrophs.** Plants are the most familiar example. Plants use the energy of sunlight to convert carbon dioxide and water into sugar and oxygen (Chapter 8). Sugars, such as glucose, contain energy in their chemical bonds that is used to synthesize ATP, which in turn can power the work of the cell.

Other organisms derive their energy directly from organic molecules such as glucose. These organisms are called **chemotrophs,** and animals are familiar examples. Animals ingest other organisms, obtaining organic molecules such as glucose that they break down in the presence of oxygen to produce carbon dioxide and water. In this process, the energy in the organic molecule is converted to energy carried in the bonds of ATP (Chapter 7).

In drawing this distinction between plants and animals, we have to be careful: Although sunlight provides the energy that plants use to synthesize glucose, plants still power most cellular processes by breaking down the sugar they make, just as animals do. And although chemotrophs harness energy from organic molecules, the energy in these organic molecules is generally derived from the sun. Bearing these two points in mind, we use the terms "phototroph" and "chemotroph" because they call our attention to the flow of energy from the sun to organisms and then from one organism to the next (discussed more fully in Chapter 25).

Organisms can also be considered in terms of their source of carbon (Fig. 6.1). Some organisms are able to convert carbon dioxide (an inorganic form of carbon) into glucose (an organic form of carbon). These organisms are **autotrophs,** or "self feeders," because they make their own organic sources of carbon. Plants again are an example, so plants are both phototrophs and autotrophs, or photoautotrophs.

Other organisms do not have the ability to convert carbon dioxide into organic forms of carbon. Instead, they obtain their carbon from organic molecules synthesized by other organisms (called preformed organic molecules)—that is, they eat other organisms or molecules derived from other organisms. Such organisms are **heterotrophs,** or "other feeders," as they rely on other organisms for their organic source of carbon. Animals obtain their carbon in this way, and so animals are both chemotrophs and heterotrophs, or chemoheterotrophs.

As we move away from the familiar examples of plants and animals and begin in Part 2 to explore the diversity of life, we will see that not all organisms fit into these two categories (Fig. 6.1). Some microorganisms gain energy from sunlight, but obtain their carbon from preformed organic molecules; such organisms are called photoheterotrophs. Other microorganisms extract energy from inorganic sources but build their own organic molecules; these organisms are termed chemoautotrophs. They are often found in extreme environments, such as deep-sea vents, where sunlight is absent and inorganic compounds such as hydrogen sulfide are plentiful.

Metabolism is the set of chemical reactions that sustain life.

The building and breaking down of sugars such as glucose, and the harnessing and release of energy in the process, are driven by chemical reactions in the cell. The term **metabolism** encompasses the entire set of these chemical reactions that convert molecules into other molecules and transfer energy in living organisms. These chemical reactions are occurring all of the time in your cells. Many of these reactions are linked, in that the products of one are the reactants of the next, forming long pathways and intersecting networks.

Metabolism is divided into two branches: **Catabolism** is the set of chemical reactions that break down molecules into smaller units and, in the process, produce ATP, and **anabolism** is the set of chemical reactions that build molecules from smaller units and require an input of energy, usually in the form of ATP (**Fig. 6.2**). For example, carbohydrates can be broken down, or catabolized, into sugars, fats into fatty acids and glycerol, and proteins into amino acids. These initial products can be broken down further to release energy stored in their chemical bonds. The synthesis of macromolecules such as sugars and proteins, by contrast, is anabolic.

6.2 ENERGY

The energy of a system has a formal definition: It is the system's capacity to do work. For a cell, this work involves processes we discussed in earlier chapters, such as synthesizing DNA, RNA, and proteins, pumping substances into and out of the cell, and moving vesicles between various compartments of a cell. The sun is a familiar source of energy, and we recognize energy in movement. On a cellular level, energy is held in chemical bonds, such as those of ATP, glucose, and lipids. How do these molecules contain energy in their chemical bonds? In this section, we discuss different sources of energy.

Kinetic and potential energy are two forms of energy.
Light, electricity, wind, and fossil fuels are all different sources of energy, and they can be classified as one of two types: kinetic energy or potential energy (**Fig. 6.3**). **Kinetic energy** is the energy of motion, and it is perhaps the most familiar form of energy. Moving objects possess kinetic energy because they perform work, resulting in the movement of themselves and the surrounding matter. For example, a ball bouncing down a set of stairs possesses kinetic energy. Kinetic energy

---

FIG. 6.2 **Catabolism and anabolism.** The energy harvested as ATP during the breakdown of molecules in catabolism can be used to synthesize molecules in anabolism.

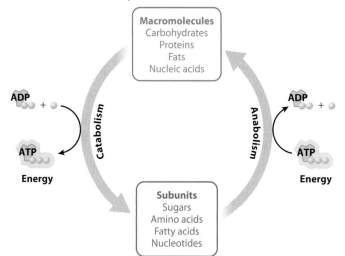

FIG. 6.3 **Potential and kinetic energy.** Some of the high potential energy of a ball at the top of a set of stairs is transformed to kinetic energy as the ball rolls down the stairs.

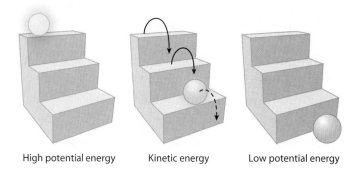

High potential energy   Kinetic energy   Low potential energy

is associated with any kind of movement, such as a person running or a muscle contracting. Similarly, light is associated with the movement of photons, electricity with the movement of electrons, and thermal energy (perceived as heat) with the movement of molecules, so these, too, are forms of kinetic energy.

Energy is not always associated with motion. An immobile object can still possess a form of energy called **potential energy,** or stored energy. Potential energy depends on the structure of the object or its position relative to its surroundings, and it is released by a change in the object's structure or position. For example, the potential energy of a ball is higher at the top of a flight of stairs than at the bottom (Fig. 6.3). If it were not blocked by the floor, it would move from the position of higher potential energy (the top of the stairs) to the position of lower potential energy (the bottom of the stairs) because of the force of gravity. Similarly, an electrochemical gradient of molecules across a cell membrane is a form of potential energy. Given the chance, the molecules move down their concentration and electrical gradients (Chapter 5).

Energy can be converted from one form to another. The ball at the top of the stairs has a certain amount of potential energy because of its position. As it rolls down the stairs, this potential energy is converted to kinetic energy associated with movement of the ball and the surrounding air. When the ball reaches the bottom of the stairs, the remaining energy is stored as potential energy. Conversely, it takes an input of energy to move the ball back to the top of the stairs, and this input of energy is stored as potential energy.

Chemical energy is a form of potential energy.

We obtain the energy we need from the food we eat, which contains chemical energy, a form of potential energy. How do food molecules contain potential energy? Recall from Chapter 2 that atoms consist of a nucleus with positively charged protons and electrically neutral neutrons, and negatively charged electrons occupying orbitals at various distances from the nucleus. Like the ball on the stairs, electrons have potential energy based on their position. The farther away an electron is from the nucleus, the more potential energy it has (**Fig. 6.4**). Given the chance, an electron will move closer to the nucleus because of the attraction between the positively charged nucleus and the negatively charged electron. When electrons move closer to the nucleus, some of this potential energy is converted to other types of energy, such as heat or light energy. Conversely, it takes an input of energy to move electrons farther from the nucleus, and this energy is stored as potential energy.

Recall, too, that a covalent bond results from the sharing of the electrons between two atoms. When these shared electrons

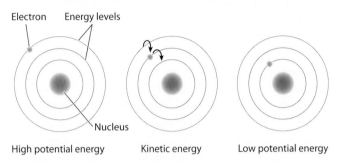

FIG. 6.4 **Potential and kinetic energy of electrons.** Some of the high potential energy of an electron farther from the nucleus is converted to the kinetic energy of light or heat as the electron moves closer to the nucleus.

Electron   Energy levels

Nucleus

High potential energy   Kinetic energy   Low potential energy

are far from both nuclei, they have a large amount of potential energy; when close, they have less potential energy. In this way, molecules carry potential energy in their chemical bonds. Organic molecules contain many covalent bonds, including carbon–carbon (C–C) bonds and carbon–hydrogen (C–H) bonds. In these bonds, the electrons are far from the two atoms, so they store a large amount of chemical potential energy. Organic molecules such as carbohydrates, lipids, and proteins are rich sources of chemical energy and therefore are sometimes called fuel molecules.

ATP is the cell's energy currency.

The chemical energy carried in carbohydrates, lipids, and proteins is harnessed by cells to do work. But cells do not use this energy all at once. Instead, through a series of chemical reactions described in Chapter 7, they package this energy into a chemical form that is readily accessible to the cell. One form of chemical energy is adenosine triphosphate, or ATP, shown in **Fig. 6.5.** The chemical energy in the bonds of ATP is used in turn to drive many cellular processes, such as muscle contraction, cell movement, and membrane pumps. In this way, ATP serves as a "go-between," acting as an intermediary between fuel molecules that store a large amount of potential energy in their bonds and the activities of the cell that require an input of energy.

ATP is composed of adenosine, which is made up of the base adenine and the five-carbon sugar ribose, attached to triphosphate, or three phosphate groups (Fig. 6.5). Its chemical relatives are ADP (adenosine diphosphate) and AMP (adenosine monophosphate), with two phosphate groups and one phosphate group, respectively. The use of ATP as an energy source in nearly all cells reflects its use early in the evolution of life on Earth.

The chemical energy of ATP is held in the bonds connecting the phosphate groups. At physiological pH, these phosphate groups are negatively charged and have a tendency to repel each other.

FIG. 6.5 The structure of ATP.

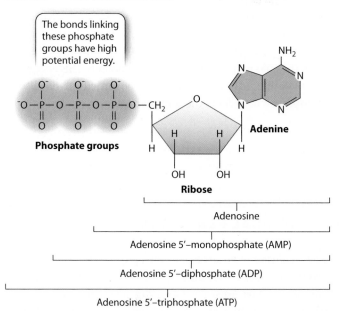

The chemical bonds connecting the phosphate groups therefore store potential energy that is released when the bonds are broken. In turn, the released energy can power the work of the cell.

6.3 THE LAWS OF THERMODYNAMICS

Energy from the sun can be converted by plants and other phototrophs into chemical potential energy held in the bonds of molecules. Chemical reactions can transfer this chemical energy between different molecules. And energy from these molecules can be used by the cell to do work. In all these instances, energy is subject to the laws of thermodynamics. In fact, all processes in a cell, from diffusion to osmosis to the pumping of ions to cell movement, are subject to these laws. There are four laws of thermodynamics, two of which are particularly relevant to biological processes.

The first law of thermodynamics: Energy is conserved.

The **first law of thermodynamics** is the law of conservation of energy. It states that the universe contains a constant amount of energy. Therefore, energy is neither created nor destroyed. New energy is never formed, and energy is never lost. Instead, energy simply changes from one form to another. For example, kinetic energy can change to potential energy and vice versa, but the total amount of energy always remains the same (**Fig. 6.6**).

FIG. 6.6 The first law of thermodynamics. When energy is transformed from one form to another, the total amount of energy remains the same.

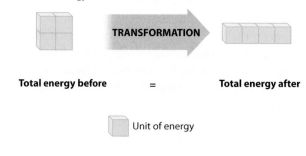

In the simple example of a ball rolling down a set of stairs (see Fig. 6.3), the potential energy stored at the top of the stairs is converted to kinetic energy associated with the movement of the ball and the surrounding air. The total amount of energy in this energy transformation is constant—that is, the difference in potential energy at the top and the bottom of the stairs is equal to the total amount of kinetic energy associated with the movement of the ball and air molecules.

Similarly, when an electron moves from a higher energy level, or shell, to a lower one, it emits light or heat (see Fig. 6.4). The difference in potential energy between the two energy levels is equal to the light or heat energy emitted, consistent with the first law.

The second law of thermodynamics: Disorder tends to increase.

When energy changes form, the *total amount of energy* remains constant. However, in going from one form of energy to another, the *energy available to do work* decreases (**Fig. 6.7**). How can the

FIG. 6.7 The second law of thermodynamics. Because the amount of disorder increases when energy is transformed from one form to another, some of the energy available to do work is lost.

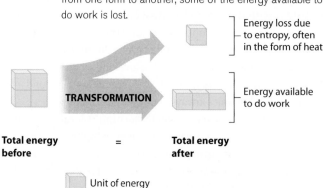

total energy remain the same, but the energy available to do work decrease? The answer is that some of the energy is available to do work, and some is not available to do work. So, energy transfers are never 100% efficient, since the amount of energy available to do work decreases every time energy changes form.

The energy that is not available to do work takes the form of an increase in disorder. In other words, there is a universal price to pay in transforming energy from one form to another, which takes the form of an increase in disorder. For example, when kinetic energy is changed into potential energy or vice versa, the amount of disorder always increases. This principle is summarized by the **second law of thermodynamics,** which states that the transformation of energy is associated with an increase in disorder of the universe. The degree of disorder is called **entropy.**

In chemical reactions, most of the entropy increase occurs through the transformation of various forms of energy into thermal energy, which we experience as heat. Thermal energy is a form of kinetic energy corresponding to the random motion of molecules, and results in a given temperature. The higher the temperature, the more rapidly the molecules move, and the higher the disorder.

Consider the contraction of a muscle, a form of kinetic energy associated with the shortening of muscle cells. The contraction of muscle is powered by chemical potential energy in fuel molecules. Some of this potential energy is transformed into kinetic energy (movement), and the rest is dissipated as thermal energy (which is why your muscles warm as you exercise). The amount of chemical potential energy is equal to the amount of kinetic energy plus the amount of thermal energy, consistent with the first law of thermodynamics. In addition, because of the entropy "tax," not all of the chemical energy stored in molecules is converted to kinetic energy, as thermal energy flowing as heat is a necessary by-product of the process.

In living organisms, catabolic reactions result in an increase of entropy as a single ordered biomolecule is broken down into several smaller ones with more freedom to move around, consistent with the second law. Anabolic reactions, by contrast, might seem to decrease entropy because they use individual building blocks to synthesize more ordered biomolecules such as proteins or nucleic acids. Do these anabolic reactions violate the second law of thermodynamics? No, because the second law of thermodynamics always applies to the universe as a whole, not to a chemical reaction in isolation. A local decrease in entropy is always accompanied by an even higher increase in the entropy of the surroundings. The production of heat in a chemical reaction increases entropy because heat is associated with the motion of molecules. The combination of the decrease in entropy associated with the building of a macromolecule and

the increase in entropy associated with heat always results in a net increase in entropy.

The key point here is that the maintenance of the high degree of function and organization of a single cell or a multicellular organism requires a constant input of energy, either from the sun or from the energy stored in chemical compounds. This energy allows molecules to be built and work to be carried out, but also leads to greater disorder in the surroundings.

→ **Quick Check 1** Cold air is more ordered (that is, it has less entropy) than hot air. The second law of thermodynamics states that entropy always increases. Do air conditioners violate this law?

6.4 CHEMICAL REACTIONS

Living organisms build and break down molecules, pump ions across membranes, move, and in general function largely through chemical reactions. As we have seen, organisms break down food molecules, storing energy in the bonds of ATP, which then powers chemical reactions that sustain life. Chemical reactions are therefore central to life processes. We describe here several features of a chemical reaction.

A chemical reaction occurs when molecules interact.

As we saw in Chapter 2, a chemical reaction is the process by which molecules, called reactants, are transformed into other molecules, called products. During a chemical reaction, atoms keep their identity, but the bonds linking the atoms change. For example, carbon dioxide (CO_2) and water (H_2O) can react to produce carbonic acid (CH_2O_3), as shown here and in **Fig. 6.8**:

$$CO_2 + H_2O \rightarrow H_2CO_3$$

FIG. 6.8 **A chemical reaction.** Atoms retain their identity during a chemical reaction as bonds are broken and new bonds formed to yield new molecules.

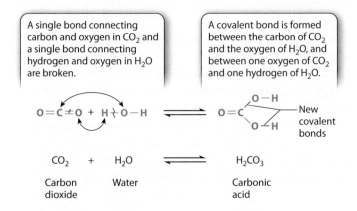

A single bond connecting carbon and oxygen in CO_2 and a single bond connecting hydrogen and oxygen in H_2O are broken.

A covalent bond is formed between the carbon of CO_2 and the oxygen of H_2O, and between one oxygen of CO_2 and one hydrogen of H_2O.

New covalent bonds

CO_2 + H_2O ⇌ H_2CO_3

Carbon dioxide   Water   Carbonic acid

The preceding reaction occurs commonly. For example, in an aqueous (watery) environment, carbonic acid exists as bicarbonate ions (HCO_3^-) and protons (H^+). This reaction occurs in the oceans, and explains why the oceans are becoming more acidic with increasing carbon dioxide levels in the atmosphere. In addition, when cells break down glucose in organisms, they produce carbon dioxide. In animals, this carbon dioxide diffuses out of cells and into the blood. Rather than remaining dissolved in solution, most of the carbon dioxide is converted into carbonic acid according to the preceding reaction.

Most chemical reactions in cells are reversible; the products can react to form the reactants. For example, carbon dioxide and water react to form carbonic acid, and carbonic acid can also dissociate to produce carbon dioxide and water. This reverse reaction also occurs in the blood, allowing carbon dioxide to be removed from the lungs or gills (Chapter 39). The reversibility of the reaction is indicated by a double arrow:

$$CO_2 + H_2O \rightleftharpoons H_2CO_3$$

The way the reaction is written defines the forward and reverse reactions: A forward reaction proceeds from left to right and the reactants are placed on the left side of the arrow; a reverse reaction proceeds from right to left and the reactants are placed on the right side of the arrow.

The direction of a reversible reaction can be influenced by the concentrations of reactants and products. For example, increasing the concentration of the reactants or decreasing the concentration of the products favors the forward reaction. This effect explains how many reactions in metabolic pathways proceed: The products of many reactions are quickly consumed by the next reaction, helping to drive the first reaction forward.

Chemical reactions are subject to the laws of thermodynamics.

Chemical reactions, like all processes in the cell, are subject to the laws of thermodynamics. We have seen that cells use chemical reactions to perform much of the work of the cell. The amount of energy available to do work is called **Gibbs free energy (G)**. In a chemical reaction, we can compare the free energy of the reactants and products to determine whether there is energy available to do work. The difference between two values is denoted by the Greek letter delta (Δ). In this case, ΔG is the free energy of the products minus the free energy of the reactants (**Fig. 6.9**). If the products of a reaction have more free energy than the reactants, then ΔG is positive and a net input of energy is required to drive the reaction forward (Fig. 6.9a). By contrast, if the products of a reaction have less free energy than the reactants, ΔG is negative and energy is released and available to do work (Fig. 6.9b).

Reactions with a negative ΔG that release energy and proceed spontaneously are called **exergonic**, and reactions with a positive ΔG that require an input of energy and are not spontaneous are called **endergonic**. Note that the term "spontaneous" does not imply instantaneous or even rapid. "Spontaneous" in this context means that a reaction releases energy; "non-spontaneous" means that a reaction requires a sustained input of energy.

Recall that the total amount of energy is equal to the energy available to do work plus the energy that is not available to do work because of the increase in disorder. We can write this relationship as an equation, in which the total amount of energy is **enthalpy (H)**, the energy available to do work is Gibbs free energy (G), and the degree of disorder is **entropy (S)** multiplied by the **absolute temperature (T)** (measured in degrees Kelvin), since temperature influences the movement of molecules (and hence the degree of disorder). Therefore,

Total amount of energy (H) =
    energy available to do work (G) + energy lost to entropy (TS)

We are interested in the energy available for a cell to do work, or G. Therefore, we express G in terms of the other two parameters, H and TS, as follows:

$$G = H - TS$$

In a chemical reaction, we can compare the total energy and entropy of the reactants with the total energy and entropy of the products to see if there is energy available to do work. As a result, we get

$$\Delta G = \Delta H - T\Delta S$$

This equation is a useful way to see if a chemical reaction takes place, what direction it proceeds in, and whether net energy is required or released. Let's take a step back and make sure it makes sense intuitively. The value of ΔG depends on *both* the change in enthalpy and the change in disorder. Catabolic reactions are those in which the products have less chemical energy in their bonds than in those of the reactants and in which the products

---

FIG. 6.9 Endergonic and exergonic reactions. An endergonic reaction requires an input of energy; an exergonic reaction releases energy.

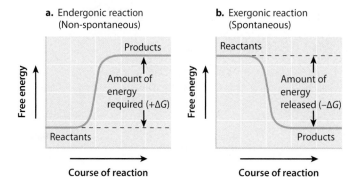

a. Endergonic reaction (Non-spontaneous)

b. Exergonic reaction (Spontaneous)

FIG. 6.10 **Energy in catabolism and anabolism.** Catabolic reactions have a negative ΔG and release energy often in the form of ATP, whereas anabolic reactions have a positive ΔG and require an input of energy often in the form of ATP.

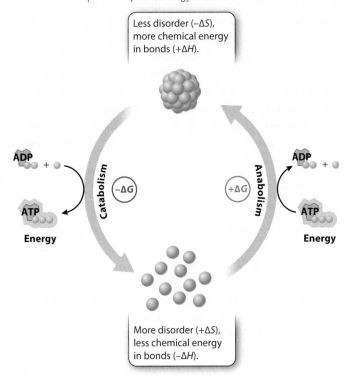

Less disorder ($-\Delta S$), more chemical energy in bonds ($+\Delta H$).

ADP +

ATP

Energy

Catabolism

$-\Delta G$

$+\Delta G$

Anabolism

ADP +

ATP

Energy

More disorder ($+\Delta S$), less chemical energy in bonds ($-\Delta H$).

are more disordered than the reactants. In other words, such reactions have a negative value of ΔH and a positive value of ΔS, and therefore a negative value of ΔG and proceed spontaneously (**Fig. 6.10**). The reverse is also true: Increasing chemical potential energy and decreasing disorder, as in the synthesis of proteins from individual amino acids and other anabolic reactions, results

in a positive value of ΔG and requires a net input of energy.

There are also cases in which the change in enthalpy and the change in entropy are both positive or both negative. In these cases, the absolute value of these parameters determines whether ΔG is positive or negative and therefore whether a reaction is spontaneous or not.

→ **Quick Check 2** How does increasing the temperature affect the change in free energy (ΔG) of a chemical reaction?

The hydrolysis of ATP releases energy.

Let's apply these concepts to a specific chemical reaction. Earlier, we introduced ATP, the molecule that drives many cellular processes using the chemical potential energy in its chemical bonds. ATP reacts with water to lose a phosphate group (HPO_4^{2-}), forming ADP and inorganic phosphate (P_i) (**Fig. 6.11**):

$$ATP + H_2O \rightarrow ADP + P_i$$

This is an example of a hydrolysis reaction, a chemical reaction in which a water molecule is split into a proton (H^+) and a hydroxyl group (OH^-). Hydrolysis reactions often break down polymers into their subunits, and in the process one product gains a proton and the other gains a hydroxyl group.

The reaction of ATP with water is an exergonic reaction that releases energy. This negative free energy difference between the products and reactants can be explained by referring to the formula we derived in the last section. Recall that the phosphate groups of ATP are negatively charged at physiological pH and repel each other. ATP has three phosphate groups, and ADP has two. Therefore, ADP contains less chemical potential energy in its bonds than does ATP, resulting in a negative value of ΔH. In addition, a single molecule of ATP is broken down into two molecules, ADP and P_i. Therefore, the reaction is also associated with an increase in entropy, or a positive value of ΔS. Since $\Delta G = \Delta H - T\Delta S$, ΔG is negative and the reaction is a spontaneous

FIG. 6.11 **ATP hydrolysis.** ATP hydrolysis is an exergonic reaction that releases free energy.

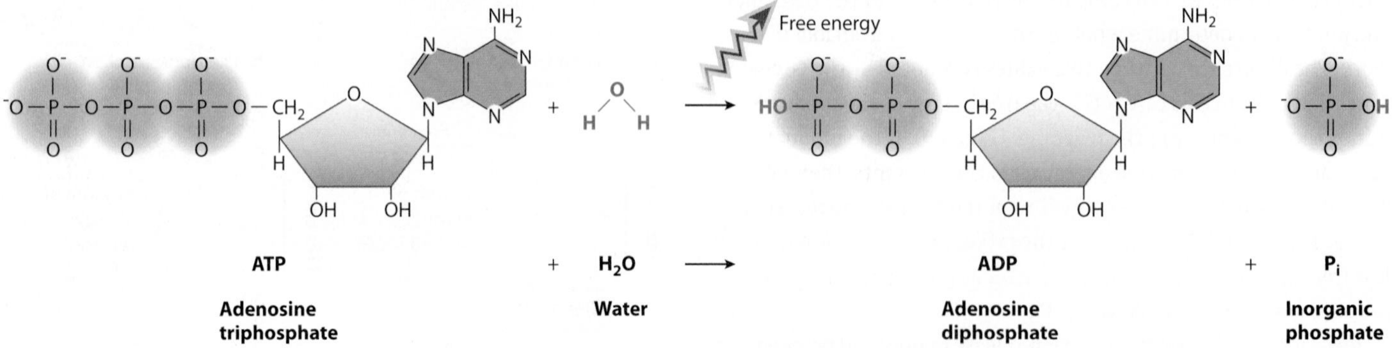

Free energy

ATP
Adenosine
triphosphate

+ **H₂O**
Water

→

ADP
Adenosine
diphosphate

+ **P_i**
Inorganic
phosphate

one that releases free energy. The release of free energy during the hydrolysis of ATP allows ATP to drive chemical reactions and other processes that require a net input of energy, as we will see next.

Non-spontaneous reactions are often coupled to spontaneous reactions.

If the conversion of reactant A into product B is spontaneous, the reverse reaction leading to the formation of B from A is not. The ΔG's for the forward and reverse reactions have the same absolute value but opposite signs. You might expect that the direction of the reaction would always be from A to B. However, in a living organism, not all chemical reactions are spontaneous. Anabolic reactions are a good example; they require an input of energy to drive them in the right direction. This raises the question: What drives non-spontaneous reactions? The coupling of a non-spontaneous reaction to a spontaneous one can drive a non-spontaneous reaction, as long as the net ΔG of the two reactions is negative.

Let's consider the following two reactions:
(1) A → B $\Delta G_1 > 0$ (energy consumed)
(2) B → C $\Delta G_2 < 0$ (energy released)

Only reaction 2 is spontaneous since $\Delta G_2 < 0$, but if the sum of ΔG_1 and ΔG_2 is negative, then the overall reaction A →→ C is spontaneous and the transformation of A into B occurs despite a positive ΔG. This type of **energetic coupling,** in which a spontaneous reaction drives a non-spontaneous one, provides the thermodynamic driving force of a non-spontaneous biochemical reaction.

In a cell, the most common reaction involving energetic coupling is the hydrolysis of ATP. This reaction can drive an endergonic reaction that requires an input of energy if the two reactions are coupled together (**Fig. 6.12a**). Coupled reactions involving ATP share a phosphate group, which is transferred between ATP and other molecules in the reaction.

Following ATP hydrolysis, the cell needs to replenish its ATP so that it can carry out additional

chemical reactions. The synthesis of ATP from ADP and P_i is an endergonic reaction with a positive ΔG, requiring an input of energy. In some cases, exergonic reactions can drive the synthesis of ATP by energetic coupling (**Fig. 6.12b**). The sum of the ΔG's of the two reactions is negative, allowing the overall reaction to proceed.

Phosphorylated molecules, like ATP, can be hydrolyzed, releasing free energy. Hydrolysis reactions can be ranked by their free energy differences. **Fig. 6.13** shows that ATP hydrolysis has an intermediate free energy difference compared to the free energy difference for hydrolysis of other common phosphorylated molecules. Those reactions that have a ΔG more negative than that of ATP hydrolysis give a phosphate group to ADP, and those reactions that have a ΔG less negative than that of ATP hydrolysis

FIG. 6.12 **Energetic coupling.** A spontaneous (exergonic) reaction drives a non-spontaneous (endergonic) reaction. (a) The hydrolysis of ATP drives the formation of glucose 6-phosphate from glucose. (b) The hydrolysis of phosphoenolpyruvate drives the synthesis of ATP.

> The coupled reaction proceeds because ΔG is less than 0 and P_i is shared between the two reactions.

a.

ATP	+	H_2O	⟶	ADP	+	P_i	$\Delta G_1 = -7$ kcal/mol	**Exergonic reaction**
Glucose	+	P_i	⟶	Glucose 6-phosphate	+	H_2O	$\Delta G_2 = +3.3$ kcal/mol	**Endergonic reaction**
Glucose	+	ATP	⟶	Glucose 6-phosphate	+	ADP	$\Delta G = -3.7$ kcal/mol	**Coupled reaction**

b.

Phosphoenolpyruvate	+	H_2O	⟶	Pyruvate	+	P_i	$\Delta G_1 = -14.8$ kcal/mol	**Exergonic reaction**
ADP	+	P_i	⟶	ATP	+	H_2O	$\Delta G_2 = +7$ kcal/mol	**Endergonic reaction**
Phosphoenolpyruvate	+	ADP	⟶	Pyruvate	+	ATP	$\Delta G = -7.8$ kcal/mol	**Coupled reaction**

FIG. 6.13 **ΔG of common hydrolysis reactions in a cell.** ATP hydrolysis has an intermediate ΔG.

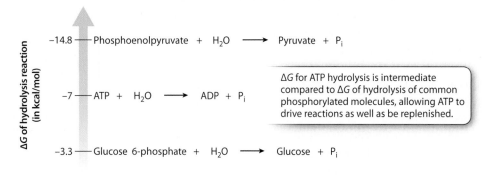

ΔG of hydrolysis reaction (in kcal/mol)

−14.8 — Phosphoenolpyruvate + H_2O ⟶ Pyruvate + P_i

−7 — ATP + H_2O ⟶ ADP + P_i

> ΔG for ATP hydrolysis is intermediate compared to ΔG of hydrolysis of common phosphorylated molecules, allowing ATP to drive reactions as well as be replenished.

−3.3 — Glucose 6-phosphate + H_2O ⟶ Glucose + P_i

receive a phosphate group from ATP by energetic coupling. Therefore, ADP is an energy acceptor and ATP an energy provider. The ATP–ADP system is at the core of energetic coupling between catabolic and anabolic reactions. In this way, ATP continually turns over in a cell.

6.5 ENZYMES AND THE RATE OF CHEMICAL REACTIONS

Up to this point, we have focused on the spontaneity and direction of chemical reactions. Now we address their rate. As mentioned earlier, a spontaneous reaction is not necessarily a fast one. For example, the breakdown of glucose into carbon dioxide and water is spontaneous with a negative ΔG, but the rate of the reaction is close to zero and the breakdown of glucose is imperceptible. However, glucose is readily broken down inside cells all the time. How is this possible? The answer is that chemical reactions in a cell are accelerated by chemical catalysts.

The rate of a chemical reaction is defined as the amount of product formed (or reactant consumed) per unit of time. Catalysts are substances that increase the rate of chemical reactions without themselves being consumed. In biological systems, the catalysts are usually proteins called **enzymes,** although, as we saw in Chapter 2, some RNA molecules have catalytic activity as well. Enzymes can increase the rate of chemical reactions dramatically. Moreover, because they are highly specific, acting only on certain reactants and catalyzing only some reactions, enzymes play a critical role in determining which chemical reactions take place from all the possible reactions that could occur in a cell. In this section, we discuss how enzymes increase the rate of chemical reactions and how that ability gives them a central role in metabolism.

Enzymes reduce the activation energy of a chemical reaction.

Earlier, we saw that exergonic reactions release free energy and endergonic reactions require free energy. Nevertheless, all chemical reactions require an input of energy to proceed, even exergonic reactions that release energy. For this type of reaction, the energy released is more than the initial input of energy, so there is a net release of energy.

Why is an input of energy needed for all chemical reactions? As a chemical reaction proceeds, existing chemical bonds break and new ones form. For an extremely brief period of time, a compound is formed in which the old bonds are breaking and the new ones are forming. This intermediate stage between reactants and products is called the **transition state.** It is highly unstable and therefore has a large amount of free energy.

In all chemical reactions, reactants adopt at least one transition state before their conversion into products. The graph in **Fig. 6.14** represents the free energy levels of the reactant, transition state, and product. This reaction is spontaneous since the free energy of the reactant is higher than the free energy of the product and ΔG is negative. However, the highest free energy value corresponds to the transition state.

To reach the transition state, the reactant must absorb energy from its surroundings (the uphill portion of the curve in Fig. 6.14). As a result, all chemical reactions, even spontaneous ones that release energy, require an input of energy that we can think of as an "energy barrier." The energy input necessary to reach the transition state is called the **activation energy (E_A).** Once the transition state is reached, the reaction proceeds, products are formed, and energy is released into the surroundings (the downhill portion of the curve in Fig. 6.14). There is an inverse correlation between the rate of a reaction and the height of the energy barrier: the lower the energy barrier, the faster the reaction; the higher the barrier, the slower the reaction.

In chemical reactions that take place in the lab, heat is a common source of energy used to overcome the energy barrier. In living organisms, reactions are accelerated by the action of enzymes. However, enzymes do not act by supplying heat. Instead, they reduce the activation energy by stabilizing the transition state and decreasing its free energy (the red line in Fig. 6.14). As the activation energy decreases, the speed of the reaction increases.

Although an enzyme accelerates a reaction by reducing the activation energy, the difference in free energy between reactants and products (ΔG) does not change. In other words, an enzyme

---

FIG. 6.14   An enzyme-catalyzed reaction. An enzyme accelerates a reaction by lowering the activation energy, E_A.

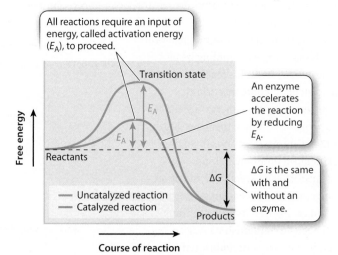

changes the path of the reaction between reactants and products, but not the starting or end point (Fig. 6.14). Consider the breakdown of glucose into carbon dioxide and water. The ΔG of the reaction is the same whether it proceeds by combustion or by the action of multiple enzymes in a metabolic pathway in a cell.

→ **Quick Check 3** Which of the following do enzymes change? ΔG; reaction rate; types of products generated; activation energy; the laws of thermodynamics.

Enzymes form a complex with reactants and products.

An important characteristic of enzymes is that, as catalysts, they participate in a chemical reaction but are not themselves consumed in the process. In other words, they emerge unchanged from a chemical reaction, ready to catalyze the same reaction again. How do enzymes increase the reaction rate without being consumed? The answer is that enzymes form a complex with the reactants and products.

In an uncatalyzed reaction, a reactant, often called a **substrate (S)**, is converted to a product (P):

$$S \rightleftharpoons P$$

In the presence of an enzyme (E), the substrate first forms a complex with the enzyme (enzyme–substrate, or ES). While still part of the complex, the substrate is converted to product (enzyme–product, or EP). Finally, the complex dissociates, releasing the enzyme and product. Therefore, a reaction catalyzed by an enzyme can be described as

$$S + E \rightleftharpoons ES \rightleftharpoons EP \rightleftharpoons E + P$$

The formation of this complex is critical for accelerating the rate of a chemical reaction. Recall from Chapter 4 that proteins adopt three-dimensional shapes and that the shape of a protein is linked to its function. Enzymes are folded into three-dimensional shapes that bring particular amino acids into proximity to form an **active site.** The active site of the enzyme is the portion of the enzyme that binds substrate and converts it to product (**Fig. 6.15**). In the active site, the enzyme and substrate form both transient covalent bonds and/or weak noncovalent interactions. Together, these interactions stabilize the transition state and decrease the activation energy.

Enzymes also reduce the energy of activation by positioning two substrates to react. The formation of the enzyme–substrate complex promotes the reaction between two substrates by aligning their reactive chemical groups and limiting their motion relative to each other.

The size of the active site is extremely small compared to the size of the enzyme. If only a small fraction of the enzyme is necessary for the catalysis of a reaction, why are enzymes so large? Of the many amino acids that form the active site, only

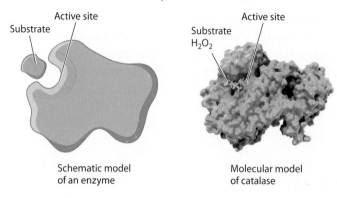

FIG. 6.15 **The active site of the enzyme catalase, shown schematically and as a surface model.** Substrate binds and is converted to product at the active site.

Schematic model of an enzyme

Molecular model of catalase

a few actively contribute to catalysis. Each of these amino acids has to occupy a very specific spatial position to align with the correct reactive group on the substrate. If the few essential amino acids were part of a short peptide, the alignment of chemical groups between the peptide and the substrate would be difficult or even impossible because the length of the bonds and the bond angles in the peptide would constrain its three-dimensional structure. In fact, in many cases the catalytic amino acids are spaced far apart in the primary structure of the enzyme, but brought close together in the formation of the active site by protein folding (**Fig. 6.16**). In other words, the large size of many enzymes is required at least in part to bring the catalytic amino acids into very specific positions in the active site of the folded enzyme.

The formation of a complex between enzymes and substrates

FIG. 6.16 Formation of the active site of an enzyme by protein folding.

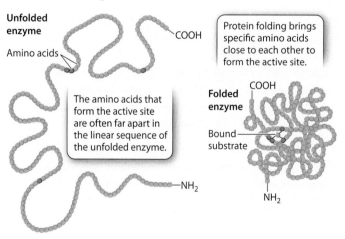

Unfolded enzyme

COOH

Amino acids

Protein folding brings specific amino acids close to each other to form the active site.

The amino acids that form the active site are often far apart in the linear sequence of the unfolded enzyme.

Folded enzyme

COOH

Bound substrate

—NH₂

NH₂

can be demonstrated experimentally, as illustrated in **Fig. 6.17** and **Fig. 6.18**, using two different techniques to answer the same question.

Enzymes are highly specific.

Enzymes are remarkably specific both for the substrate and the reaction that is catalyzed. In general, enzymes recognize either a unique substrate or a class of substrates that share common chemical structures. In addition, enzymes catalyze only one reaction or a very limited number of reactions.

For example, the enzyme succinate dehydrogenase acts only on succinate, whereas the enzyme β- (beta-) galactosidase is specific for a class of molecules. The enzyme β-galactosidase catalyzes the cleavage of the glycosidic bond that links galactose to glucose in the disaccharide lactose, as well as any glycosidic bond that links galactose to one of several types of

HOW DO WE KNOW?

FIG. 6.17

Do enzymes form complexes with substrates?

BACKGROUND The idea that enzymes form complexes with substrates to catalyze a chemical reaction was first proposed in 1888 by the Swedish chemist Svante Arrhenius. One of the earliest experimental demonstrations in support of this idea was made by American chemist Kurt Stern. He studied an enzyme called catalase, which is very abundant in animal and plant tissues. Catalase converts hydrogen peroxide (H_2O_2), which is toxic to cells, to water (H_2O) and oxygen (O_2):

$$2H_2O_2 \quad \rightarrow \quad 2H_2O \quad + \quad O_2$$

Hydrogen peroxide Water Oxygen

Catalase is very efficient, able to convert hydrogen peroxide to water and oxygen very rapidly.

HYPOTHESIS Stern hypothesized that catalase forms a complex with hydrogen peroxide.

METHOD Stern used spectral analysis to test his hypothesis. He shined a white light on the reaction as it took place. Different molecules absorb different wavelengths of light. The maximum absorption of a wavelength by each different molecule is called the absorption peak. By analyzing the patterns of absorption peaks as the reaction proceeded, Stern could determine whether or not an intermediate complex was formed.

RESULTS A schematic representation of the absorption peaks is shown here. Note the appearance of a new absorption peak in panel II, consistent with the formation of an enzyme–substrate complex.

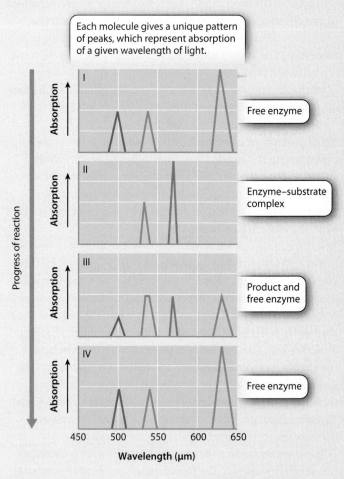

Each molecule gives a unique pattern of peaks, which represent absorption of a given wavelength of light.

I — Free enzyme
II — Enzyme–substrate complex
III — Product and free enzyme
IV — Free enzyme

Wavelength (μm)

CONCLUSION The simplest interpretation of the data is that catalase forms a complex with hydrogen peroxide during its conversion to water and oxygen, providing support for the initial hypothesis.

FOLLOW-UP WORK As Stern wrote, "It remains to be seen to which extent the findings of this study apply to enzyme action in general." In other words, the next steps were to see if other enzymes also work by forming a complex with their substrates.

SOURCE Stern, K. G. 1936. "On the Mechanism of Enzyme Action: A Study of the Decomposition of Monoethyl Hydrogen Peroxide by Catalase and of an Intermediate Enzyme–Substrate Compound." *J. Biol. Chem.* 114:473–494.

FIG. 6.18

Do enzymes form complexes with substrates?

BACKGROUND The enzyme β-galactosidase catalyzes the cleavage of the glycosidic bond that links galactose to glucose in the disaccharide lactose. Lactose belongs to a family of molecules called β-galactosides since it contains a galactose unit attached to the rest of the molecule by a glycosidic bond. In a related compound called β-thiogalactoside, the oxygen atom in the glycosidic bond is replaced by sulfur. The enzyme β-galactosidase binds β-thiogalactoside but cannot cleave or release it.

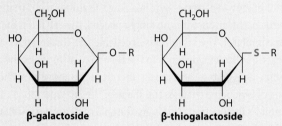

β-galactoside   **β-thiogalactoside**

METHOD A container is separated into two compartments by a semipermeable membrane. The membrane is permeable to β-galactoside and β-thiogalactoside, but not permeable to the enzyme.

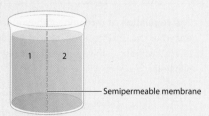

Semipermeable membrane

EXPERIMENT 1 Radioactively labeled β-thiogalactoside (S) is added to compartment 1 and the movement of S is followed by measuring the level of radioactivity in the two compartments.

RESULT Over time, the level of radioactivity is the same in the two compartments.

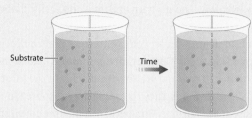

Substrate   Time

EXPERIMENT 2 Radioactively labeled β-thiogalactoside (S) is added to compartment 1, enzyme (E) is added to compartment 2, and the movement of S is followed by measuring the level of radioactivity in the two compartments.

RESULT Over time, the level of radioactivity is greater in compartment 2 than in compartment 1.

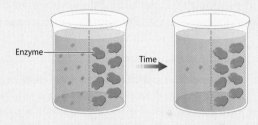

Enzyme   Time

CONCLUSION These results can be explained if the substrate diffuses from compartment 1 to compartment 2, forms a complex with the enzyme, and is not released. In other words, E and S form a complex.

SOURCE Adapted from Doherty, D. G., and F. Vaslow. 1952. "Thermodynamic Study of an Enzyme–Substrate Complex of Chymotrypsin." *J. Am. Chem. Soc.* 74:931–936.

molecule. In this case, the enzyme does not recognize the whole substrate, but a particular structural motif within it, and very small differences in the structure of this motif affect the activity of the enzyme. For example, β-galactosidase cleaves β-galactoside but does not cleave α- (alpha-) galactoside, which differs from β-galactoside only in the orientation of the glycosidic bond. Hence, the enzyme is able to discriminate between two identical bonds with different orientations within a molecule. The specificity of enzymes can be attributed to the structure of their active sites. The enzyme active site interacts only with substrates having a precise three-dimensional structure.

Enzyme activity can be influenced by inhibitors and activators.

The activity of enzymes can be influenced by **inhibitors** and **activators.** Inhibitors decrease the activity of enzymes, whereas activators increase the activity of enzymes. Enzyme inhibitors are quite common. They are synthesized naturally by many plants and animals as a defense against predators. Similarly, pesticides and herbicides often target enzymes to inactivate them. Many drugs used in medicine are enzyme inhibitors, including drugs used to treat infections as well as cancer and other diseases. Given the importance of chemical reactions and the role of enzymes in metabolism, it is not surprising that enzyme inhibitors have such widespread applications.

Inhibitors bind either to the active site of the enzyme or elsewhere, but in both cases they hinder the enzyme's ability to accelerate the conversion of reactants to products. Inhibitors fall into two classes. **Irreversible inhibitors** usually form covalent bonds with enzymes and irreversibly inactivate them. **Reversible inhibitors** form weak bonds with enzymes and easily dissociate from them.

Reversible inhibitors can act competitively or non-competitively with enzymes (**Fig. 6.19**). **Competitive inhibitors** bind to the active site of the enzyme and prevent the binding of the substrate (Fig. 6.19a). In other words, they compete with substrate for the active site of the enzyme. Competitive inhibitors are often structurally similar to the substrate. By binding to the active site of the enzyme, competitive inhibitors reduce the affinity of the enzyme for the substrate. Therefore, competitive inhibitors can be overcome by increasing the concentration of substrate.

Non-competitive inhibitors usually have a structure very different from that of the substrate and bind to the enzyme at a site different from the active site (Fig. 6.19b). When the inhibitor is bound, the enzyme is still able to bind the substrate and there is no competition between the binding of the substrate and the inhibitor. Therefore, the affinity of the enzyme for its substrate is unchanged by a non-competitive inhibitor. However, a non-competitive inhibitor slows down the reaction by altering the shape of the enzyme and reducing its activity.

Allosteric enzymes in the cell are regulated by activators and inhibitors.

Enzyme activators and inhibitors are sometimes important in the normal operation of a cell—for example, to regulate a metabolic pathway. Consider the synthesis of isoleucine from threonine, a pathway found in some bacteria. This conversion requires five reactions, each catalyzed by a different enzyme (**Fig. 6.20**). Once the bacterium has enough isoleucine for its needs, it would be a waste of energy to continue synthesizing the amino acid. To shut down the pathway once it is no longer needed, the cell relies on an enzyme inhibitor. The inhibitor is isoleucine, the final product of the five reactions. Isoleucine binds to the first enzyme in the pathway, threonine dehydratase, at a site distinct from the active site. The binding of isoleucine changes the shape of the enzyme and in this way inhibits its function. This is an example of **negative feedback**, in which the final product inhibits the first step of the reaction.

Threonine dehydratase is an example of an **allosteric enzyme.** Allosteric enzymes change their shape or conformation

---

FIG. 6.19 **(a) Competitive and (b) non-competitive inhibition.** Both types of inhibitor reduce the activity of an enzyme by binding to it reversibly, but competitive inhibitors bind the active site and non-competitive inhibitors bind a different site.

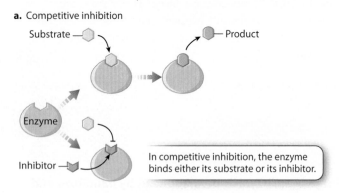

a. Competitive inhibition

Substrate — Product

Enzyme

Inhibitor

In competitive inhibition, the enzyme binds either its substrate or its inhibitor.

b. Non-competitive inhibition

Active site

Enzyme

Inhibitor site

In non-competitive inhibition, the binding sites of the substrate and inhibitor are different. The binding of a non-competitive inhibitor causes a decrease in the rate at which the enzyme converts the substrate to product.

FIG. 6.20 **The regulation of threonine dehdyratase, an allosteric enzyme.** The enzyme is inhibited by the final product of this synthetic pathway and activated by the initial substrate.

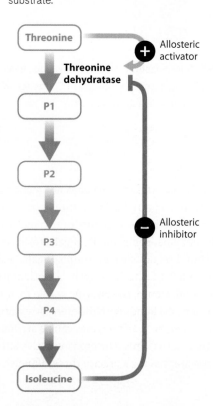

Threonine

Allosteric activator

Threonine dehydratase

P1

P2

P3

P4

Isoleucine

Allosteric inhibitor

on binding to a substrate, activator, or inhibitor, and this change in shape in turn influences the activity of the enzyme, either activating or inhibiting it. Threonine dehydratase is allosterically inhibited by isoleucine, as we have seen. In addition, it is allosterically activated by the first substrate in the series of reactions, threonine (Fig. 6.20). Threonine binds to the enzyme and changes its conformation in a way that increases its activity. At a low concentration of threonine, the rate of the reaction is very slow. As the concentration of threonine increases, the activity of the enzyme increases. At a particular threshold, a small increase in threonine concentration results in a large increase in reaction rate. Finally, when there is excess substrate, the reaction rate slows down. In effect, the allosteric enzyme adjusts the rate of a reaction depending on substrate concentration.

In the next two chapters, we examine more closely two key metabolic processes, cellular respiration and photosynthesis. Both of these processes require many chemical reactions acting in a coordinated fashion. Allosteric enzymes catalyze key reactions in metabolism and are usually found at or near the start of a metabolic pathway or at the crossroads between two metabolic pathways. Allosteric enzymes are one way that the cell coordinates the activity of multiple metabolic pathways.

? CASE 1 The First Cell: Life's Origins
What naturally occurring elements might have spurred the first reactions that led to life?
Many enzymes are not just made up of protein, but also contain metal ions. These ions are one type of **cofactor,** a substance that associates with an enzyme and plays a key role in its function. Metallic cofactors, especially iron, magnesium, manganese, cobalt, copper, zinc, and molybdenum, bind to diverse proteins, including those used in DNA synthesis, nitrogen metabolism, and the transport of electrons for cellular respiration and photosynthesis, processes that are discussed in the next two chapters. With this in mind, scientists have asked whether metal ions might, by themselves, catalyze chemical reactions thought to have played a role in the origin of life. They do. For example, magnesium and zinc ions added to solutions can accelerate the linking of nucleotides to form RNA and DNA molecules.

Enzymes that contain iron and sulfur clustered together are particularly important in the transport of electrons within cells. Iron–sulfur minerals, especially pyrite (or fool's gold, FeS_2), form commonly in mid-ocean hydrothermal vent systems and other environments where oxygen is absent. It has been proposed that reactions now carried out in cells by iron–sulfur proteins reflect chemical reactions that took place spontaneously on the early Earth. The idea that your cells preserve an evolutionary memory of ancient hydrothermal environments may seem like science fiction, but it finds support in laboratory experiments. For example, the reaction of H_2S and FeS to form pyrite has been shown to catalyze a number of plausibly pre-biotic chemical reactions, including the formation of pyruvate (a key intermediate in energy metabolism discussed in Chapter 7). Thus, the metals in enzymes help connect the chemistry of life to the chemistry of Earth.

Core Concepts Summary

6.1 METABOLISM IS THE SET OF BIOCHEMICAL REACTIONS THAT TRANSFORMS BIOMOLECULES AND TRANSFERS ENERGY.

Organisms can be grouped according to their source of energy: Phototrophs acquire energy from sunlight and chemotrophs obtain energy from chemical compounds. page 6-2

Organisms can also be grouped according to the source of carbon they use to build organic molecules: Heterotrophs obtain carbon from organic molecules, and autotrophs obtain carbon from inorganic carbon, such as carbon dioxide. page 6-2

Catabolism is the set of reactions that break down molecules and release energy, and anabolism is the set of reactions that build molecules and require energy. page 6-3

6.2 THE ENERGY OF A SYSTEM IS ITS CAPACITY TO DO WORK.

Kinetic energy is the energy of motion. page 6-3

Potential energy is stored energy and depends on the structure of an object or its position relative to its surroundings. page 6-4

Chemical energy is a form of potential energy held in the bonds of molecules. page 6-4

6.3 THE LAWS OF THERMODYNAMICS GOVERN ENERGY FLOW IN BIOLOGICAL SYSTEMS.

The first law of thermodynamics states that energy cannot be created or destroyed. page 6-5

The second law of thermodynamics states that there is an increase in disorder or entropy in the universe over time. page 6-5

6.4 CHEMICAL REACTIONS ARE SUBJECT TO THE LAWS OF THERMODYNAMICS.

In a chemical reaction, atoms themselves do not change, but the bonds linking the atoms change to form new molecules. page 6-6

Many chemical reactions are reversible. page 6-7

The direction of reversible reactions is influenced by the concentration of reactants and products. page 6-7

Gibbs free energy (*G*) is the amount of energy available to do work. page 6-7

Three thermodynamic parameters define a chemical reaction: Gibbs free energy (*G*), enthalpy (*H*), and entropy (*S*), and the change of free energy in a chemical reaction is described by $\Delta G = \Delta H - T\Delta S$. page 6-7

Exergonic reactions are spontaneous ($\Delta G < 0$) and release energy. page 6-7

Endergonic reactions are non-spontaneous ($\Delta G > 0$) and require energy. page 6-7

The hydrolysis of ATP is an exergonic reaction that is used to drive many endergonic reactions in a cell. page 6-8

In living systems, non-spontaneous reactions are often coupled to spontaneous ones. page 6-9

6.5 THE RATE OF BIOCHEMICAL REACTIONS IS CONTROLLED BY PROTEIN CATALYSTS CALLED ENZYMES.

Enzymes reduce the free energy level of the transition state between reactants and products, thereby reducing the energy input, or activation energy, required for a chemical reaction to proceed. page 6-10

During catalysis, the substrate and product form a complex with the enzyme. Transient covalent bonds and/or weak noncovalent interactions stabilize the complex. page 6-11

The size of the active site of an enzyme is small compared to the size of the enzyme as a whole and the active site amino acids occupy a very specific spatial arrangement. page 6-11

An enzyme is very specific toward its substrate and the types of reactions it catalyzes. page 6-12

Inhibitors reduce the activity of enzymes. They can act irreversibly or reversibly. page 6-13

Activators increase the activity of enzymes. page 6-13

Allosteric enzymes change their shape and activity on binding to substrates or other molecules that act as activators or inhibitors. Allosteric enzymes are often found at or near the start of a metabolic pathway or at the crossroads of multiple pathways. page 6-14

Self-Assessment

1. Describe four ways in which organisms obtain energy and carbon from the environment.

2. Distinguish between catabolism and anabolism.

3. Define energy; describe the two forms that it takes and provide an example of each.

4. Explain how molecules contain chemical energy in their bonds.

5. Draw the structure of ATP, indicating the bonds that are broken during hydrolysis.

6. Name and describe the first and second laws of thermodynamics.

7. Given a set of thermodynamic parameters, indicate whether a chemical reaction is spontaneous or not.

8. Describe how the hydrolysis of ATP can drive non-spontaneous reactions in a cell.

9. Give three characteristics of enzymes.

10. Explain how protein folding allows for enzyme specificity.

Do you understand the chapter's Core Concepts? Log into BIO**P◎RTAL** to check your answers to the Self-Assessment questions, then practice what you've learned and reinforce this chapter's concepts by working through the problems and multimedia tutorials provided there.

🛜 http://courses.bfwpub.com/yourbioportal/index.php

CHAPTER 7

CELLULAR RESPIRATION

Harvesting Energy from Carbohydrates and Other Fuel Molecules

Core Concepts

7.1 Cellular respiration is a series of catabolic reactions that convert the energy stored in fuel molecules into ATP.

7.2 Glycolysis is the partial oxidation of glucose and results in the production of pyruvate, a small amount of ATP, and high-energy electron carriers.

7.3 Pyruvate is oxidized to acetyl-CoA, connecting glycolysis to the citric acid cycle.

7.4 The citric acid cycle results in the complete oxidation of fuel molecules and the generation of ATP and high-energy electron carriers.

7.5 The electron transport chain transfers high-energy electrons from electron carriers to oxygen, using the energy to pump protons and synthesize ATP by oxidative phosphorylation.

7.6 Glucose can be broken down in the absence of oxygen by fermentation, producing a modest amount of energy in the form of ATP.

7.7 Metabolic pathways are integrated, allowing control of the energy level of cells.

The ability to harness energy from the environment is a key attribute of life. We have seen that energy is needed for all kinds of tasks—among them cell movement and division, muscle contraction, growth and development, and the synthesis of macromolecules. Organic molecules such as carbohydrates, lipids, and proteins are good sources of energy. Some organisms, like humans and other heterotrophs, obtain organic molecules by consuming them in their diet. Others, like plants and other autotrophs, synthesize these molecules on their own, as we discuss more fully in the next chapter. Regardless of how these molecules are obtained, nearly all organisms—animals, plants, fungi, and microbes—break them down in the process of **cellular respiration,** releasing energy that can be used to do the work of the cell. Cellular respiration is a series of chemical reactions that convert the energy stored in fuel molecules into a chemical form that can be readily used by cells.

It is tempting to think that organic molecules are converted to energy in this process, but this is not the case. Recall from Chapter 6 that the first law of thermodynamics (the law of conservation of energy) states that energy cannot be created or destroyed. Biological processes, like all processes, are subject to the laws of thermodynamics. As a result, the process of cellular respiration converts the chemical potential energy stored in organic molecules to a form of chemical potential energy that is useful to cells: **adenosine triphosphate,** or **ATP.** ATP is the universal energy currency for all cells (Chapter 6).

It is also easy to forget that organisms other than animals, such as plants, use cellular respiration. If plants use sunlight as a source of energy, why would they need cellular respiration? As we will see in the next chapter, plants use the energy of sunlight to make carbohydrates. Plants then break down these carbohydrates in the process of cellular respiration to produce ATP.

In this chapter, we discuss the breakdown, storage, and mobilization of sugars such as glucose, the synthesis of ATP, and the coordination and regulation of metabolic pathways that supply the energy needs of a cell.

7.1 AN OVERVIEW OF CELLULAR RESPIRATION

In the last chapter, we saw that catabolism describes the set of chemical reactions that break down molecules into smaller units. In the process, these reactions release chemical energy and store it in molecules of ATP. Anabolism, by contrast, is the set of chemical reactions that build molecules from smaller units. Anabolic reactions require an input of energy, usually in the form of ATP.

Cellular respiration is one of the major sets of catabolic reactions in a cell. During cellular respiration, fuel molecules such as glucose, fatty acids, and proteins are catabolized into smaller units, releasing the energy stored in their chemical bonds to power the work of the cell.

Cellular respiration occurs in four stages.

Cellular respiration is a series of catabolic reactions that convert the energy stored in food molecules, such as glucose, into ATP. It can occur in the presence of oxygen (termed aerobic respiration) or in the absence of oxygen (termed anaerobic respiration). Most organisms are capable of aerobic respiration; some bacteria respire anaerobically (Chapter 26). Here we focus on aerobic respiration. Oxygen is consumed in aerobic respiration, and carbon dioxide and water are produced. The process occurs in four stages (**Fig. 7.1**).

In stage 1, glucose, fatty acids, or amino acids are partially broken down and a modest amount of energy is released. In this chapter, we focus on the breakdown of glucose to make pyruvate, a process known as **glycolysis.**

In stage 2, pyruvate is converted to another molecule called acetyl-coenzyme A (acetyl-CoA) and carbon dioxide is produced.

Stage 3 is the **citric acid cycle.** During this stage, acetyl-CoA is broken down and more carbon dioxide is released.

In stages 1–3, chemical energy is transferred to two types of energy-storing molecules: ATP and **electron carriers.** ATP was discussed in Chapter 6. Electron carriers are molecules that store and transfer energy in the form of "high-energy" or "excited" electrons, discussed more fully below.

Stage 4 is **oxidative phosphorylation.** In this series of reactions, electron carriers generated in stages 1–3 donate their high-energy electrons to an **electron transport chain** (also called a respiratory chain). Electron transport chains transfer electrons along a series of membrane-associated proteins to a final electron acceptor and harness the energy of the electrons to produce a large amount of ATP. In aerobic respiration, oxygen is the final electron acceptor, so oxygen is consumed and water is produced in the process.

In eukaryotes, glycolysis takes place in the cytoplasm, and the citric acid cycle and oxidative phosphorylation take place in mitochondria. The electron transport chain is made up of proteins associated with the inner mitochondrial membrane (Chapter 5). In some bacteria, these reactions take place in the cytoplasm, and the electron transport chain is located in the plasma membrane. It is thought that mitochondria were once free-living bacteria but are now unable to live outside their host eukaryotic cell. This idea, known as the endosymbiotic theory, is discussed more fully in Chapter 27.

Before turning to the details of the four stages of cellular respiration, we take a moment to consider how energy is stored and used in cells. In particular, we focus on why carbohydrates and lipids are such good sources of energy.

FIG. 7.1   Cellular respiration. In most organisms, cellular respiration consumes oxygen and produces carbon dioxide, water, and ATP.

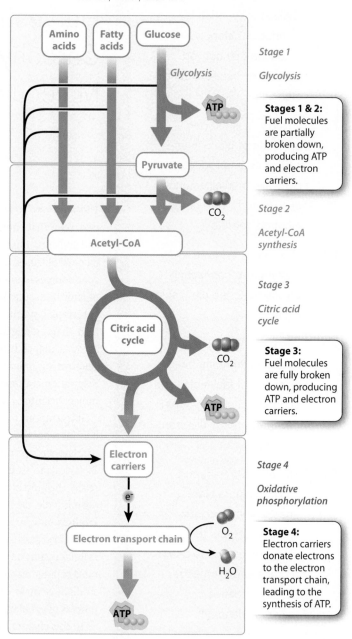

Cellular respiration involves a series of redox reactions.

You know from everyday experience that carbohydrates and lipids are good sources of energy. The key to understanding how energy is stored in these molecules is to understand **oxidation–reduction reactions** ("redox reactions" for short). In biological systems, oxidation–reduction reactions are often used to store or release chemical energy.

Oxidation is the loss of electrons, and reduction is the gain of electrons. The loss and gain of electrons always occur together in a single oxidation–reduction reaction: Electrons are transferred from one molecule to another so that one molecule loses electrons and one molecule gains those electrons.

A familiar example of an oxidation–reduction reaction is the reaction of iron and oxygen to make iron oxide—that is, rust. The overall reaction can be written as follows:

$$4Fe + 3O_2 \rightarrow 2Fe_2O_3$$

We can also write this reaction as two half-reactions in order to follow the electrons:

$$4Fe \rightarrow 2Fe_2^{3+} + 12e^-$$
$$3O_2 + 12e^- \rightarrow 2O_3^{2-}$$

As you can see from these half-reactions, iron loses electrons and is therefore oxidized, while oxygen gains electrons and is reduced.

Oxidation
$$4Fe \rightarrow 2Fe_2^{3+} + 12e^-$$
$$3O_2 + 12e^- \rightarrow 2O_3^{2-}$$
Reduction

The electrons lost by iron are gained by oxygen, so the original reaction can be written as follows:

Oxidation
$$4Fe + 3O_2 \rightarrow 2Fe_2O_3$$
Reduction

In many biological systems, electrons are not completely transferred between molecules. Instead, there is a change in electron density around an atom. In this case, oxidation is a decrease in electron density and reduction is an increase in electron density. Another way to think about these reactions is that electrons are partially lost or gained. The breakdown of the sugar glucose provides an example. The overall reaction can be written as follows:

$$C_6H_{12}O_6 + 6O_2 \rightarrow 6CO_2 + 6H_2O + energy$$
Glucose Oxygen Carbon Water
dioxide

This reaction is an example of an oxidation–reduction reaction in which glucose is oxidized to carbon dioxide and at the same time oxygen is reduced to water:

Oxidation
$$C_6H_{12}O_6 + 6O_2 \rightarrow 6CO_2 + 6H_2O + energy$$
Reduction

To understand why this is an oxidation–reduction reaction, consider where the electrons are in the reactants and products. Let's first compare glucose and carbon dioxide. The carbon atoms of glucose are bound to other carbon atoms, hydrogen atoms, and oxygen atoms. In the case of C—C and C—H covalent bonds, electrons are shared about equally between the two atoms (**Fig. 7.2**). By contrast, in carbon dioxide, they are not shared equally. The oxygen atom is more electronegative than the carbon atom, so the electrons that are shared between carbon and oxygen spend more time near the oxygen atom (Fig. 7.2a). As a result,

---

FIG. 7.2 **Electron sharing in covalent bonds.** Electrons are more likely to be found near the more electronegative atom in a bond.

a. Carbon atoms in glucose are oxidized.

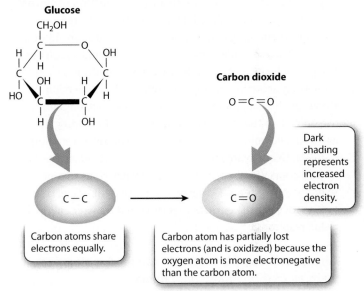

b. Oxygen atom in water is reduced.

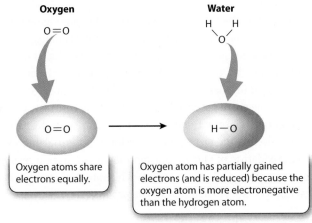

in the preceding reaction, carbon has partially lost electrons to oxygen. We say that the carbon atoms in glucose are oxidized, or simply that glucose is oxidized.

Let's consider the reduction reaction by comparing oxygen gas and water (Fig. 7.2b). In oxygen gas, electrons are shared equally between two oxygen atoms. In water, the electrons that are shared between hydrogen and oxygen spend more time near oxygen because oxygen is more electronegative than hydrogen. As a result, in the preceding reaction, the electron density around the oxygen atom has increased, so oxygen has partially gained electrons and is reduced.

Because oxygen gains electrons, it is called an **electron acceptor.** It also oxidizes glucose, so it can be referred to as an **oxidizing agent.** Glucose, conversely, is an **electron donor** and therefore a **reducing agent.**

Oxidation and reduction reactions are defined by the loss or gain of electrons. But note that in the oxidation of glucose, electrons always travel with hydrogen atoms. Therefore, the movement of hydrogen atoms can be used as an aid to recognize which molecules become oxidized and which ones become reduced. For example, we can see that the carbon atoms of glucose lose hydrogen atoms in the conversion to carbon dioxide; therefore, glucose loses electrons and is oxidized. In the same reaction, oxygen gains hydrogen atoms in becoming water; therefore, it gains electrons and is reduced. Using hydrogen atoms as a marker for electrons is often a convenient way to follow redox reactions that occur in biological systems. However, the movement of electrons is key, as they are the entities that carry and transfer energy in redox reactions.

Chemical energy is stored in reduced molecules such as carbohydrates and lipids.

We can now address the question of why reduced molecules, such as carbohydrates and lipids, have so much energy. The answer has to do with how the atoms of these molecules share electrons.

The shared electrons of C—C and C—H bonds characteristic of carbohydrates and lipids have high potential energy. The high potential energy results from the fact that the electrons are, on average, far from the nucleus of the atoms. As discussed in Chapter 6, the farther an electron is from the nucleus, the more potential energy it has. By contrast, when electrons are close to the nucleus of an atom, as in the case of carbon dioxide and water, they have lower potential energy. So the oxidation of glucose during cellular respiration results in a large release of energy because the potential energy of the reactants is higher than that of the products.

The reaction for the oxidation of glucose helps us focus on the starting reactants, final products, and release of energy. However, it misses the many intermediate steps that take place as the cell oxidizes glucose. Tossing a match into the gas tank of a car would release a tremendous amount of energy in the form of an explosion, but this energy would not be used productively. Similarly, if all the energy stored in glucose were released at once, most of it would be released as heat and the cell would not be able to harness it to do work. The energy in organic molecules is released gradually in a series of chemical reactions (**Fig. 7.3**). By oxidizing glucose slowly and in a controlled manner, the chemical energy stored in glucose can be harnessed in the chemical bonds of other molecules, such as ATP and electron carriers. ATP carries energy in its chemical bonds (Chapter 6). Electron carriers contain chemical energy in the form of high-energy electrons, which can be harnessed to produce ATP.

Electron carriers transport high-energy electrons.

As we just saw, many of the chemical reactions involved in cellular respiration are redox reactions that store energy in the form of electron carriers. Two important electron carriers in cells are the molecules nicotinamide adenine dinucleotide (NAD^+/NADH) and flavin adenine dinucleotide (FADH/ $FADH_2$). These electron carriers exist in two forms—an oxidized form (NAD^+ and FAD) and a reduced form (NADH and $FADH_2$). The oxidized form accepts electrons in many of the reactions of cellular respiration and becomes reduced. The reduced form has high potential energy. The electrons it gains in redox reactions are then donated to the electron transport chain. The electron transport chain transfers these electrons to oxygen, the final electron acceptor, releasing energy used to synthesize ATP.

Electron transport chains are used in respiration to extract energy from fuel molecules such as glucose, as well as in photosynthesis to extract energy from sunlight (Chapter 8).

ATP is generated by substrate-level phosphorylation and oxidative phosphorylation.

The chemical energy stored in a molecule of glucose is used to produce ATP in two different ways during cellular respiration. In some reactions, a phosphorylated organic molecule directly transfers a phosphate group to ADP. The free energy difference (ΔG) of hydrolysis of these phosphorylated molecules is more negative than that of ATP hydrolysis and so can drive the synthesis of ATP by energetic coupling (Chapter 6). This way of generating ATP is called **substrate-level phosphorylation** because a phosphate group is transferred to ADP from an organic

FIG. 7.3 **Energy is released gradually in cellular respiration.** (a) Glucose is oxidized slowly through many reactions. (b) Many of these reactions release energy in the form of ATP and electron carriers.

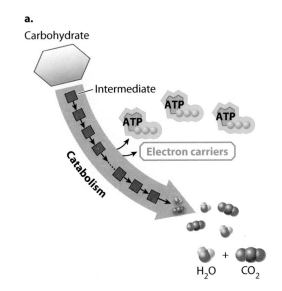

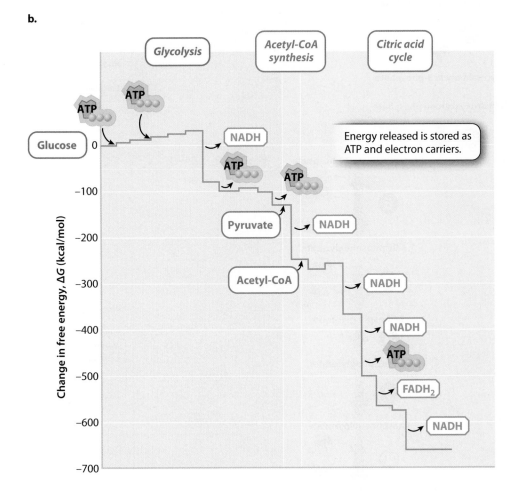

Energy released is stored as ATP and electron carriers.

molecule, which acts as a phosphate donor or substrate. Substrate-level phosphorylation produces only a small amount of the total ATP generated in the process of cellular respiration.

Most of the ATP generated in cellular respiration is produced in an entirely different manner— by oxidative phosphorylation. ATP is generated indirectly in the reactions of oxidative phosphorylation, through the reduction of electron carriers, the transfer of high-energy electrons from electron carriers to the electron transport chain, and the subsequent synthesis of ATP from ADP and inorganic phosphate (P_i).

→ **Quick Check 1** For each of the following pairs of molecules, indicate which member of the pair has higher and which has lower levels of chemical energy: ADP/ATP; NAD^+/NADH; FAD/$FADH_2$; CO_2/$C_6H_{12}O_6$; oxidized molecules/corresponding reduced molecules.

7.2 GLYCOLYSIS: THE SPLITTING OF SUGAR

Glucose is the most common fuel molecule in animals, plants, and microbes. It is the starting molecule for glycolysis, which results in the partial oxidation of glucose and the synthesis of a relatively small amount of ATP and electron carriers. Glycolysis literally means "splitting sugar," an apt name because in glycolysis a 6-carbon sugar (glucose) is split in two, yielding two 3-carbon molecules. The process is anaerobic because oxygen is not consumed. Glycolysis evolved very early in the evolution of life, when oxygen was not present in Earth's atmosphere.

FIG. 7.4   **Glycolysis.** Glucose is partially oxidized to pyruvate, with the net production of 2 ATP and 2 NADH.

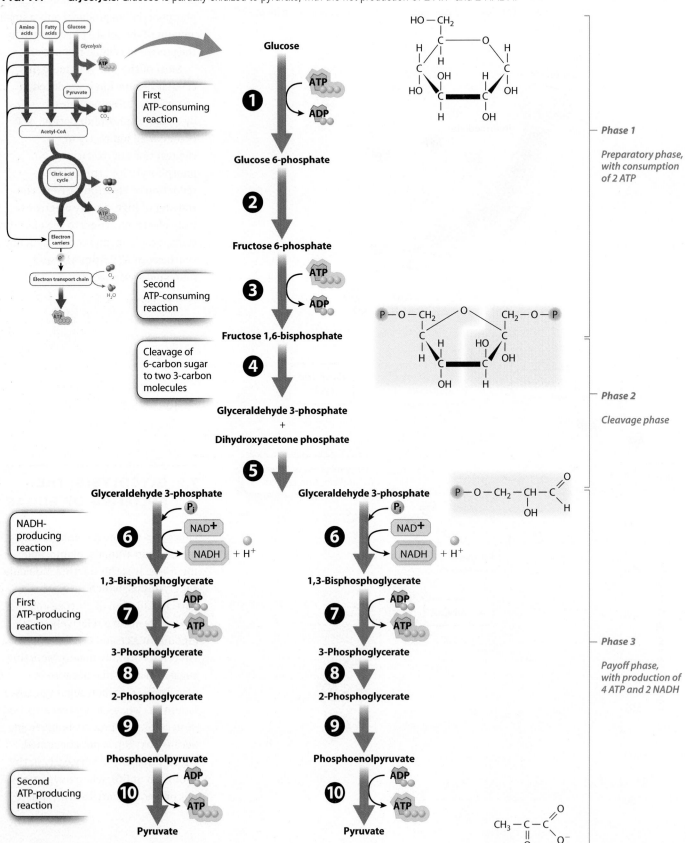

TABLE 7.1   Approximate Total ATP Yield in Cellular Respiration

PATHWAY	SUBSTRATE-LEVEL PHOSPHORYLATION	OXIDATIVE PHOSPHORYLATION	TOTAL ATP
Glycolysis (Glucose → 2 pyruvate)	2 ATP	2 NADH = 5 ATP	7
Acetyl-CoA Synthesis (2 Pyruvate → 2 acetyl-CoA)	0 ATP	2 NADH = 5 ATP	5
Citric acid cycle (2 turns, 1 for each acetyl-CoA)	2 ATP	6 NADH = 15 ATP 2 $FADH_2$ = 3 ATP	20
Total	4 ATP	28 ATP	32

It occurs in nearly all living organisms and is therefore probably the most widespread metabolic pathway among organisms.

Glycolysis is the partial breakdown of glucose.

Glycolysis begins with a molecule of glucose and produces two 3-carbon molecules of pyruvate and a net total of two molecules of ATP and two molecules of the electron carrier NADH. ATP is produced directly by the addition of a phosphate group to ADP, or substrate-level phosphorylation.

Glycolysis is a series of 10 chemical reactions (**Fig. 7.4**). These reactions can be divided into three phases. The first phase (reactions 1–3) prepares glucose for the next two phases by the addition of two phosphate groups to glucose, producing fructose 1,6-bisphosphate. This phase requires an input of energy. To supply that energy and the phosphate groups, two molecules of ATP are hydrolyzed per molecule of glucose. In other words, the first phase of glycolysis is an endergonic process. The phosphorylation of glucose has two important consequences. While glucose enters and exits cells through specific membrane transporters, phosphorylated glucose is trapped inside the cell. In addition, the presence of two negatively charged phosphate groups in proximity destabilizes the molecule so that it can be broken apart in the second phase of glycolysis.

The second phase (reactions 4 and 5) is the cleavage phase. In reaction 4, the 6-carbon molecule fructose 1,6-bisphosphate is split into two 3-carbon molecules, glyceraldehyde 3-phosphate and its isomer dihydroxyacetone phosphate. Then, in reaction 5, dihydroxyacetone phosphate is converted to glyceraldehyde 3-phosphate. For each molecule of glucose entering glycolysis, two 3-carbon glyceraldehyde 3-phosphate molecules enter the third phase.

Reactions 6–10 are the third and final phase of glycolysis. This phase ends with the production of two molecules of pyruvate. It is sometimes called the payoff phase because ATP

and the electron carrier NADH are produced. Later, NADH will contribute to the synthesis of ATP during oxidative phosphorylation.

In summary, glycolysis begins with a single molecule of glucose (six carbons) and produces two molecules of pyruvate (three carbons each). These reactions yield four molecules of ATP and two molecules of NADH. However, two ATP molecules are consumed during the initial phase of glycolysis, resulting in a net gain of two ATP molecules and two molecules of NADH (Fig. 7.4; **Table 7.1**). The overall chemical equation for glycolysis is as follows:

$$\text{Glucose} + 2\,NAD^+ + 2\,ADP + 2\,P_i \rightarrow$$
$$2\,\text{pyruvate} + 2\,ATP + 2\,NADH + 2H^+ + 2H_2O$$

→   **Quick Check 2** At the end of glycolysis, but before the subsequent steps in cellular respiration, which molecules contain the energy held in the original glucose molecule?

7.3 ACETYL-CoA SYNTHESIS

Glycolysis occurs in almost all living organisms, but it does not generate very much energy in the form of ATP. The end product, pyruvate, still contains a good deal of chemical potential energy in its bonds. In the presence of oxygen, pyruvate can be further broken down to release more energy, first to acetyl-CoA and then even further in a series of reactions known as the citric acid cycle. The synthesis of acetyl-CoA is a key step that links glycolysis to the citric acid cycle. In eukaryotes, this is the first step that takes place inside the mitochondria.

The oxidation of pyruvate connects glycolysis to the citric acid cycle.

The end product of glycolysis is pyruvate, which can be transported into mitochondria. Mitochondria are rod-shaped organelles surrounded by a double membrane (**Fig. 7.5**; Chapter 5). The inner and outer mitochondrial membranes are not close to each other in all areas because the inner membrane has folds that project inward. These membranes define two spaces. The space between the inner and outer membranes is called the **intermembrane space,** and

FIG. 7.5   Mitochondrial membranes and compartments.

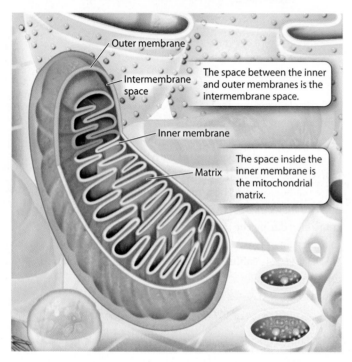

the space enclosed by the inner membrane is called the mitochondrial **matrix.**

Pyruvate is transported into the mitochondrial matrix, where it is converted into acetyl-CoA (**Fig. 7.6**). First, part of the pyruvate molecule is oxidized and splits off to form carbon dioxide, the most oxidized (and therefore the least energetic) form of carbon. The electrons lost in this process are donated to NAD$^+$, which is reduced to NADH. The remaining part of the pyruvate molecule—an acetyl group ($CH_3OC—$)—still contains a large amount of potential energy that can be harnessed. It is transferred to coenzyme A (CoA), a molecule that carries the acetyl group to the next set of reactions. All these reactions are catalyzed by a group of enzymes called the pyruvate dehydrogenase complex.

Overall, the synthesis of one molecule of acetyl-CoA from pyruvate results in the formation of one molecule of carbon dioxide and one molecule of NADH. Recall, however, that a single molecule of glucose forms two molecules of pyruvate during glycolysis. Therefore, two molecules of carbon dioxide, two molecules of NADH, and two molecules of acetyl-CoA are produced from a single starting glucose molecule in this stage of cellular respiration (Table 7.1). Acetyl-CoA is the substrate of the first step in the citric acid cycle.

7.4 THE CITRIC ACID CYCLE

The citric acid cycle is the step in cellular respiration in which fuel molecules are completely oxidized. It is also called the Krebs cycle and the tricarboxylic acid (TCA) cycle. During the citric acid cycle, the chemical energy in the bonds of acetyl-CoA is transferred to ATP by substrate-level phosphorylation and to the electron carriers NADH and FADH$_2$. In this way, the citric acid cycle supplies high-energy electrons to the electron transport chain, leading to the production of much more energy in the form of ATP than is obtained by glycolysis alone.

The citric acid cycle produces ATP and electron carriers.

Like the synthesis of acetyl-CoA, the citric acid cycle takes place in the mitochondrial matrix. It is composed of eight reactions and is called a cycle because the starting molecule, oxaloacetate, is regenerated at the

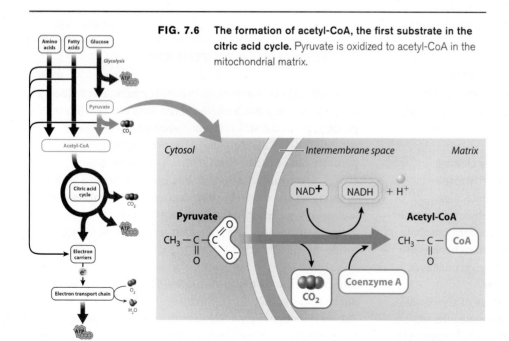

FIG. 7.6   The formation of acetyl-CoA, the first substrate in the citric acid cycle. Pyruvate is oxidized to acetyl-CoA in the mitochondrial matrix.

FIG. 7.7 **The citric acid cycle.** The acetyl group of acetyl-CoA is completely oxidized, with the net production of one ATP, three NADH, and one $FADH_2$.

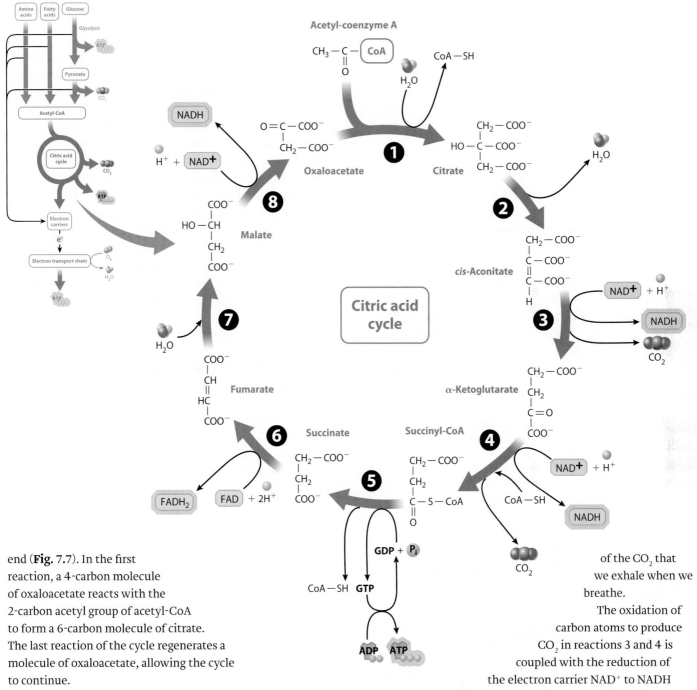

end (**Fig. 7.7**). In the first reaction, a 4-carbon molecule of oxaloacetate reacts with the 2-carbon acetyl group of acetyl-CoA to form a 6-carbon molecule of citrate. The last reaction of the cycle regenerates a molecule of oxaloacetate, allowing the cycle to continue.

The citric acid cycle results in the complete oxidation of the acetyl group of acetyl-CoA. Since the first reaction creates a molecule with six carbons and the last reaction regenerates a 4-carbon molecule, two carbons are eliminated during the cycle. These carbons are released as carbon dioxide in reactions 3 and 4. Along with the release of carbon dioxide from pyruvate in its conversion to acetyl-CoA, these reactions are the sources of the CO_2 released during cellular respiration and therefore the sources

of the CO_2 that we exhale when we breathe.

The oxidation of carbon atoms to produce CO_2 in reactions 3 and 4 is coupled with the reduction of the electron carrier NAD^+ to NADH (Fig. 7.7). In this way, energy released in the oxidation reactions is transferred to NADH. Additional electron carriers are produced in reactions 6 and 8, which are also redox reactions. In fact, the citric acid cycle produces a large quantity of electron carriers: three molecules of NADH and one molecule of $FADH_2$ per turn of the cycle. These electron carriers donate high-energy electrons in the next stage of cellular respiration to power the synthesis of ATP.

Reaction 5 is a substrate-level phosphorylation reaction that generates a molecule of GTP (Fig. 7.7). GTP can transfer its terminal phosphate to a molecule of ADP to form ATP. Reaction 5 is the only substrate-level phosphorylation in the citric acid cycle.

Overall, two molecules of acetyl-CoA produced from a single molecule of glucose yield two molecules of ATP, six molecules of NADH, and two molecules of $FADH_2$ in the citric acid cycle (Table 7.1).

→ **Quick Check 3** At the end of the citric acid cycle, but before the subsequent steps of cellular respiration, which molecules contain the energy held in the original glucose molecule?

? CASE 1 The First Cell: Life's Origins
What were the earliest energy-harnessing reactions?

Some bacteria run the citric acid cycle in reverse, incorporating carbon dioxide into organic molecules instead of liberating it. Running the citric acid cycle in reverse requires energy, which is supplied by sunlight (Chapter 8) or chemical reactions (Chapter 26).

Why would an organism run the citric acid cycle in reverse? The answer is that the intermediates generated step by step as the cycle turns provide the building blocks for synthesizing the cell's key biomolecules. This is true whether the cycle is run in the reverse or forward direction (**Fig. 7.8**). Pyruvate, for example, is the starting point for the synthesis of sugars and the amino

FIG. 7.8   Molecules produced by the citric acid cycle. Many organic molecules can be synthesized from citric acid cycle intermediates.

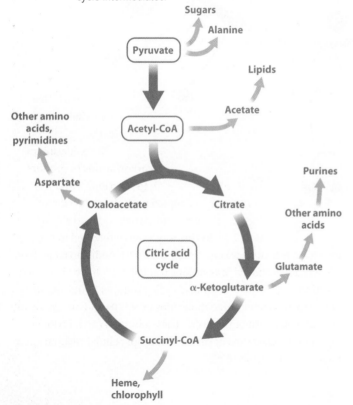

acid alanine; acetate is the starting point for the synthesis of the cell's lipids; oxaloacetate is modified to form different amino acids and pyrimidine bases; and α- (alpha-) ketogluterate is modified to form other amino acids. For organisms that run the cycle in the forward direction, the citric acid cycle is used to generate both energy-storing molecules (ATP and electron carriers) and intermediates in the synthesis of other molecules. For organisms that run the cycle in reverse, it is used to generate intermediates in the synthesis of other molecules and also to reduce carbon dioxide and incorporate carbon into organic molecules.

The centrality of the citric acid cycle to both the synthesis of biomolecules and to meeting the energy requirements of cells suggests to some biologists that this cycle evolved early, appearing in some of the first cells to feature metabolism. This early appearance of the citric acid cycle, in turn, implies that the great variety of biosynthetic and energy-yielding pathways found in modern cells evolved through the extension and modification of this deeply rooted cycle. As always in evolution, new cellular capabilities arose by the modification of preexisting capabilities. Complex networks of highly specific pathways evolved from a simpler, more general set of reactions.

7.5 THE ELECTRON TRANSPORT CHAIN AND OXIDATIVE PHOSPHORYLATION

The complete oxidation of glucose during glycolysis and the citric acid cycle results in the production of two kinds of electron carriers: NADH and $FADH_2$. We are now going to see how the energy stored in these electron carriers is used to synthesize ATP.

The energy in these electron carriers is released in a series of redox reactions that occur as electrons pass through a chain of protein complexes in the inner mitochondrial membrane to the final electron acceptor, oxygen, which is reduced to water. The energy in these electrons is not converted directly into the chemical energy of ATP, however. Instead, the passage of electrons is coupled to the transfer of protons (H^+) across the inner mitochondrial membrane, creating a concentration and charge gradient (Chapter 5). This electrochemical gradient provides a source of potential energy that is then used to drive the synthesis of ATP.

We next explore the properties of the electron transport chain, the proton gradient, and the synthesis of ATP.

The electron transport chain transfers electrons and pumps protons.

Electrons are not directly transported from NADH and $FADH_2$ to oxygen. Instead, they are transported along a series of four large protein complexes that form the electron transport chain (complexes I to IV). These are shown in **Fig. 7.9**. These membrane proteins are embedded in the mitochondrial inner membrane (see Fig. 7.5). The inner mitochondrial membrane contains one of the highest concentrations of proteins found in eukaryotic membranes.

FIG. 7.9 **The electron transport chain.** (a) The electron transport chain consists of four complexes (I to IV) in the inner mitochondrial membrane. (b) Electrons flow from electron carriers to oxygen, the final electron acceptor. (c) The proton gradient formed from the electron transport chain has potential energy that is used to synthesize ATP.

a. The electron transport chain in cellular respiration

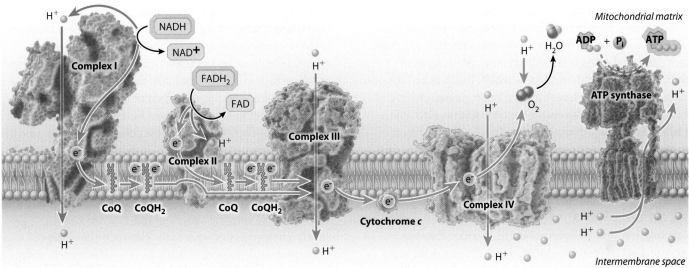

b. Electron transport

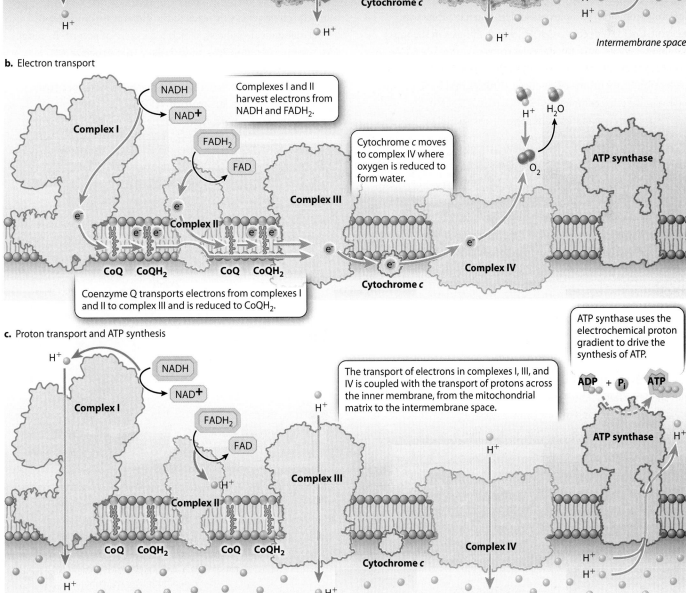

Complexes I and II harvest electrons from NADH and FADH$_2$.

Cytochrome *c* moves to complex IV where oxygen is reduced to form water.

Coenzyme Q transports electrons from complexes I and II to complex III and is reduced to CoQH$_2$.

ATP synthase uses the electrochemical proton gradient to drive the synthesis of ATP.

c. Proton transport and ATP synthesis

The transport of electrons in complexes I, III, and IV is coupled with the transport of protons across the inner membrane, from the mitochondrial matrix to the intermembrane space.

Electrons enter the electron transport chain via either complex I or II. Electrons donated by NADH enter through complex I, and electrons donated by $FADH_2$ enter through complex II (complex II is the same enzyme that catalyzes step 6 in the citric acid cycle). These electrons are transported through either complex I or II to complex III and then through complex IV.

Within each protein complex of the electron transport chain, electrons are passed from electron donors to electron acceptors. Each donor and acceptor is a redox couple, consisting of an oxidized and a reduced form of a molecule. The electron transport chain contains many of these redox couples. As electrons are passed from donors to acceptors, the energy of the electrons is reduced. Each electron acceptor therefore binds electrons more strongly than the previous one in the chain. Oxygen is the final electron acceptor, and it has the highest affinity for electrons. When oxygen accepts an electron, it is reduced to water.

Electrons also must be transported between the four complexes (Fig. 7.9). **Coenzyme Q** (CoQ), also called ubiquinone, accepts electrons from both complexes I and II. When it accepts an electron, CoQ is reduced to $CoQH_2$, which diffuses in the inner membrane, docks, and transfers electrons to complex III. Complex III in turn transfers electrons to **cytochrome c**. When it accepts an electron, cytochrome *c* is reduced, diffuses in the membrane, and interacts with complex IV.

These electron transfer steps are each associated with the release of energy as electrons are passed from the high-energy electron carriers NADH and $FADH_2$ to the final low-energy (high-affinity) electron acceptor, oxygen. Some of this energy is used to reduce the next carrier in the chain, but in complexes I, III, and IV some of it is used to pump protons (H^+) across the inner mitochondrial membrane, from the mitochondrial matrix to the intermembrane space (Fig. 7.9). Thus, the transfer of electrons through complexes I, III, and IV is coupled with the pumping of protons. The result is an accumulation of protons in the intermembrane space.

→   **Quick Check 4** Animals breathe in air that contains more oxygen than the air they breathe out. Where is oxygen consumed?

The proton gradient is a source of potential energy.

Like all membranes, the inner mitochondrial membrane is selectively permeable: Protons cannot passively diffuse across this membrane, and the movement of other molecules is controlled by transporters and channels (Chapter 5). We have just seen that the movement of electrons through membrane-embedded protein complexes is coupled with the pumping of protons from the mitochondrial matrix into the intermembrane space. The consequence is a proton gradient, a difference in proton concentration across the inner membrane.

The proton gradient has two components: a chemical gradient due to the difference in concentration and an electrical gradient due to the difference in charge between the two sides of the

membrane. To reflect the dual contribution of the concentration gradient and the electrical gradient, the proton gradient is also called an electrochemical gradient.

The proton gradient is a source of potential energy, as discussed in Chapters 5 and 6. It stores energy much in the same way that a battery or a dam does. Through the actions of the electron transport chain, protons have a high concentration in the intermembrane space and a low concentration in the mitochondrial matrix. As a result, there is a tendency for protons to diffuse back to the mitochondrial matrix, driven by a difference in concentration and charge on the two sides of the membrane. This movement, however, is blocked by the membrane, so the gradient holds potential energy. That energy can be harnessed if a pathway is opened through the membrane because, as we will see shortly, the resulting movement of the protons through the membrane can be used to perform work.

In sum, the oxidation of the electron carriers NADH and $FADH_2$ formed during glycolysis, acetyl-CoA synthesis, and the citric acid cycle leads to the generation of a proton electrochemical gradient, which is a source of potential energy. This source of potential energy is used to synthesize ATP.

ATP synthase converts the energy of the proton gradient into the energy of ATP.

In 1961, Peter Mitchell proposed a hypothesis to explain how the energy stored in the proton electrochemical gradient is used to synthesize ATP. In 1978, he was awarded the Nobel Prize in Chemistry for work that fundamentally changed the way we understand how energy is harnessed by a cell.

FIG. 7.10   **ATP synthase.** ATP synthase drives the synthesis of ATP by means of an electrochemical proton gradient.

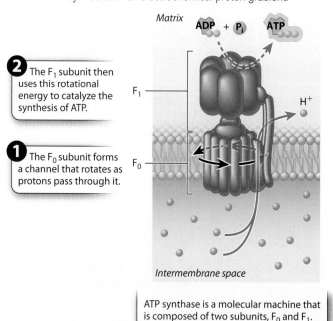

Matrix

2 The F_1 subunit then uses this rotational energy to catalyze the synthesis of ATP.

1 The F_0 subunit forms a channel that rotates as protons pass through it.

ADP + P_i ATP

F_1 H^+

F_0

Intermembrane space

ATP synthase is a molecular machine that is composed of two subunits, F_0 and F_1.

According to Mitchell's hypothesis, the gradient of protons provides a source of potential energy that is converted into chemical energy stored in ATP. First, for the potential energy of the proton gradient to be released, there must be an opening in the membrane for the protons to flow through. Mitchell suggested that protons in the intermembrane space diffuse down their electrical and concentration gradients through a transmembrane protein channel into the mitochondrial matrix. Second, the movement of protons through the enzyme must be coupled with the synthesis of ATP. This coupling is made possible by **ATP synthase,** a remarkable enzyme composed of two distinct subunits called F_0 and F_1 (**Fig. 7.10**). F_0 forms the channel in the inner mitochondrial membrane through which protons flow; F_1 is the catalytic unit that synthesizes ATP. Proton flow through the channel (F_0) makes it possible for the enzyme (F_1) to synthesize ATP.

Proton flow through the F_0 channel causes it to rotate, converting the energy of the proton gradient into mechanical rotational energy, a form of kinetic energy. The rotation of the F_0 subunit leads to rotation of the F_1 subunit in the mitochondrial matrix (Fig. 7.10). The rotation of the F_1 subunit in turn causes conformational changes that allow it to catalyze the synthesis of ATP from ADP and P_i. In this way, mechanical rotational energy is converted into the chemical energy of ATP.

Direct experimental evidence for Mitchell's hypothesis did not come for over a decade. One of the key experiments that provided support for Mitchell's hypothesis is illustrated in **Fig. 7.11.**

HOW DO WE KNOW?

FIG. 7.11

Can a proton gradient drive the synthesis of ATP?

BACKGROUND Peter Mitchell's hypothesis that a proton gradient can drive the synthesis of ATP was proposed before experimental evidence supported it and was therefore met with skepticism. In the 1970s, biochemist Efraim Racker and his collaborator Walther Stoeckenius tested the hypothesis.

EXPERIMENT Racker and Stoeckenius built an artificial system consisting of a membrane, a bacterial proton pump activated by light, and ATP synthase.

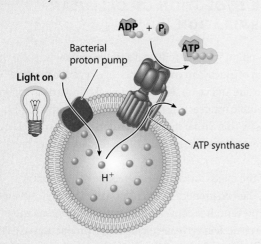

They measured the concentration of protons in the external medium and the amount of ATP produced in the presence and absence of light.

RESULTS In the presence of light, the concentration of protons increased inside the vesicles, suggesting that protons were taken up by the vesicles.

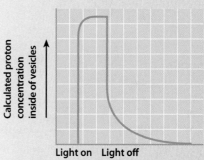

In the dark, the concentration of protons returned to the starting level. ATP was generated in the light, but not in the dark.

Condition	Relative level of ATP
Light	594
Dark	23

INTERPRETATION In the presence of light, the proton pump was activated and protons were pumped to one side of the membrane, leading to the formation of a proton gradient. The proton gradient, in turn, powered synthesis of ATP via ATP synthase.

CONCLUSION A membrane, proton gradient, and ATP synthase are sufficient to synthesize ATP. This result provided experimental evidence for Mitchell's hypothesis.

SOURCES Mitchell, P. 1961. "Coupling of Phosphorylation to Electron and Hydrogen Transfer by a Chemiosmotic Type of Mechanism." *Nature* 191:144–148; Racker, E., and W. Stoeckenius. 1974. "Reconstitution of Purple Membrane Vesicles Catalyzing Light-Driven Proton Uptake and Adenosine Triphosphate Formation." *J. Biol. Chem.* 249:662–663.

FIG. 7.12   The flow of energy in cellular respiration. A single glucose molecule yields 32 ATP molecules.

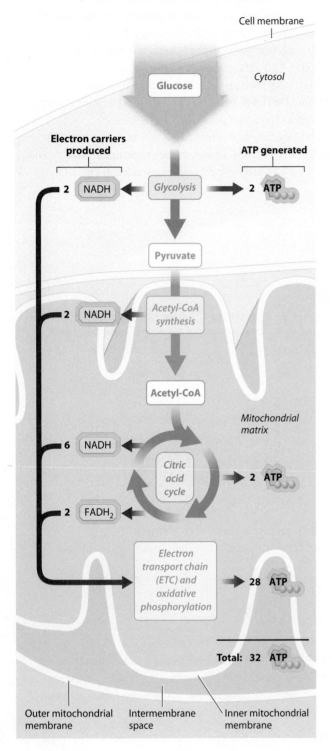

→   **Quick Check 5** Uncoupling proteins are proteins spanning the inner mitochondrial membrane that allow protons to pass through the membrane and bypass the channel of ATP synthase. Describe the consequences to the proton gradient and ATP production.

Approximately 2.5 molecules of ATP are produced for each NADH that donates electrons to the chain and 1.5 molecules of ATP for each $FADH_2$. Therefore, overall, the complete oxidation of glucose yields about 32 molecules of ATP from glycolysis, acetyl-CoA synthesis, the citric acid cycle, and oxidative phosphorylation (Table 7.1). The energy held in the bonds of glucose is now stored in a molecule that can be readily used by cells.

It is worth taking a moment to follow the flow of energy in cellular respiration, illustrated in its full form in **Fig. 7.12**. We began with glucose and noted that it held chemical potential energy in its covalent bonds. This energy is released slowly in a series of reactions and captured in chemical form. Some of these reactions generate ATP directly by substrate-level phosphorylation. Others are redox reactions that transfer energy to the electron carriers NADH and $FADH_2$. These electron carriers donate electrons to the electron transport chain, which uses the energy stored in the electron carriers to pump protons across the inner membrane of the mitochondria. In other words, the energy of the electron carriers is transformed into energy stored in a proton electrochemical gradient. ATP synthase then converts the energy of the proton gradient to rotational energy, which drives the synthesis of ATP. The cell now has a form of energy that it can use in many ways to perform work.

7.6 ANAEROBIC METABOLISM AND THE EVOLUTION OF CELLULAR RESPIRATION

Up to this point, we have followed a single metabolic path: the breakdown of glucose in the presence of oxygen to produce carbon dioxide and water. However, metabolic pathways more often resemble intersecting roads rather than a single, linear path. We saw this earlier in the discussion of the citric acid cycle, where intermediates in the cycle often feed into other metabolic pathways.

One of the major forks in the metabolic road occurs at pyruvate, the end product of glycolysis (section 10.2). When oxygen is present, it is converted to acetyl-CoA, which then enters the citric acid cycle, resulting in the production of ATP and electron carriers to fuel the electron transport chain, as we saw.

When oxygen is not present, however, pyruvate is metabolized along a number of different pathways. These pathways occur in many living organisms today and played an important role in the early evolution of life on Earth.

Fermentation extracts energy from glucose in the absence of oxygen.

Pyruvate, the end product of glycolysis, is a molecule shared by many metabolic pathways and it therefore has many possible fates in the cell. In the presence of oxygen, most of the pyruvate is used to synthesize acetyl-CoA, which in turn fuels the citric acid cycle. In the absence of oxygen, pyruvate can be broken down by **fermentation,** which does not rely on oxygen or a similar outside electron acceptor. Fermentation is accomplished through a wide variety of metabolic pathways that extract energy from fuel molecules such as glucose. Fermentation pathways are important for anaerobic organisms that live without oxygen, as well as some organisms such as yeast that favor fermentation over oxidative phosphorylation even in the presence of oxygen. It is also sometimes used in aerobic organisms when oxygen cannot be delivered fast enough to meet the cell's metabolic needs, as in exercising muscle.

Recall that during glycolysis, glucose is oxidized to form pyruvate, and NAD^+ is reduced to form NADH. For glycolysis to continue, NADH must be oxidized to NAD^+. The regeneration of NAD^+ is important because without it glycolysis would grind to a halt. In the presence of oxygen, NAD^+ is regenerated when NADH donates its electrons to the electron transport chain. In the absence of oxygen during fermentation, NADH is oxidized to NAD^+ when pyruvate or a derivative of pyruvate is reduced.

There are many fermentation pathways, especially in bacteria. Two of the major ones are **lactic acid fermentation** and **ethanol fermentation** (**Fig. 7.13**). Lactic acid fermentation occurs in animals and bacteria. During lactic acid fermentation, electrons from NADH are transferred to pyruvate to produce lactic acid and NAD^+ (Fig. 7.13a). The overall chemical reaction is written as follows:

$$\text{Glucose} + 2\,\text{ADP} + 2\,P_i \rightarrow 2\,\text{lactic acid} + 2\,\text{ATP} + 2H_2O$$

Ethanol fermentation occurs in plants and fungi. During ethanol fermentation, pyruvate releases carbon dioxide to form acetaldehyde, and electrons from NADH are transferred to acetaldehyde to produce ethanol and NAD^+ (Fig. 7.13b). The overall chemical reaction is written as follows:

$$\text{Glucose} + 2\,\text{ADP} + 2\,P_i \rightarrow 2\,\text{ethanol} + 2CO_2 + 2\,\text{ATP} + 2H_2O$$

In both fermentation pathways, NADH is oxidized to NAD^+. However, NADH and NAD^+ do not appear in the overall chemical equations because there is no net production or loss of either molecule. NAD^+ molecules that are reduced during glycolysis are oxidized when lactic acid or ethanol is formed.

FIG. 7.13   **Lactic acid and ethanol fermentation pathways.**

a. Lactic acid fermentation

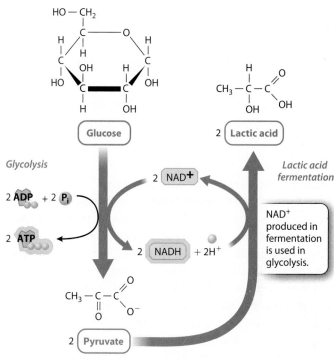

b. Ethanol fermentation

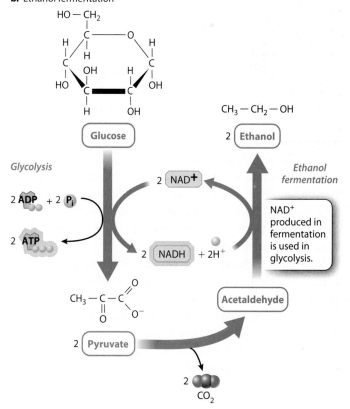

The breakdown of a molecule of glucose by fermentation yields only two molecules of ATP. The energetic gain is relatively small compared to the total yield of aerobic respiration because the end products, lactic acid and ethanol, still contain a large amount of chemical energy in their bonds and are not fully oxidized. The modest yield explains why organisms that produce ATP by fermentation must consume a large quantity of fuel molecules to power the cell.

→ **Quick Check 6** Breadmaking involves ethanol fermentation and typically uses yeast, sugar, flour, and water. Why are yeast and sugar used?

❓ CASE 1 The First Cell: Life's Origins
How did early cells meet their energy requirements?
The four stages of cellular respiration lead to the full oxidation of glucose, resulting in the release of a large amount of energy stored in its chemical bonds. The first stage, glycolysis, results in only the partial oxidation of glucose, so just some of the energy held in its chemical bonds is released. Nearly all organisms are capable of partially breaking down glucose, suggesting that glycolysis evolved very early in the history of life.

Life first evolved about 4 billion years ago in the absence of atmospheric oxygen. The earliest organisms probably used one of the fermentation pathways to generate the ATP necessary to power cellular processes because fermentation does not require atmospheric oxygen. This process occurs in the cytoplasm and does not require proteins embedded in specialized membranes.

As we have seen, cellular respiration involves an electron transport chain, composed of proteins embedded in a membrane and capable of transferring high-energy electrons from one protein to the next and pumping protons. The resulting proton gradient powers the synthesis of ATP. Like fermentation, cellular respiration can occur in the absence of oxygen, but in that case molecules other than oxygen, such as sulfate and nitrate, are the final electron acceptor (Chapter 26). This form of respiration is known as anaerobic respiration and occurs in some present-day bacteria. The electron transport chain in these bacteria is located in the plasma membrane, not in an internal membrane.

How might such a system have evolved? An intriguing possibility is that early prokaryotes evolved pumps to drive protons out of the cell in response to an increasingly acidic environment (**Fig. 7.14**). Some pumps might have used the energy of ATP to pump protons, while others used electron transport proteins to pump protons (Fig. 7.14a). At some point, proton pumps powered by electron transport might have become efficient enough that the protons could pass back

through the ATP-driven pumps, running them in reverse to synthesize ATP (Fig. 7.14b).

Organisms capable of producing oxygen, the cyanobacteria, did not evolve until about 2.5 billion years ago, maybe earlier. The evolution of this new form of life introduced oxygen into Earth's atmosphere. This dramatic change led to the evolution of new life-forms with new possibilities for extracting energy from fuel molecules such as glucose. Aerobic respiration, in which oxygen serves as the final electron acceptor in the electron transport chain, generates much more energy than does anaerobic respiration or fermentation.

FIG. 7.14   **The possible evolution of the electron transport chain and oxidative phosphorylation.**

a.

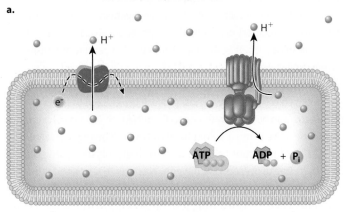

Early cells evolved mechanisms to pump protons out of the cell, powered by ATP and electron transport.

b.

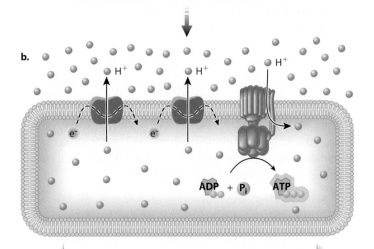

Eventually, electron-transport-powered pumps became efficient enough to run the ATP-driven pump in reverse.

The evolution of cellular respiration illustrates that evolution often works in a stepwise fashion, building on what is already present. In this case, aerobic respiration picked up where anaerobic respiration left off, making it possible to harness more energy from organic molecules to power the work of the cell.

7.7 METABOLIC INTEGRATION

In this chapter, we have focused on the breakdown of glucose. What happens if there is more glucose than is needed by the cell? As well as glucose, you probably consume diverse carbohydrates, lipids, and proteins. How are these broken down? And how are these various metabolic pathways coordinated so that the intracellular level of ATP is maintained in a narrow range? In this final section, we consider how the cell responds to these challenges.

Excess glucose is stored as glycogen in animals and starch in plants.

Glucose is a readily available form of energy in organisms, but it is not always broken down immediately. Excess glucose can be stored in cells and then mobilized—that is, broken down—when necessary. Glucose can be stored in two major forms: as **glycogen** in animals and **starch** in plants (**Fig. 7.15**). Both these molecules are large branched polymers of glucose.

Carbohydrates that are consumed by animals are broken down into simple sugars and circulate in the blood. The level of glucose in the blood is tightly regulated. When the blood glucose level is high, as it is after a meal, glucose molecules that are not consumed by glycolysis are linked together to form glycogen in liver and muscle. Glycogen stored in muscle is used to provide ATP for muscle contraction. By contrast, the liver does not store glycogen primarily for its own use, but is a central glycogen storehouse for the whole body, able to release glucose into the bloodstream when it is needed elsewhere. Glycogen provides a source of glucose 6-phosphate to feed glycolysis when the level of blood glucose is low. Glucose molecules located at the end of glycogen chains can be cleaved one by one, and they are released in the form of

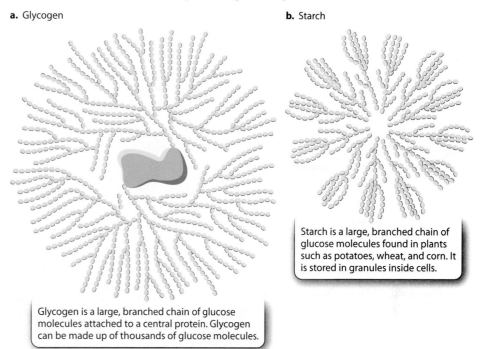

FIG. 7.15 **Storage forms of glucose.** (a) Glycogen is a storage form of glucose in animal cells and (b) starch is a storage form of glucose in plant cells.

a. Glycogen

b. Starch

Starch is a large, branched chain of glucose molecules found in plants such as potatoes, wheat, and corn. It is stored in granules inside cells.

Glycogen is a large, branched chain of glucose molecules attached to a central protein. Glycogen can be made up of thousands of glucose molecules.

glucose 1-phosphate. Glucose 1-phosphate is then converted into glucose 6-phosphate, an intermediate in glycolysis (see Fig. 7.4). One glucose molecule cleaved off a glycogen chain produces three and not two molecules of ATP by glycolysis because the ATP-consuming step 1 of glycolysis is bypassed.

Sugars other than glucose contribute to glycolysis.

The carbohydrates in your diet are digested to produce a variety of sugars (**Fig. 7.16**). Some of these are disaccharides (maltose, lactose, and sucrose) with two sugar units; others are monosaccharides (fructose, mannose, and galactose) with a single sugar unit. The disaccharides are hydrolyzed into monosaccharides, which are transported into cells.

The hydrolysis of some disaccharides produces glucose molecules that directly enter glycolysis. What happens to other monosaccharides? They, too, enter glycolysis, although not as glucose. Instead, they are converted into intermediates of glycolysis that come later in the pathway. For example, fructose is produced by the hydrolysis of sucrose (table sugar) and receives a phosphate group to form either fructose 6-phosphate or fructose 1-phosphate. In the liver, fructose 1-phosphate is cleaved and converted into glyceraldehyde 3-phosphate, which enters glycolysis at reaction 6 (see Fig. 7.4).

FIG. 7.16   Common sugars in your diet.

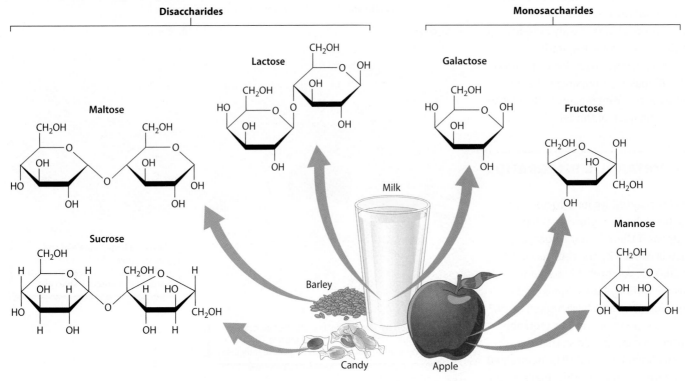

Fatty acids and proteins are useful sources of energy.

In addition to carbohydrates, lipids are also a good source of energy. We know this from common experience. Butter, oils, ice cream, and the like all contain lipids and are high in calories, which are units of energy. We can also infer that lipids are a good source of energy from their chemical structure. Recall from Chapter 2 that a type of fat called triacylglycerol is composed of three fatty acid molecules bound to a glycerol backbone. These fatty acid molecules are rich in carbon–carbon and carbon–hydrogen bonds, which, as we saw earlier, carry chemical energy.

Following a meal, the small intestine very quickly absorbs triacylglycerols, which are then transported by the bloodstream and either consumed or stored in fat (adipose) tissue. Triacylglycerols are broken down inside cells to glycerol and fatty acids. Then, the fatty acids themselves are shortened by a series of reactions that sequentially remove two carbon units from their ends (**Fig. 7.17**). This process is called **β- (beta-) oxidation.** It does not produce ATP, but releases a large number of NADH and FADH$_2$ molecules that

FIG. 7.17   **β-oxidation of fatty acids.** The fatty acids from lipids are broken down to produce NADH and FADH$_2$ as well as acetyl-CoA.

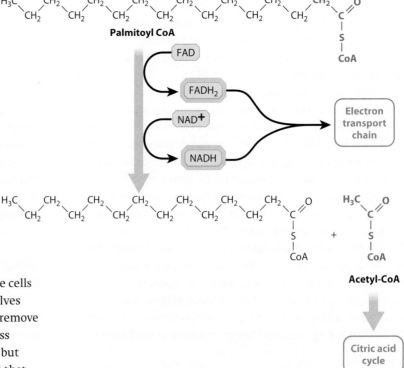

provide high-energy electrons for the synthesis of ATP by oxidative phosphorylation. In addition, the end product of the reaction is acetyl-CoA, which feeds the citric acid cycle and leads to the production of an even larger quantity of electron carriers.

The oxidation of fatty acids produces a large amount of ATP. For example, the complete oxidation of a molecule of palmitic acid, a fatty acid containing 16 carbons, yields about 106 molecules of ATP. By contrast, glycolysis yields just 2 molecules of ATP, and the complete oxidation of a glucose molecule produces about 32 molecules of ATP (Table 7.1). Fatty acids therefore are a useful and efficient source of energy, but they cannot be used by all tissues of the body. Notably, the brain and red blood cells depend primarily on glucose for energy.

Proteins, like fatty acids, are a source of chemical energy that can be broken down, if necessary, to power the cell. Proteins are typically first broken down to amino acids, some of which can then enter glycolysis and others the citric acid cycle.

The intracellular level of ATP is a key regulator of cellular respiration.

ATP is the key end product of cellular respiration, holding in its bonds energy that can be used for all kinds of cellular processes. ATP is constantly being turned over in a cell, broken down to ADP and P_i to supply the cell's energy needs, and re-synthesized by fermentation and cellular respiration. The level of ATP inside a cell can therefore be an indicator of how much energy a cell has available. When ATP levels are high, the cell has a high amount of free energy and is poised to carry out cellular processes. In this case, pathways that generate ATP are slowed, or down-regulated. By contrast, when ATP levels are low, the cell activates, or up-regulates, pathways that lead to ATP synthesis. Other intermediates of cellular respiration, such as NADH, have a similar effect in that high NAD^+ levels stimulate cellular respiration, whereas high NADH levels inhibit it (**Fig. 7.18**).

How is this kind of coordinated response of the cell possible? The cell uses several mechanisms, one of which is the regulation of enzymes that control key steps of the pathway. One of these key reactions is reaction 3 of glycolysis—the conversion of fructose 6-phosphate to fructose 1,6-bisphosphate (see Fig. 7.4). This is a key step in glycolysis because it is highly endergonic and irreversible. As a result, it is considered a "committed" step and is subject to tight control. This reaction is catalyzed by the enzyme phosphofructokinase-1 (PFK-1), which can be thought of as a metabolic valve that regulates the rate of glycolysis.

FIG. 7.18   Regulation of cellular respiration. Cellular respiration is inhibited by its products, including ATP and NADH, and activated by its substrates, including ADP and NAD^+.

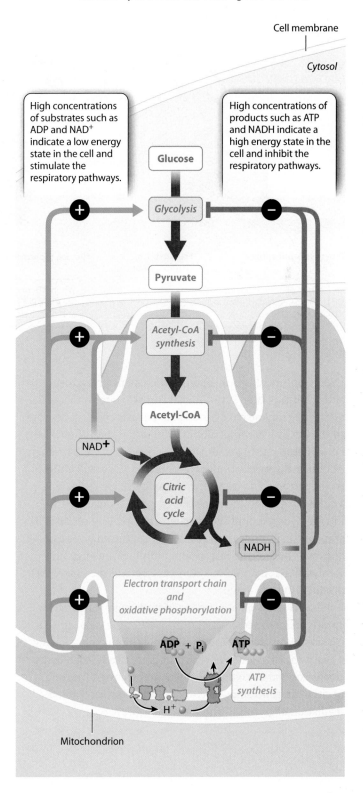

FIG. 7.19. **Regulation of PFK-1.** The regulation of the glycolytic enzyme phosphofructokinase-1 (PFK-1) is an example of integrated metabolic control.

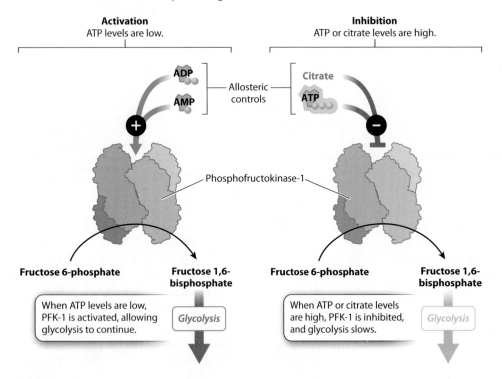

Exercise requires several types of fuel molecules and the coordination of metabolic pathways.

In the last two chapters, we considered what energy is and how it is harnessed by cells. Let's apply the concepts we discussed to a familiar example: exercise. Exercise such as running, walking, and swimming is a form of kinetic energy, powered by ATP in muscle cells. Where does this ATP come from?

Muscle cells, like all cells, do not contain a lot of ATP, and stored ATP is depleted by exercise in a matter of seconds. As a result, muscle cells rely on fuel molecules to generate ATP. For a short sprint or a burst of activity, muscle can convert stored glycogen to glucose, and then break down glucose anaerobically to pyruvate and lactic acid by lactic acid fermentation. This pathway is rapid, but it does not generate a lot of ATP. In addition, it is limited by the production of lactic acid, which lowers the pH of the blood.

PFK-1 is an allosteric enzyme with many activators and inhibitors (**Fig. 7.19**). Recall from Chapter 6 that an allosteric enzyme changes its shape and activity in response to the binding of molecules at a site other than the active site. ADP and AMP are allosteric activators of PFK-1. When ADP and AMP are abundant, one or the other will bind to the enzyme and cause the enzyme's shape to change. The shape change activates the enzyme, increasing the rate of glycolysis and the synthesis of ATP. When ATP is in abundance, it binds to the same site on the enzyme as ADP and AMP, but in this case binding inhibits the enzyme's catalytic activity. As a result, glycolysis and the rate of ATP production slow down.

PFK-1 is also regulated by one of its downstream products, citrate, an intermediate in the citric acid cycle (see Fig. 7.7). Citrate acts as an allosteric inhibitor of the enzyme, slowing its activity. High levels of citrate indicate that it is not being consumed and glucose breakdown can be slowed. The role of citrate in controlling glycolysis illustrates the coordinated regulation of glycolysis and the citric acid cycle.

For longer, more sustained exercise, other metabolic pathways come into play. Muscle cells contain many mitochondria, which produce ATP by aerobic respiration. The energy yield of aerobic respiration is much greater than that of fermentation, but the process is slower. This slower production of ATP by aerobic respiration in part explains why runners cannot maintain the pace of a sprint for longer runs.

For even longer exercise, liver glycogen supplements muscle glycogen: The liver releases glucose into the blood that is taken up by muscle cells and oxidized to produce ATP. In addition, fatty acids are released from adipose tissue and taken up by muscle cells, where they are broken down by β-oxidation. β-oxidation yields even more ATP than does the complete oxidation of glucose, but the process is again slower. Storage forms of energy molecules, such as fatty acids and glycogen, contain large reservoirs of energy, but are slower to mobilize. Thus, exercise takes coordination between different cells, tissues, and metabolic pathways to ensure adequate ATP to meet the needs of working muscle.

Core Concepts Summary

7.1 CELLULAR RESPIRATION IS A SERIES OF CATABOLIC REACTIONS THAT CONVERT THE ENERGY STORED IN FUEL MOLECULES INTO ATP.

Cellular respiration is a four-stage process that includes (1) glycolysis; (2) pyruvate oxidation and acetyl-CoA synthesis; (3) the citric acid cycle; and (4) oxidative phosphorylation. page 7-2

The complete oxidation of glucose in the presence of oxygen to make carbon dioxide and water is an oxidation–reduction reaction. page 7-3

In oxidation–reduction reactions, electrons are transferred from one molecule to another. Oxidation is the loss of electrons, and reduction is the gain of electrons. page 7-3

The chemical bonds of sugar molecules like glucose have high potential energy because the electrons that are shared by neighboring atoms are on average far from the nucleus. page 7-4

The chemical energy in glucose and other fuel molecules is released slowly in a series of chemical reactions that produce energy-storing molecules, including ATP and the electron carriers NADH and $FADH_2$. page 7-4

Electron carriers transfer electrons to an electron transport chain, which harnesses the energy of these electrons to generate ATP. page 7-4

ATP is generated by substrate-level phosphorylation and oxidative phosphorylation in cellular respiration. page 7-4

7.2 GLYCOLYSIS IS THE PARTIAL OXIDATION OF GLUCOSE AND RESULTS IN THE PRODUCTION OF PYRUVATE, A SMALL AMOUNT OF ATP, AND HIGH-ENERGY ELECTRON CARRIERS.

Glycolysis takes place in the cytoplasm. page 7-2

Glycolysis is a series of 10 reactions in which glucose is converted to pyruvate. page 7-7

Glycolysis involves preparatory, cleavage, and payoff phases. page 7-7

For each molecule of glucose consumed during glycolysis, a net gain of two molecules of ATP and two molecules of NADH is produced. page 7-7

The synthesis of ATP in glycolysis results from the direct transfer of a phosphate group to ADP, a process called substrate-level phosphorylation. page 7-7

7.3 PYRUVATE IS OXIDIZED TO ACETYL-CoA, CONNECTING GLYCOLYSIS TO THE CITRIC ACID CYCLE.

The conversion of pyruvate to acetyl-CoA results in the production of one molecule of NADH and one molecule of carbon dioxide. page 7-7

Acetyl-CoA synthesis occurs in the mitochondrial matrix. page 7-7

Acetyl-CoA is the first substrate in the citric acid cycle. page 7-8

7.4 THE CITRIC ACID CYCLE RESULTS IN THE COMPLETE OXIDATION OF FUEL MOLECULES AND THE GENERATION OF ATP AND HIGH-ENERGY ELECTRON CARRIERS.

The citric acid cycle takes place in the mitochondrial matrix. page 7-8

The acetyl group of acetyl-CoA combines with oxaloacetate, followed by a series of decarboxylation and redox reactions that regenerate oxaloacetate. page 7-9

A complete turn of the citric acid cycle results in the production of one molecule of GTP (which is converted to ATP), three molecules of NADH, and one molecule of $FADH_2$. page 7-9

Citric acid cycle intermediates are starting points for the synthesis of many different organic molecules. page 7-10

7.5 THE ELECTRON TRANSPORT CHAIN TRANSFERS ELECTRONS FROM ELECTRON CARRIERS TO OXYGEN, USING THE ENERGY TO PUMP PROTONS AND SYNTHESIZE ATP BY OXIDATIVE PHOSPHORYLATION.

NADH and $FADH_2$ donate electrons to the electron transport chain. page 7-10

In the electron transport chain, electrons move from one redox carrier to the next. page 7-10

The electron transport chain is made up of four complexes. Complexes I and II accept electrons from NADH and $FADH_2$ respectively. The electrons are transferred from these two complexes to coenzyme Q. page 7-10

Reduced coenzyme Q transfers electrons to complex III and cytochrome c transfers electrons to complex IV. Complex IV contains oxygen, the final electron acceptor. page 7-12

The transfer of electrons through the electron transport chain is coupled with the movement of protons across the inner mitochondrial membrane into the intermembrane space. page 7-12

The buildup of protons in the intermembrane space results in a proton electrochemical gradient, which stores potential energy. page 7-12

The movement of protons back into the mitochondrial matrix through the F_0 subunit of ATP synthase is coupled with the formation of ATP, a reaction catalyzed by the F_1 subunit of ATP synthase. page 7-13

7.6 GLUCOSE CAN BE BROKEN DOWN IN THE ABSENCE OF OXYGEN BY FERMENTATION, PRODUCING A MODEST AMOUNT OF ENERGY IN THE FORM OF ATP.

Pyruvate, the end product of glycolysis, is processed differently in the presence and the absence of oxygen. page 7-14

In the absence of oxygen, pyruvate enters one of several fermentation pathways. page 7-15

In lactic acid fermentation, pyruvate is reduced to lactic acid. page 7-15

In ethanol fermentation, pyruvate is converted to acetaldehyde, which is reduced to ethanol. page 7-15

During fermentation, NADH is oxidized to NAD^+, allowing glycolysis to proceed. page 7-15

Glycolysis and fermentation are ancient biochemical pathways and were likely used in the common ancestor of all organisms living today. page 7-16

7.7 METABOLIC PATHWAYS ARE INTEGRATED, ALLOWING CONTROL OF THE ENERGY LEVEL OF CELLS.

Excess glucose is polymerized and stored in molecules called glycogen (in animals) and starch (in plants). page 7-17

Other monosaccharides derived from the digestion of dietary carbohydrates are converted into intermediates of glycolysis. page 7-17

Fatty acids contained in triacylglycerols are an important form of energy storage in cells. The breakdown of fatty acids is called β-oxidation. page 7-18

Phosphofructokinase-1 controls a key step in glycolysis. It has many allosteric activators, including ADP and AMP, and allosteric inhibitors, including ATP and citrate. page 7-20

The ATP in muscle cells used to power exercise is generated by lactic acid fermentation, aerobic respiration, and β-oxidation. page 7-20

Self-Assessment

1. Name and describe the four major stages of cellular respiration.

2. Explain what an oxidation–reduction reaction is and why the breakdown of glucose in the presence of oxygen to produce carbon dioxide and water is an example of an oxidation–reduction reaction.

3. Describe two ways in which ATP is generated in cellular respiration.

4. Write the overall chemical equation for glycolysis, noting the starting and ending products and highlighting the energy-storing molecules that are produced.

5. Describe two different metabolic pathways that pyruvate can enter.

6. Name the products of the citric acid cycle.

7. Describe how the movement of electrons along the electron transport chain leads to the generation of a proton gradient.

8. Describe how a proton gradient generates ATP.

9. Explain how muscle tissue generates ATP during short-term and long-term exercise.

Do you understand the chapter's Core Concepts? Log into BIO*PORTAL* to check your answers to the Self-Assessment questions, then practice what you've learned and reinforce this chapter's concepts by working through the problems and multimedia tutorials provided there.

🛜 http://courses.bfwpub.com/yourbioportal/index.php

CHAPTER 8

PHOTOSYNTHESIS

Using Sunlight to Build Carbohydrates

Core Concepts

Walk through a forest and you will be struck, literally if you aren't careful, by the substantial nature of trees. Where does the material to construct these massive organisms come from? Because trees grow upward from a firm base in the ground, a reasonable first guess is the soil. In the first recorded experiment on this topic, the Flemish chemist and physiologist Jan Baptist van Helmont (1580–1644) found that the initial 300 pounds of soil into which he had planted a small willow tree decreased by only 2 ounces over a 5-year period. During this same period, the tree gained more than 150 pounds. Van Helmont concluded that water must be responsible for the tree's growth. He was, in fact, half right: A tree is roughly half liquid water. But what he missed entirely is that the other half of his tree had been created out of thin air.

The process that allowed Van Helmont's tree to increase in mass using substances pulled from the air is called **photosynthesis.** Photosynthesis is a biochemical process for building carbohydrates from sunlight and carbon dioxide (CO_2) taken from the air. These carbohydrates are used as both structural components of the plant and as a source of energy used to produce ATP.

8.1 THE NATURAL HISTORY OF PHOTOSYNTHESIS

Carbohydrates have more energy stored in their chemical bonds than is contained in the bonds of the CO_2 molecules from which they are synthesized during photosynthesis. Therefore, to build carbohydrates using CO_2 requires an input of energy. In photosynthesis, this energy comes from sunlight.

Photosynthesis is a redox reaction.

Energy is added to molecules during carbohydrate synthesis through the transfer of high-energy electrons. It is this addition of energy and electrons that allows the incoming CO_2 molecules to form the higher-energy bonds found in a carbohydrate molecule. In Chapter 7, we saw that **reduction** reactions are reactions in which a molecule acquires electrons and gains energy, whereas **oxidation** reactions are reactions in which a molecule loses electrons and releases energy. During photosynthesis, CO_2 molecules are reduced to form higher-energy carbohydrate molecules (**Fig. 8.1**).

Where do the electrons used to reduce CO_2 come from? These electrons can only come from the oxidation of other molecules, illustrating once again that reduction–oxidation (or redox) reactions always come in pairs. In photosynthesis carried out by plants and many algae, the ultimate **electron donor** is water. However, as we will see in Chapter 26, photosynthetic bacteria can use a variety of other electron donors. The oxidation of water results in the production of electrons, protons, and O_2. Thus, oxygen is formed in photosynthesis as a by-product of water's role as a source of electrons. We can demonstrate that water is the source of the oxygen released during photosynthesis using isotopes, molecules that can be distinguished on the basis of their molecular mass (**Fig. 8.2**).

Overall, then, the equation for photosynthesis can be described as follows:

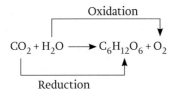

$$CO_2 + H_2O \longrightarrow C_6H_{12}O_6 + O_2$$

(Oxidation, over the arrow; Reduction, under the arrow)

The oxidation of water is linked with the reduction of CO_2 through a series of redox reactions in which electrons are passed from one compound to another. This series of reactions constitutes the **photosynthetic electron transport chain.** The process begins with the absorption of light by protein–pigment complexes known as **photosystems.** Photosystems use absorbed light energy to drive redox reactions and thereby set the photosynthetic electron transport chain in motion. In turn, the movement of electrons through this transport chain is used to drive the synthesis of ATP and NADPH. And finally, ATP and NADPH are the

---

FIG. 8.1 **Overview of photosynthesis.** In photosynthesis, energy from sunlight is used to reduce CO_2 to form carbohydrates.

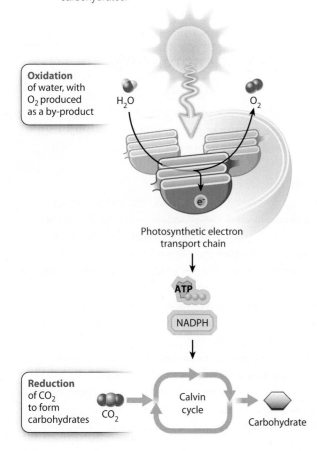

HOW DO WE KNOW?

FIG. 8.2

Does the oxygen released by photosynthesis come from H_2O or CO_2?

BACKGROUND The reactants in photosynthesis are water and carbon dioxide. Therefore, it is unclear where the oxygen that is produced in the reaction comes from.

METHOD Most of the oxygen in the atmosphere is ^{16}O, with 8 protons and 8 neutrons. A small amount (0.2%) is ^{18}O, with 8 protons and 10 neutrons. ^{16}O and ^{18}O are stable isotopes. The relative abundance of molecules containing ^{16}O versus ^{18}O can be measured using a mass spectrometer. H_2O and CO_2 containing a high percentage of ^{18}O can be used to determine whether the oxygen produced in photosynthesis comes from water or carbon dioxide.

EXPERIMENT

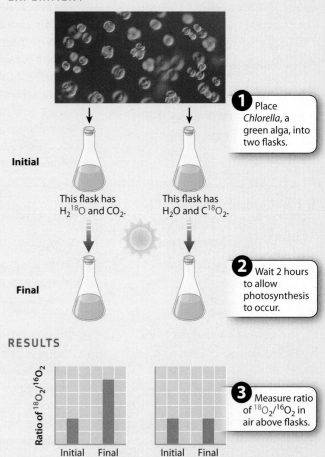

① Place *Chlorella*, a green alga, into two flasks.

Initial

This flask has $H_2^{18}O$ and CO_2.

This flask has H_2O and $C^{18}O_2$.

② Wait 2 hours to allow photosynthesis to occur.

Final

RESULTS

(Graphs: Ratio of $^{18}O_2/^{16}O_2$, with Initial and Final bars for each flask)

③ Measure ratio of $^{18}O_2/^{16}O_2$ in air above flasks.

CONCLUSION The ratio of $^{18}O_2/^{16}O_2$ only increases when water contains ^{18}O, but not when carbon dioxide contains ^{18}O. This finding indicates that the oxygen produced in photosynthesis comes from water, not carbon dioxide.

FOLLOW-UP WORK Carbon also has several isotopes, and their measurement has been used to determine the source of increased CO_2 in the atmosphere today (Chapter 25).

SOURCE Adapted from Ruben, S., M. Randall, M. Kamen, and J. L. Hyde. 1941. "Heavy Oxygen (O^{18}) as a Tracer in the Study of Photosynthesis." *Journal of the American Chemical Society.* 63:877–879.

energy sources needed to synthesize carbohydrates using CO_2 in a process called the **Calvin cycle** (see Fig. 8.1).

Each year, photosynthesis removes more than 100 billion metric tons of carbon from the atmosphere, while incorporating more than 100 terawatts (a terawatt is 10^{12} watts) of solar energy into chemical bonds. To put these quantities in perspective, the energy captured by photosynthesis in a year is 10 times the energy of all the oil and coal used worldwide in 2006. Fossil fuels are themselves the legacy of ancient photosynthesis: Oil has its origin in the bodies of marine phytoplankton and the organisms that graze on them, while coal represents the geologic remains of terrestrial (land) plants. Thus, one motivation to understand photosynthesis is the sheer magnitude and importance of this process for life on Earth. Before exploring the details of how photosynthesis actually occurs, let's look at what types of organisms are photosynthetic, where they live, how they have evolved to be photosynthetic, and what structural components are needed to allow cells to capture energy in this remarkable way.

→ **Quick Check 1** If you want to produce carbohydrates containing the heavy oxygen (^{18}O) isotope, should you water your plants with $H_2{}^{18}O$ or inject $C^{18}O_2$ into the air?

Photosynthesis is widely distributed.

Photosynthesis occurs among prokaryotic as well as eukaryotic organisms, on land as well as in the sea. Approximately 50% of global photosynthesis is carried out by terrestrial organisms, with the other half taking place in the ocean. The majority of photosynthetic organisms in marine environments are unicellular. About half of oceanic photosynthesis is carried out by phytoplankton (single-celled marine eukaryotes), while the other half is carried out by cyanobacteria (photosynthetic bacteria). On land, photosynthesis is dominated by multicellular plants.

Photosynthesis takes place almost everywhere sunlight is available to serve as a source of energy. In the ocean, photosynthesis occurs in the surface layer about 100 m deep, called the **photic zone,** through which enough sunlight penetrates to enable photosynthesis. On land, photosynthesis occurs most readily in environments that are both moist and warm. However, photosynthetic organisms have evolved adaptations that allow them to tolerate a wide range of environmental conditions, like those illustrated in **Fig. 8.3.** In very dry regions, a combination of photosynthetic bacteria and unicellular algae forms an easily disturbed layer on the

---

FIG. 8.3 **Photosynthesis in extreme environments.** (a) Desert crust in Utah formed by photosynthetic bacteria and algae. (b) A hot spring in Yellowstone National Park. The yellow color is due to photosynthetic bacteria. (c) The surface of a permanent snow pack. The red color is due to photosynthetic algae.

surface of the soil known as desert crust. Photosynthetic bacteria are also found in the hot springs of Yellowstone National Park at temperatures up to 75 °C. At the other extreme, unicellular eukaryotic algae can grow on the surfaces of glaciers, causing the surface of the snow to appear red. In section 8.4, we discuss why photosynthetic organisms growing in such extreme environments often appear red or yellow rather than green.

The evolutionary history of photosynthesis includes both horizontal gene transfer and endosymbiosis.

The most ancient forms of photosynthesis have simple photosynthetic electron transport chains with only a single photosystem. However, a single photosystem cannot capture enough energy to pull electrons from (oxidize) water and then use them to reduce CO_2. Thus, photosynthetic organisms with a single photosystem must use more easily oxidized compounds, such as H_2S, as electron donors. These organisms are limited to environments where the electron-donor molecules are abundant. Because these organisms do not use water as an electron donor, they do not produce O_2 during photosynthesis (Chapter 26).

A major event in the history of life was the evolution of photosynthetic electron transport chains that could bridge the energy difference between the oxidation of water and the reduction of CO_2. Water is abundant, but it is extremely difficult to pull electrons from water. The first organisms to accomplish this feat were the cyanobacteria. These photosynthetic bacteria incorporated two different photosystems into a single photosynthetic electron transport chain. Having two photosystems allows the energy level of the electrons moving through the photosynthetic electron chain to be increased in two steps, much as a series of locks serves to raise the elevation of boats traveling through a canal. The addition of light energy in the first step allows electrons to be pulled from a water molecule, while the addition of light energy in the second step raises the energy level of these electrons so that they can be used to reduce CO_2. Stripping electrons from water results in the release of oxygen. Indeed, all the oxygen in Earth's atmosphere results from photosynthesis by organisms containing two photosystems.

Each of the two photosystems present in cyanobacteria has a high degree of similarity to the single photosystem found in other lineages of photosynthetic bacteria. The structural similarity is so great as to make it highly unlikely that the two photosystems in cyanobacteria evolved independently. An alternative hypothesis is that the genetic material associated with one photosystem was transferred to a bacterium with

the other photosystem, resulting in a single bacterium with the genetic material to produce both types of photosystems (**Fig. 8.4**). The transfer of genetic material between organisms that are not parent and offspring is called **horizontal gene transfer,** and it is common among prokaryotes, where it provides an important means of producing genetic diversity. The mechanisms of horizontal gene transfer are discussed more fully in Chapter 26.

Photosynthesis is hypothesized to have gained a foothold among eukaryotic organisms when a free-living cyanobacterium was engulfed by a eukaryotic cell (Fig. 8.4). Over time, the engulfed cyanobacterium lost its ability to survive outside of its host cell and evolved into the chloroplast, the organelle in eukaryotic cells that carries out photosynthesis. The process in which one cell takes up residence inside of another cell is called endosymbiosis. Therefore, the idea that chloroplasts and mitochondria (Chapter 7) arose in this way is called the endosymbiotic hypothesis. It is discussed in Chapter 27.

FIG. 8.4   **The evolutionary history of photosynthesis.** Bacteria with a single photosystem obtained two photosystems by horizontal gene transfer and later, by endosymbiosis, became the chloroplasts of eukaryotic cells.

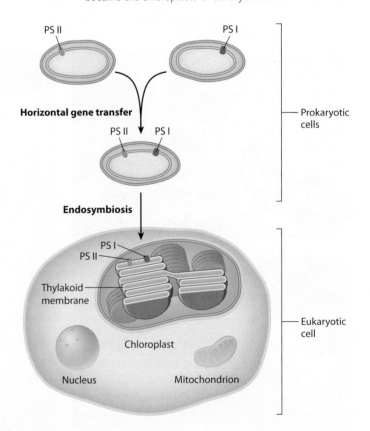

The photosynthetic electron transport chain takes place on specialized membranes.

The ability to absorb sunlight and convert it into chemical forms allows photosynthetic organisms to produce their own food. However, high-energy electrons moving through the photosynthetic electron transport chain have the potential to damage the cell. To prevent damage, the movement of electrons through the photosynthetic electron transport chain is constrained: The electrons follow a defined network of pathways through large protein complexes embedded in specialized "photosynthetic" membranes. These protein complexes provide a scaffold along which the pigments and other elements of the photosynthetic electron transport chain are arrayed. In fact, the movement of electrons through the photosynthetic electron transport chain is not controlled by the specificity of individual enzymes. Instead, it depends upon the spatial arrangement of the sites where the redox reactions take place within and between these major protein complexes.

Chloroplasts are enclosed by a double membrane. Filling much of the center of the chloroplast is a third, highly folded, membrane known as the **thylakoid membrane** (**Fig. 8.5**). The photosynthetic electron transport chain is located on the thylakoid membrane.

The name "thylakoid" is derived from *thylakois,* the Greek word for "sac." Thylakoid membranes form structures that resemble flattened sacs, which are grouped into structures called **grana** (singular, granum) that look like stacks of interlinked pancakes. Grana are connected to one another by membrane bridges so that the thylakoid forms a single continuous membrane. Thus, while it may look as though the individual grana are independent from one another, in fact the thylakoid membrane encloses a common fluid-filled interior compartment called the **lumen.** The region surrounding the thylakoid membrane is called the **stroma.** Carbohydrate synthesis takes place in the stroma, whereas sunlight is captured and transformed via the photosynthetic electron transport chain on the thylakoid membrane.

The outer membrane of the chloroplast double membrane is thought to have originated from the plasma membrane of the ancestral eukaryotic cell, which surrounded the ancestral cyanobacterium as it was being engulfed. The inner chloroplast membrane is thought to correspond to the plasma membrane of the ancestral free-living cyanobacterium. The thylakoid membrane then corresponds to the internal photosynthetic membrane found in cyanobacteria. Finally, the stroma corresponds to the cytoplasm of the ancestral cyanobacterium.

A photosynthetic cell can have more than 100 chloroplasts. Photosynthetic cells also contain mitochondria. Although

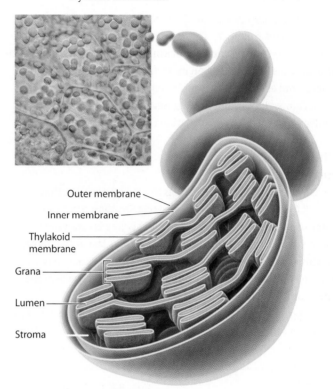

FIG. 8.5 **Chloroplast structure.** Chloroplasts contain highly folded thylakoid membranes.

Outer membrane
Inner membrane
Thylakoid membrane
Grana
Lumen
Stroma

photosynthetic organisms are correctly described as autotrophs because they can form carbohydrates from CO_2, they also require mitochondrial respiration, in which carbohydrates are broken down to generate ATP to meet the cell's energy requirements (Chapter 7). Cellular respiration is therefore one of several features that heterotrophic organisms like ourselves share with photosynthetic organisms.

We now consider the underlying biochemistry of photosynthesis. Though in this chapter we focus on photosynthesis as carried out by eukaryotic cells, there is a remarkable diversity in the way photosynthesis is carried out in bacteria. We discuss this diversity in Chapter 26. Because carbohydrates are the major product of photosynthesis, we first examine the Calvin cycle, the biochemical pathway used in photosynthesis to synthesize carbohydrates from CO_2. Once we understand what energy forms are needed to drive this autotrophic pathway, we turn our attention to how energy is captured from sunlight. Finally, we examine some of the challenges of coordinating these two metabolic stages and consider ways in which photosynthetic organisms cope with the inherent biochemical challenges of photosynthesis.

8.2 THE CALVIN CYCLE

The Calvin cycle consists of 15 chemical reactions that synthesize carbohydrates from CO_2. These reactions can be grouped into three main steps: (1) **carboxylation,** in which CO_2 absorbed from the air is added to a 5-carbon molecule; (2) **reduction,** in which energy and electrons are transferred to the molecules formed from carboxylation; and (3) **regeneration** of the 5-carbon molecule needed for carboxylation (**Fig. 8.6**).

The incorporation of CO_2 is catalyzed by the enzyme rubisco.

The first step of the Calvin cycle is a carboxylation reaction (Fig. 8.6). Specifically, CO_2 is added to a 5-carbon sugar called **ribulose-1,5-bisphosphate** (**RuBP**). This step is catalyzed by the enzyme **ribulose bisphosphate carboxylase oxygenase,** or **rubisco** for short. Although many enzymes are active in the Calvin cycle, rubisco has a disproportionate influence over the functioning of the entire pathway.

Compared to other enzymes, rubisco is surprisingly slow. As a result, photosynthetic cells must produce large amounts of this single enzyme. In fact, rubisco is the most abundant protein on Earth and constitutes as much as half of the total protein found in a leaf. As the principal gatekeeper through which CO_2 becomes incorporated into carbohydrates, rubisco plays a key role in the processes that permit life on Earth.

Before rubisco can act as a carboxylase, RuBP and CO_2 must diffuse into its active site. Once the active site is occupied, carboxylation proceeds spontaneously. The product is a 6-carbon compound that immediately breaks into two molecules of **3-phosphoglycerate** (**3-PGA**). These 3-carbon molecules are the first stable products of the Calvin cycle. However, if O_2 instead of CO_2 diffuses into the active site, the reaction can still proceed, although O_2 is added to RuBP in place of CO_2. An enzyme like rubisco that adds O_2 to a substrate molecule is called an oxygenase, explaining part of this enzyme's long name. The addition of O_2 by rubisco creates a major challenge for photosynthesis, a topic we discuss in section 8.4.

NADPH is the reducing agent of the Calvin cycle.

Rubisco is responsible for the addition of the carbon atoms needed for the formation of carbohydrates, but by itself rubisco does not increase the amount of energy stored within the

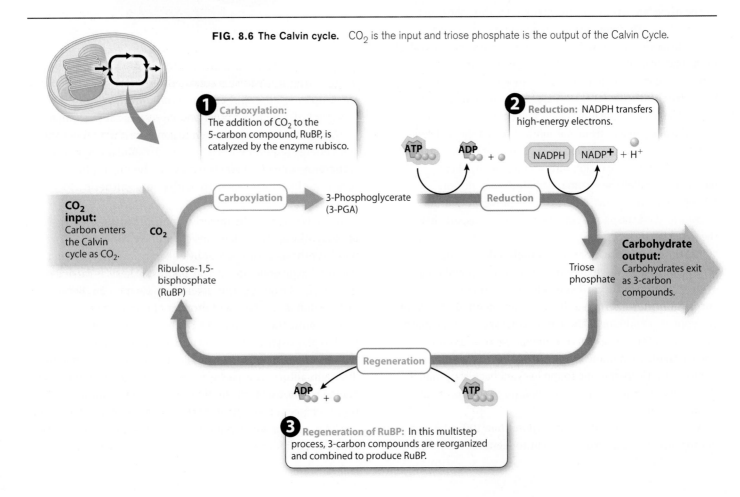

FIG. 8.6 The Calvin cycle. CO_2 is the input and triose phosphate is the output of the Calvin Cycle.

1 Carboxylation: The addition of CO_2 to the 5-carbon compound, RuBP, is catalyzed by the enzyme rubisco.

2 Reduction: NADPH transfers high-energy electrons.

ATP   ADP + ●

NADPH   NADP**+** + H$^+$

Carboxylation

3-Phosphoglycerate (3-PGA)

Reduction

CO_2 **input:** Carbon enters the Calvin cycle as CO_2.

CO_2

Ribulose-1,5-bisphosphate (RuBP)

Triose phosphate

Carbohydrate output: Carbohydrates exit as 3-carbon compounds.

ADP + ●   ATP

Regeneration

3 Regeneration of RuBP: In this multistep process, 3-carbon compounds are reorganized and combined to produce RuBP.

newly formed bonds. For this energy increase to take place, the carbon compounds formed by rubisco must be reduced. **Nicotinamide adenine dinucleotide phosphate** (**NADPH**) is the reducing agent used in the Calvin cycle. NADPH transfers the energy and electrons that allow carbohydrates to be synthesized from CO_2, the most oxidized of all carbon compounds (Fig. 8.6).

NADPH is produced by the photosynthetic electron transport chain. Like all components of the Calvin cycle, NADPH can move freely within the stroma of the chloroplast. Although NADPH is a powerful reducing agent, energy and electrons are transferred from NADPH only under the catalysis of a specific enzyme, thus providing a high degree of control over the fate of these high-energy electrons. In the Calvin cycle, the reduction of 3-PGA involves two steps: (1) ATP is used to phosphorylate 3-PGA, and (2) NADPH transfers two high-energy electrons to the phosphorylated compound. Because two molecules of 3-PGA are formed each time rubisco catalyzes the incorporation of one molecule of CO_2, two ATP and two NADPH are required for each molecule of CO_2 incorporated by rubisco. NADPH provides most of the energy incorporated in the bonds of the carbohydrate molecules produced by the Calvin cycle. Nevertheless, ATP plays an essential role in preparing 3-PGA for the addition of energy and electrons from NADPH.

These energy transfer steps result in the formation of glyceraldehyde 3-phosphate (GAP), which is reversibly interconverted to dihydroxyacetone phosphate (DHAP) by the enzyme triose phosphate isomerase. Together GAP and DHAP constitute a pool of 3-carbon carbohydrate molecules known as **triose phosphates.** Triose phosphates are the true products of the Calvin cycle because they are the molecules exported from the chloroplast. Larger sugars, such as glucose and sucrose, are assembled from triose phosphates in the cytoplasm. However, if every triose phosphate molecule produced by the Calvin cycle were exported from the chloroplast, RuBP could not be regenerated and the Calvin cycle would grind to a halt. Thus, for every six triose phosphate molecules that are produced, only one can be withdrawn from the Calvin cycle.

The regeneration of RuBP requires ATP.

Of the 15 chemical reactions that make up the Calvin cycle, 12 are directly involved in the last step, the regeneration of RuBP (Fig. 8.6). The large number of reactions involved in this step reflects the degree of reshuffling of carbon atoms needed to produce three 5-carbon RuBP molecules from five 3-carbon triose phosphate molecules. ATP is required for the regeneration of RuBP, raising the Calvin cycle's total energy requirements to two molecules of NADPH and three molecules of ATP for each molecule of CO_2 incorporated by rubisco. Thus, NADPH and ATP play distinct roles

in the formation of carbohydrates from CO_2. NADPH provides energy that is incorporated into the higher-energy bonds that characterize carbohydrate molecules, whereas ATP provides energy that is needed to regenerate RuBP.

The Calvin cycle does not utilize sunlight directly. For this reason this pathway is sometimes referred to as the light-independent or even the "dark" reactions of photosynthesis. However, this pathway cannot operate without the energy input provided by a steady supply of NADPH and ATP. Both are supplied by the photosynthetic electron transport chain, in which light is captured and transformed into chemical energy. Thus, under natural conditions, photosynthesis, including the Calvin cycle, occurs only in the light.

→ **Quick Check 2** The Calvin cycle requires both ATP and NADPH. Which of these provides the major input of energy needed to synthesize carbohydrates?

The steps of the Calvin cycle were determined using radioactive CO_2.

In a series of experiments conducted between 1948 and 1954 (**Fig. 8.7**), the American chemist Melvin Calvin and colleagues supplied radioactively labeled CO_2 ($^{14}CO_2$) to the unicellular green alga *Chlorella* and then plunged the cells into boiling alcohol, thus halting all enzymatic reactions. By examining the compounds that became radioactively labeled, Calvin and his colleagues were able to determine the identity of the carbon compounds produced in photosynthesis (Experiment 1 in Fig. 8.7).

Figuring out the chemical reactions that connected these labeled compounds, however, required both ingenuity and hard work. For example, by using a very short exposure to $^{14}CO_2$, Calvin and colleagues determined that the incorporation of CO_2 results in the production of 3-PGA (Experiment 2 in Fig. 8.7).

To determine how 3-PGA is formed, they supplied radioactive $^{14}CO_2$ to label the products, but then cut off the supply of $^{14}CO_2$ to block the carboxylation reaction. In this experiment, the amount of RuBP increased relative to the amount seen in the first experiment. They concluded that the first step was the addition of CO_2 to RuBP (Experiment 3 in Fig. 8.7).

Carbohydrates are stored in the form of starch.

The Calvin cycle is capable of producing more carbohydrates than the cell needs or, in a multicellular organism, more than the cell is able to export. If carbohydrates accumulated in the cell, they would upset the osmotic balance, causing water to enter the cell. Instead, excess carbohydrates are converted to starch, a storage form of carbohydrates discussed in Chapter 2. Because starch molecules are not soluble, they provide a means of carbohydrate storage that

FIG. 8.7

How is CO_2 used to synthesize carbohydrates?

BACKGROUND In the 1940s, radioactive $^{14}CO_2$ became available in quantities that allowed experiments. Melvin Calvin and Andrew Benson used $^{14}CO_2$ to follow the incorporation of CO_2 into

EXPERIMENTS AND RESULTS

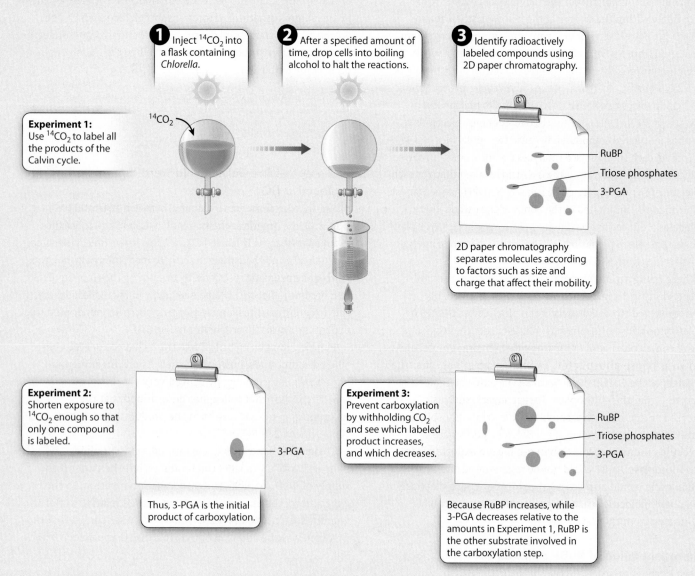

1 Inject $^{14}CO_2$ into a flask containing *Chlorella*.

2 After a specified amount of time, drop cells into boiling alcohol to halt the reactions.

3 Identify radioactively labeled compounds using 2D paper chromatography.

Experiment 1: Use $^{14}CO_2$ to label all the products of the Calvin cycle.

$^{14}CO_2$

RuBP
Triose phosphates
3-PGA

2D paper chromatography separates molecules according to factors such as size and charge that affect their mobility.

Experiment 2: Shorten exposure to $^{14}CO_2$ enough so that only one compound is labeled.

3-PGA

Thus, 3-PGA is the initial product of carboxylation.

Experiment 3: Prevent carboxylation by withholding CO_2 and see which labeled product increases, and which decreases.

RuBP
Triose phosphates
3-PGA

Because RuBP increases, while 3-PGA decreases relative to the amounts in Experiment 1, RuBP is the other substrate involved in the carboxylation step.

CONCLUSION The initial step in the Calvin cycle unites the 5-carbon RuBP with CO_2, resulting in the production of two molecules of 3-PGA.

FOLLOW-UP WORK In the 1950s, Marshall Hatch and colleagues showed that some plants, including corn and sugar cane, accumulate a 4-carbon compound as the first product in photosynthesis. In Chapter 29, we explore how C4 photosynthesis allows plants to avoid the oxygenase reaction of rubisco.

SOURCE Calvin, M., and H. Benson. 1949. "The Path of Carbon in Photosynthesis IV: The Identity and Sequence of the Intermediates in Sucrose Synthesis." *Science* 109:140–142.

FIG. 8.8 A chloroplast containing starch granules, shown here in yellow.

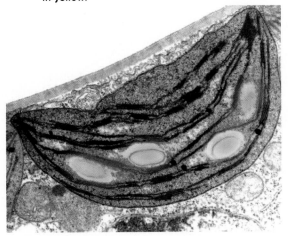

does not affect the cell's osmotic balance. The formation of starch during the day provides photosynthetic cells with a source of carbohydrates that they can use during the night (**Fig. 8.8**).

8.3 CAPTURING SUNLIGHT INTO CHEMICAL FORMS

To use sunlight to power the Calvin cycle, the cell must be able to convert light energy into both NADPH and ATP. NADPH is the reducing agent used to synthesize carbohydrates from CO_2, whereas ATP is required for the regeneration of RuBP. The production of both molecules is the task of the photosynthetic electron transport chain. NADPH is produced by the linear flow of electrons through the photosynthetic electron transport chain from water to $NADP^+$. To produce ATP, the photosynthetic electron transport chain functions as a proton pump, leading to the accumulation of protons in the thylakoid lumen. The resulting proton gradient is used to drive the synthesis of ATP, just as it drives the synthesis of ATP in mitochondrial respiration (Chapter 7).

Photosystems use light energy to set the photosynthetic electron transport chain in motion.

The function of a photosystem is to convert absorbed light energy into the movement of electrons, making it a key element in the photosynthetic electron transport chain. To understand how a photosystem works, we need to know a little about light. Light is a type of electromagnetic radiation, as are radio waves, X-rays, and other forms of radiation. Electromagnetic radiation is energy in the form of waves; the type of electromagnetic energy depends on the wavelength. **Visible light** is the portion of the electromagnetic spectrum apparent to our eyes, and it includes the range of wavelengths used in photosynthesis. The wavelengths of visible light are from 400 nm to 700 nm.

Pigments are molecules that absorb some wavelengths of visible light (**Fig. 8.9**). Pigments look colored because they reflect light enriched in the wavelengths that they do not absorb. Physically, a photosystem is a complex of proteins and pigments that is embedded in the thylakoid membrane. **Chlorophyll** is the major photosynthetic pigment; it appears green because it is poor at absorbing green wavelengths. The chlorophyll molecule consists of a large, light-absorbing "head" containing a magnesium atom at its center and a long hydrocarbon "tail" that allows the pigment to be anchored in the lipid membrane.

The thylakoid membrane also contains other pigments, most notably the orange-yellow carotenoids. Carotenoids are able to absorb light from regions of the visible spectrum that are poorly absorbed by chlorophyll. Thus, the presence of these **accessory pigments** allows photosynthetic cells to absorb a broader range of visible light than would be possible with just chlorophyll alone. As we will see in section 8.4, carotenoids play an important role in protecting the photosynthetic electron transport chain from damage.

Absorption of visible light by a chlorophyll molecule results in one of its electrons being elevated to a higher energy state

FIG. 8.9 Light wavelengths absorbed by leaves. The electromagnetic spectrum below highlights the range of visible wavelengths used in photosynthesis; the graph shows the extent to which these wavelengths are absorbed by pigments in an intact leaf.

Electromagnetic spectrum

High energy ◄————————————► Low energy

| Gamma rays | X-rays | Ultra-violet | **Visible light** | Infra-red | Micro-waves | Radio waves |

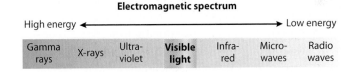

Visible light is only one part of the electromagnetic spectrum.

400 nm   700 nm

Shorter ◄————————► Longer
wavelengths   wavelengths

Leaves efficiently absorb light across most of the visible spectrum.

Absorption

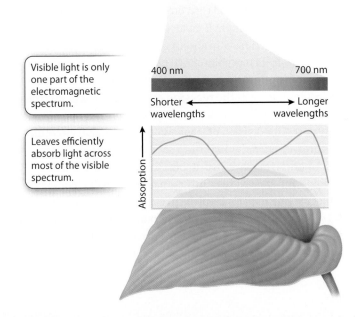

FIG. 8.10   **Absorption of light energy by chlorophyll.** Absorption of light energy by (a) an isolated chlorophyll molecule in the lab and (b) a chlorophyll molecule in a plant cell.

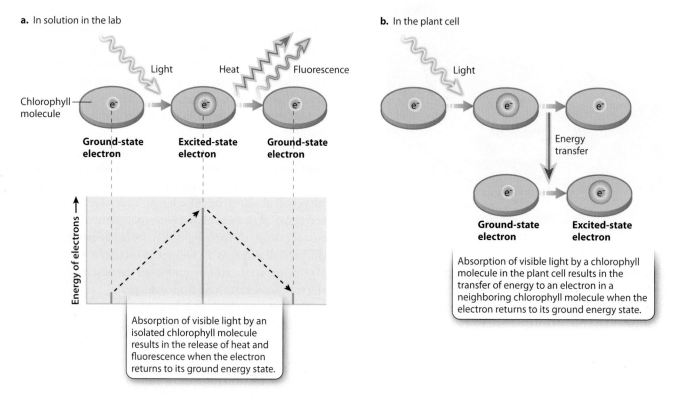

a. In solution in the lab

b. In the plant cell

Absorption of visible light by an isolated chlorophyll molecule results in the release of heat and fluorescence when the electron returns to its ground energy state.

Absorption of visible light by a chlorophyll molecule in the plant cell results in the transfer of energy to an electron in a neighboring chlorophyll molecule when the electron returns to its ground energy state.

(**Fig. 8.10**). For chlorophyll molecules that have been isolated in the laboratory, this absorbed light energy is rapidly released, allowing the electron to return to its initial "ground" energy state (Fig. 8.10a). Most of the energy (>95%) is converted into heat; a small amount is reemitted as light (fluorescence). By contrast, for chlorophyll molecules situated within the photosystems of the thylakoid, something entirely different occurs: The absorbed light energy is transferred to another chlorophyll molecule and then on to another (Fig. 8.10b).

Most of the chlorophyll molecules in the thylakoid membrane function as an antenna: Absorbed light energy is transferred from one chlorophyll molecule to another until it is finally transferred to a specially configured pair of chlorophyll molecules known as the **reaction center.** As we will see, the reaction center is where light energy is converted into electron transport. This division of labor among chlorophyll molecules was discovered in the 1940s in a series of experiments by the American biophysicists Robert Emerson and William Arnold, who showed that only a small fraction of chlorophyll molecules are directly involved in electron transport (**Fig. 8.11**). We now know that several hundred antenna chlorophyll molecules are associated with each reaction center. The antenna chlorophylls allow the photosynthetic electron

transport chain to operate efficiently. Without the antenna to gather light energy, reaction centers would sit idle much of the time, even in bright sunlight.

The chlorophyll molecules that make up the antenna are precisely spaced so that when a chlorophyll molecule absorbs light it transfers energy, but not electrons, to an adjacent chlorophyll molecule (see Fig. 8.10b). A good analogy for this form of energy transfer is the transfer of vibrational energy between two tuning forks held close together. The transfer of energy between antenna chlorophyll molecules is highly efficient, so little energy is lost as heat, in contrast to what happens with an isolated chlorophyll molecule. Light energy absorbed by the antenna is passed from one chlorophyll molecule to the next until eventually it is transferred to the reaction center, as shown in **Fig. 8.12a.**

The reaction center chlorophylls have a configuration distinct from that of the antenna chlorophylls. As a result, reaction center chlorophylls are able to transfer both absorbed light energy *and* an associated high-energy electron to an adjacent molecule that acts as an electron acceptor. When the transfer takes place, the reaction center becomes oxidized and the adjacent electron-acceptor molecule is reduced. The result is the conversion of light energy into a chemical form. This electron transfer sets in motion

FIG. 8.11

Do chlorophyll molecules operate on their own or in groups?

BACKGROUND By about 1915, scientists knew that chlorophyll was the pigment responsible for absorbing light energy in photosynthesis. However, it was unclear how these pigments contributed to the reduction of CO_2. The American physiologists Robert Emerson and William Arnold set out to determine the nature of the "photochemical unit" by quantifying how many chlorophyll molecules were needed to incorporate one CO_2 molecule into carbohydrate.

EXPERIMENT Emerson and Arnold exposed flasks of the green alga *Chlorella* to flashes of light of such short duration (10^{-5} s) that each chlorophyll molecule could be "excited" only once, and the time between flashes was long enough to allow the reactions resulting from this light energy to run to completion. In step 1, they recorded the maximum rate of CO_2 uptake by increasing the intensity of the light flashes until the rate could not go any higher. In step 2, they determined the concentration of chlorophyll present in their solution of cells. They then compared the maximum rate of CO_2 uptake to the number of chlorophyll molecules.

RESULTS

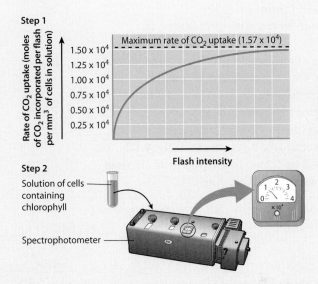

CONCLUSION Because the maximum rate of CO_2 uptake per flash was much smaller than the amount of chlorophyll in their flask, Emerson and Arnold concluded that each photochemical unit contains many chlorophyll molecules.

FOLLOW-UP WORK Emerson and Arnold's work was followed by studies that demonstrated that the photosynthetic electron-transport chain contains two photosystems (photosynthetic units) arranged in series.

SOURCE Emerson, R., and W. Arnold. 1932. "The Photochemical Reaction in Photosynthesis." *Journal of General Physiology.* 16:191–205.

FIG. 8.12 **The reaction center.** (a) Antenna chlorophylls deliver absorbed light energy to the reaction center, where energy and electrons are transported to the electron transport chain. (b) After the reaction center has lost an electron, it is reduced by gaining an electron, so it is ready to absorb additional light energy.

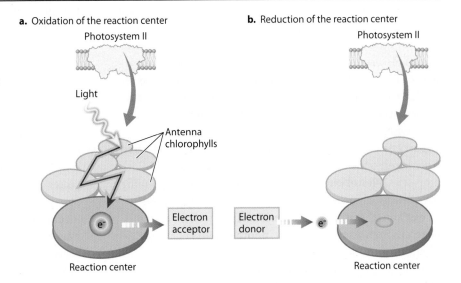

the light-driven chain of redox reactions that constitute the photosynthetic electron transport chain.

Once the reaction center has lost an electron, it is no longer able to absorb light. From a visual perspective, it has been bleached. Thus, for the photosystem to continue contributing electrons to the photosynthetic electron transport chain, another electron must be delivered to take the place of the one that has entered the transport chain (**Fig. 8.12b**). As we will see below, these replacement electrons ultimately come from water.

→   **Quick Check 3** How do antenna chlorophylls differ from reaction center chlorophylls?

The photosynthetic electron transport chain connects two photosystems.

Experiments conducted in the 1940s led to the surprising finding that photosynthetic cells use light energy at only half the maximum efficiency predicted. We now know that the reason that the efficiency is lower than predicted is that the photosynthetic electron transport chain includes not one but two photosystems arranged in series. Two photosystems are necessary to provide enough energy to pull electrons from water and then use them to reduce $NADP^+$.

If you follow the flow of electrons from water, through both photosystems, and on to $NADP^+$, as shown in **Fig. 8.13,** you can see a large increase in the energy level of the electrons as they pass through each of the two photosystems. You can also see that every other step along the photosynthetic electron transport chain is associated with a small decrease in the energy level of the electrons. Because the overall energy trajectory has an up-down configuration resembling a "Z," the photosynthetic electron transport chain is sometimes referred to as the **Z scheme.**

For the two photosystems to work together to move electrons from water to NADPH, they must have distinct chemical properties. **Photosystem II** supplies electrons to the beginning of the electron transport chain. When photosystem II loses an electron (that is, when it is itself oxidized), it is able to pull electrons from water. In contrast, **photosystem I** energizes electrons with a second input of light energy so they have enough energy to reduce $NADP^+$. The key point here is that photosystem I when oxidized is not a sufficiently strong oxidant

FIG. 8.13   **The Z scheme.** The use of water as an electron donor requires input of light energy at two places in the photosynthetic electron transport chain.

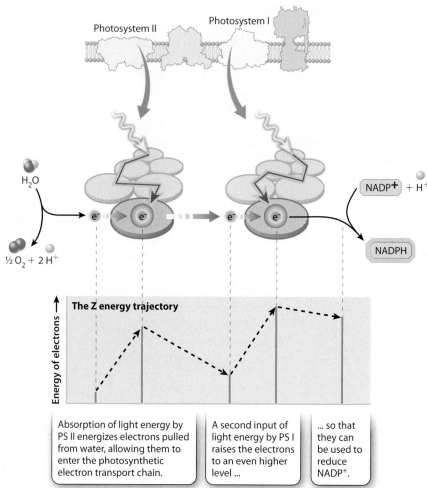

to split water, whereas photosystem II cannot produce electrons with enough energy to form NADPH.

The major protein complexes of the photosynthetic electron transport chain include the two photosystems as well as the **cytochrome b_6f complex,** through which electrons pass between photosystem II and photosystem I (**Figure 8.14**). Small, relatively mobile compounds convey electrons between these protein complexes. Plastoquinone, a lipid-soluble mobile compound, carries electrons from photosystem II to the cytochrome b_6f complex, while plastocyanin, a water-soluble protein, carries electrons from the cytochrome b_6f complex to photosystem I by diffusing through the thylakoid lumen. The modular nature of the photosynthetic electron transport chain, interconnected by diffusible elements, enables this pathway to adjust in response to changes in the availability of light.

Water, as the electron donor, sits at one end of the photosynthetic electron transport chain, whereas $NADP^+$, the

FIG. 8.14 **The photosynthetic electron transport chain.** (a) An overview of the production of NADPH and ATP. (b) The linear flow of electrons from H_2O to NADPH. (c) The use of a proton electrochemical gradient to synthesize ATP.

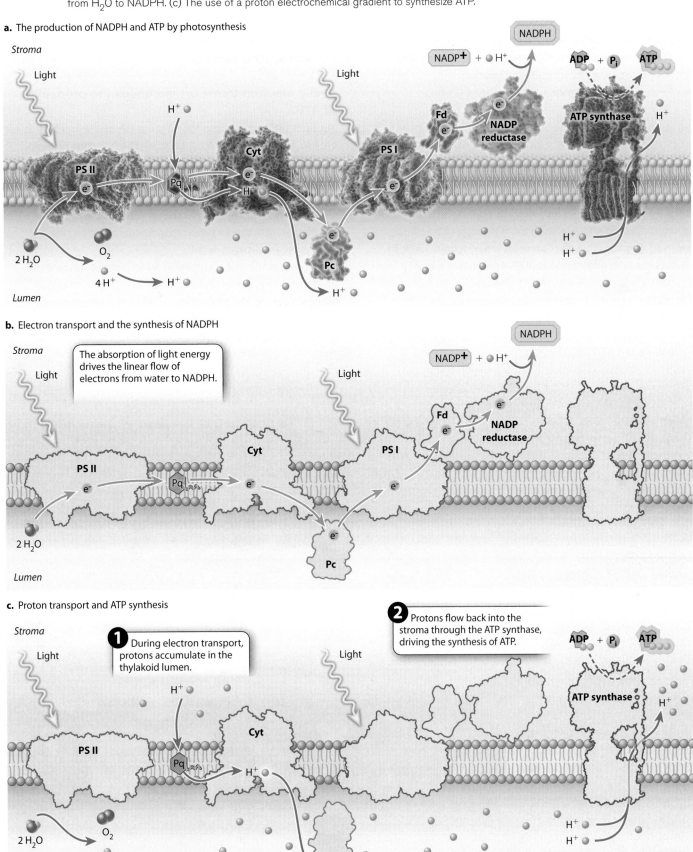

a. The production of NADPH and ATP by photosynthesis

b. Electron transport and the synthesis of NADPH

The absorption of light energy drives the linear flow of electrons from water to NADPH.

c. Proton transport and ATP synthesis

1 During electron transport, protons accumulate in the thylakoid lumen.

2 Protons flow back into the stroma through the ATP synthase, driving the synthesis of ATP.

electron acceptor that transports high-energy electrons to the Calvin cycle, sits at the other. NADPH is formed when high-energy electrons are passed from photosystem I to a membrane-associated protein called ferredoxin (Fig. 8.14b). The enzyme ferredoxin–NADP⁺ reductase then catalyzes the formation of NADPH by transferring two high-energy electrons to NADP⁺ as well as a proton from the surrounding solution:

$$NADP^+ + 2e^- + H^+ \longrightarrow NADPH$$

→　**Quick Check 4** Why are two photosystems needed if H_2O is used as an electron donor?

The accumulation of protons in the thylakoid lumen drives the synthesis of ATP.

So far, we have considered only how the photosynthetic electron transport chain leads to the formation of NADPH. However, we know that the Calvin cycle also requires ATP. In chloroplasts as in mitochondria, ATP is synthesized by ATP synthase, a transmembrane protein powered by the movement of protons across the membrane. In chloroplasts, the ATP synthase is oriented such that the movement of protons from the thylakoid lumen to the stroma results in the synthesis of ATP, as shown in Fig. 8.14c.

How do protons accumulate in the thylakoid lumen? Two features of the photosynthetic electron transport chain are responsible for the build-up of protons in the thylakoid lumen. First, the oxidation of water releases protons and O_2 into the lumen (Fig. 8.14c). Second, the cytochrome-b_6f complex, the protein complex situated between photosystem II and photosystem I, functions as a proton pump. As electrons transit through the cytochrome-b_6f complex, some of the energy that is released by each redox reaction is used to drive protons from the stroma side of the thylakoid membrane to the lumen (Fig. 8.14c).

These two mechanisms are quite powerful. When the photosynthetic electron transport chain is operating at full capacity, the concentration of protons in the lumen can be more than 1000 times greater than that in the stroma (equivalent to a difference of 3 pH units). This accumulation of protons on one side of the thylakoid membrane can then be used to power the synthesis of ATP. If offered a pathway through the membrane, protons diffuse from this region of

higher concentration and net positive charge to the region of lower concentration and net negative charge in the stroma, releasing energy. The pathway most readily available is through a channel in the ATP synthase. When protons pass through this enzyme, some of the energy that is released is used to drive the synthesis of ATP (Chapter 7).

Cyclic electron transport increases the production of ATP.

Sunlight varies in intensity throughout the day. When light levels are low, light is shared evenly between the two photosystems. However, as light levels increase, the light energy absorbed begins to overwhelm the capacity of the Calvin cycle to make use of NADPH. The danger is that when there is no NADP⁺ returning from the Calvin cycle to act as the terminal electron acceptor for the photosynthetic electron transport chain, the high-energy electrons can damage the cell.

To prevent this from happening, electrons are shunted into an alternative pathway that increases the production of ATP while decreasing the production of NADPH. Electrons from photosystem I are redirected from ferredoxin back into the electron transport chain (**Fig. 8.15**). These electrons reenter the photosynthetic electron transport chain upstream of the cytochrome-b_6f proton pump. Because these electrons

---

FIG. 8.15　Cyclic electron transport. When light levels are high, some electrons are diverted from NADPH synthesis back into the electron transport chain, entering upstream of the cytochrome-b_6f proton pump.

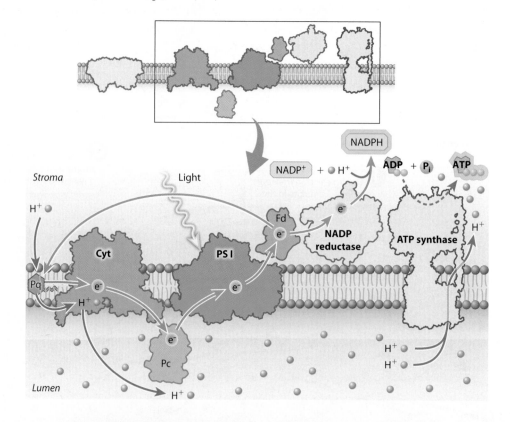

eventually return to photosystem I, this alternative pathway is referred to as **cyclic electron transport,** in contrast to the linear movement of electrons from water to NADPH.

Cyclic electron transport leads to the production of ATP because as the high-energy electrons from ferredoxin pass through the cytochrome-b_6f complex, additional protons are pumped into the lumen. As a result, there are more protons in the lumen that can be used to drive the synthesis of ATP. In addition, a subset of the photosystem II antennae migrate through the thylakoid membrane to become associated with photosystem I. This redistribution of light-harvesting capacity increases the rate of cyclic electron transport relative to linear electron transport, further enhancing the production of ATP.

The spatial organization of the thylakoid membrane contributes to its functioning.

We are now ready to understand how the major components of the photosynthetic electron transport chain are positioned on the thylakoid membrane in a manner consistent with their roles in photosynthesis. To do this, we must revisit the peculiar shape of this photosynthetic membrane, shown in Fig. 8.5. Recall that, despite its convoluted arrangement, the thylakoid membrane forms a single large sac, with the lumen on the inside and the stroma on the outside. The convoluted arrangement of interlinked granal stacks increases the total surface area of the thylakoid that can be accommodated within a single chloroplast. Nevertheless, the tight packing of the granal stacks means that only membranes on the outside of each granal stack and the links between grana are in direct contact with the stroma. The inner folds of the granal stacks have no direct contact with the stroma.

The components of the photosynthetic electron transport chain are distributed in such a way as to make tight packing possible, increasing surface area without sacrificing function. Photosystem I and the ATP synthase are concentrated on the outer regions of the granal stacks (**Fig. 8.16**). From there they can readily supply NADPH and ATP to the stroma, where these molecules are used to power the Calvin cycle. In contrast, photosystem II is located primarily on the closely packed inner regions of the thylakoid membrane that have little contact with the stroma. The cytochrome-b_6f complex, which is located between the two photosystems, has a relatively even distribution.

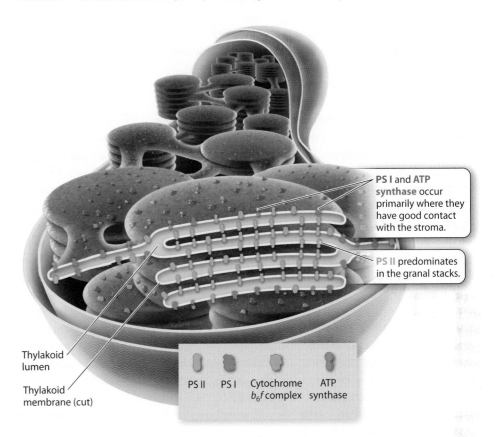

FIG. 8.16 Distribution of PS I, PS II, and ATP synthase in the thylakoid membrane.

PS I and **ATP synthase** occur primarily where they have good contact with the stroma.

PS II predominates in the granal stacks.

Thylakoid lumen

Thylakoid membrane (cut)

PS II   PS I   Cytochrome b_6f complex   ATP synthase

This distribution of components to different regions is made possible by the presence of the mobile compounds that carry electrons between the major components of the photosynthetic electron transport chain. In particular, the diffusion of the protein plastocyanin through the lumen allows photosystem II and photosystem I to be located in different regions of the thylakoid membrane. The close packing of thylakoid membrane regions helps explain why the thylakoid membrane and the inner mitochondrial membrane look so different, even though they both support electron transport chains.

? CASE 1 The First Cell: Life's Origins
How did early cells meet their energy requirements?

Photosynthesis is a highly complex process, involving the coordination of many reactions and enzymes. This complexity is the result of several billion years of evolution. The first organisms that were able to draw upon sunlight as an energy source would have been much simpler.

How simple? The earliest reaction centers may have used light energy to drive the movement of electrons from a soluble inorganic electron donor in the surrounding medium to an electron-acceptor molecule within the cell. Reduced iron, Fe^{2+}, is thought to have been abundant in the early ocean, and therefore could have served as the first electron donor. Alternatively, the first forms of light-driven electron transport may have been coupled to the net movement of protons across the membrane, allowing for the synthesis of ATP.

Similarly, it is unlikely that these first photosynthetic organisms employed chlorophyll, a complex molecule whose biosynthetic pathway contains at least 17 enzymatic steps. Because some of the intermediate compounds leading to chlorophyll are themselves capable of absorbing light energy, perhaps each of these now-intermediate compounds was, at one time, a functional end product used by an early photosynthetic organism. Selection for chemical variants with increased efficiency or the ability to absorb new portions of the visible spectrum may then have led to the further elaboration of this pathway. Selection would have eventually resulted in the chlorophyll pigments that are used by photosynthetic organisms today.

8.4 CHALLENGES TO PHOTOSYNTHETIC EFFICIENCY

The efficient functioning of photosynthesis faces two major challenges. The first is that if more energy is generated than the Calvin cycle can use, excess light energy can damage the cell. The second challenge stems from rubisco's ability to catalyze the addition of either carbon dioxide or oxygen to RuBP. The addition of oxygen instead of carbon dioxide can substantially reduce the amount of carbohydrate produced.

Excess light energy can cause damage.

Photosynthesis is an inherently dangerous enterprise. Unless the photosynthetic reactions are carefully controlled, molecules will be formed that can damage cells through the indiscriminate oxidization of lipids, proteins, and nucleic acids (**Fig. 8.17**).

Under normal conditions, the redox reactions that make up the photosynthetic electron transport chain do not allow either absorbed light energy or the resulting high-energy electrons to stray. However, when NADP$^+$ is in short supply, either the absorbed light energy or the energy and the associated electron can be transferred to O$_2$, resulting in the formation of highly reactive forms of oxygen known collectively as **reactive oxygen species** (Fig. 8.17a).

NADP$^+$ is returned to the photosynthetic electron transport chain by the Calvin cycle's consumption of NADPH. Thus, any factor that causes the rate of NADP$^+$ regeneration to fall behind the rate of light-driven electron transport can potentially lead to damage. Such an imbalance is likely to occur, for example, in the middle of the day when light intensity is highest. Photosynthetic cells could prevent excess light energy by synthesizing sufficient quantities of Calvin cycle enzymes to process all the energy

absorbed by chlorophyll even at full sunlight. This strategy, however, would be energetically expensive because light levels vary dramatically over the course of the day. When light levels are low, such as in the morning and late afternoon, Calvin cycle enzymes would sit idle.

The rate at which the Calvin cycle can utilize NADPH is also influenced by a number of factors that are independent of light intensity. For example, cold temperatures cause the enzymes of the Calvin cycle to function more slowly, but they have little impact on the absorption of light energy by the photosynthetic electron transport chain. On a cold, sunny day, more light energy is absorbed than can be used by the Calvin cycle. Other factors that depress the rate at which the Calvin cycle can function include shortages of nitrogen, which reduces protein levels overall, and of CO$_2$.

Photosynthetic organisms employ two major lines of defense to deal with the stresses that occur when the Calvin cycle cannot keep up with light harvesting (Fig. 8.17b). First among these are chemicals that detoxify reactive oxygen species. Ascorbate (vitamin C), beta-carotene, and other antioxidants are able to neutralize reactive oxygen species. These compounds exist in high concentration in chloroplasts. Some of these antioxidant molecules are brightly colored, like the red pigments found in algae that live on snow shown in Fig. 8.3c. The presence of antioxidant compounds is one of the many reasons that eating photosynthetic tissues is good for your health.

A second line of defense is to prevent reactive oxygen species from forming in the first place. **Xanthophylls** are yellow-orange pigments that slow the formation of reactive oxygen species by reducing excess light energy. These pigments accept absorbed light energy directly from chlorophyll and then convert this energy to heat (Fig. 8.17b). Photosynthetic organisms that live in extreme environments often appear brown or yellow because of high levels of xanthophyll pigments, as seen in Figs. 8.3a and 8.3b. Plants that lack xanthophylls grow poorly when exposed to moderate light levels and die in full sunlight.

Converting absorbed light energy into heat is beneficial at high light levels, but at low light levels it would decrease the production of carbohydrates. Therefore, this ability is switched on only when the photosynthetic electron transport chain is working at high capacity. The creation of a strong proton gradient across the thylakoid membrane at high light levels activates the enzyme that converts inactive xanthophyll molecules into their light-absorbing form.

Xanthophyll pigments are predominantly associated with photosystem II. When activated by high light, these light-absorbing pigments reduce linear electron transport, but

FIG. 8.17 **Defenses against reactive oxygen species.** (a) Reactive oxygen species are generated when excess light energy and electrons are transferred to oxygen. (b) Defenses against the reactive oxygen species include antioxidants that neutralize reactive oxygen species and xanthophylls that convert excess light energy into heat.

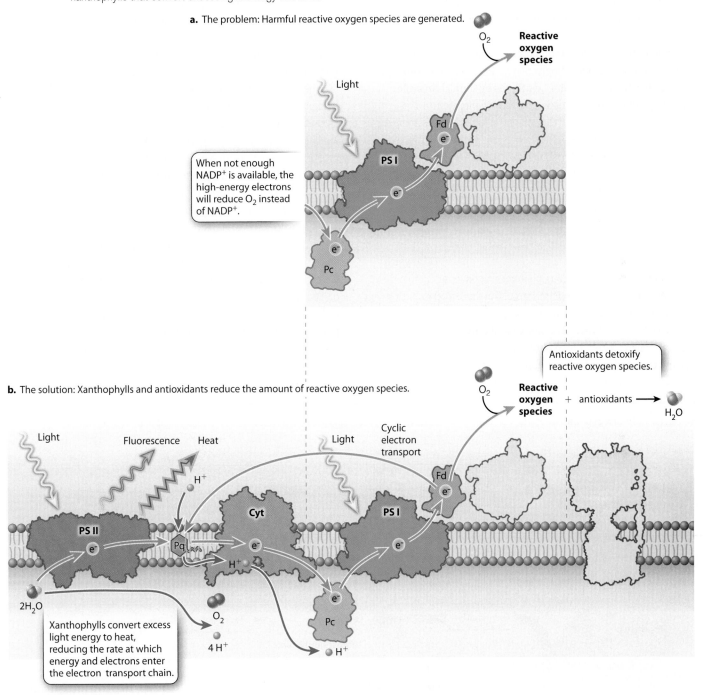

a. The problem: Harmful reactive oxygen species are generated.

O_2 → **Reactive oxygen species**

Light

When not enough $NADP^+$ is available, the high-energy electrons will reduce O_2 instead of $NADP^+$.

PS I

Fd
e⁻

e⁻

e⁻
Pc

Antioxidants detoxify reactive oxygen species.

b. The solution: Xanthophylls and antioxidants reduce the amount of reactive oxygen species.

O_2 → **Reactive oxygen species** + antioxidants ⟶ H_2O

Light Fluorescence Heat

H^+

Cyclic electron transport

Light

Cyt

PS I

Fd
e⁻

PS II

Pq

e⁻

e⁻

e⁻

H^+

$2H_2O$

Xanthophylls convert excess light energy to heat, reducing the rate at which energy and electrons enter the electron transport chain.

O_2

$4 H^+$

e⁻
Pc

H^+

allow cyclic electron transport to continue. Light absorbed by photosystem I thus remains available to power the synthesis of ATP, which can then be used to help repair cellular components that have been damaged by reactive oxygen species.

Photorespiration leads to a net loss of energy and carbon.
A major challenge to photosynthetic efficiency is the fact that rubisco can add O_2 to RuBP instead of CO_2. The idea that an enzyme could make a "mistake" may seem surprising, yet, from

the point of view of a very large enzyme, CO_2 and O_2 have a lot in common: They are similar in size, have similar chemical bonds, and are both uncharged. Moreover, O_2 is approximately 500 times more abundant in the atmosphere than CO_2.

When rubisco adds O_2 instead of CO_2 to RuBP, the result is one molecule with three carbon atoms (3-PGA) and one molecule with only two carbon atoms (2-phosphoglycolate). The production of 2-phosphoglycolate creates a serious problem because this molecule cannot be utilized by the Calvin cycle either to produce triose phosphate or to regenerate RuBP.

A metabolic pathway to recycle 2-phosphoglycolate is present in photosynthetic cells. However, this pathway is not able to return all of the carbon atoms in 2-phosphoglycolate to the Calvin cycle; some are released as CO_2. Because the overall effect of oxygenation is a release of CO_2 in the presence of light, this process is referred to as **photorespiration** (**Fig. 8.18**). However, unlike respiration, which produces ATP, photorespiration actually consumes ATP. In photorespiration, ATP is used to drive the reactions that convert a portion of the carbon atoms in 2-phosphoglycolate into 3-PGA, which can reenter the Calvin cycle. Thus, photorespiration represents a net energy drain on two accounts: First, it results in the oxidation and loss, in the form of CO_2, of carbon atoms that had previously been incorporated and reduced by the Calvin cycle, and second, it consumes ATP.

Rubisco plays a key role in photosynthesis, and yet it is an enzyme that makes mistakes, "confusing" O_2 and CO_2. What accounts for its evolutionary success? A partial answer is that rubisco first evolved long before oxygen appeared in Earth's atmosphere. Still, why would photorespiration persist in the face of what must be strong evolutionary pressure to reduce or eliminate the unwanted oxygenation reaction?

The difficulty is that for rubisco to favor the addition of CO_2 over O_2 requires a high degree of selectivity, and the price of selectivity is speed. The better rubisco is at discriminating between CO_2 and O_2, the slower its catalytic rate. Nowhere is this trade-off more evident than in land plants, whose photosynthetic cells acquire CO_2 from an O_2-rich and CO_2-poor atmosphere. The rubiscos of land plants are highly selective, but incredibly slow, with catalytic rates on the order of three reactions per second. To put this rate in perspective, it is not uncommon for metabolic enzymes to achieve a catalytic rate of a hundred thousand reactions per second.

This trade-off between selectivity and speed is a key constraint for photosynthetic organisms. For land plants, rubisco's low catalytic rate means that photosynthetic cells must produce huge amounts of this enzyme; as much as 50% of the total protein within a leaf is rubisco. At the same time, the low concentration of CO_2 in the atmosphere (0.0385%) relative to O_2 (21%) means that as much as one-quarter of the reduced carbon formed in photosynthesis can be lost via photorespiration.

→   **Quick Check 5** Why does rubisco have such a low catalytic rate (that is, why is it so slow)?

FIG. 8.18   **Photorespiration.**   Carbon and energy are lost when rubisco acts as an oxygenase in the process called photorespiration.

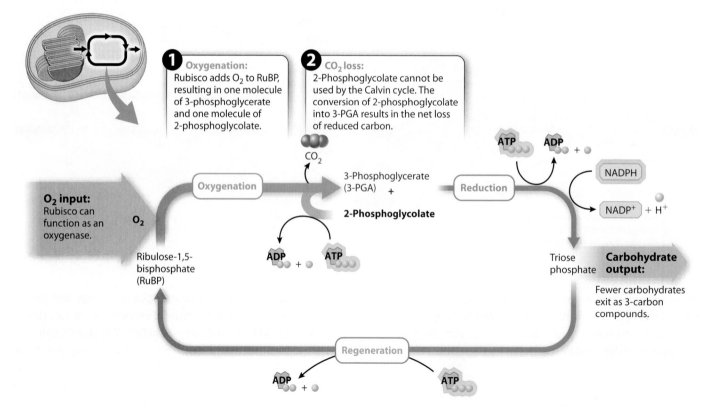

Photosynthesis captures just a small percentage of incoming solar energy.

Typically, only 1% to 2% of the sun's energy that lands on a leaf ends up in carbohydrates. Does this mean that photosynthesis is incredibly wasteful? Or is this process, the product of billions of years of evolution, surprisingly efficient? This is not an idle question. The effects of rising CO_2 concentrations on Earth's climate, the search for a renewable, carbon-neutral fuel to power our transportation sector, and the agricultural demands of our skyrocketing human population all point to photosynthesis as a metabolic process relevant to solving some of our most pressing global issues.

Photosynthetic efficiency is typically calculated relative to the total energy output of the sun (**Fig. 8.19**). However, only visible light has the appropriate energy levels to produce the high-energy electrons required by the photosynthetic electron transport chain. Most of the sun's output (~60%) is not absorbed by chlorophyll and thus cannot be used in photosynthesis. In addition, leaves are not perfect at absorbing visible light—about 8% is either reflected or passes through the leaf. Finally, even under optimal conditions, not all of the light energy absorbed by chlorophyll can be transferred to the reaction center and instead is given off as heat (also ~8%). As we have seen, when light levels are high, excess light is actively converted into heat by xanthophyll pigments.

The photosynthetic electron transport chain therefore captures at most about 24% of the sun's usable energy arriving at the surface of a leaf (100% − 60% − 8% − 8% = 24%). While this number may appear low, it is on a par with the number of high-performance photovoltaic cells in solar panels, which convert sunlight into electricity. This comparison is even more impressive when you consider that photosynthetic organisms must build and maintain all their biochemical machinery. However, energy is lost at another step as well. The incorporation of CO_2 into carbohydrates results in considerable loss in free energy, equivalent to ~20% of the total incoming solar radiation. Much of this loss in free energy is due to photorespiration.

In total, therefore, the maximum energy conversion efficiency of photosynthesis is calculated to be around 4% (24% − 20%). Efficiencies achieved by real plants growing in nature, however, are typically much lower, on the order of 1% to 2%. In Chapter 29, we explore the many factors that can constrain the

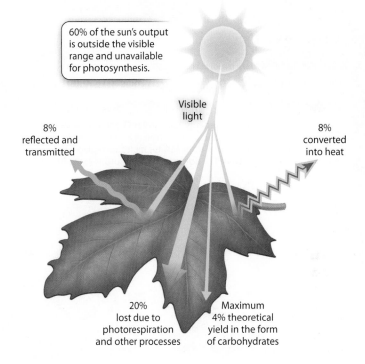

FIG. 8.19 Photosynthetic efficiency. Maximum photosynthetic efficiency is theoretically around 4% of incoming solar energy, but actual yields are closer to 1% to 2%.

60% of the sun's output is outside the visible range and unavailable for photosynthesis.

Visible light

8% reflected and transmitted

8% converted into heat

20% lost due to photorespiration and other processes

Maximum 4% theoretical yield in the form of carbohydrates

photosynthetic output of land plants, and see how some plants have evolved ways to minimize losses in productivity due to drought and photorespiration.

Cellular respiration and photosynthesis are complementary metabolic processes. Cellular respiration breaks down carbohydrates in the presence of oxygen to supply the energy needs of the cell, producing carbon dioxide and water as byproducts, while photosynthesis uses carbon dioxide and water in the presence of sunlight to build carbohydrates, releasing oxygen as a byproduct. We summarize the two processes in **Fig. 8.20**.

→ **Quick Check 6** In what ways is photorespiration similar to cellular respiration (Chapter 7) and in what ways does it differ?

Harnessing Energy: Photosynthesis and Cellular Respiration

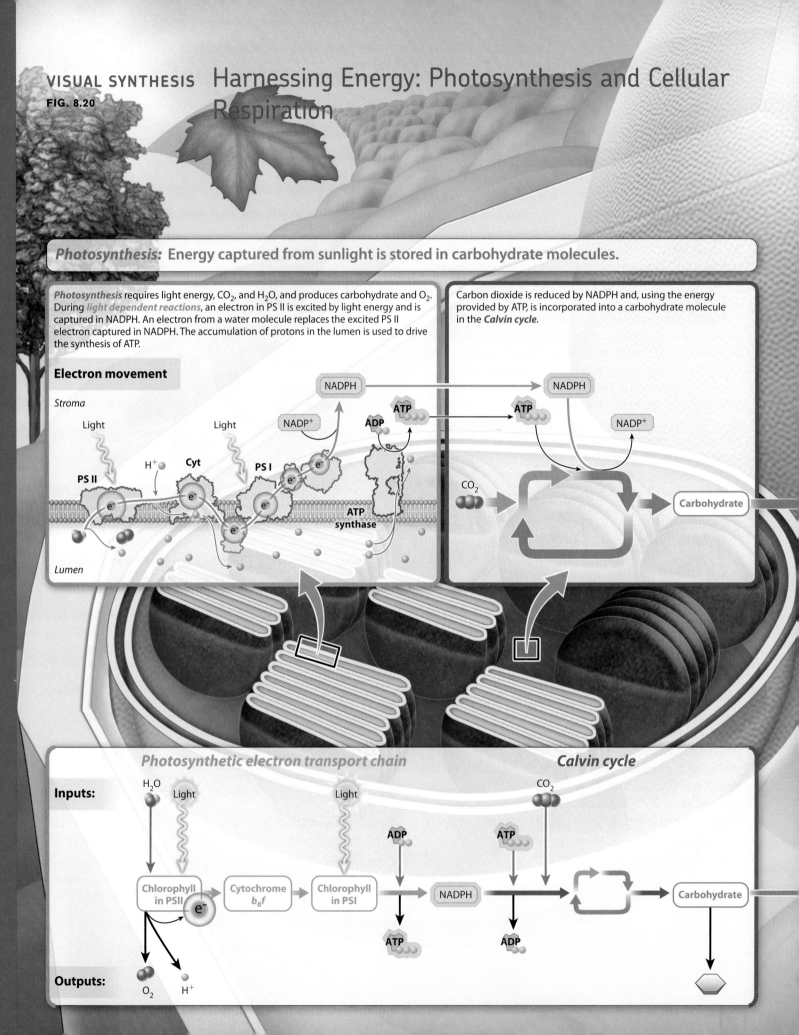

Photosynthesis: Energy captured from sunlight is stored in carbohydrate molecules.

Photosynthesis requires light energy, CO_2, and H_2O, and produces carbohydrate and O_2. During *light dependent reactions*, an electron in PS II is excited by light energy and is captured in NADPH. An electron from a water molecule replaces the excited PS II electron captured in NADPH. The accumulation of protons in the lumen is used to drive the synthesis of ATP.

Carbon dioxide is reduced by NADPH and, using the energy provided by ATP, is incorporated into a carbohydrate molecule in the *Calvin cycle*.

Electron movement

Stroma

Light

NADPH

NADPH

$NADP^+$

ATP

ADP

ATP

$NADP^+$

H^+ **Cyt**

PS I

e^-

e^-

e^-

CO_2

Carbohydrate

PS II

e^-

e^-

e^-

ATP synthase

Lumen

Photosynthetic electron transport chain

Calvin cycle

Inputs:

H_2O Light

Light

CO_2

ADP

ATP

Chlorophyll in PSII

e^-

Cytochrome b_6f

Chlorophyll in PSI

NADPH

Carbohydrate

ATP

ADP

Outputs:

O_2 H^+

Aerobic respiration: Energy released from the oxidation of carbohydrates is used to make ATP.

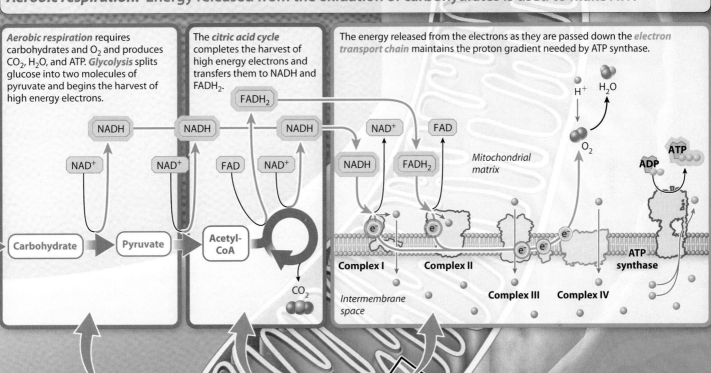

Aerobic respiration requires carbohydrates and O_2 and produces CO_2, H_2O, and ATP. *Glycolysis* splits glucose into two molecules of pyruvate and begins the harvest of high energy electrons.

The *citric acid cycle* completes the harvest of high energy electrons and transfers them to NADH and $FADH_2$.

The energy released from the electrons as they are passed down the *electron transport chain* maintains the proton gradient needed by ATP synthase.

FADH₂

NADH   NADH   NADH

NAD⁺   NAD⁺   FAD   NAD⁺

NAD⁺   FAD

NADH   FADH₂

Mitochondrial matrix

H⁺   H₂O

O₂

ADP   ATP

Carbohydrate → Pyruvate → Acetyl-CoA

e⁻   e⁻

e⁻   e⁻   e⁻

Complex I   Complex II

Complex III   Complex IV

ATP synthase

Intermembrane space

CO_2

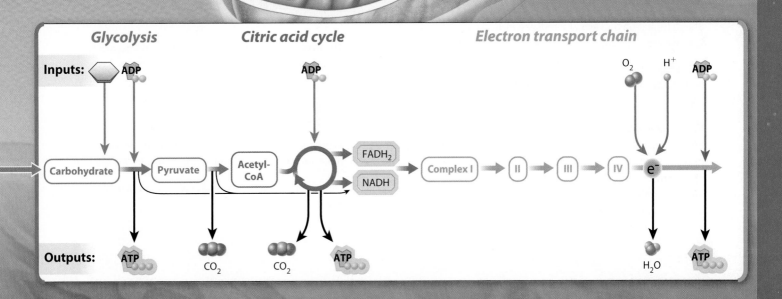

Glycolysis   **Citric acid cycle**   **Electron transport chain**

Inputs: ADP   ADP O_2 H⁺   ADP

Carbohydrate → Pyruvate → Acetyl-CoA → Complex I → II → III → IV → e⁻

FADH₂

NADH

Outputs: ATP CO_2 CO_2 ATP H_2O ATP

Core Concepts Summary

8.1 PHOTOSYNTHESIS IS THE MAJOR PATHWAY BY WHICH ENERGY AND CARBON ARE INCORPORATED INTO CARBOHYDRATES.

In photosynthesis, water is oxidized to form oxygen, and carbon dioxide is reduced to form carbohydrates. page 8-1

Photosynthesis consists of two sets of reactions: (1) the Calvin cycle, in which carbon dioxide is reduced to form carbohydrates, and (2) light-harvesting reactions, in which ATP and NADPH are generated to drive the Calvin cycle. page 8-2

The evolution of photosynthesis involved horizontal gene transfer in bacteria and endosymbiosis in eukaryotes. page 8-4

In eukaryotes, photosynthesis takes place in chloroplasts: The Calvin cycle occurs in the stroma, and the light-harvesting reactions take place on the thylakoid membrane. page 8-5

8.2 THE CALVIN CYCLE IS A THREE-STEP PROCESS THAT RESULTS IN THE INCORPORATION OF CARBON DIOXIDE INTO CARBOHYDRATES.

The three steps of the Calvin cycle are (1) carboxylation; (2) reduction; and (3) regeneration. page 8-6

The first step is the addition of CO_2 to the 5-carbon sugar RuBP. This step is catalyzed by the enzyme rubisco, considered the most abundant protein on Earth. The resulting 6-carbon compound immediately breaks down into two 3-carbon compounds. page 8-6

The second step is phosphorylation of the 3-carbon compounds by ATP followed by reduction by NADPH to produce 3-carbon triose phosphate molecules that are exported from the chloroplast to the cytosol, where they are used to build larger sugars. page 8-7

The third step is the regeneration of RuBP from five 3-carbon molecules. page 8-7

Starch formation provides chloroplasts with an osmotically inactive way of storing carbohydrates. page 8-7

8.3 THE LIGHT-HARVESTING REACTIONS USE SUNLIGHT TO PRODUCE ATP AND NADPH REQUIRED BY THE CALVIN CYCLE.

Visible light is absorbed by chlorophyll. The absorbed light energy can be released as heat, reemitted as light (fluorescence), or transferred to an adjacent chlorophyll molecule. Special chlorophyll molecules in the reaction center transfer both energy and electrons, thus initiating the photosynthetic electron transport chain. page 8-9

The electron transport chain consists of multisubunit protein complexes and diffusible compounds. Water is the electron donor and $NADP^+$ is the final electron acceptor. page 8-9

Antenna chlorophylls transfer absorbed light energy to the reaction center. page 8-10

Reaction centers are located within pigment–protein complexes known as photosystems. page 8-10

The linear transport of electrons from water to NADPH requires the energy input of two photosystems. page 8-12

Photosystem II pulls electrons from water, resulting in the production of oxygen and protons on the lumen side of the membrane. Photosystem I passes electrons to $NADP^+$, producing NADPH for use in the Calvin cycle. page 8-12

The buildup of protons drives ATP synthase to produce ATP on the stroma side of the membrane, where it is used by the Calvin cycle. page 8-14

8.4 PHOTOSYNTHESIS FACES SEVERAL CHALLENGES TO ITS EFFICIENCY.

An imbalance between the light-harvesting reactions and the Calvin cycle can lead to the formation of reactive oxygen species. page 8-16

Protection from excess light energy includes antioxidant molecules that neutralize reactive oxygen species and xanthophyll pigments that dissipate excess light energy as heat. page 8-16

Rubisco can act catalytically on oxygen as well as on carbon dioxide. When it acts as an oxygenase, there is a loss of energy and reduced carbon from the Calvin cycle. page 8-18

Rubisco has evolved to favor carbon dioxide over oxygen, but the cost of this selectivity is reduced speed. page 8-18

The synthesis of carbohydrates via the Calvin cycle results in significant energy losses, largely due to photorespiration. page 8-18

The maximum theoretical efficiency of photosynthesis is approximately 4% of total incident solar energy. page 8-19

Self-Assessment

1. Write the overall photosynthetic reaction and identify which molecules are oxidized and which molecules are reduced.

2. Describe how photosynthesis evolved in prokaryotes and in eukaryotes.

3. Explain the functions of the Calvin cycle and the light harvesting reactions in photosynthesis.

4. Name the major inputs and outputs of the Calvin cycle.

5. Describe the three major steps in the Calvin cycle and the role of the key enzyme rubisco.

6. Explain why photosynthetic electron transport requires two photosystems.

7. Describe the role of cyclic electron transport.

8. List two strategies that plants use to limit the formation and effects of reactive oxygen species.

9. Explain the trade-off that rubisco faces in terms of selectivity and enzymatic speed.

10. Estimate the overall efficiency of photosynthesis and where in the pathway energy is dissipated.

Do you understand the chapter's Core Concepts? Log into BIO*PORTAL* to check your answers to the Self-Assessment questions, then practice what you've learned and reinforce this chapter's concepts by working through the problems and multimedia tutorials provided there.

🛜 **http://courses.bfwpub.com/yourbioportal/index.php**

Cancer

WHEN GOOD CELLS GO BAD

Imagine a simple vaccine that could prevent about 500,000 cases of cancer worldwide every year. You'd think such a discovery would be hailed as a miracle. Not quite. A vaccine to prevent cervical cancer—which affects about half a million women and kills as many as 275,000 annually—has been available since 2006. But in the United States, the vaccine has stirred unanticipated controversy.

Cancer is uncontrolled cell division. Cell division is a normal process that occurs during development of a multicellular organism and subsequently as part of the maintenance and repair of adult tissues. It is carefully regulated so that it occurs only at the right time and place. But sometimes, this careful regulation can be disrupted. When the normal checks on cell division become derailed, cancer can result.

Most cancers are caused by inherited or acquired mutations, but nearly all cases of cervical cancer are caused by a virus called human papillomavirus (HPV). There are hundreds of strains of HPV. Some of these strains cause minor problems such as common warts and plantar warts in men and women. Other strains are sexually transmitted. Some can cause genital warts in men and women but aren't associated with cancer. However, a handful of "high-risk" HPV strains are strongly tied to cancer of the cervix. More than 99% of cervical cancer cases are believed to arise from HPV infections.

HPV infects epithelial cells, a type of cell that lines the body cavities and covers the outer surface of the body. Once inside a cell, the virus hijacks the cellular machinery to produce new viruses. The high-risk strains of HPV take

When the normal checks on cell division become derailed, cancer can result.

it one step further: Those viruses that aren't fought off by the immune system can permanently integrate their own eight-gene DNA sequence into the host cell's DNA.

Once integrated into the DNA of human epithelial cells, two viral genes, *E6* and *E7*, ramp up their activity and produce two proteins. These viral proteins inhibit the activity of key tumor suppressor genes. Tumor suppressor genes code for proteins that keep cell division in check by slowing down cell division, repairing DNA replication errors, or instructing defective cells to die. When tumor suppressors are prevented from doing these jobs, cancer can grow.

HPV strikes in two ways. The viral E6 protein inhibits a protein called p53, an important tumor suppressor, which in healthy cells controls responses to cellular stresses such as DNA damage. However, when bound by E6, p53 becomes essentially inactive. Meanwhile, the viral E7 protein inhibits a protein called Rb, which normally blocks transcription factors that promote cell division. Without Rb and p53 to put the brakes on cell division, cervical cells divide uncontrollably.

As they grow and multiply, the abnormal cells push through the basal lamina, a thin layer that separates the epithelial cells lining the cervix from the connective tissue beneath. Untreated, invasive cancer can spread to other organs. Once cancer travels beyond its primary location, the situation is grim. Most cancers cannot be cured after they have spread.

The U.S. Food and Drug Administration (FDA) has approved two vaccines for HPV, both of which protect against the high-risk strains responsible for cervical cancer. Medical groups such as the American Academy of Pediatrics and governmental organizations such as the Centers for Disease Control and Prevention (CDC) recommend

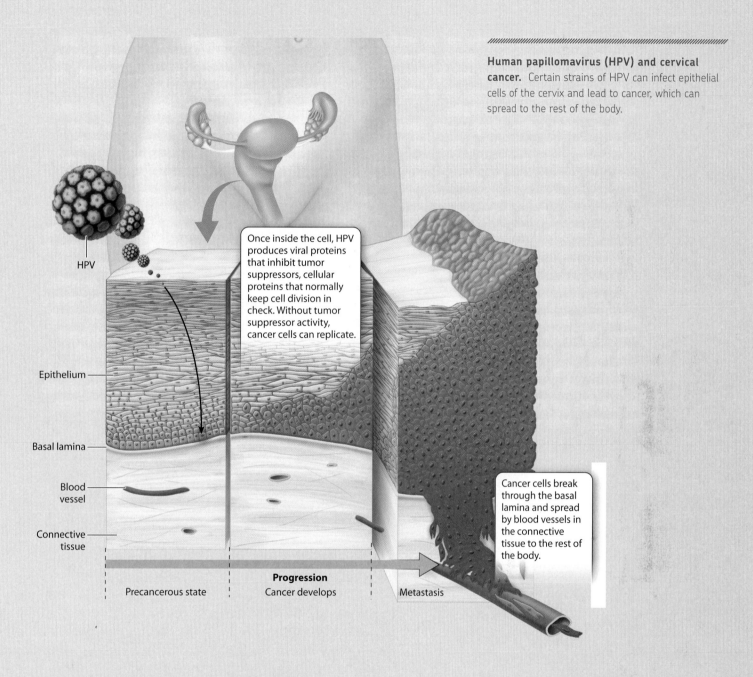

Human papillomavirus (HPV) and cervical cancer. Certain strains of HPV can infect epithelial cells of the cervix and lead to cancer, which can spread to the rest of the body.

HPV

Once inside the cell, HPV produces viral proteins that inhibit tumor suppressors, cellular proteins that normally keep cell division in check. Without tumor suppressor activity, cancer cells can replicate.

Epithelium

Basal lamina

Blood vessel

Connective tissue

Cancer cells break through the basal lamina and spread by blood vessels in the connective tissue to the rest of the body.

Progression

Precancerous state | Cancer develops | Metastasis

vaccinating girls at age 11 or 12, before they become sexually active. In addition, recent CDC guidelines also recommend vaccinating boys because they can transmit the virus to women when they become sexually active.

On the basis of these recommendations, Virginia and Washington, D.C., require that middle-school girls receive the vaccine, and many other states are considering similar legislation. But there are critics of these mandates. Some say the government shouldn't be making medical decisions. Others argue that the vaccine condones sexual activity among young girls and boys. Still others have expressed concern over the vaccine's safety.

Studies have found the HPV vaccine to be safe, a conclusion backed by a 2010 report from the Institute of Medicine, an independent nonprofit organization that advises the U.S government on issues of health. In spite of these findings, the HPV vaccine has not been widely accepted. The CDC found that by 2010, a full 5 years after the vaccine was introduced, only 32% of teenage girls had been vaccinated.

Proponents of HPV vaccination say those numbers should cause concern. HPV is common: A 2007 study found that nearly 27% of American women ages 14–59 were infected with the virus. Among

20- to 24-year-olds, the infection rate was nearly 45%. Certainly, not everyone who contracts HPV will develop cancer. Most people manage to clear the virus from their bodies within 2 years of infection. But in some cases, the virus hangs on and cancer results.

Because cancer is often difficult to treat, especially in its later stages, many researchers focus on early detection or prevention. Early detection of cervical cancer can be made from routinely taken Pap smears, in which cells from the cervix are collected and observed under a microscope. Cervical cancer is also an obvious target for prevention, since it is caused by a virus that can be averted with a conventional vaccine. However, most cancers are not caused by viruses, and developing vaccines to prevent those cancers is a trickier proposition—but researchers are pushing ahead.

At the Mayo Clinic in Rochester, Minnesota, researchers are working to design vaccines to prevent breast and ovarian cancers from recurring in women who have been treated for these diseases. The researchers have zeroed in on proteins on the surface of cancerous cells. Cells communicate with one another by releasing signaling molecules that are picked up by receptor molecules on another cell's surface, much the way a radio antenna picks up a radio signal sent across a distance. Cellular communication is critical for a functioning organism. Sometimes, though, the signaling process goes awry.

The Mayo Clinic team is focusing on two cell surface receptors that, when malfunctioning, lead to cancer. One, Her2/neu, promotes the growth of aggressive breast cancer cells. The other, folate receptor α (alpha) protein, is frequently overexpressed in breast and ovarian tumors. The researchers hope to train patients' immune systems to generate antibodies that recognize these proteins, and then destroy the cancerous cells. The approach successfully prevented tumors in mice. Now the researchers are testing the vaccines in humans.

Even if these new therapies turn out to be successful, cancer researchers have much more work to do. Cancer is not one disease but many, and most of them are caused by a complex interplay of genetics and environmental factors. Any number of things can go wrong as cells communicate, grow, and divide. But as researchers learn more about the cellular processes involved, they can step in to prevent or treat cancer. As the HPV vaccine shows, there is significant progress to be made.

? CASE 2 QUESTIONS

1. How do cell signaling errors lead to cancer? *See page 9-15.*
2. How can doctors test for the spread of cancer? *See page 10-5.*
3. How do cancer cells spread throughout the body? *See page 10-18.*
4. What genes are involved in cancer? *See page 11-17.*

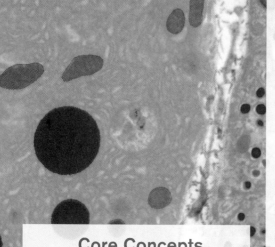

CHAPTER 9

CELL COMMUNICATION

Core Concepts

9.1 Cells communicate primarily by sending and receiving chemical signals.

9.2 Cell signaling can be classified according to the distance between the signaling and responding cells.

9.3 Signaling molecules bind to and activate specific cell-surface and intra-cellular receptors.

9.4 Signals are transmitted across the plasma membrane, are often amplified in the cytosol leading to a cellular response, and are eventually terminated.

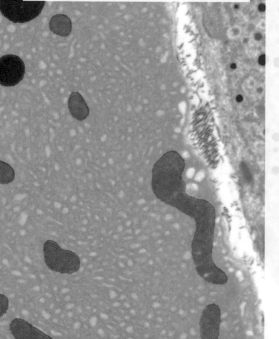

Up to this point, we have considered how life works by looking mainly at what happens inside individual cells. We have seen how a cell uses the information stored in genes to synthesize the proteins necessary to carry out their functions. We have also seen how the plasma membrane actively keeps the environment inside the cell different from that outside it. Finally, we have explored how a cell harvests and uses energy from the environment. Most cells, however, do not exist in isolation. Instead, they exist in sometimes simple, but more often highly complex, communities of cells.

Successful communities have several features in common. First, individuals within a community communicate with one another. Cells respond to information provided by neighboring cells or to information provided by the surrounding environment. Second, individuals or groups of individuals within a community have particular skills that enable them to perform specific tasks essential to the well-being of the community. Cells in multicellular organisms have specialized functions: Muscle cells are specialized for contraction, red blood cells for transporting oxygen, and skin cells for establishing a physical barrier. Third, members of a community stick together—literally, in the case of cells. Most cells in multicellular organisms are physically attached to other cells or to other materials in their surroundings. The physical associations among some cells are very strong. In other instances, the connections between cells are transient and far less elaborate.

In the next three chapters, we consider communities of cells. In Chapter 9, we look at how cells communicate with one another. In Chapter 10, we consider cell shape and structure, which are both important for the ability of cells to perform their specific tasks, and we examine how cells physically interact with one another. Finally, in Chapter 11, we examine the means by which new members are added to cellular communities through cell division.

9.1 PRINCIPLES OF CELL COMMUNICATION

As members of our own communities, we often base our actions on information we receive from others in the group, responding very differently to a friendly handshake or affectionate hug than to a hard shove or violent blow. We also glean information from inanimate things around us: We respond differently when we walk barefoot on hot pavement than when we take a seat in a comfortable chair. Similarly, the activities of virtually all cells are influenced by their physical surroundings, including interactions with other members of the community of cells. Cells receive large amounts of information from their surroundings, from numerous sources and in different ways. Often, information is conveyed from one cell to another in the form of small molecules secreted into the environment. Other information is provided by physical contact with neighboring cells. Still other information is provided by the meshwork of proteins and polysaccharides that underlies or surrounds most cells in multicellular organisms (Chapter 10).

In this section, we take a look at general principles of cell communication, including how cells send and receive signals and how a cell responds after it receives a signal. These basic principles apply to all living organisms, both prokaryotes and eukaryotes, and both unicellular and multicellular organisms.

Cells communicate using chemical signals that bind to specific receptors.

An example from prokaryotes illustrates some important principles underlying cell communication. *Streptococcus pneumoniae* (also known as pneumococcus) is a disease-causing bacterium that is associated not only with pneumonia but also with meningitis and some kinds of arthritis. Many bacteria, including pneumococcus, are able to take up DNA from the environment and incorporate it into their own genome. By this means, individual bacterial cells can share genes with advantageous properties, including the ability to resist antibiotic drugs.

In the 1960s, it was observed that the rate of DNA uptake by pneumococcal cells increased sharply once the bacterial population reached a certain density. Scientists concluded that the bacteria were able to coordinate DNA uptake across the population so that uptake occurred only at the appropriate time. How is it possible that these bacteria "know" how many other bacteria are present and are able to communicate this information to one another?

In the 1990s, scientists discovered a peptide consisting of 17 amino acids that is continuously synthesized and released by pneumococcal cells. Not long after, a receptor for this peptide was discovered on the surface of the pneumococcal cells. The binding of this peptide to its receptor causes a bacterium to express the genes required for DNA uptake. When the bacteria are at low density, the concentration of the peptide is too low to activate the genes required for DNA uptake (**Fig. 9.1a**). As the population density increases, so does the concentration of the peptide, until it reaches a level high enough to cause the cells to turn on the genes necessary for DNA uptake (**Fig. 9.1b**).

This simple example of DNA uptake by pneumococcus illustrates the four essential elements involved in communication between all cells, whether prokaryotic or, as shown in **Fig. 9.2**, eukaryotic. These elements are a **signaling cell,** a **signaling molecule,** a **receptor molecule**, and a **responding cell.** The signaling cell is the source of the signaling molecule, which binds to a receptor molecule on or in the responding cell. In the case of pneumococcus, the bacterial cells are both the signaling cells and the responding cells. In other cases, the signaling and responding cells may be different cells. Nevertheless, the general idea that cells are able to communicate by sending a signaling molecule that binds to a receptor on a responding cell is universal among both prokaryotes and eukaryotes. These four players

FIG. 9.1   **Communication among bacterial cells.**

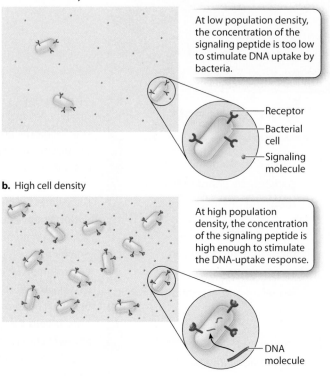

a. Low cell density

At low population density, the concentration of the signaling peptide is too low to stimulate DNA uptake by bacteria.

Receptor
Bacterial cell
Signaling molecule

b. High cell density

At high population density, the concentration of the signaling peptide is high enough to stimulate the DNA-uptake response.

DNA molecule

interact in very much the same way in diverse types of cellular communication.

Signaling involves receptor activation, signal transduction, response, and termination.

What happens after a signaling molecule binds to a receptor on a responding cell? On binding the signal, the receptor is turned on, or **activated** (**Fig. 9.3**). Once activated, the receptor transmits the message through the cytoplasm, often by intracellular signaling

FIG. 9.2   **Four components required for cellular communication: a signaling cell, a signaling molecule, a receptor, and a responding cell.**

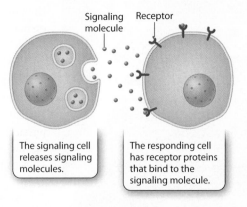

Signaling molecule   Receptor

The signaling cell releases signaling molecules.

The responding cell has receptor proteins that bind to the signaling molecule.

FIG. 9.3 Steps in cell signaling: receptor activation, signal transduction, response, and termination.

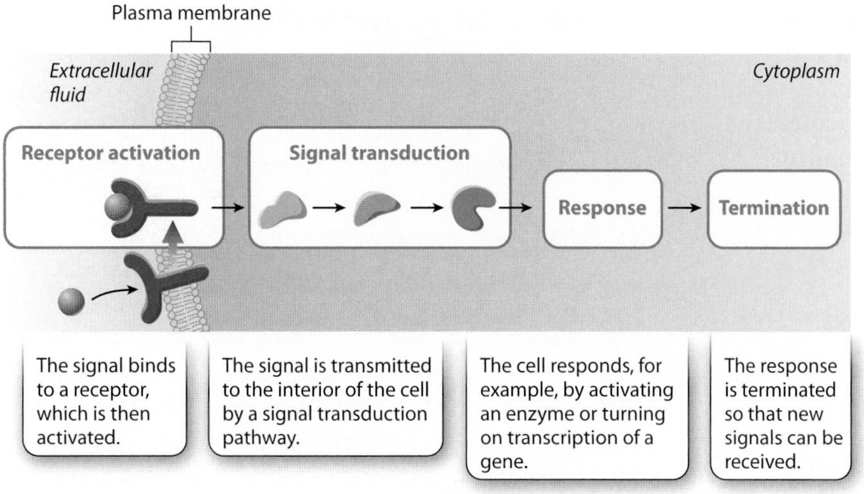

Plasma membrane

Extracellular fluid

Cytoplasm

| Receptor activation | Signal transduction | Response | Termination |

The signal binds to a receptor, which is then activated.

The signal is transmitted to the interior of the cell by a signal transduction pathway.

The cell responds, for example, by activating an enzyme or turning on transcription of a gene.

The response is terminated so that new signals can be received.

pathways or cascades, in a process called **signal transduction.** The message is carried from outside the cell into the cytosol or nucleus. Along the way, the initial signal is often amplified, so that a small signal can have a large effect on the responding cell.

Next, there is a cellular **response,** which can take different forms depending on the nature of the signal and the type of responding cell. For example, signaling pathways can activate enzymes or turn on genes that cause the cell to divide, change shape, or signal other cells. Finally, the signal is terminated. **Termination** allows the cell to respond to new signals.

In the case of pneumococcal cells, the peptide-signaling molecule binds to a receptor on the cell surface. When enough receptors are bound by the signaling molecule, the message is relayed by signal-transduction pathways to the nucleoid in the cytosol, where genes are turned on that express proteins involved in DNA uptake from the environment. Eventually, when the density of bacteria is low, the initiating signal falls below a critical threshold and gene expression is turned back off. This example is relatively simple. Remarkably, however, other signaling pathways in a wide range of organisms involve the same four players and a common

series of steps, which have been evolutionarily conserved over long periods of time.

9.2 TYPES OF CELL SIGNALING

In prokaryotes and unicellular eukaryotes, cell communication is communication between individuals. In complex multicellular eukaryotes, cell signaling involves communication between cells that make up an individual. The same principles apply in both instances, but there are differences to be considered. In multicellular organisms, the distance between communicating cells varies considerably. In addition, many cells in multicellular organisms are physically attached to one another, in which case the signaling molecule is not released from the signaling cell. In this section, we explore communication over long and short distances, as well as communication among cells that are physically associated with one another.

Endocrine signaling acts over long distances.
Signaling molecules released by a cell may have to travel great distances in the body, usually via the circulatory system, to reach their target responding cells. Signaling by means of molecules that travel through the bloodstream is called **endocrine signaling** (**Fig. 9.4a** and Chapter 38).

FIG. 9.4 Types of cell communication. Cell communication can be classified according to the distance between the signaling and responding cells.

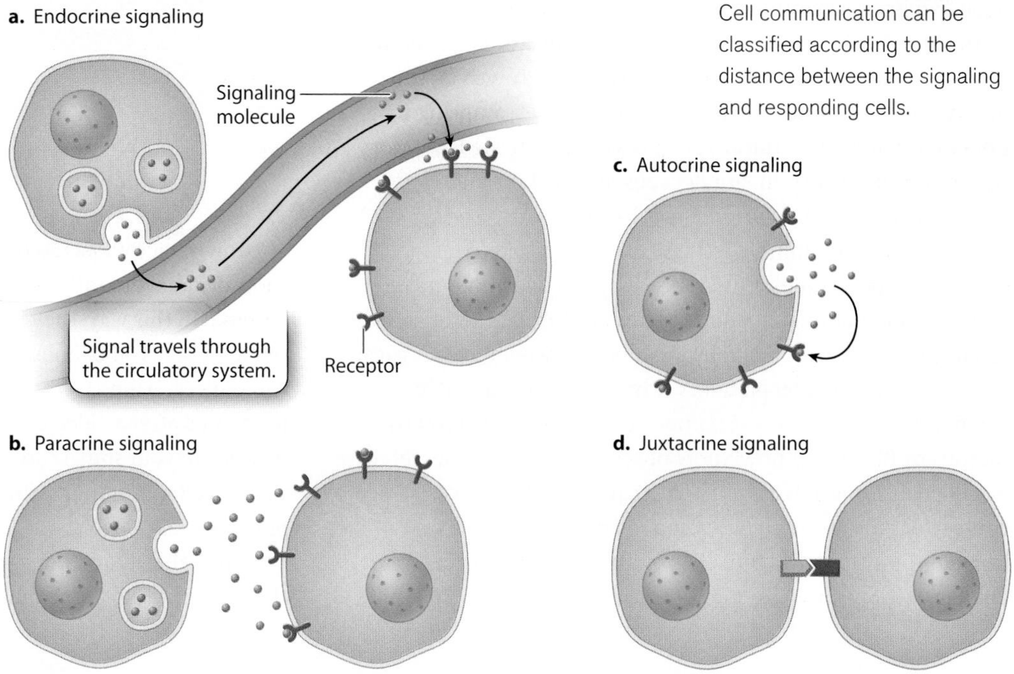

a. Endocrine signaling

Signaling molecule

Signal travels through the circulatory system.

Receptor

b. Paracrine signaling

c. Autocrine signaling

d. Juxtacrine signaling

Familiar examples of endocrine-signaling molecules include the mammalian steroid hormones estradiol (an estrogen) and testosterone (an androgen). These hormones travel from the ovaries and the testes, respectively (although there are other minor sources of these hormones), through the bloodstream, to target cells in various tissues throughout the body. The increased amount of estrogen in girls during puberty causes the development of breast tissue and the beginning of menstrual cycles. The increased amount of testosterone in boys during puberty causes the growth of muscle cells, the deepening of the voice, and the growth of facial hair (Chapter 42).

→ **Quick Check 1** If a hormone is released into the bloodstream and therefore comes into contact with many cells, what determines which cells in the body respond to the hormone?

Paracrine and autocrine signaling act over short distances.

In contrast to endocrine signaling, **paracrine signaling** (**Fig. 9.4b**) involves two cells that are close together. In this case, a signaling molecule needs to diffuse only a short distance to the nearest neighboring cell in order to bind its receptor and deliver its message. Signaling molecules in paracrine communication travel distances of up to 20 cell diameters, or a few hundred micrometers. In some cases, signaling molecules may be secreted by a cell and then bind to receptors on the very same cell, as we saw in the case of pneumococcal cells. Such cases, where signaling cell and responding cell are one and the same, are examples of **autocrine signaling** (**Fig. 9.4c**). Paracrine and autocrine signaling are especially important to multicellular organisms during the development of the embryo (Chapter 20).

In paracrine signaling, the signal is usually a small, soluble molecule, such as a **growth factor.** The first growth factor discovered was found by scientists who were attempting to understand how to maintain cultures of cells in the laboratory for use in their research. For decades, medical research has worked with cells maintained in culture. Initially, these cultured cells had limited use because they failed to divide outside the body unless they were supplied with unidentified factors from mammalian blood serum. In 1974, American scientists Nancy Kohler and Allan Lipton discovered that these factors are secreted by platelets (**Fig. 9.5**). Consequently, the first growth factor was named "platelet-derived growth factor," or PDGF. We now know of scores of proteins secreted by cells that function as growth factors, and in most cases their effects are confined to neighboring cells. These effects include the stimulation of cell growth, cell division, and changes in gene expression.

FIG. 9.5

Where do growth factors come from?

BACKGROUND Cells can be grown outside the body in culture. However, they survive and grow well only under certain conditions. Researchers hypothesized that there are substances that are required for growth of cells in culture, but the nature and source of these substances was unknown. A key insight came from the observation that chicken cells grew much better if they were cultured in the presence of blood serum rather than blood plasma. Blood serum is the liquid component of blood that is collected after blood has been allowed to clot. Blood plasma is also the liquid component of blood, but it is collected from blood that has not clotted. American biologists Nancy Kohler and Allan Lipton were interested in identifying the source of the factor in blood serum that allows cells to survive in culture.

HYPOTHESIS Since Kohler and Lipton knew that clotting depends on the release of substances from platelets, they hypothesized that a growth-promoting factor was activated or introduced into the blood by platelets during the clotting reaction.

EXPERIMENT 1 The investigators first confirmed earlier observations using cells called fibroblasts, which they took from mice. They cultured two sets of fibroblasts in small plastic dishes. To one of the cultures they added serum; to the other culture they added plasma. Then they monitored the rate of cell division in both culture dishes for nine days.

RESULTS 1 They observed that the rate of cell division in the fibroblasts cultured in serum was far greater than that of the cells cultured in plasma, as expected (Fig. 9.5a).

Growth factors secreted by cells in an embryo work over short distances to influence the kind of cells their neighbors will become. In this way, they help shape the structure of the adult's tissues, organs, and limbs. For example, in developing vertebrates, paracrine signaling by the growth factor Sonic Hedgehog (yes, it's named after a video game character) ensures that the motor neurons in your spinal cord are located properly, that the bones of your vertebral column form correctly, and that your thumb and pinky fingers are on the correct sides of your hands.

A specialized form of paracrine signaling in many organisms is the communication between neurons (nerve cells), or between

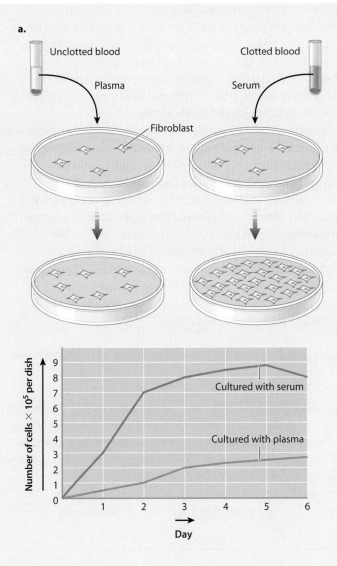

a.

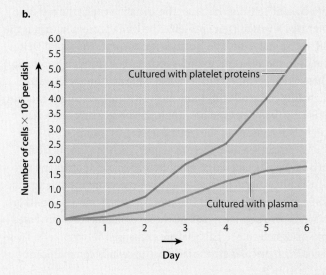

EXPERIMENT 2 To see if the factor is released directly from platelets, they prepared a solution of proteins made from purified platelets, added these proteins to cultured fibroblasts, and measured cell growth.

RESULTS 2 They found that the solution of platelet proteins also caused an increase in the growth of fibroblasts compared to the growth of fibroblasts in plasma (Fig. 9.5b).

b.

CONCLUSION Kohler and Lipton concluded that the growth-promoting factor is a protein that is released by platelets on activation and clot formation, and therefore normally present in serum.

FOLLOW-UP WORK Subsequent work over the next few years by these and other scientists resulted in the purification and characterization of the growth factor we know today as platelet-derived growth factor, or PDGF.

SOURCE Kohler, N., and A. Lipton. 1974. "Platelets as a Source of Fibroblast Growth-Promoting Activity." *Experimental Cell Research* 87:297–301.

neurons and muscle cells (Chapter 35). When neurotransmitters, a type of signaling molecule, are released from a neuron, they diffuse across a very small space, called a synapse, between the signaling cell and the responding cell. If the adjacent cell is a neuron, it often responds by transmitting the nerve impulse further and then releasing additional neurotransmitters. If the responding cell is a muscle cell, it often responds by contracting.

Juxtacrine signaling depends on direct cell–cell contact.
In some cases, a cell communicates with another cell through direct physical contact, without a chemical signal that diffuses or circulates through an external medium. This type of communication is called contact-dependent signaling, or **juxtacrine signaling** (**Fig. 9.4d**). It requires that the two communicating cells be in physical contact with each other. A transmembrane protein on the surface of one cell acts as the signaling molecule, and a transmembrane protein on the surface of an adjacent cell acts as the receptor.

As an example of juxtacrine signaling, let's look at the development of the central nervous system of vertebrate animals. In the brain and spinal cord, neurons transmit information in the form of electrical signals from one part of the body to another. The neurons in the central nervous system are greatly outnumbered by supporting cells, called glial cells, that nourish and insulate the neurons. Both the neurons and the glial cells start out as similar cells in the embryo, but some of these undifferentiated cells become neurons and many more become glial cells.

For reasons that are not entirely clear, the amount of a transmembrane protein called Delta dramatically increases on the surface of some of these undifferentiated cells. Delta binds to a transmembrane protein called Notch on the surface of adjacent cells. In this case, the signaling cell is the cell with elevated levels of Delta protein. The Delta protein in turn is the signaling molecule, and Notch is its receptor. The signal Delta sends to the adjacent, undifferentiated cell through Notch is a message to become a glial cell and not a neuron. Because one signaling cell sends this same message to all the cells it touches, it is easy to understand how there can be so many more glial cells than neurons in the central nervous system.

As you can see from these examples, the ways in which cells of a developing embryo communicate with one another and the way neurons signal muscle cells or other neurons are based on the same principles at work in DNA uptake by pneumococcal cells in response to a peptide signal. All these communications are based on small-molecule signals that are exchanged between cells. These signaling molecules are the language of cellular communication.

9.3 RECEPTORS AND RECEPTOR ACTIVATION

Receptors are proteins that receive and interpret information carried by signaling molecules. Regardless of the distance

between communicating cells, a message is received by a cell when the signaling molecule binds noncovalently to its appropriate and usually highly specific receptor protein. For this reason, the signaling molecule is often referred to as a **ligand** (from the Latin *ligare*, which means "to bind"). The signaling molecule binds to a specific location on the receptor protein called the **ligand-binding site.**

Almost without exception, the binding of a signaling molecule to the ligand-binding site of a receptor causes a conformational change in the receptor. We say that the conformational change "activates" the receptor because it is through this change that the receptor passes the message from the signaling molecule to the interior of the cell. In many ways, this change in receptor shape is similar to the change that occurs when a substrate binds to the active site of an enzyme (Chapter 6). The conformational change in the receptor ultimately triggers various chemical reactions or other changes in the cytosol, and is therefore a crucial step in the reception and interpretation of communications from other cells.

Receptors can be on the cell surface or in the interior of the cell.

The location of a particular receptor in a cell depends largely on whether the signaling molecule is polar or nonpolar (**Fig. 9.6**). Many signaling molecules, such as the growth factors we just encountered, are small, polar proteins that cannot pass through the hydrophobic core of the plasma membrane. The receptor proteins for these signals are on the outside surface of the responding cell (Fig. 9.6a).

Receptor proteins for growth factors and other polar ligands are transmembrane proteins with an extracellular

---

FIG. 9.6   Cell-surface and intracellular receptors. (a) Cell-surface receptors interact with polar signaling molecules that cannot cross the plasma membrane. (b) Intracellular receptors interact with nonpolar signaling molecules that can cross the plasma membrane.

a. Cell-surface receptor

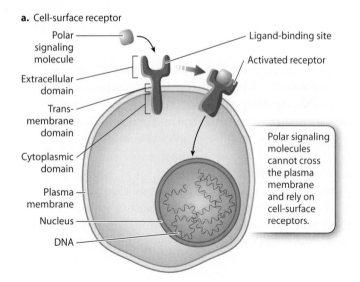

b. Intracellular receptor

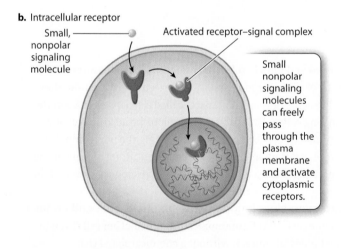

domain, a short transmembrane domain, and a cytoplasmic domain. When a signaling molecule binds to the ligand-binding site in the extracellular domain, the entire molecule, including the cytoplasmic domain of the receptor, undergoes a conformational change, and as a result the molecule is activated. In this way, the receptor acts as a bridge between the inside and outside of the responding cell that carries the message of the hydrophilic signal across the hydrophobic core of the plasma membrane. The type of receptor determines which signaling pathway is activated and ultimately determines how the cell responds to the signaling molecule. We discuss several examples of signaling pathways in section 9.4.

Some nonpolar signaling molecules, such as the steroid hormones involved in endocrine signaling, don't need a receptor on the cell surface in order to relay information to the interior of the cell. Since steroids are derived from cholesterol, they are hydrophobic and pass easily through the hydrophobic core of the phospholipid bilayer and into the target cell. Once inside, steroid hormones bind to receptor proteins located in the cytosol or in the nucleus to form receptor–steroid complexes (Fig. 9.6b). Steroid–receptor complexes formed in the cytosol enter the nucleus, where they act as transcriptional regulators to control the expression of specific genes. Steroid receptors located in the nucleus are often already bound to DNA and need only to bind their steroid counterpart to become active.

The importance of steroid hormones and their receptors cannot be overstated. Sex hormones, glucocorticoids (which raise blood glucose levels), and ecdysone (involved in insect molting) are examples of steroid hormones. However, since the majority of information received by cells is transmitted across the plasma membrane through transmembrane receptors, we focus our attention on the sequence of events that takes place when receptors on the surface of cells bind their ligands.

There are three major types of cell-surface receptor, which act like molecular switches.

As we saw earlier, receptor activation occurs after a signaling molecule binds to the ligand-binding site on its receptor. Many receptors, in fact, act as binary molecular switches, existing in only two alternative states, either "on" or "off," like a light switch without a dimmer (**Fig. 9.7a**). Receptors behave similarly to a light switch. When bound to their signaling molecule, the molecular switch is turned on. When the signaling molecule is no longer bound, the switch is turned off.

There are thousands of different receptor proteins on the surface of any given cell. Most of them can be placed into one of three groups according to the way they are activated. The first type of cell-surface receptor is called a **G protein-coupled receptor** (**Fig. 9.7b**). As its name suggests, this type of receptor couples to, or associates with, **G proteins,** proteins that bind to

---

FIG. 9.7 **Three types of cell-surface receptor.** G protein-coupled receptors (b), receptor kinases (c), and ligand-gated ion channels (d) can be either "off" (not activated) or "on" (activated), and in this way they act like a light switch (a).

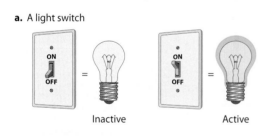

a. A light switch

ON
OFF

Inactive

ON
OFF

Active

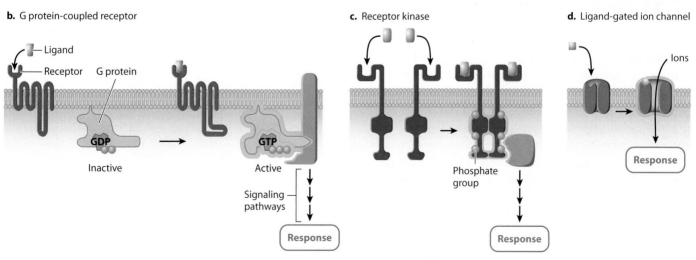

b. G protein-coupled receptor

Ligand

Receptor   G protein

GDP

Inactive

GTP

Active

Signaling pathways

Response

c. Receptor kinase

Phosphate group

Response

d. Ligand-gated ion channel

Ions

Response

the guanine nucleotides GTP and GDP. When a G protein is bound to GTP, it is active, and when it is bound to GDP, it is inactive. When a ligand binds to a G protein-coupled receptor, the receptor binds to and activates the G protein by replacing GDP with GTP. As long as the G protein is bound to GTP, it is in the "on" position and the signal is propagated.

→   **Quick Check 2** Is the term "G protein" just a shorter name for a G protein-coupled receptor?

The second type of receptor is an enzyme called a **receptor kinase** (**Fig. 9.7c**). A kinase is an enzyme that adds a phosphate group to another molecule in a process called phosphorylation. **Phosphatases** have the opposite effect and remove a phosphate group, a process called dephosphorylation. Usually (but not always), when a protein is phosphorylated by a kinase, it becomes active and is switched on. When the protein is dephosphorylated by a phosphatase, it is switched off and becomes inactive.

Receptors in the third group, the **ligand-gated ion channels,** alter the flow of ions across the plasma membrane when bound by their ligand (**Fig. 9.7d**). Recall from Chapter 5 that channel proteins help ions and other molecules diffuse into and out of the cell by providing a hydrophilic pathway through the hydrophobic core of the phospholipid bilayer. Most of the time, the channels are closed to prevent the free movement of ions across the membrane. However, when a signaling molecule binds to the extracellular ligand-binding site of the channel protein, the channel undergoes a conformational change that opens it and allows ions to flow in and out. The channel remains open as long as the signaling molecule remains bound. This type of signaling is especially important for neurons and muscle cells, since their primary functions depend on a rapid change in ion transport across the plasma membrane.

9.4 SIGNAL TRANSDUCTION, RESPONSE, AND TERMINATION

In this section, we focus on what happens after a signaling molecule binds to its receptor and flips a molecular switch. Although the molecular switches are different, the subsequent steps are similar. Following the binding of a ligand and receptor activation, most signaling pathways involve signal transduction and amplification, a cellular response, and termination of the signal. We examine the signaling pathways activated by G protein-coupled receptors, receptor kinases, and ligand-gated ion channels. We also consider the role of signal transduction in cancer and how different signaling pathways intersect with one another.

Signals transmitted by G protein-coupled receptors are amplified and regulated at several steps.

Signaling by G protein-coupled receptors is widespread, and its effects are diverse. The receptors are highly conserved evolutionarily and are found in virtually every eukaryotic organism. In humans, more than 900 different G protein-coupled receptors have been found. Signaling through these receptors makes possible our senses of sight, smell, and taste. They also enable the cells that express them to respond to a number of different hormones. Despite this great variability in the nature of the signals, the signal transduction events triggered by these receptors are remarkably similar.

FIG. 9.8   **Activation of a G protein through a G protein-coupled receptor.** A G protein-coupled receptor is activated when it binds a signaling molecule, which leads to exchange of GDP for GTP, separation of the α subunit of the G protein, and downstream effects.

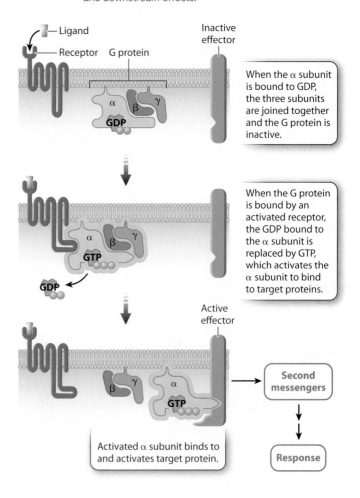

When the α subunit is bound to GDP, the three subunits are joined together and the G protein is inactive.

When the G protein is bound by an activated receptor, the GDP bound to the α subunit is replaced by GTP, which activates the α subunit to bind to target proteins.

Activated α subunit binds to and activates target protein.

As we saw in section 9.3, G protein-coupled receptors are transmembrane proteins that bind signaling molecules. These receptors are positioned in proximity to G proteins, which are located on the cytoplasmic side of the plasma membrane. When a signaling molecule binds to the receptor, the cytoplasmic domain of the receptor binds to and activates the nearby G protein by exchanging GDP with GTP. The activated G protein goes on to activate additional proteins in the signaling pathway.

G proteins are composed of three subunits called the α (alpha), β (beta), and γ (gamma) subunits (**Fig. 9.8**). The α subunit is the part of the G protein that binds to either GDP or GTP. When the α subunit is bound to GDP, the three subunits are joined and the G protein is inactive. When the G protein is bound by an activated receptor, the GDP bound to the α subunit is replaced by GTP, which causes the α subunit to separate from the β and γ subunits. The isolated GTP-bound α subunit is now active and able to bind to specific target proteins in the cell, activating them in turn.

Let's consider an example. You're startled or you're scared, and you experience that strange feeling in the pit of the stomach and rapid heartbeat that we've all felt at one time or another. This effect, which accompanies fright or other forms of stress, is mediated by adrenaline, a hormone released by the adrenal glands that binds to a G protein-coupled receptor. When adrenaline binds to its G protein-coupled receptor on cardiac muscle cells, GDP in the G protein is replaced by GTP and activates the G protein. The GTP-bound α subunit of the activated G protein then binds to and activates an enzyme in the cell membrane called adenylyl cyclase. Adenylyl cyclase converts the nucleotide ATP into cyclic AMP, abbreviated as cAMP. This molecule is one of several intermediate, cytosolic signaling molecules known as **second messengers** (adrenaline being the first messenger). Once formed, cAMP binds to and activates another enzyme, a kinase called protein kinase A, or PKA. The phosphorylation of specific proteins in the heart muscle by PKA causes the rate of contraction to increase (**Fig. 9.9**). As long as adrenaline is bound to its receptor, the heart rate remains high, resulting in increased blood flow to the brain and skeletal muscles needed to deal with the stress.

A little adrenaline goes a long way as a result of signal amplification. A single receptor bound to adrenaline can activate several individual G protein molecules and continues to do so until the adrenaline leaves the binding site of the receptor. Every one of the activated G protein α subunits binds to an adenylyl cyclase molecule and, as long as the α subunit remains bound, the enzyme continues to generate cAMP. Every cAMP molecule binds to an available protein kinase A molecule, and likewise, as long as cAMP remains bound, the kinase continues to phosphorylate its target proteins. These sequential molecular changes in the cytosol amplify the signal so that a very small amount of signaling molecule has a large effect on a responding cell.

In this example, the adrenaline signal is amplified in three places: (1) Each receptor activates multiple G proteins; (2) each molecule of adenylyl cyclase produces large amounts of the second messenger cAMP; and (3) each protein kinase A

FIG. 9.9 **Adrenaline signaling in heart muscle.** Adrenaline binds to a G protein-coupled receptor, leading to production of the second messenger cAMP, activation of protein kinase A, and increased heart rate.

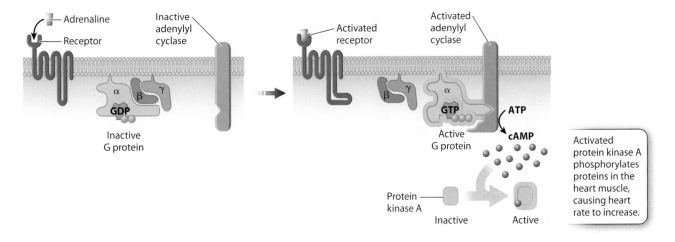

molecule activated by cAMP activates multiple protein targets by phosphorylation (**Fig. 9.10**).

After a good scare, we eventually calm down and our heartbeat returns to normal. This change means that the signal initiated by adrenaline has been terminated. Let's look at how this happens (**Fig. 9.11**). First, most ligands, including adrenaline, do not bind

to their receptors permanently. The amount of time a signaling molecule remains bound to its receptor depends on how tightly the receptor holds on to it, a property called **binding affinity.** Once adrenaline leaves the receptor, the receptor reverts to its inactive conformation and no longer activates adjacent G proteins. If the concentration of adrenaline in the system is high enough, then as

FIG. 9.10 Amplification of G protein signaling. Signaling through G protein-coupled receptors is amplified at several places, so that a small amount of signal can produce a large response in the cell.

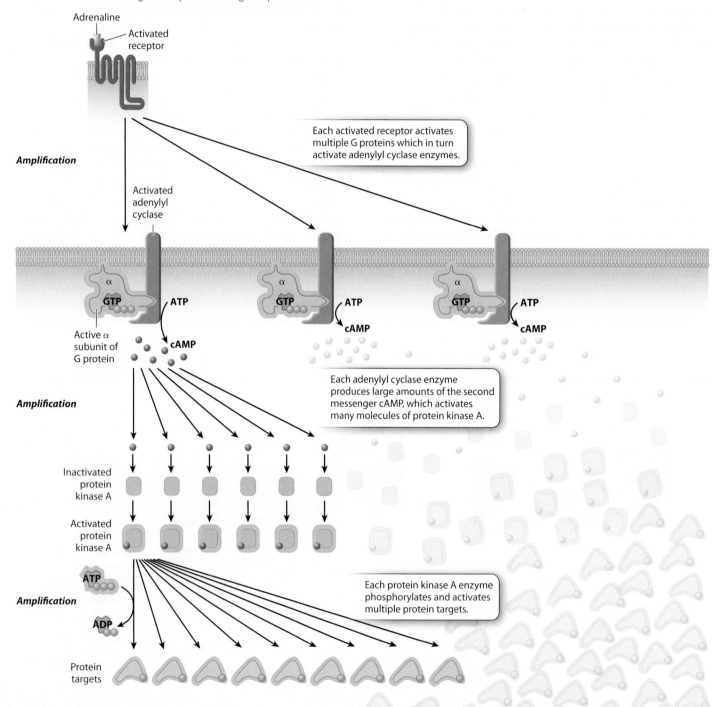

FIG. 9.11 **Termination of a G protein signal.** G protein-coupled signaling is terminated at several places, allowing the cell to respond to new signals.

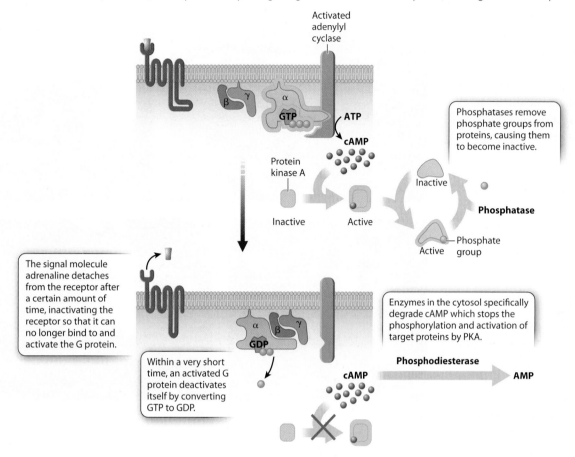

soon as one adrenaline molecule leaves the receptor, another takes its place and reactivates the receptor. However, once the concentration of adrenaline returns to normal low levels, the receptors are no longer continually occupied and they become inactive.

Even once a receptor has been turned off, a signal will continue to be transmitted unless all the other components of the signaling pathway are also inactivated. In our example of the adrenaline-signaling pathway, a second place where the signal is terminated is at the G protein itself (Fig. 9.11). As we saw earlier, the α subunit is able to bind to and activate other proteins only when it is bound to GTP. G proteins have enzymatic activity, and they are able to catalyze the hydrolysis of GTP to GDP and inorganic phosphate. This means that an active, GTP-bound α subunit in the "on" position automatically turns itself "off" by converting the GTP to GDP. In fact, the α subunit converts GTP to GDP almost as soon as a molecule of GTP binds to it. Thus, a G protein is able to activate adenylyl cyclase, and adenylyl cyclase is able to make cAMP only during the very short time it takes the α subunit to convert its bound GTP to GDP, a timescale on the order of seconds. Without an active receptor to generate more active G protein α subunits, transmission of the signal quickly comes to a halt.

Farther down the pathway, enzymes shut down other components. An enzyme converts the second messenger cAMP to AMP, which inactivates protein kinase A. Phosphatases remove the phosphate groups, inactivating proteins targeted by protein kinase A (Fig. 9.11). In fact, most signaling events counteract kinases and phosphatases at one or more points in the pathway as a means of increasing or decreasing the response of the cell to the signal.

→ **Quick Check 3** Name four ways in which the adrenaline signal to the heart is terminated.

Receptor kinases phosphorylate each other and activate intracellular signaling pathways.

Like the communication that takes place through G protein-coupled receptors, signaling through receptor kinases causes cells to respond in many ways. During embryonic development, receptor kinase signaling is responsible for the formation and elongation of structures called limb buds that eventually become our arms and legs. As adults, insulin signaling through its receptor kinase enables virtually every cell in our body to transport glucose across the plasma membrane into the cytosol. When we cut a finger, platelet-derived growth factor is released from platelets in the blood and binds to its receptor kinase on the surface of cells at the site of the wound, where it triggers the cell division necessary to repair the damaged tissue.

Signaling through receptor kinases takes place in most eukaryotic organisms, and the structure and function of these receptors has been remarkably conserved evolutionarily. A receptor kinase called Kit has been studied in a number of animal models. In vertebrates, signaling through the Kit receptor kinase is important for the production of pigment in skin, feathers, scales, and hair. The conserved function of this receptor is obvious in individuals with mutations in the *kit* gene, as

FIG. 9.12   **Mutations in the Kit receptor kinase.** Similar patterns of incomplete pigmentation are present in mammals, reptiles, birds, and fish with this mutated receptor.

shown in **Fig. 9.12**. (By convention, the name of a protein, like Kit, is capitalized and in roman type. The name of the gene that encodes the protein, like *kit,* is italicized and all lower case.) As you can see from Fig. 9.12, mammals, reptiles, birds, and fish with a mutation in the *kit* gene have a remarkably similar appearance.

Let's take a look at how receptor kinases work. The cytoplasmic portion of these receptors is a kinase, that is, an enzyme that phosphorylates other molecules. When a signaling

molecule binds to the extracellular portion of the receptor, a conformational change causes the receptor to partner up with another receptor kinase bound to another molecule of the same ligand in a process called **dimerization.** Dimerization activates the cytoplasmic kinase domains of the paired receptors, causing them to phosphorylate each other at multiple sites on their cytoplasmic tails (**Fig. 9.13**). The addition of these phosphate groups provides places on the receptor where other proteins bind and become active.

FIG. 9.13   **Receptor kinase activation and signaling.** Receptor kinases bind signaling molecules, dimerize, phosphorylate each other, and activate intracellular signal molecules.

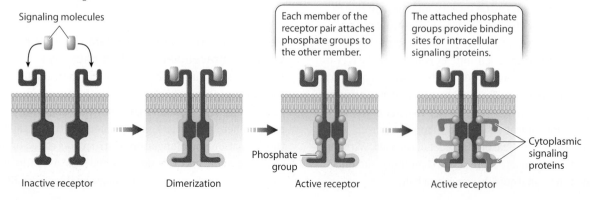

Signaling through receptor kinases follows the same basic sequence of events that we saw in signaling though G protein-coupled receptors. Binding of the ligand activates the receptor, which causes a set of cytoplasmic proteins to become sequentially activated, and, since many of these proteins are enzymes, the signal is amplified. And as we saw earlier in the G protein-coupled pathway, intracellular signaling proteins in receptor kinase pathways are also activated by GTP binding and phosphorylation, and are inactivated by GTP hydrolysis to GDP and dephosphorylation by phosphatases.

Now let's look at an example of signaling through a receptor kinase pathway. Think about the last time you got a paper cut. The cut likely bled for a minute or two, and then the bleeding stopped. If the cut was small, it probably healed completely in a week or so. PDGF has a lot to do with getting the healing process started. When platelets in the blood encounter damaged tissue, they release a number of proteins, including PDGF. PDGF is the signaling molecule that binds to PDGF-specific receptor kinases on the surface of cells at the site of a wound, causing the receptors to dimerize and become active. The activated receptors then recruit and activate additional signaling proteins present in the cytosol.

One of these cytoplasmic signaling proteins is **Ras,** which is very similar to the α subunit of G proteins. In the absence of a signal, Ras is bound to GDP and is inactive. However, when Ras binds to an activated receptor kinase, it releases GDP and binds GTP to become active. Activated GTP-bound Ras triggers the activation of a series of kinases that together are called the mitogen-activated protein kinase pathway, or, for short, the **MAP kinase pathway** (**Fig. 9.14**). The final activated kinase in the series enters the nucleus, where it phosphorylates its target proteins. Some of these proteins include regulators of transcription that switch on genes needed for the cell division so that your paper cut can heal.

The signals received by receptor kinases are amplified as the signal is passed from kinase to kinase. Each phosphorylated kinase in the series activates multiple molecules of the downstream kinase, each of which in turn activates many molecules of another kinase still farther downstream. In this way, a very small amount of signaling molecule in the environment (PDGF, in our example) can cause a large-scale response in the cell.

Receptor kinase signaling is also reversed or terminated by the same basic mechanisms that are at work in G protein-coupled receptor pathways. For example, protein phosphatases play important roles in the inactivation of receptor kinases and the other enzymes of the MAP kinase pathway. Furthermore, Ras is a GTPase, just like the G protein α subunit. Shortly after Ras binds to GTP and becomes active, Ras converts GTP to GDP, making it inactive. Without an active receptor kinase to generate more active Ras, activation of MAP kinase pathway components stops.

FIG. 9.14 **The MAP kinase pathway.** Some receptor kinases signal through Ras, which in turn activates the MAP kinase pathway, leading to changes in gene expression.

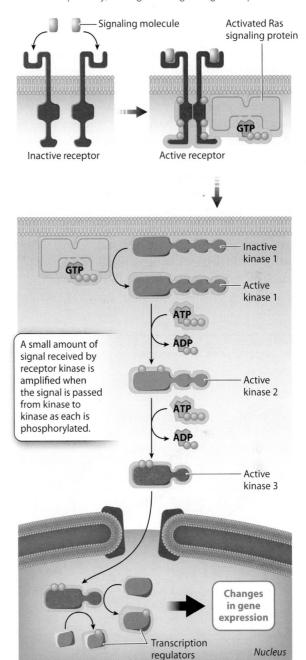

Signaling molecule

Activated Ras signaling protein

GTP

Inactive receptor

Active receptor

Inactive kinase 1

GTP

Active kinase 1

ATP

ADP

A small amount of signal received by receptor kinase is amplified when the signal is passed from kinase to kinase as each is phosphorylated.

Active kinase 2

ATP

ADP

Active kinase 3

Changes in gene expression

Transcription regulators

Nucleus

Ligand-gated ion channels alter the movement of ions across the plasma membrane.

Let's turn our attention now to the third group of receptors, the ligand-gated ion channels. Instead of activating cytosolic enzymes, these receptors function as ion channels to regulate the permeability of the cell membrane to ions. Nevertheless, the same principles of cell communication apply here as well: A signal binds to a receptor, which is activated and causes a cellular response until the signal is terminated.

There are many examples of ion-gated channels, each specific for one or more different ions. Ion-gated channels are particularly important in neurons and muscle cells. The plasma membranes of neurons and muscle cells are often referred to as "excitable membranes" because of the dramatic changes that take place in the membrane and in the entire cell when ions, especially sodium ions (Na^+), are permitted to flow into the cell. At rest, almost all of the Na^+ channels of neurons and muscle cells are closed, and in fact, these cells expend large amounts of ATP to pump Na^+ out of the cell. As a result, the concentration of Na^+ inside the cell is very low compared to its concentration outside the cell.

The difference in Na^+ concentration also contributes to a difference in electrical charge across the plasma membrane, called the **membrane potential.** At rest, the inside of the cell has a negative charge relative to the outside. This charge difference is in part the result of the large amount of positively charged sodium ions outside the cell and the high concentration of negatively charged ions and proteins in the cytosol. When a signaling molecule released by a neuron binds a ligand-gated Na^+ channel,

the channel opens, allowing Na^+ to move down its concentration gradient into the cell. The influx causes a drastic decline in the charge difference between the outside and inside of the cell. In turn, this change in membrane potential causes the cell to respond: The neuron responds by sending a nerve impulse, and the muscle cell responds by contracting.

Let's look more closely at the signal that sets off a muscle contraction (**Fig. 9.15**). When a neuron sends a signal to a muscle cell, it causes the muscle cell to shorten, and when many muscle cells shorten, the muscle as a whole contracts. The signaling molecule released from the neuron is a neurotransmitter called acetylcholine, which diffuses across the small space called the neuromuscular junction between the neuron and the muscle cell, until it encounters and binds to its receptor on the muscle cell. The acetylcholine receptor is a ligand-gated ion channel, so when acetylcholine binds to the extracellular ligand binding site, the conformational change that takes place opens the channel, and Na^+ ions rush into the muscle cell. The sudden influx of Na^+ ions changes the membrane potential, activating the contractile machinery of the cell and causing it to contract.

FIG. 9.15   Ligand-gated ion channels. Ligand-gated ion channels open in response to a bound signaling molecule.

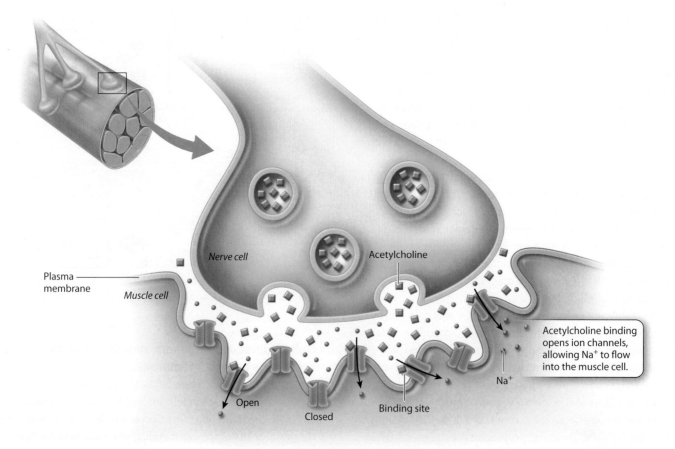

Plasma membrane

Muscle cell

Nerve cell

Acetylcholine

Open

Closed

Binding site

Na^+

Acetylcholine binding opens ion channels, allowing Na^+ to flow into the muscle cell.

This sort of cell signaling needs a mechanism for shutting off just as the other receptor pathways do. In the case of ligand-gated channels, there are several places where regulation takes place. An important point of regulation is the length of time the ligand remains in the binding site of the receptor, since the occupation of the binding site causes the channel to remain open. A second point of regulation is provided by an enzyme called acetylcholinesterase, which is present in the neuromuscular junction and terminates the acetylcholine signal by rapidly breaking it down. When the binding site is unoccupied, the channel reverts to the closed conformation. The flow of Na^+ ions into the cells ceases and the membrane potential returns to its resting state.

This signaling pathway is the target of a deadly poison known as curare. Native hunters of South America isolate curare from indigenous plants and rub it on arrowheads to kill their prey. Curare blocks the acetylcholine receptor, thereby relaxing voluntary muscles, including the diaphragm, which supports normal breathing. The result is death by asphyxiation. Interestingly, during the twentieth century, curare and its derivatives were used as a component of anesthesia to relax muscles during surgery. Today, anesthesiologists routinely use much safer and more effective blockers of the acetylcholine receptor to ease the manipulation of muscles and tissues during surgery.

? CASE 2 Cancer: When Good Cells Go Bad
How do cell signaling errors lead to cancer?
Many cancers arise when something goes wrong with the way a cell responds to a signal that leads to cell division or, in some cases, when a cell behaves as if it has received a signal for cell division when in fact it hasn't. Problems with cell signaling that can lead to cancer can take place at just about every step in the cell-signaling process. In some rare cases, a tumor may form as the result of the overproduction of a signaling molecule or the production of an altered form of a signaling molecule. More frequently, the source of the problem is in the receptor. For example, individuals with some forms of cancer have from 10 to 100 times the normal number of receptors for a signaling molecule called epidermal growth factor (EGF), making the cell more responsive to the normally low levels of EGF in the environment. Under normal conditions, binding of EGF to its receptor leads to the controlled division of cells. But in these cancer patients, the heightened response of the signaling pathway leads to abnormal gene expression and excess cell division.

Individuals with other cancers, including certain breast cancers, have mutant EGF receptors that activate intracellular pathways even when EGF isn't present. One of these mutant receptors, called Her2/neu, is the target of antibody therapy. Antibodies are proteins synthesized by cells of the immune

system that target foreign substances in the body for destruction. Pharmaceutical companies are able to produce antibodies that specifically target the Her2/neu receptor. When these antibodies are used as a form of chemotherapy, they bind to the cancer cells with Her2/neu on their surfaces, targeting them for destruction by the immune system.

Farther down the pathway, mutant forms of the Ras protein are often present in cancers. One especially harmful mutation prevents Ras from converting its bound GTP to GDP. The protein remains locked in the active, GTP-bound state, causing the sustained activation of the MAP kinase pathway. More than 30% of all human cancers involve abnormal Ras activity as a result of one or more mutations in the *ras* gene.

Signaling pathways can intersect with one another in a cell.
In this chapter, we have focused on individual signaling pathways to emphasize the general principles of communication between cells. In each case, we saw that a cell releases or has a cell-surface signaling molecule, which binds to and activates a cell-surface or intracellular receptor. Binding of the signaling molecule to the receptor induces a conformational change in the receptor, causing it to become active. The activated receptor in turn causes changes in the interior of the cell, frequently turning on a signal-transduction cascade that is amplified, leading to a cellular response. Cellular responses can vary depending on the nature of the signal and type of cell. They include turning genes on or off, changes in cellular metabolism, and cell division. Eventually, the signal and response terminate.

Focusing on each pathway one at a time allowed us to understand how each pathway operates. But in the context of an organism, cell signaling can be quite complex. There are scores upon scores of different signaling molecules, most of which have their own specific receptor. The receptors may or may not be present on or in a particular cell, and if a certain receptor is present, the number of copies of that receptor may vary widely.

In addition, the cellular response to a particular signaling molecule can vary from one kind of cell to another. For example, in mammalian cells the MAP kinase pathway promotes cell division, whereas in yeast cells it triggers sexual reproduction. The various effects that activating the MAP kinase pathway can have on the cell depends in part on the different sets of proteins that are found in different cell types.

It is also important to realize that different signaling molecules can bind to a single cell and activate several signaling pathways simultaneously, so that the final response of a cell depends on how the pathways intersect with one another. The integration of different signals gives cells a wide range of possible responses to their environment. Receiving two different signals may enhance a particular response, such as cell growth; or one signal may inhibit a component of the signaling pathway triggered by the other signal, resulting in a weakened response. Thus, cells are able to use a similar set of signaling cascades to communicate with other cells and respond to the environment in myriad different ways.

For example, recent studies have shown that enzymes in the MAP kinase pathway can be inhibited by active PKA. Recall that PKA is activated by elevated cAMP levels associated with the G protein-coupled receptor pathway. The regulation of the MAP kinase pathway by PKA therefore illustrates how one signaling pathway can inhibit another.

Researchers have made use of this molecular cross talk. Many

patients with breast cancer have elevated MAP kinase activity in their tumor cells. When human breast cancer cells are genetically modified to express an activated G protein α subunit, their growth after transplantation into mice is significantly inhibited. In addition, in cell culture, elevated cAMP levels block cells from responding to growth factors that signal through Ras to the MAP kinase pathway. As we understand more about how different signaling pathways integrate their outputs in specific cell types, we will stand a better chance of tailoring therapies to inhibit the pathway components relevant to a particular cancer.

Core Concepts Summary

9.1 CELLS COMMUNICATE PRIMARILY BY SENDING AND RECEIVING CHEMICAL SIGNALS.

There are four essential players in communication between two cells: a signaling cell, a signaling molecule, a receptor, and a responding cell. page 9-2

The signaling molecule binds to its receptor on the responding cell, leading to receptor activation, signal transduction and amplification, response, and eventually termination of the signal and response. page 9-2

9.2 CELL SIGNALING CAN BE CLASSIFIED ACCORDING TO THE DISTANCE BETWEEN THE SIGNALING AND RESPONDING CELLS.

Endocrine signaling takes place over long distances and relies on the circulatory system for delivery of signaling molecules. page 9-3

Paracrine signaling takes place over short distances between neighboring cells. page 9-4

Autocrine signaling occurs when a cell signals itself. page 9-4

Juxtacrine communication depends on physical contact between cells. page 9-5

9.3 SIGNALING MOLECULES BIND TO AND ACTIVATE SPECIFIC CELL-SURFACE AND INTRACELLULAR RECEPTORS.

A signaling molecule, or ligand, binds to the ligand-binding site of the receptor. Binding causes the receptor to undergo a conformational change that activates the receptor. page 9-6

Receptors for polar signaling molecules, including growth factors, are located on the plasma membrane. page 9-6

Receptors for nonpolar signaling molecules, such as steroid hormones, are located in the cytosol or in the nucleus. page 9-7

There are three major types of cell-surface receptor: G protein-coupled receptors, receptor kinases, and ligand-gated ion channels. All act as molecular switches. page 9-7

G protein-coupled receptors associate with G proteins, which are active when bound to GTP and inactive when bound to GDP. page 9-8

Receptor kinases are activated by phosphorylation and inactivated by dephosphorylation. page 9-8

Ligand-gated ion channels open in response to a signal, allowing the movement of ions across the plasma membrane. page 9-8

9.4 SIGNALS ARE TRANSMITTED ACROSS THE PLASMA MEMBRANE AND ARE OFTEN AMPLIFIED IN THE CYTOSOL, LEADING TO A CELLULAR RESPONSE FOLLOWED BY TERMINATION.

G proteins are associated with G protein-coupled receptors that bind signaling molecules. page 9-8

G proteins are composed of three subunits, denoted α, β, and γ. When a G protein encounters an activated receptor, the α subunit exchanges GDP for GTP, dissociates from the β and γ subunits, and becomes active. page 9-9

Second messengers like cAMP amplify the signal in the cytosol (brought to the cell by the extracellular first messenger). page 9-9

Intracellular, cytosolic signals are short-lived before they are terminated. page 9-11

Ligand binding to a receptor kinase causes it to dimerize with another receptor bound to the same ligand. The two receptor kinases become active when they phosphorylate each other's cytoplasmic domains, allowing activation of intracellular signaling pathways. page 9-12

The phosphorylated receptors are bound by other proteins, which cause the subsequent activation of other cytosolic signaling molecules, such as Ras. page 9-13

When Ras is activated, the GDP to which it is bound is released and is replaced by GTP. The active, GTP-bound Ras temporarily binds to and activates the first in a series of kinases. page 9-13

Neurons communicate with other neurons and with muscle cells using ligand-gated ion channels, which lead to movement of ions across the membrane and a change in the membrane charge or potential. page 9-14

Cancer can be caused by malfunction of any step in the signaling processes involved in cell division. page 9-15

Mutations in receptor kinases and Ras are frequently associated with human cancers. page 9-15

Several signaling pathways can take place simultaneously in a single cell, and the cellular response depends on the integration of several signals. page 9-15

Self-Assessment

1. Name the four players in cell communication.

2. Name the steps that are often involved in cell communication.

3. Describe one way in which endocrine-, paracrine-, autocrine-, and juxtacrine-signaling pathways are similar to one another and one way they differ from one another.

4. Explain how cells respond to external signals even when those signals cannot enter the cell.

5. Explain how signals can be specific in targeting only some cells, even if they are released into the bloodstream and come into contact with many cells.

6. List several possible types of responses a cell might have to a signaling molecule.

7. Compare and contrast cell-surface receptors and intracellular receptors in terms of their location, chemical properties of their signaling molecules, and types of responses mediated.

8. List several ways in which a signal may be amplified in an intracellular signaling pathway.

9. Describe ways in which the response of a cell to a signal can be terminated.

Do you understand the chapter's Core Concepts? Log into BIO *PORTAL* to check your answers to the Self-Assessment questions, then practice what you've learned and reinforce this chapter's concepts by working through the problems and multimedia tutorials provided there.

 http://courses.bfwpub.com/yourbioportal/index.php

CELL FORM AND FUNCTION

Cytoskeleton, Cellular Junctions, and Extracellular Matrix

Core Concepts

10.1 Tissues and organs are communities of cells that perform a specific function.

10.2 The cytoskeleton is composed of microtubules, microfilaments, and intermediate filaments that help to maintain cell shape.

10.3 The cytoskeleton interacts with motor proteins to permit the movement of cells and substances within cells.

10.4 Cells adhere to other cells and the extracellular matrix by means of cell adhesion molecules and junctional complexes.

10.5 The extracellular matrix provides structural support and informational cues.

A recurring theme in this book, and in all of biology, is that form and function are inseparably linked. This is true at every level of structural organization, from molecules to organelles to cells and to organisms themselves. We saw in Chapter 4 that the function of proteins depends on their shape. In Chapters 7 and 8, we saw that the function of organelles like mitochondria and chloroplasts depends on the large internal surface areas of the inner membrane of mitochondria and the thylakoid membrane of chloroplasts.

The functions of different cell types are also reflected in their shape and internal structural features (**Fig. 10.1**). Consider a typical red blood cell. It is shaped like a disk that is slightly indented in the middle, and it lacks a nucleus and other organelles (Fig. 10.1a). This unusual shape and internal organization allow it to be remarkably flexible as it carries oxygen in the bloodstream. Because it is able to deform readily, it can pass through blood vessels with diameters smaller than that of the red blood cell itself. Cells in the liver (Fig. 10.1b) that synthesize proteins and glycogen look very different from muscle cells (Fig. 10.1c) that contract to exert force. A neuron (Fig. 10.1d), with its long and extensively branched extensions that communicate with other cells, is structurally nothing like a cell lining the intestine (Fig. 10.1e) that absorbs nutrients.

As we saw in Chapter 9, cells often exist in communities, forming tissues and organs in multicellular organisms. Again, form and function are intimately linked. Think of the branching structure and large surface area of the mammalian lung, which is well adapted for gas exchange, or the muscular heart, adapted for pumping blood through large circulatory systems.

In this chapter, we look at what determines cell shape. We also examine the different ways cells adhere to one another to build tissues and organs, and see how this adhesion differs depending on the function of the cellular community. We also learn about the physical environment outside cells, which is synthesized by cells themselves and influences their behavior.

10.1 TISSUES AND ORGANS

At the beginning of Chapter 9, we considered the features that enable a group of individuals to function as a community. One of these is the presence of members able to perform specialized tasks. In addition, community members stick together and respond to their surrounding environment. Now, think of our own tissues and organs—a heart, a stomach, a kidney, a brain—all are communities of cells that work together to perform highly specific and important tasks in response to cues from the environment.

FIG. 10.1 **Diverse cell types.** Cells differ in shape and are well adapted for their various functions.

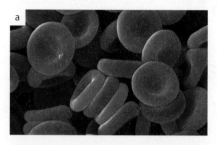

The shape of a red blood cell maximizes its surface area for gas exchange and allows it to deform as it passes through the circulatory system.

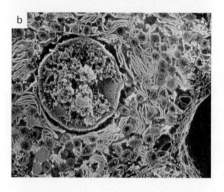

Hepatocytes (liver cells) contain large amounts of rough ER needed for protein synthesis.

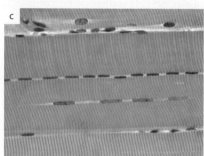

Long, multinucleated muscle cells are packed with actin and myosin needed for contraction.

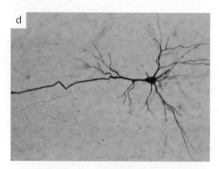

Long extensions of the plasma membrane allow neurons to communicate with other cells.

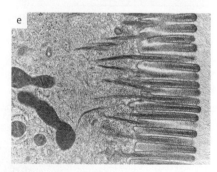

Microvilli on intestinal epithelial cells increase their absorptive surface area.

Tissues and organs are communities of cells.

A biological **tissue** is a collection of cells that work together to perform a specific function. Two or more tissues often combine and function together as an **organ,** such as a heart or lung. Animals and plants have tissues and organs that allow them to carry out the various processes necessary to sustain them. In animals, for example, four types of tissue—epithelial, connective, nervous, and muscle—combine to make up all the organs of the body. Plants are made up of just three types of tissue: dermal (the outer protective layer), ground (the bulk of the plant body), and vascular (the channels that transport nutrients and water throughout the plant).

Tissues and organs have distinctive shapes that reflect how they work and what they do. In the same way, the different cell types that make up these organs have distinctive shapes based on what they do in the organ. In animals, the shape of cells is determined and maintained by structural protein networks in the cytoplasm called the **cytoskeleton.** The shape and structural integrity of tissues and organs depend on the ability of cells to adhere to one another. In turn, the adhesion of cells to one another depends on cell adhesion molecules and other cytosolic proteins that assemble into structures called **cellular junctions.** Equally important to a strong, properly shaped tissue or organ is the ability of cells to adhere to a meshwork of proteins and polysaccharides outside the cell called the **extracellular matrix.** In plants, the extracellular matrix provides both a mechanism for cells to adhere to one another and structural support that maintains their shape.

The structure of skin relates to its function.

To start our investigation of the cytoskeleton, cellular junctions, and the extracellular matrix, let's consider a community of cells very familiar to all of us—our own skin (**Fig. 10.2**). The structure of mammalian skin is clearly tied to its function. Skin has two main layers. The outer layer, the **epidermis,** serves as a water-resistant, protective barrier. The layer beneath the epidermis is the **dermis.** This layer of the skin supports the epidermis, both physically and by supplying it with nutrients. It also provides a cushion surrounding the body.

As you can see in Fig. 10.2, the epidermis is several cell layers thick. Cells arranged in one or more layers are called epithelial cells and together make up a type of animal tissue called **epithelial tissue.** Epithelial tissue covers the outside of the body and lines many internal structures, such as the digestive tract and vertebrate blood vessels. The epidermal layer of skin is primarily composed of epithelial cells called keratinocytes. The epidermis also contains melanocytes that produce the pigment that gives skin its coloration. Different kinds of epithelial cells are specialized to carry out different functions, such as protection, secretion, and absorption.

Keratinocytes in the epidermis are specialized to protect underlying tissues and organs. They are able to perform this function in part because of their elaborate system of cytoskeletal filaments. These filaments are often connected to the cellular

FIG. 10.2   **The skin.** The skin is a community of cells organized into two layers—the epidermis and dermis—that together provide protection for the underlying tissues of the body.

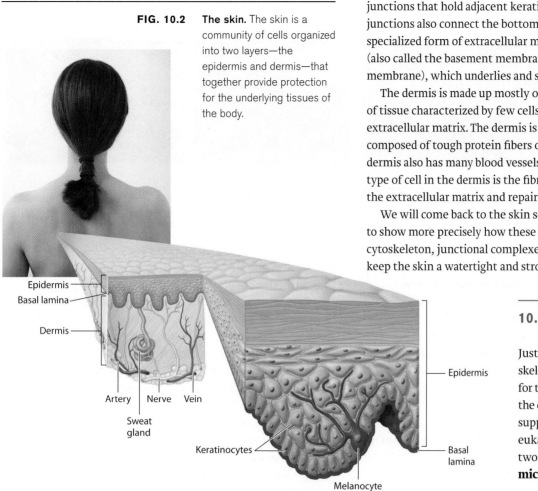

junctions that hold adjacent keratinocytes together. Cellular junctions also connect the bottom layer of keratinocytes to a specialized form of extracellular matrix called the **basal lamina** (also called the basement membrane, although it is not in fact a membrane), which underlies and supports all epithelial tissues.

The dermis is made up mostly of **connective tissue,** a type of tissue characterized by few cells and substantial amounts of extracellular matrix. The dermis is strong and flexible because it is composed of tough protein fibers of the extracellular matrix. The dermis also has many blood vessels and nerve endings. The main type of cell in the dermis is the fibroblast. Fibroblasts synthesize the extracellular matrix and repair wounds.

We will come back to the skin several times in this chapter to show more precisely how these multiple connections among cytoskeleton, junctional complexes, and the extracellular matrix keep the skin a watertight and strong protective barrier.

10.2 THE CYTOSKELETON

Just as the bones of vertebrate skeletons provide internal support for the body, the protein fibers of the cytoskeleton provide internal support for cells (**Fig. 10.3**). All eukaryotic cells have at least two cytoskeletal elements, **microtubules** and **microfilaments.**

FIG. 10.3   **Three types of cytoskeletal element.** (a) Microtubules; (b) microfilaments; and (c) intermediate filaments.

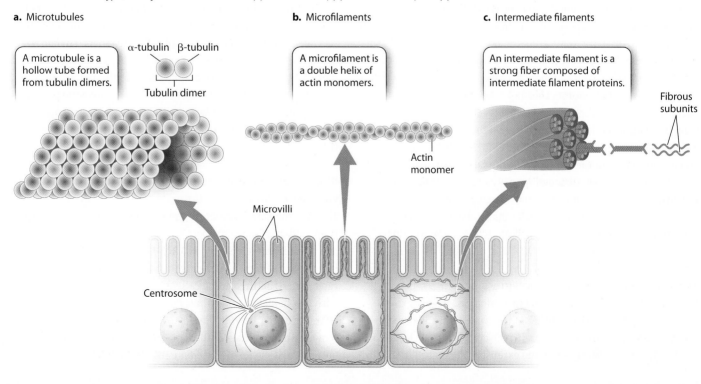

a. Microtubules

A microtubule is a hollow tube formed from tubulin dimers.

α-tubulin   β-tubulin

Tubulin dimer

b. Microfilaments

A microfilament is a double helix of actin monomers.

Actin monomer

c. Intermediate filaments

An intermediate filament is a strong fiber composed of intermediate filament proteins.

Fibrous subunits

Microvilli

Centrosome

FIG. 10.4   Cilia and flagella in diverse cell types. Cilia and flagella, composed of microtubules, move cells or propel substances by them.

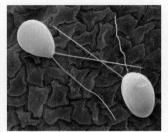

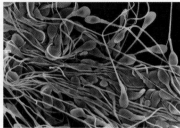

Coordinated beating of the cilia that cover the paramecium moves the cell through its environment.

The cilia in these human airway epithelial cells propel mucus containing debris out of the lungs.

These unicellular algae are propelled by two flagella.

Some cells of multicellular organisms, including sperm cells, swim by movement of a flagellum.

Animal cells have a third element, **intermediate filaments.** All three of these cytoskeletal elements are long chains, or polymers, made up of protein subunits. In addition to providing structural support, microtubules and microfilaments enable the movement of many cells and the movement of substances within cells. We first consider the structural role of the cytoskeleton and return to its role in cell motility and intracellular transport in section 10.3.

Microtubules are hollow, tubelike polymers of tubulin dimers.

Microtubules, which are hollow tubelike structures, have the largest diameter of the three cytoskeletal elements (Fig. 10.3a). They are polymers of protein dimers. Each protein dimer is made up of two slightly different **tubulin** proteins, called α (alpha) and β (beta) tubulin. One α tubulin and one β tubulin combine to make a tubulin dimer. These tubulin dimers are assembled into microtubules.

Microtubules have diverse functions. In animal cells, microtubules radiate outward to the cell periphery from a microtubule organizing center called the **centrosome.** This spokelike arrangement of microtubules helps cells withstand compression and thereby maintain their shape. Many organelles are tethered to microtubules, which guide the arrangement of organelles in the cell. Microtubules also provide tracks for the transport of material from one part of the cell to another. They are found specially arranged in **cilia** and **flagella,** organelles that propel the movement of cells or substances surrounding the cell (**Fig. 10.4**). Finally, microtubules form the **spindle apparatus** that separates replicated chromosomes during eukaryotic cell division (Chapter 11).

Microfilaments are helical polymers of actin.

Microfilaments are polymers of **actin** monomers, arranged to form a helix. They are the thinnest of the three cytoskeletal fibers and are present in various locations in the cytoplasm (see Fig. 10.3b). They are relatively short and extensively branched in the cell cortex, the area of the cytoplasm just beneath the plasma membrane. At the cortex, microfilaments reinforce the plasma membrane and organize proteins associated with it. These cortical microfilaments are also important in maintaining the shape of a cell. For example, in absorptive epithelial cells such as those in the small intestine, bundles of microfilaments are found in microvilli, hairlike projections that extend from the surface of the cell (**Fig. 10.5**). Longer bundles of microfilaments form a band that extends around the circumference of epithelial cells. This band is attached to a type of cell junction called an adherens junction, which connects a cell to its neighbors (section 10.4). As a result, the band provides a great deal of structural support not only to individual epithelial cells, but also to the entire epithelial layer of cells.

In addition to providing structural support to the cell, microfilaments are important for the transport of materials inside cells, especially plant cells. Furthermore, microfilaments are responsible for changes in the shape of many types of cells. An exceptionally dramatic example of such a shape change is the shortening of a muscle cell when it contracts, discussed more fully in the next section. Microfilaments are found at the front edge of migrating cells, where they can move the plasma membrane forward. Finally, microfilaments, arranged in a structure called the contractile ring separate the daughter cells at the end of animal cell division (Chapter 11).

Intermediate filaments are polymers of proteins that vary according to cell type.

The intermediate filaments of animal cells are so named because their diameter is intermediate between that of microtubules and microfilaments (see Fig. 10.3c). They are polymers of intermediate filament proteins that combine to form strong, cable-like structures in the cell. As a result, they provide cells with mechanical strength. We have seen that different cell types all use the same tubulin dimers to form microtubules and the same actin monomers to form microfilaments. By contrast, the proteins making up intermediate filaments differ from one cell

FIG. 10.5 **Microfilaments in intestinal microvilli.** Actin microfilaments help to maintain the structure of microvilli in the intestine.

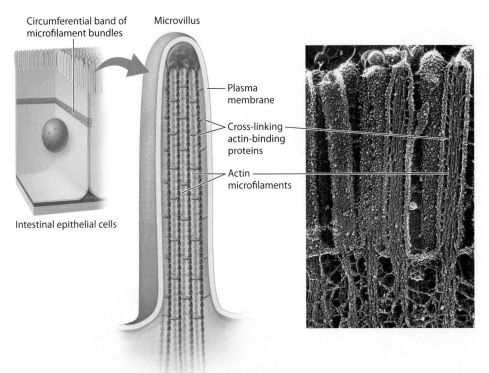

Circumferential band of microfilament bundles

Microvillus

Plasma membrane

Cross-linking actin-binding proteins

Actin microfilaments

Intestinal epithelial cells

type to another. For example, in epithelial cells, these protein subunits are keratins; in fibroblasts, they are vimentins; and in neurons, they are neurofilaments. Some intermediate filaments, called lamins, are even found inside the nucleus, where they provide support for the nuclear envelope (**Fig. 10.6**). In fact, there

FIG. 10.6 **Intermediate filaments in the cytoplasm and the nucleus of a cell.**

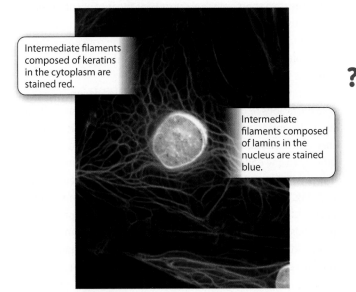

Intermediate filaments composed of keratins in the cytoplasm are stained red.

Intermediate filaments composed of lamins in the nucleus are stained blue.

are well over 100 different kinds of intermediate filaments.

Once assembled, many intermediate filaments become attached at the cytoplasmic side of cellular junctions called desmosomes (**Fig. 10.7**; section 10.4). Like the association of microfilaments with adherens junctions, the anchoring of intermediate filaments to desmosomes provides strong support for the cells. In the case of epithelial cells, this anchoring results in structural continuity from one cell to another that greatly strengthens the entire epithelial tissue, enhancing the ability of epithelial cell layers to withstand physical stress. This is especially important in a wide range of tissues that are regularly subject to such stress, including the skin and the lining of the intestine.

Genetic defects that disrupt the intermediate filament network can have severe consequences. For example, individuals with epidermolysis bullosa, a rare genetic disease, have defective keratin genes inherited from their parents. Intermediate filaments do not polymerize properly in these individuals, weakening connections between the layers of cells that make up the epidermis. As a consequence, the outer layers can detach, resulting in extremely fragile skin that blisters in response to the slightest trauma (Fig. 10.7). The sensitivity to physical stress is so extreme that infants with epidermolysis bullosa often suffer significant damage to the skin during childbirth. Therefore, caesarean section is sometimes recommended in cases where the disease is diagnosed during pregnancy.

? CASE 2 Cancer: When Good Cells Go Bad
How can doctors test for the spread of cancer?
Cancer is characterized by uncontrolled cell division. Many types of cancer result in the formation of a mass of cells called a tumor. In most cases, the tumor itself is not the problem. The real concern is that tumor cells will metastasize, or spread to other parts of the body, where they can affect the function of distant organs. One way physicians check for metastasis is to look for intermediate filament proteins in places where they don't belong. For example, the presence of certain keratins in the bloodstream is an indicator of metastasis.

Physicians may also examine lymph nodes for signs that a cancer has spread. Lymph nodes are part of the lymphatic system,

FIG. 10.7   **Intermediate filaments in the epidermis of the skin.** Intermediate filaments bind to cellular junctions called desmosomes, forming a strong, interconnected network. Epidermolysis bullosa is a blistering disease of the skin caused by a defect in intermediate filaments.

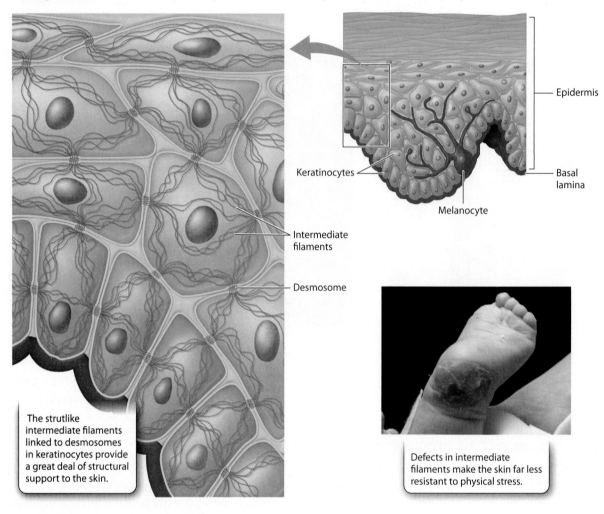

Epidermis

Keratinocytes

Basal lamina

Melanocyte

Intermediate filaments

Desmosome

The strutlike intermediate filaments linked to desmosomes in keratinocytes provide a great deal of structural support to the skin.

Defects in intermediate filaments make the skin far less resistant to physical stress.

which collects extracellular fluid from tissues in the body and returns it to the circulatory system. Each part of the body drains into a specific set of lymph nodes. So if a patient is diagnosed with a melanoma, a cancer of melanocytes, a surgeon can remove the lymph node that drains the area of the body where the cancer is. A pathologist then examines the cells of the lymph node for the presence of melanocyte keratins. Since the cells of the lymph node do not normally contain melanocyte keratins, the presence of these intermediate filament proteins in the lymph node helps doctors determine how advanced the cancer is and thus design the best course of treatment. This lymph node test is useful in detecting other kinds of cancer as well, including cancers of the breast and prostate.

Microtubules and microfilaments are dynamic structures.

When we think of the parts of a skeleton, we are inclined to think of our bones. Unlike our bones, which undergo remodeling but do not change rapidly, microtubules and microfilaments are highly dynamic structures. They become longer by the addition of subunits to their ends, and shrink by the loss of subunits. The growth and shrinkage of microtubules and microfilaments are influenced by many factors, including the concentration of free tubulin and actin subunits and the activity of regulatory proteins that attach to the cytoskeleton.

The rate at which protein subunits are added depends on the concentrations of tubulin and actin in that region of the cell. At high concentrations of subunits, microtubules and microfilaments may grow at both ends, although these subunits are added more quickly to one end than to the other. The faster-growing end is called the plus end and the slower-growing end is called the minus end (**Fig. 10.8**). The minus ends of microtubules in animal cells are positioned at the organizing center of the centrosome, and the plus ends project outward toward the plasma membrane.

In addition, microtubules have an important property not shared by the other cytoskeletal elements: Their

FIG. 10.8 Different rates of growth at the plus and minus ends of microtubules and microfilaments. The plus end grows quickly and the minus end grows slowly.

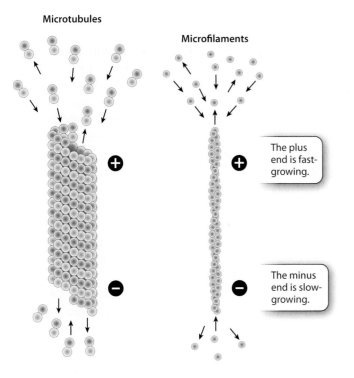

Microtubules

Microfilaments

The plus end is fast-growing.

The minus end is slow-growing.

FIG. 10.9 Dynamic instability. The plus ends of microtubules undergo cycles of rapid shrinkage followed by slow growth.

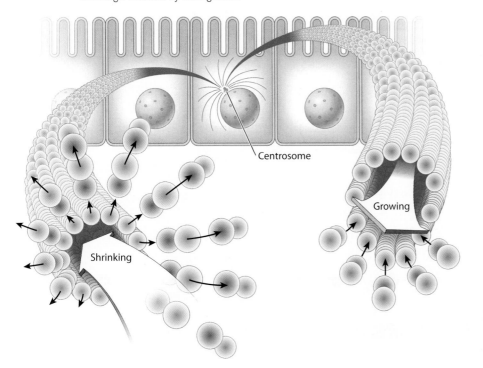

Centrosome

Growing

Shrinking

plus ends undergo seemingly random cycles of rapid shrinkage (depolymerization) followed by slower growth (polymerization). These cycles of shrinkage and growth are called **dynamic instability** (**Fig. 10.9**). The dramatic shrinkage is often called microtubule catastrophe and takes place because the plus end of a microtubule is structurally unstable. Once depolymerization has occurred, tubulin dimers are added to reassemble the microtubule.

Dynamic instability might seem like an undesirable feature for a component of the cytoskeleton, but it is actually very important for many functions of microtubules. For example, it allows microtubules to explore the space of the cell by growing into new areas and then shrinking back. This ability is especially important in the process of dividing chromosomes between the two daughter cells during cell division. In Chapter 11, we will see that the segregation of chromosomes requires that each chromosome be attached to two microtubules. The way that microtubules encounter chromosomes fast enough to form these attachments is by random exploration of the cytoplasm, which is driven by dynamic instability.

The cytoskeleton is an ancient feature of cells.

Actin and tubulin are found in all eukaryotic cells, and evolutionarily they are highly conserved. The amino acid sequences of yeast tubulin and human tubulin are 75% identical. Similar comparisons of actin from amoebas and animals show that they are 80% identical after close to a billion years of evolution. In fact, a mixture of yeast and human actin monomers forms hybrid microfilaments able to function normally in the cell.

Not long ago, it was believed that cytoskeletal proteins were present only in eukaryotic cells. However, a number of studies have shown that many prokaryotes also have a system of proteins similar in structure to the cytoskeletal elements of eukaryotic cells and are involved in similar processes, including the separation of daughter cells during cell division. Interestingly, at least one of these prokaryotic cytoskeleton-like proteins is expressed in chloroplasts and mitochondria of some eukaryotic cells. The presence of this protein in these organelles lends support to the theory that chloroplasts and mitochondria were once independent prokaryotic cells that developed a symbiotic relationship with ancestral eukaryotic cells. This idea is called the endosymbiotic theory and we discuss it in more detail in Chapter 27.

10.3 CELLULAR MOVEMENT

In addition to providing structure and support, some cytoskeletal elements also allow cellular movement. We can think of cellular movement in three different ways. First, there is the movement of the cell itself, and many cells are capable of moving great distances on their own. The second kind of movement is the change in shape of a cell, as when a contracting muscle cell shortens. Changes in cell shape are also common in embryos and are an essential part of early development. The third kind of cellular movement is the movement of molecules and organelles within a cell. For example, melanocytes in the epidermis transport their packets of melanin along their branching dendrites to deliver them to neighboring keratinocytes (see Fig. 10.2). Similarly, in neurons, neurotransmitters are transported from the cell body to the end of the axon, where they are stored until they are needed. In this section, we discuss the molecular basis for these kinds of cellular movement.

Motor proteins associate with microtubules and microfilaments to cause movement.

A motor is a device that imparts motion. We saw that microtubules and microfilaments have some capacity to move by polymerization and depolymerization, but on their own their capacity for movement is fairly limited. However, when joined by small accessory proteins called **motor proteins,** microtubules and microfilaments are capable of causing amazing movements.

First let's consider how these motor proteins contribute to a change in cell shape. Motor proteins cause muscle contraction by moving the actin microfilaments inside muscle cells. The cytoplasm of muscle cells shown in Fig. 10.1c is packed with actin microfilaments that are anchored to the ends of the cell. **Myosin,** a motor protein found in muscle cells, binds to actin and undergoes a conformational change. As a result, the actin microfilaments slide relative to myosin, causing the cell to shorten, or contract (**Fig. 10.10**). The energy required for the conformational change in myosin and the movement of actin microfilaments comes from the energy stored in ATP and is discussed in Chapter 37.

In other cells, myosin attached to various types of cellular cargo, such as transport vesicles, works by a similar mechanism to move materials from one part of the cell to another, using microfilaments as tracks (**Fig. 10.11a**).

FIG. 10.10 Muscle contraction. The shortening of a muscle cell is driven by interactions between the motor protein myosin and actin microfilaments.

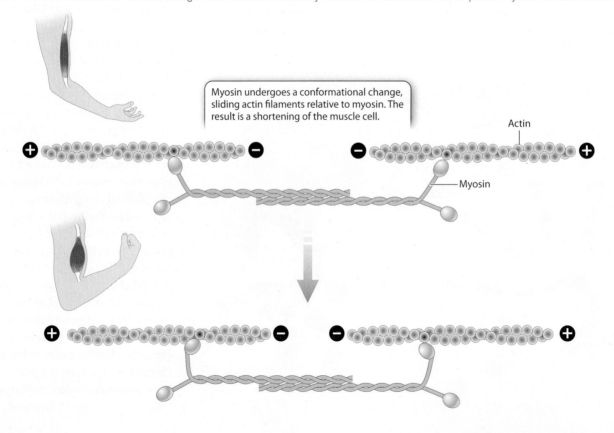

Myosin undergoes a conformational change, sliding actin filaments relative to myosin. The result is a shortening of the muscle cell.

Actin

Myosin

FIG. 10.11 **Intracellular transport.** The motor protein myosin interacts with microfilaments and the motor protein kinesin interacts with microtubules to move vesicles in the cell.

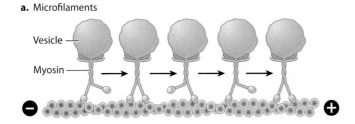

a. Microfilaments

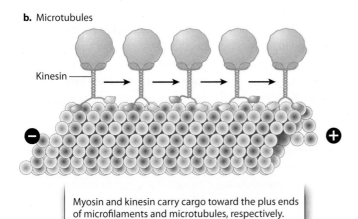

b. Microtubules

Myosin and kinesin carry cargo toward the plus ends of microfilaments and microtubules, respectively.

Microtubules also function as tracks for transport within the cell. Transport along microtubules takes place in a similar fashion to transport along microfilaments, except that the two motor proteins that transport cargo are **kinesin** and **dynein.** Kinesin is similar in structure to myosin and transports cargo toward the plus end of microtubules at the periphery of the cell (**Fig. 10.11b**). By contrast, dynein carries its load away from the plasma membrane toward the minus end. As with myosin, movement along microtubules by kinesin and dynein is driven by conformational changes in the motor proteins and is powered by energy harvested from ATP.

Let's look at an especially striking example of this system at work in the specialized skin cells called melanophores present in some vertebrates. Melanophores are similar to the melanocytes in our skin, but rather than hand off their melanin to other cells, as in humans, melanophores keep their pigment granules and move them around the cell in response to hormones or neuronal signals. This redistribution of melanin within the cell allows animals such as fish or amphibian embryos to change color. For example, at night the melanin granules in the skin of a zebrafish embryo are dispersed throughout the melanophores, making it darkly colored. As morning comes and the day brightens, the pigment granules are aggregated at the center of the cell around the centrosome, causing the embryo's color to lighten (**Fig. 10.12**). The melanin granules

FIG. 10.12 **Color change in zebrafish embryos driven by motor proteins kinesin and dynein.** Melanin granules are redistributed along microtubules in the melanophores of the skin.

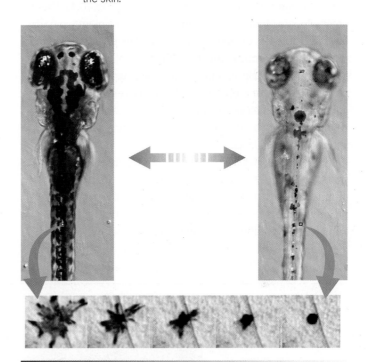

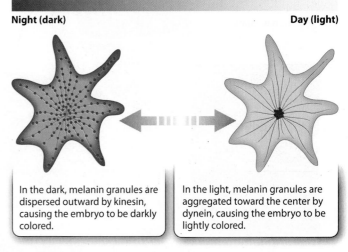

Night (dark)   **Day (light)**

In the dark, melanin granules are dispersed outward by kinesin, causing the embryo to be darkly colored.

In the light, melanin granules are aggregated toward the center by dynein, causing the embryo to be lightly colored.

in the melanophores move back and forth along microtubules, transported by kinesin and dynein. Kinesin moves the granules out toward the plus end of the microtubule during dispersal, and dynein moves them back toward the minus end during aggregation. The daytime and nighttime camouflage provided by this mechanism of color change keeps young, developing organisms from being spotted by hungry predators lurking below.

→ **Quick Check 1** Would a defect in dynein or kinesin cause a zebrafish embryo to remain darkly colored after daybreak?

Organelles with special arrangements of microtubules propel cells through the environment.

Many single-celled eukaryotic organisms that live in aquatic environments propel themselves through the water by means of the motion of short cilia or long flagella (see Fig. 10.4). These organelles are fiberlike extensions of the plasma membrane that have microtubules extending their entire length. Some cells of multicellular organisms also have cilia or flagella. For example, the sperm cells of algae, some plants, and many animals are propelled by one or more flagella. Epithelial cells in a number of animal tissues, such as the lining of the trachea and the upper respiratory tract, have cilia that move substances along the surface of the cell layer.

The microtubules in cilia and flagella are distributed in a characteristic "9 + 2" arrangement, that is, nine pairs of microtubules are located around the periphery of these organelles and two microtubules are at the center (**Fig. 10.13**). The outer microtubules are connected to the center pair by cross-linking proteins and to their neighbors by dynein molecules. Energy harvested by the hydrolysis of ATP powers the motion of cilia and flagella. Dynein undergoes a conformational change that causes the pairs of microtubules to slide past each other. The sliding of the microtubules results in a whiplike motion in the case of flagella and an oarlike rowing motion in the case of cilia.

Actin polymerization moves cells forward.

Both single-celled amoebas foraging for food on the bottom of a pond and mammalian white blood cells chasing down foreign bacteria rely on actin polymerization to get from one place to another. In fact, many cells move through their environment by crawling across a substrate or by squeezing between other cells and burrowing through connective tissues, rather than by using cilia or flagella. This type of movement relies on microfilaments. Commonly, new microfilaments are assembled and extended at one end of the cell and existing microfilaments are pulled

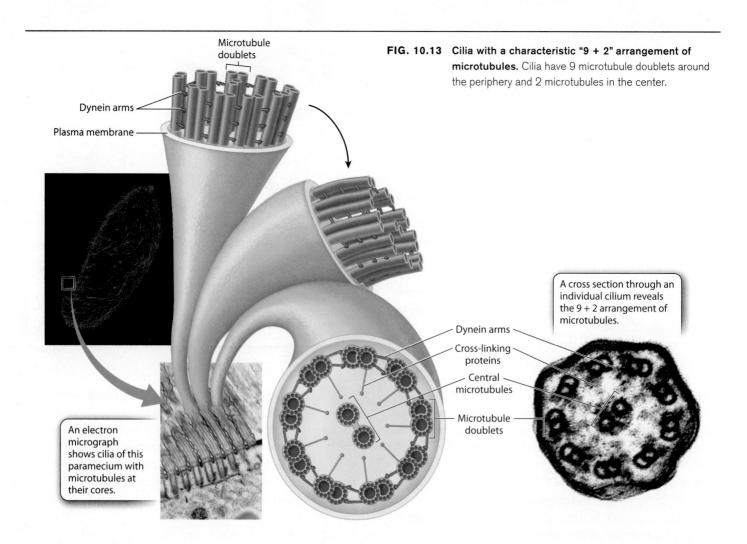

FIG. 10.13 Cilia with a characteristic "9 + 2" arrangement of microtubules. Cilia have 9 microtubule doublets around the periphery and 2 microtubules in the center.

Microtubule doublets

Dynein arms

Plasma membrane

A cross section through an individual cilium reveals the 9 + 2 arrangement of microtubules.

Dynein arms

Cross-linking proteins

Central microtubules

Microtubule doublets

An electron micrograph shows cilia of this paramecium with microtubules at their cores.

FIG. 10.14 Cell migration. Cells move by extending a lamellipodium at the leading edge and contracting microfilaments at the trailing edge.

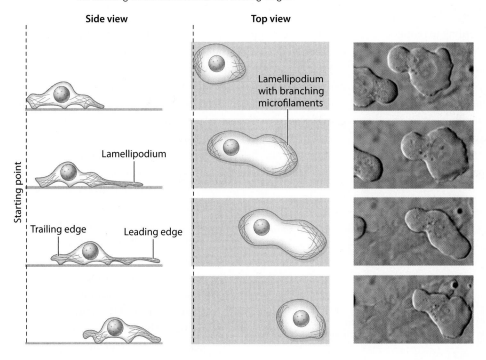

together at the other end (**Fig. 10.14**). The polymerization of actin into a microfilament exerts a considerable amount of force, enough to push the plasma membrane out into a thin, sheetlike structure called a lamellipodium, from the Greek for "thin-layered foot." New points of adhesion are established between the lamellipodium and the substrate.

Meanwhile, bundles of actin filaments at the other end of the cell contract by the interactions of myosin and actin, squeezing the cytoplasm and its contents forward toward the lamellipodium. The edge of the cell where the lamellipodium forms is called the leading edge, and the end where contraction takes place is called the trailing edge. Repeated cycles of actin polymerization at the leading edge and microfilament contraction at the trailing edge propel the cell forward. Cells are able to migrate considerable distances by this method.

Cells do not have permanent "front" and "back" ends. Instead, the locations of the leading and trailing edges can change in an instant. This flexibility allows a migrating cell to change its direction of movement, toward a source of nutrients, for example. The formation of a lamellipodium is triggered when a cell-surface receptor binds to a nutrient molecule or other substance, so the lamellipodium forms in the region of the plasma membrane where the signal is strongest. In this way, cells can follow the concentration gradient of a nutrient to its source.

10.4 CELL ADHESION

The cell, as we know, is the fundamental unit of living organisms (Chapter 1). Some conservative estimates place the number of cells in an adult human being at between 50 and 75 trillion, whereas others place the number at well above 100 trillion. Whichever estimate is more accurate, humans, as well as all complex multicellular organisms, are made up of a *lot* of cells! What then keeps us (or any other plant or animal) from slumping into a pile of cells? And what keeps cells organized into tissues, and tissues into organs?

Multicellular organisms are made up of much more than cells. The cells in most tissues and organs are connected to a complex meshwork of proteins and polysaccharides known as the extracellular matrix. The architecture and structural integrity of a particular tissue or organ depends on these attachments between cells and the extracellular matrix. In this section, we explore the means by which cells are connected to one another and to proteins in the extracellular environment.

Cells are attached to one another and to the extracellular matrix by cell-surface proteins called **cell adhesion molecules.** The regions in the plasma membrane where cells make contact with and adhere to other cells or the extracellular matrix are called **cellular junctions.** Together, cell adhesion molecules, cellular junctions, and the extracellular matrix keep us (and all multicellular organisms) intact. The importance of cell adhesion is reflected by the fact that between 5% and 10% of the genes in the human genome are involved in attaching cells to one another or to the extracellular matrix.

Cell adhesion molecules allow cells to attach to other cells and to the extracellular matrix.

In 1907, American embryologist H. V. Wilson discovered that if he pressed a live sponge through fine cloth he could break up the sponge into individual cells. Then if he swirled the cells together, they would coalesce back into a group resembling a sponge. If he swirled together the cells from sponges of two different species, he observed that the cells sorted themselves out—that is, cells from one species of sponge associated only with cells from that same species (**Fig. 10.15a**). Fifty years later, German-born embryologist Johannes Holtfreter observed that if he took neuronal cells and skin cells from an amphibian embryo and treated them the same way that Wilson had treated sponge cells, the embryonic cells would sort themselves according to tissue type (**Fig. 10.15b**).

Cells can sort themselves because of the presence of various cell adhesion molecules. While a number of cell adhesion molecules are now known, the **cadherins** (for *ca*lcium-*d*ependent ad*here*nce prote*ins*) are especially important in the adhesion of cells to other cells. There are many different kinds of cadherins, and a given cadherin may bind only to another cadherin of the same type. This property explains

Holtfreter's observations of the cells from amphibian embryos. E-cadherin (for "epidermal cadherin") is present on the surface of embryonic epidermal cells, and N-cadherin (for "neural cadherin") is present on neuronal cells. The epidermal cells adhered to one another through E-cadherin, and the neuronal cells adhered to each other through N-cadherin.

Cadherins are transmembrane proteins (Chapter 5). The extracellular domain of a cadherin molecule binds to the extracellular domain of a cadherin of the same type on an adjacent cell (**Fig. 10.16a**). The cytoplasmic portion of the protein is linked to the internal cytoskeleton. This arrangement provides structural continuity from the cytoskeleton of one cell to the cytoskeleton of another, increasing the strength of tissues and organs.

In addition to being stably connected to other cells, cells also attach to proteins of the extracellular matrix. This type of attachment provides structural reinforcement, especially to tissues under physical stress like the epidermis of the skin and the lining of the digestive tract. The cell adhesion molecules that enable cells to adhere to the extracellular matrix are called **integrins.** Like the cadherins, integrins are transmembrane proteins, and their cytoplasmic domain is linked to the cytoskeleton (**Fig. 10.16b**). Also like the cadherins, integrins are of many different types, each with a specificity for a different extracellular matrix protein. Integrins are present on the surface of virtually every animal cell. Though integrins have not been observed in plants, integrin-like proteins are present on the surface of some plant cells as well. We return to integrins and how they interact with the extracellular matrix in section 10.5.

Adherens junctions and desmosomes connect adjacent animal cells and are anchored to the cytoskeleton.

Cadherins are not distributed randomly in the plasma membrane but are located in adherens junctions

---

FIG. 10.15 Cell type-specific cell adhesion. Experiments showed that cells from (a) sponges and from (b) amphibian embryos are in each case able to adhere to one another in a specific manner.

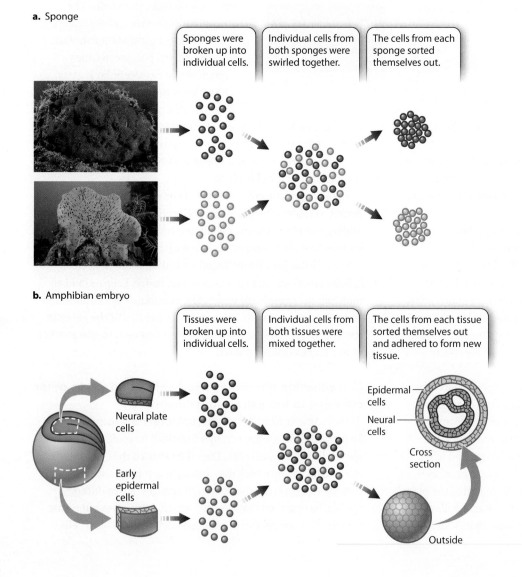

a. Sponge

| Sponges were broken up into individual cells. | Individual cells from both sponges were swirled together. | The cells from each sponge sorted themselves out. |

b. Amphibian embryo

| Tissues were broken up into individual cells. | Individual cells from both tissues were mixed together. | The cells from each tissue sorted themselves out and adhered to form new tissue. |

Neural plate cells

Early epidermal cells

Epidermal cells

Neural cells

Cross section

Outside

FIG. 10.16 Cell adhesion by (a) cadherins and (b) integrins. Cadherins are transmembrane proteins that connect cells to other cells; integrins are transmembrane proteins that connect cells to the extracellular matrix.

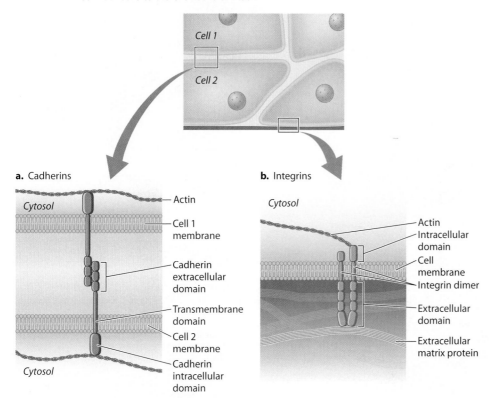

a. Cadherins

Cytosol

Actin

Cell 1 membrane

Cadherin extracellular domain

Transmembrane domain

Cell 2 membrane

Cadherin intracellular domain

Cytosol

b. Integrins

Cytosol

Actin
Intracellular domain

Cell membrane

Integrin dimer

Extracellular domain

Extracellular matrix protein

and desmosomes. These junctional complexes anchor cells to one another and are reinforced by the cytoskeleton (**Fig. 10.17**).

In our earlier discussion of microfilaments (section 10.2), we saw that a long bundle of actin microfilaments forms a band that extends around the circumference of epithelial cells, such as epithelial cells that line the intestine. This band of actin is attached to the plasma membrane by cadherins in a beltlike junctional complex called an **adherens junction** (Fig. 10.17). The cadherins in the adherens junction of one cell attach to the cadherins in the adherens junctions of adjacent cells. This arrangement establishes a physical connection among the actin cytoskeletons of all cells present in an epithelial layer of cells.

Desmosomes are buttonlike points of adhesion that hold the plasma membrane of adjacent cells together (Fig. 10.17). Cadherins are at work here, too, strengthening the connection between cells in a manner similar to adherens junctions. The cadherins in the desmosome of one cell bind to the cadherins in the desmosomes of adjacent cells. The cytoplasmic domain of these cadherins is linked to intermediate filaments in the cytoskeleton. This second type of physical connection among neighboring cells greatly enhances the structural integrity of epithelial cell layers.

The structural support provided by desmosomes and their associated network of intermediate filaments is crucial to the function of several organs, such as the skin and heart. Mutations in several of the genes for desmosomal proteins are responsible for a number of serious diseases. In these instances, intercellular connections are profoundly weakened. The results range from serious skin conditions due to fragile epidermis, as we saw with epidermolysis bullosa, to a high risk of early heart failure due to severe weakening of the heart muscle.

→   **Quick Check 2** Adherens junctions and desmosomes both attach cells to other cells and are made up of cadherins. How, then, are they different?

Tight junctions prevent the movement of substances through the space between animal cells.

Epithelial cells, which form layers or sheets that cover or line other tissues and organs, define the boundaries of many of these tissues, including the digestive tract, respiratory tract, and outer layer of the skin. Like any effective boundary, a layer of epithelial cells must limit or control the passage of material across it. Adherens junctions and desmosomes provide strong connections between cells, but they do not prevent the free passage of materials through the spaces between the cells they connect. Junctional complexes called **tight junctions** (Fig. 10.17) establish a seal between cells so that the only way a substance can travel from one side of a sheet of epithelial cells to the other is by moving *through* the cells by means of one of the cellular transport mechanisms discussed in Chapter 5.

A tight junction is a band of interconnected strands of integral membrane proteins that, like adherens junctions, encircles the epithelial cell. It also binds to tight-junction proteins on adjacent cells. Unlike adherens junctions, however, tight junctions are not connected to the cytoskeleton. Their function is to prevent passage of materials in between cells, not to anchor the cells together.

Cells that have tight junctions have two distinct sides because the tight junction divides the plasma membrane into two distinct regions (Fig. 10.17). The portion of the plasma

FIG. 10.17 Junctional complexes. Junctional complexes connect cells to other cells or to the basal lamina and are reinforced by the cytoskeleton.

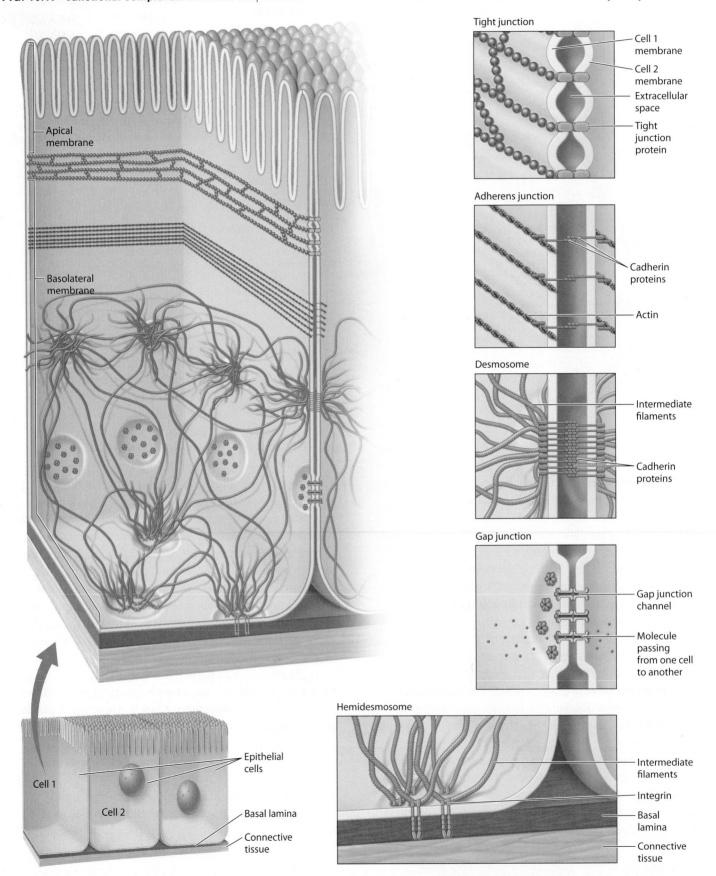

TABLE 10.1 Interactions among cellular junctions, cell adhesion molecules, and cytoskeleton elements.

DIFFERENT TYPES OF CELLULAR JUNCTION	USE SPECIFIC CELL ADHESION MOLECULES	TO ANCHOR THEMSELVES TO THE CYTOSKELETON
Adherens junctions	Cadherins	Microfilaments
Desmosomes	Cadherins	Intermediate filaments
Hemidesmosomes	Integrins	Intermediate filaments

membrane in contact with the lumen, or the inside of any tubelike structure like the gut, is called the apical membrane. The apical membrane defines the "top" side of the cell. The rest of the plasma membrane is the basolateral membrane, which defines the bottom ("baso") and sides ("lateral") of the cell. These two regions of the plasma membrane are structurally different because the tight junction prevents lipids and proteins in the membrane on one side of the junction from diffusing to the other side. As a result, the apical and basolateral membranes of a cell are likely to have different integral membrane proteins, which causes them to be functionally different as well. In the small intestine, for example, glucose is transported from the lumen into intestinal epithelial cells by transport proteins on the apical side of the cells, and is transported out of the cells into the circulation by facilitated diffusion through glucose transporters restricted to the basolateral sides of the cells.

From this discussion, we see that cellular junctions and cytoskeletal elements interact to create stable communities of cells in the form of tissues and organs. These interactions are specific, with certain junctions associated with specific components of the cytoskeletal network. These interactions are summarized in **Table 10.1.**

Gap junctions and plasmodesmata allow the passage of substances from one cell to another.

Not all junctions are involved in anchoring cells in place or sealing off one side of a layer of cells from the other. The **gap junctions** (Fig. 10.17) of animal cells and **plasmodesmata** of plant cells are connections between the plasma membranes of adjacent cells that permit materials to pass directly from the cytoplasm of one cell to the cytoplasm of another. Gap junctions are formed when a set of integral membrane proteins arranged in a ring connects to a similar ring of proteins in the membrane of another cell. Ions and signaling molecules pass through these junctions, allowing cells to communicate. In the heart, for example, ions pass though gap junctions connecting cardiac muscle cells. This rapid electrical communication allows the muscle cells to beat in a well-timed, coordinated rhythm.

Plasmodesmata (the singular form is "plasmodesma") are passages through the cell walls of adjacent plant cells. They are similar to gap junctions in that they allow cells to exchange ions and small molecules directly, but the similarity ends there. In plasmodesmata, the plasma membranes of the two connected cells are actually continuous. The size of the opening is considerably larger than that of gap junctions, large enough for cells to transfer RNA molecules and proteins, a capability that is especially important during plant embryonic development. Plasmodesmata allow plant cells to send signals to one another despite being enclosed within rigid cell walls.

→ **Quick Check 3** Which type(s) of junction prevent substances from moving through the space between cells? Which one(s) permit the exchange of cytoplasmic materials?

10.5 THE EXTRACELLULAR MATRIX

So far, we have looked at how the cytoskeleton maintains the shape of cells. We have also seen how the stable association of animal cells with one another and with the extracellular matrix is made possible by cellular junctions, and that these junctions are reinforced by the cytoskeleton. As important as the cytoskeleton and cellular junctions are to the structure of cells and tissues, it is the extracellular matrix that provides the molecular framework that ultimately determines the structural architecture of plants and animals.

The extracellular matrix is synthesized, secreted, and modified by many different kinds of cell. It is an insoluble meshwork composed of proteins and polysaccharides. There are many different forms of extracellular matrix, which differ in the amount, type, and organization of the proteins and polysaccharides that make them up.

In plants, the extracellular matrix takes the form of the cell wall, which provides the support needed by individual cells and results in turgor pressure (Chapter 5). Collectively, the interconnected cell walls of a plant act as an internal framework to support the entire organism. In animals, the extracellular matrix is present in most tissues and is especially abundant in connective tissue, where it provides support and protection, and in the basal lamina found underneath all epithelial tissue. In both plants and animals, the extracellular matrix not only contributes structural support but also provides informational cues that determine the activity of the cells that are in contact with it.

The extracellular matrix of plants is the cell wall.

The paper we write on, the cotton fibers in the clothes we wear, the wood in the chairs we sit on are, in fact, the extracellular matrix of plants. In plants, the extracellular matrix forms the cell wall, and the main component of the plant cell wall is the polysaccharide cellulose discussed in Chapter 2. Its presence in the cell wall of every plant makes cellulose the most widespread organic macromolecule on Earth.

The plant cell wall represents possibly one of the most complex examples of an extracellular matrix. It is certainly one of the most diverse in the functions it performs. Cell walls maintain the shape and turgor pressure of plant cells, allow plant cells to grow, and act as a barrier that prevents foreign materials and pathogens from reaching the plasma membrane. In many plants, cell walls collectively serve as a skeletal support structure for the entire plant.

The plant cell wall is composed of as many as three layers: the outermost middle lamella, the primary cell wall, and, closest to the plasma membrane, the secondary cell wall (**Fig. 10.18**). The middle lamella is made first, and is synthesized during the late stages of cell division. It is made of a gluelike complex carbohydrate, and it is the main mechanism by which plant cells adhere to one another. The primary cell wall is formed next and consists mainly of cellulose fibers, but it also contains a number of other molecules, including pectin and several proteins. The primary cell wall is laid down while the cells are still growing. It is assembled by enzymes on the surface of the cell and remains thin and flexible. Once cell growth has stopped, the secondary cell wall is constructed in many, but not all, plant cells. It also is made largely of cellulose fibers but in addition contains a substance called lignin. Lignin hardens the cell wall and makes it water resistant. In woody plants, the cell wall can be up to 25% lignin. The rigid secondary cell wall permits the growth of woody plants to tremendous heights. Giant sequoia trees grow to more than 300 feet and are supported entirely by the lignin-reinforced cellulose fibers of the interconnected cell walls.

For a plant cell to grow, the cell wall must accommodate an increase in cell volume and surface area. Even though the matrix of cellulose and other polysaccharides of the primary cell wall is relatively flexible compared to the lignin-containing secondary cell wall, it is still very strong. When a plant cell grows, additional cell wall components must be synthesized to expand the area of the wall. Unlike the extracellular matrix components that are secreted by animal cells, the cellulose polymer is assembled outside the cell, on the extracellular surface of the plasma membrane. Both the glucose monomers that form the polymer and the enzymes that attach them are delivered to the cell surface by arrays of microtubules. Here is yet another example of how the cytoskeleton plays an indispensable role in regulating the shape of cells.

FIG. 10.18 **The three layers of the plant cell wall: middle lamella, primary cell wall, and secondary cell wall.** The major component of the plant cell wall is cellulose, a polymer of glucose.

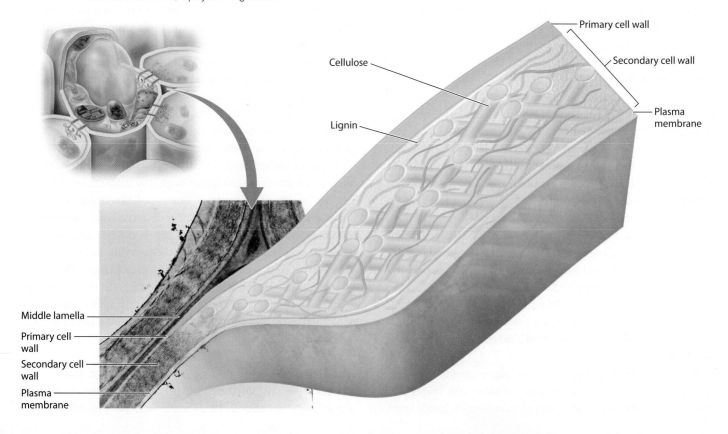

The extracellular matrix is abundant in connective tissues of animals.

The extracellular matrix of animals, like that of plants, is secreted by cells and is a mixture of proteins and polysaccharides. The animal extracellular matrix is composed of large fibrous proteins, including collagen, elastin, and laminin, which impart tremendous tensile strength. These fibrous proteins are embedded in a gel-like polysaccharide matrix. The matrix is negatively charged, attracting positively charged ions and water molecules that provide protection against compression and other physical stress.

The extracellular matrix can be found in abundance in animal connective tissue (**Fig. 10.19**). Connective tissue underlies all epithelial tissues, as we have seen. For example, the dermis of the skin is connective tissue, providing support and nutrients to the overlying epidermis. A number of cell types, including the fibroblasts that synthesize most of the extracellular matrix proteins, reside in this tissue. Connective tissue is unusual compared to other tissue types in that it is dominated by the extracellular matrix and has a low cell density. Consequently, the extracellular matrix determines the properties of different types of connective tissue. Other more specialized types of animal connective tissue include bone, cartilage, and tendon.

Collagen is the most abundant protein in the extracellular matrix of animals, and in fact is the most abundant animal protein on the planet. There are more than 20 different forms of collagen, and in humans collagen accounts for almost a quarter of the protein present in the body. Over 90% of this collagen is type I collagen, which is present in the dermis of your skin, where it provides strong, durable support for the overlying epidermis. The tendons that connect your muscles to bones and the ligaments that connect your bones to other bones are able to withstand the physical stress placed on them because they are made up primarily of collagen.

Collagen's strength is related to its structure. Like a rope or a cable, collagen is composed of intertwined fibers that make it much stronger than if it were a single fiber of the same diameter. A collagen molecule consists of three polypeptides wound around one another in a triple helix. A bundle of collagen molecules forms a fibril, and the fibrils are assembled into fibers (**Fig. 10.20**). Once multiple collagen fibers are assembled into a ligament or tendon, the final structure is incredibly strong.

FIG. 10.19   Animal connective tissue. Connective tissue is composed of protein fibers in a gel-like polysaccharide matrix.

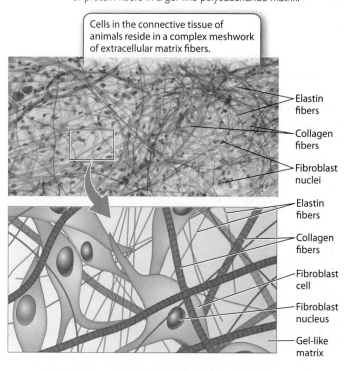

Cells in the connective tissue of animals reside in a complex meshwork of extracellular matrix fibers.

Elastin fibers

Collagen fibers

Fibroblast nuclei

Elastin fibers

Collagen fibers

Fibroblast cell

Fibroblast nucleus

Gel-like matrix

FIG. 10.20   Collagen. Type I collagen molecules are arranged in a triple helix and are grouped into bundles called fibrils, which in turn are grouped into bundles called fibers, resulting in tremendous strength like a steel cable.

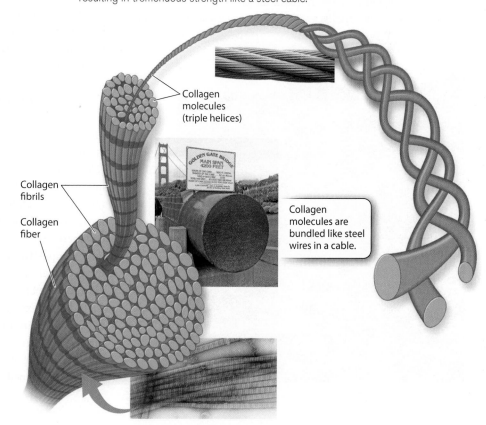

Collagen molecules (triple helices)

Collagen fibrils

Collagen fiber

Collagen molecules are bundled like steel wires in a cable.

The basal lamina is a special form of extracellular matrix.

The basal lamina is a specialized layer of extracellular matrix that is present beneath all epithelial tissues, including the lining of the digestive tract, epidermis of the skin, and endothelial cells that line the blood vessels of vertebrates (**Fig. 10.21**). The role of the basal lamina is to provide structural foundation for these epithelial tissues. The basal lamina is made of several proteins, including a special type of collagen. The triple-helical structure of collagen provides flexible support to the epithelial sheet and also provides a scaffold on which other proteins are assembled.

Epithelial cells are firmly anchored to the basal lamina by a version of the desmosome called a **hemidesmosome** (see Fig. 10.17). Integrins are the prominent cell adhesion molecules in hemidesomsomes. Their extracellular domains bind to the extracellular matrix proteins in the basal lamina, and their cytoplasmic domains are linked to intermediate filaments of the cytoskeleton. The intermediate filaments connected to hemidesomsomes are linked to those connected to the desmosomes in the lateral membrane. The result is a firmly anchored and tremendously reinforced layer of cells.

A migrating cell must be able to attach to extracellular matrix proteins in order to move forward. These contacts are also made by means of integrins. Cell migration in animals is normal and necessary during embryonic development (Chapter 42), wound

---

FIG. 10.21 The basal lamina. The basal lamina, found beneath epithelial tissue, is a specialized form of extracellular matrix.

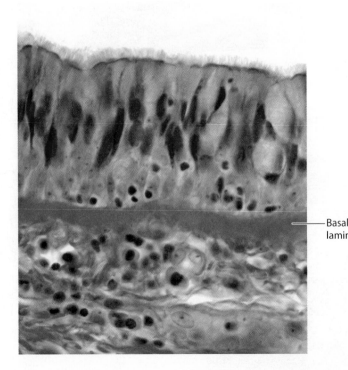

Basal lamina

healing, and the immune response to infection (Chapter 43). However, inappropriate cell migration can have devastating consequences, as we discuss now.

? CASE 2 Cancer: When Good Cells Go Bad
How do cancer cells spread throughout the body?

Nonmalignant, or benign, tumors are encapsulated masses of cells that divide continuously because regulation of cell division has gone awry (Chapter 11). As the tumor grows, its border pushes outward against adjacent tissues. Benign tumors are rarely life threatening unless the tumor interferes with the function of a vital organ.

Malignant tumors are different. They contain some cells that can metastasize, that is, break away from the main tumor and colonize distant sites in the body. Metastatic tumor cells have an enhanced ability to adhere to extracellular matrix proteins, especially those in the basal lamina. This is significant because for a cell to metastasize, it must enter and leave the bloodstream through capillaries. Since all blood vessels, including capillaries, have a basal lamina, a metastatic tumor cell needs to cross a basal lamina at least twice—once on the way into the bloodstream and again on the way out (**Fig. 10.22**). Since cells attach to basal lamina proteins by means of integrins, many studies have compared the integrins in metastatic and non-metastatic cells in the search for potential targets for treatment.

In some types of cancer, the number of specific integrins on the cell surface is an indicator of metastatic potential. Melanoma provides an example. A specific type of integrin is present in high amounts on metastatic melanoma cells but is absent on non-metastatic cells from the same tumor. In laboratory tests, blocking these integrins eliminates the melanoma cell's ability to cross an artificial basal lamina. Drugs targeting this integrin protein are currently in clinical trials.

Extracellular matrix proteins influence cell shape and gene expression.

The extracellular matrix is not an inert, three-dimensional environment in which cells live; instead, it plays an active role. Cells continue to interact with the extracellular matrix long after they have synthesized it or moved into it, and these interactions can have profound effects on the cell. Biologists have observed the results of these interactions in experiments conducted with cells grown in culture in the laboratory. For example, fibroblasts that secrete components of the extracellular matrix are in turn influenced by the extracellular matrix. Fibroblasts cultured on a two-dimensional surface coated with extracellular matrix proteins attach to the matrix and flatten as they maximize their adhesion to the matrix. By contrast, the same cells cultured in a three-dimensional gel of extracellular matrix look and behave like the spindle-shaped, highly migratory fibroblasts present in

FIG. 10.22 Metastatic cancer cells. Some cancer cells spread from the original site of cancer formation to the bloodstream and then to distant organs of the body.

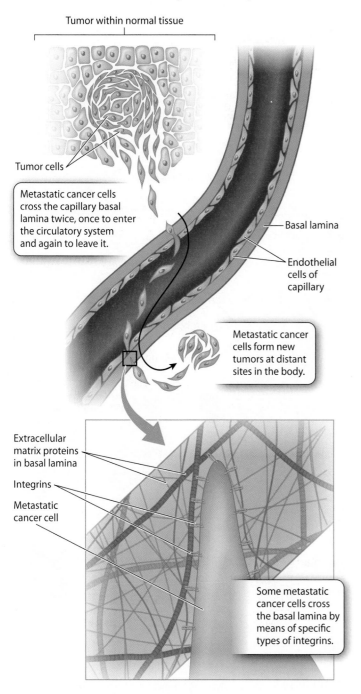

Tumor within normal tissue

Tumor cells

Metastatic cancer cells cross the capillary basal lamina twice, once to enter the circulatory system and again to leave it.

Basal lamina

Endothelial cells of capillary

Metastatic cancer cells form new tumors at distant sites in the body.

Extracellular matrix proteins in basal lamina

Integrins

Metastatic cancer cell

Some metastatic cancer cells cross the basal lamina by means of specific types of integrins.

FIG. 10.23 Cell shape determined by the structure of the extracellular matrix. Fibroblasts adopt different shapes depending on whether they are grown on a two-dimensional or a three-dimensional matrix.

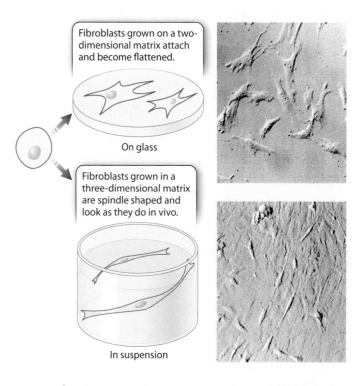

Fibroblasts grown on a two-dimensional matrix attach and become flattened.

On glass

Fibroblasts grown in a three-dimensional matrix are spindle shaped and look as they do in vivo.

In suspension

FIG. 10.24 Cell shape determined by composition of the extracellular matrix. Neurons adopt different shapes depending on whether or not they are cultured with the extracellular matrix protein laminin.

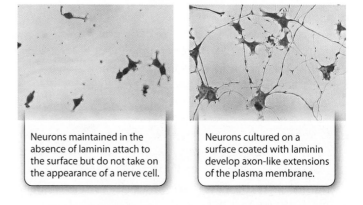

Neurons maintained in the absence of laminin attach to the surface but do not take on the appearance of a nerve cell.

Neurons cultured on a surface coated with laminin develop axon-like extensions of the plasma membrane.

living connective tissue (**Fig. 10.23**). So the structure of the extracellular matrix can influence the shape of cells.

A second example is provided by nerve cells. When these cells are grown in culture on a plastic surface, they attach to the surface of the dish, but do not take on a neuron-like shape.

However, when these cells are grown on the same surface coated with the extracellular matrix protein laminin, they develop long extensions that resemble the axons and dendrites of normal nerve cells (**Fig. 10.24**). In this case, the composition of the extracellular matrix can affect the shape of cells.

FIG. 10.25

Can extracellular matrix proteins influence gene expression?

BACKGROUND The adhesion of cells to the extracellular matrix is required for cell division, DNA synthesis, and proper cell shape. Research by Iranian-American cell biologist Mina Bissell and colleagues indicated that cellular interaction with extracellular matrix proteins influences gene expression. Bissell discovered that mammary cells expressed and secreted high levels of the milk protein β-casein when grown in a three-dimensional collagen matrix but not in a two-dimensional collagen matrix. American cell biologist Joan Caron followed up these studies using liver cells called hepatocytes.

HYPOTHESIS Caron hypothesized that a specific protein in the extracellular matrix is necessary for the expression of the protein albumin from hepatocytes grown in culture. Albumin is a major product of liver cells.

EXPERIMENT Caron cultured hepatocytes on a thin layer of type I collagen, which does not induce albumin synthesis. Next, she added a mixture of several different extracellular matrix proteins to the culture and looked for changes in albumin gene expression and protein secretion into the media. She then tested individual extracellular matrix proteins from the mixture to see which one was responsible for the increase in albumin gene expression.

RESULTS Caron found that when she cultured cells on collagen with a combination of three extracellular matrix proteins—laminin, type IV collagen, and heparin sulfate proteoglycan (HSPG)—the cells synthesized albumin mRNA and secreted albumin protein for several weeks, but if she cultured the cells on collagen alone, they did not (top and middle graphs). In addition, when she tested individual extracellular matrix proteins, she found that laminin, but not any of the other proteins, caused an increase in albumin gene expression (bottom graph).

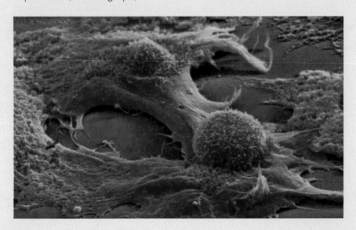

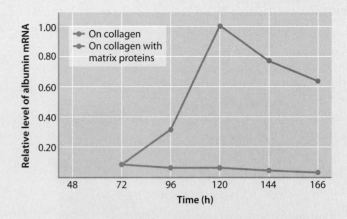

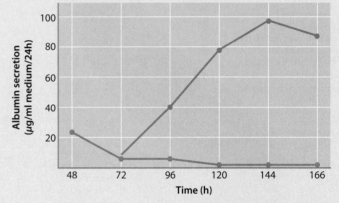

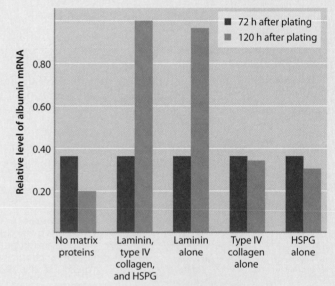

CONCLUSION Caron's hypothesis was supported by the experiments. A specific extracellular matrix protein, laminin, influences the expression of albumin by hepatocytes.

FOLLOW-UP WORK Bissell continued her work with mammary cells and found that the expression of the β-casein gene was also increased by laminin in the same way as the albumin gene in hepatocytes.

SOURCES Lee, E. Y., W. H. Lee, C. S. Kaetzel, G. Parry, and M. J. Bissell. 1985. "Interaction of Mouse Mammary Epithelial Cells with Collagen Substrata: Regulation of Casein Gene Expression and Secretion." PNAS 82:1419–1423; Caron, J. M. 1990. "Induction of Albumin Gene Transcription in Hepatocytes by Extracellular Matrix Proteins." Molecular and Cellular Biology 10:1239–1243.

In addition to influencing cell shape, the structure and composition of the extracellular matrix can influence gene expression of the cells that are grown in it. Mouse mammary epithelial cells grown in culture on plain glass coated with collagen remain alive and apparently healthy, and even make and secrete a minimal amount of milk proteins, including β-casein, when stimulated by the milk-inducing hormone prolactin. However, if the mammary epithelial cells are grown in three-dimensional collagen gels, they synthesize and secrete up to 10 times more β-casein.

→   **Quick Check 4**   Do you think cadherins or integrins are responsible for the dependence of mammary cells on the extracellular matrix for their ability to produce milk proteins? Why?

Two related experiments that further explore the importance of extracellular matrix proteins in the regulation of gene expression are described in **Fig. 10.25**. Taken together, these experiments demonstrate that there is a dynamic interplay between the extracellular matrix and the cells that synthesize it.

Core Concepts Summary

10.1 TISSUES AND ORGANS ARE COMMUNITIES OF CELLS THAT PERFORM A SPECIFIC FUNCTION.

A tissue is a collection of cells that work together to perform a specific function. page 10-2

Two or more tissues often work together to form an organ. page 10-2

Cytoskeletal structures determine the shape of the cell. page 10-2

Cell junctions connect cells to one another and to the extracellular matrix, a meshwork of proteins and polysaccharides outside the cell. page 10-2

10.2 THE CYTOSKELETON IS COMPOSED OF MICROTUBULES, MICROFILAMENTS, AND INTERMEDIATE FILAMENTS THAT HELP TO MAINTAIN CELL SHAPE.

All eukaryotic cells have microtubules and microfilaments. Animal cells also have intermediate filaments. page 10-3

Microtubules, microfilaments, and intermediate filaments are polymers of protein subunits. page 10-4

Microtubules provide structural support and maintain cytoplasmic organization. They are hollow polymers of tubulin dimers. page 10-4

Microfilaments also provide structural support necessary to maintain the shape of a cell. They are polymers of actin monomers. page 10-4

Microtubules and microfilaments are dynamic structures and can assemble and disassemble rapidly. page 10-4

Intermediate filaments are polymers of proteins that differ depending on cell type. They do not exhibit the dynamic properties of microtubules and microfilaments and provide stable structural support for many types of cells. page 10-5

Microtubules and microfilaments have a plus end and a minus end, determined by the rate at which subunits are added. page 10-6

Microtubules go through rounds of growth and rapid shrinkage called dynamic instability. page 10-7

The cytoskeleton is an ancient feature of cells. Some prokaryotic cells have protein polymer-like systems that function similarly to microtubules and microfilaments. page 10-7

10.3 THE CYTOSKELETON INTERACTS WITH MOTOR PROTEINS TO PERMIT THE MOVEMENT OF CELLS AND SUBSTANCES WITHIN CELLS.

Motor proteins associated with microtubules and microfilaments enable intracellular transport and cell movement. Myosin binds to actin in microfilaments. Dynein and kinesin bind to tubulin to facilitate microtubule-dependent movement. page 10-8

Microfilaments are involved in intracellular vesicle transport and enable many cells to move by crawling across a surface or through a tissue. page 10-8

Microtubules provide intracellular tracks along which cargo is transported in the cytoplasm. page 10-9

Flagella and cilia are organelles that contain microtubules that propel cells through aqueous environments. page 10-10

10.4 CELLS ADHERE TO OTHER CELLS AND THE EXTRACELLULAR MATRIX BY MEANS OF CELL ADHESION MOLECULES AND JUNCTIONAL COMPLEXES.

Cell adhesion molecules allow cells to attach to other cells and to extracellular matrix proteins. page 10-11

Cadherins are transmembrane proteins that allow cells to adhere to other cells. Integrins are transmembrane proteins that facilitate cell adhesion to the extracellular matrix. page 10-12

Adherens junctions form a continuous band around the circumference of a cell. Desmosomes are buttonlike points of adhesion between cells. page 10-13

Cadherins in adherens junctions are anchored to the microfilaments of the cytoskeleton. Cadherins in desmosomes are anchored to intermediate filaments. page 10-13

Tight junctions prevent the passage of substances through the space between cells. They also divide the plasma membrane into apical and basolateral regions. page 10-13

Gap junctions and plasmodesmata allow the passage of substances from the cytoplasm of one cell to that of its neighbor. page 10-15

10.5 THE EXTRACELLULAR MATRIX PROVIDES STRUCTURAL SUPPORT AND INFORMATIONAL CUES.

The extracellular matrix is an insoluble meshwork of proteins and polysaccharides secreted by the cells it surrounds. It provides structural support to cells, tissues, and organs. page 10-15

In plants, the extracellular matrix is found in the cell wall, and the main component of the plant cell wall is the polysaccharide cellulose. page 10-16

In animals, the extracellular matrix is found in abundance in connective tissue. page 10-17

Collagen is the primary component of connective tissues in animals and is exceptionally strong. page 10-17

A highly specialized extracellular matrix called the basal lamina is present under all epithelial cell layers. Cells are anchored to the basal lamina by integrins in hemidesmosomes. page 10-18

In addition to providing structural support for cells, the extracellular matrix can influence cell shape, movement, and gene expression. page 10-18

Self-Assessment

1. Name three types of filaments that make up the cytoskeleton, including the subunits of each, and state which cytoskeletal element is not present in plant cells.

2. Explain how microtubules and microfilaments are dynamic structures.

3. Describe the functions of the three major motor proteins that are required for cellular movements involving the cytoskeleton.

4. Compare the cytoskeletal dynamics in cells that move by beating cilia or flagella with cells that move by crawling.

5. Identify the cytoskeletal component linked to adherens junctions, desmosomes, and hemidesmosomes.

6. Compare and contrast the structural features and functional roles of cadherins and integrins.

7. Name examples of the extracellular matrix in plants and animals.

8. Explain the functional relationships among the basal lamina, integrins, and intermediate filaments in epithelial tissues.

9. Predict the effect of inadequate or inappropriate adhesion of a cell to the extracellular matrix on gene expression in the cell.

Do you understand the chapter's Core Concepts? Log into BIOPORTAL to check your answers to the Self-Assessment questions, then practice what you've learned and reinforce this chapter's concepts by working through the problems and multimedia tutorials provided there.

🛜 http://courses.bfwpub.com/yourbioportal/index.php

CHAPTER 11

CELL DIVISION

Variations, Regulation, and Cancer

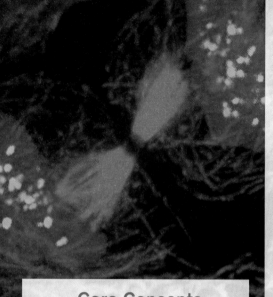

Core Concepts

11.1 During cell division, a single parental cell divides into two daughter cells.

11.2 Mitotic cell division is the basis of asexual reproduction in unicellular eukaryotes and the process by which cells divide in multicellular eukaryotes.

11.3 Meiotic cell division is essential for sexual reproduction, the production of offspring that combines genetic material from two parents.

11.4 The cell cycle is regulated so that cell division occurs only at appropriate times.

11.5 Cancer is uncontrolled cell division that usually results from mutations in genes that control cell division.

Cells come from preexisting cells. This is one of the fundamental principles of biology and a key component of the cell theory, which was introduced in Chapter 1. **Cell division** is the process by which cells make more cells. In multicellular organisms, which begin life as a single cell, cell division produces the millions, billions, or in the case of humans, trillions of cells that make up the fully developed organism. Even after a multicellular organism has achieved its adult size, cell division continues. In plants, cell division is essential for continued growth. In many animals, cell division replaces worn-out blood cells, skin cells, and cells that line much of the digestive tract. And if you fall and scrape your knee, the cells at the site of the wound begin dividing to replace the damaged cells and heal the scrape.

Cell division is also important in reproduction. In bacteria, for example, a new generation is created when the parent cell divides and forms two daughter cells. This type of reproduction is called **asexual reproduction.** When a single bacterium reproduces by cell division, it first makes identical copies of its genetic material so that each of the two daughter cells has the same genetic material as the parent cell. There are many connotations to the word "sex," but strictly speaking, sex is the combining of genetic material from two individuals. Since the genetic material in the bacterial daughter cells comes from just one parent, reproduction occurred without sex, or asexually. In principle, the daughter cells are genetically identical to the parental cell, but because DNA replication is not completely error free, the daughter cells may carry small genetic differences or mutations compared to the parent cell.

By contrast, **sexual reproduction** results in offspring that receive genetic material from two parents. Half the genetic material is supplied by the female parent and is present in the egg; the other half is contributed by the male's sperm. Eggs and sperm are specialized cells called **gametes.** A female gamete and a male gamete merge during fertilization to form a new organism (Chapter 42). A unique feature of gametes is that they contain half the number of chromosomes as the other cells in the parent organism. So when fertilization occurs, the combination of genetic material from the egg and the sperm results in a new organism with the same number of chromosomes as the parents. The production of gametes comes about by a form of cell division that results in daughter cells with half the number of chromosomes as the parent cell. As we will see, the products of this cell division are *not* genetically identical to the parent.

What determines when cells divide and, importantly, when they should not? And what determines which cells divide? To answer these questions, we must understand the process of cell division and how it is controlled. This discussion will lay the groundwork for exploring how cancer results from a loss of control of cell division.

11.1 CELL DIVISION

Cell division is the process by which a single cell becomes two daughter cells. While this process may seem simple, successful cell division must satisfy several important requirements. First, the two daughter cells must each receive the full complement of genetic material (DNA) present in the single parent cell. Second, the parent cell must be large enough to divide in two and still contribute sufficient cytoplasmic components such as proteins, lipids, and other macromolecules to each daughter cell. Satisfying these requirements means that key cellular components must be duplicated before cell division takes place. This duplication of material is achieved in a series of steps that constitute the life cycle of every cell. When you think of a life cycle, you might think of various stages beginning with birth and ending with death. In the case of a single cell, the life cycle begins and ends with cell division.

In this section, we explore the different mechanisms by which prokaryotic and eukaryotic cells divide. Prokaryotic cells divide by **binary fission.** When eukaryotic cells divide, they first divide the nucleus during **mitosis,** then divide the cytoplasm into two daughter cells during **cytokinesis.** As we discuss, it is likely that mitosis evolved from binary fission.

Prokaryotic cells reproduce by binary fission.

The majority of prokaryotic cells, namely bacteria and archaeons, divide by binary fission. In this form of cell division, a cell replicates its DNA, increases in size, and divides into two daughter cells. Each daughter cell receives one copy of the replicated parental DNA. The molecular mechanisms that drive binary fission have been studied most extensively in bacteria. The process of binary fission is similar in archaeons, as well as in chloroplasts and mitochondria, organelles within plant and animal cells which evolved from free-living prokaryotic cells (Chapters 5 and 27).

Let's consider the process of binary fission in the intestinal bacterium *Escherichia coli* (**Fig. 11.1**). The circular genome of *E. coli* is attached by proteins to the inside of the plasma membrane. DNA replication is initiated at a specific location on the circular DNA molecule and proceeds in opposite directions around the circle. The result is two DNA molecules, both attached to the plasma membrane. The cell then grows. As the cell elongates, the two DNA attachment sites move apart. When the cell is about twice its original size and the DNA molecules are well separated, a constriction forms at the midpoint of the cell. Eventually, new membrane and cell wall are synthesized at the site of the constriction, dividing the single cell into two. The result is two daughter cells, each having the same genetic material as the parent cell.

Like most cellular processes, binary fission requires the coordination of many components in both time and space. Recent research has identified several genes whose products play a key role in bacterial cell division. One of these genes, called *FtsZ*, has been especially well studied. The protein it encodes forms a ring at the site of constriction where the new cell wall forms between the two daughter cells. *FtsZ* is present in the genomes of diverse bacteria and archaeons, suggesting that it plays a fundamental role in prokaryotic cell division. Interestingly, it appears to be evolutionarily related to tubulin, which you will recall from Chapter 10 makes up the dynamic microtubules found in eukaryotic cells that are important in intracellular transport, cell movement, and cell division.

→ **Quick Check 1** What do you predict would be the consequence of a mutation in *FtsZ* that disrupts the function of the protein it encodes?

FIG. 11.1 **Binary fission.** Cell division in bacteria and archaeons occurs by binary fission.

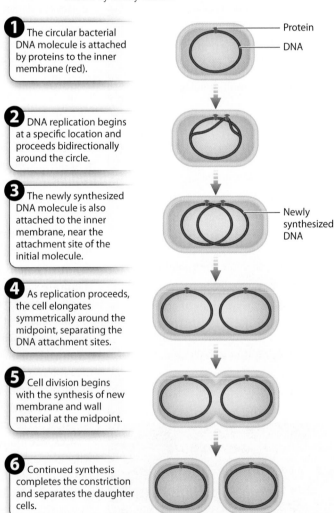

1 The circular bacterial DNA molecule is attached by proteins to the inner membrane (red). — Protein — DNA

2 DNA replication begins at a specific location and proceeds bidirectionally around the circle.

3 The newly synthesized DNA molecule is also attached to the inner membrane, near the attachment site of the initial molecule. — Newly synthesized DNA

4 As replication proceeds, the cell elongates symmetrically around the midpoint, separating the DNA attachment sites.

5 Cell division begins with the synthesis of new membrane and wall material at the midpoint.

6 Continued synthesis completes the constriction and separates the daughter cells.

Eukaryotic cells reproduce by mitotic cell division.

The basic steps of binary fission that we just saw—replication of DNA, segregation of replicated DNA to daughter cells, and division of one cell into two—occur in all forms of cell division. However, cell division in eukaryotes is more complicated than cell division in prokaryotes. Instead of the single, relatively small, circular DNA molecule that is the genome of prokaryotic cells, the genome of eukaryotic cells is typically much larger and organized into one or more linear chromosomes, each of which needs to be replicated and separated into daughter cells. And whereas the DNA of prokaryotes is attached to the inside of the plasma membrane, allowing separation of replicated DNA into daughter cells by cell growth, the DNA of eukaryotes is located in the nucleus. As a result, eukaryotic cell division requires first the breakdown and then the re-formation of the nuclear envelope, as well as mechanisms other than cell growth to separate replicated DNA. As we saw in Chapter 10 and discuss in more detail in section 11.2, chromosomes of dividing eukaryotic cells attach to the mitotic spindle, which separates them into daughter cells.

Interestingly, some unicellular eukaryotes exhibit forms of cell division that have characteristics of binary fission and mitosis. For example, dinoflagellates, like all eukaryotes, have a nucleus and linear chromosomes. However, unlike most eukaryotes, the nuclear envelope does not break down but stays intact during cell division. Furthermore, the replicated DNA is attached to the nuclear envelope. The nucleus then grows and divides in a manner reminiscent of binary fission. These and observations of intermediate forms of cell division in other organisms strongly suggest that mitosis evolved from binary fission.

The cell cycle describes the life cycle of a eukaryotic cell.

Cell division in eukaryotic cells proceeds through a number of steps that make up the **cell cycle** (**Fig. 11.2**). The cell cycle consists of two distinct stages: **M phase** and **interphase.** During M phase, the parent cell divides into two daughter cells. M phase consists of two different events: (1) mitosis, the separation of the chromosomes into two nuclei, and (2) cytokinesis, the division of the cell itself into two separate cells. Usually, these two processes go hand in hand, with cytokinesis usually beginning even before mitosis is complete. In most mammalian cells, M phase lasts about an hour.

The second stage of the cell cycle, called interphase, is the time between two successive M phases (Fig. 11.2). This stage lasts about 10 to 14 hours in most actively multiplying mammalian cells. For many years, it was thought that the relatively long period of interphase is uneventful. Today we know that during this stage the cell makes many preparations for division. These preparations include replication of the DNA in the nucleus so that each daughter cell receives a copy of the genome, and an increase in

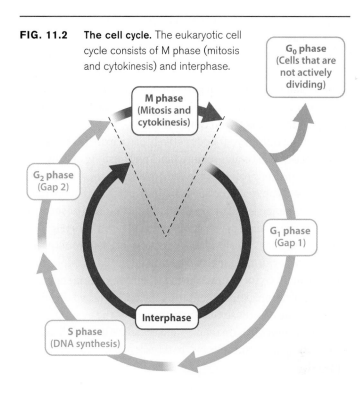

FIG. 11.2 **The cell cycle.** The eukaryotic cell cycle consists of M phase (mitosis and cytokinesis) and interphase.

cell size so that each daughter cell receives sufficient amounts of cytoplasmic and membrane components to survive on its own.

Interphase can be divided into three phases, as shown in Fig. 11.2. Among the many preparations that the cell must make during interphase, one particularly important task is the replication of the entire DNA content of the nucleus. Since replication involves the synthesis of DNA, this stage is called **S phase** ("S" standing for "synthesis").

In most cells, S phase does not immediately precede or follow mitosis but is separated from it by two gap phases: G_1 **phase** between the end of M phase and the start of S phase, and G_2 **phase** between the end of S phase and the start of M phase. Many essential processes occur during both "gap" phases, despite the name. For example, both the size and protein content of the cell increase in preparation for division. In addition, the G_1 phase is a time when specific regulatory proteins are made and activated. Once active, the regulatory proteins, many of which are kinases, then promote the activity of enzymes that synthesize DNA. Thus, G_1 is a time of preparation for S-phase DNA synthesis, and G_2 is a time of preparation for M-phase mitosis and cytokinesis.

The time it takes for cells to pass through the cell cycle depends on the type of cell and the organism's stage of development. Actively dividing cells in some human tissues such as the intestine and skin require frequent replenishing. Cells in these tissues usually need about 12 hours to complete the cell cycle. Most other actively dividing cells in your body take about 24 hours to complete the cycle. A unicellular eukaryote like yeast can complete an entire cell cycle in just 90 minutes. Champions in the race through the cell cycle are the cells of the embryos of some frog species, in which early cell divisions divide the cytoplasm of the large egg cell into many smaller cells and so do not require any growth period in between cell divisions. Consequently, there are virtually no G_1 and G_2 phases and as little as 30 minutes pass between cell divisions.

Not all the cells in your body actively participate in the cell cycle, since not all tissues require rapid replenishing of cells. Instead, many cells pause in the cell cycle somewhere between M phase and S phase for periods ranging from days to more than a year. This period is called the **G_0 phase** and is distinguished from G_1 by the absence of preparations for DNA synthesis (Fig. 11.2). Although cells in G_0 have exited the cell cycle, they are active in other ways, performing specialized functions. For example, liver cells remain in G_0 for as much as a year, carrying out metabolism and detoxification, before reentering the cell cycle and dividing. Other cells such as those that form the lens of the eye and nerve cells enter G_0 permanently and therefore are nondividing cells. Thus, many brain cells lost to disease or damage cannot be replaced.

11.2 MITOTIC CELL DIVISION

Mitotic cell division (mitosis followed by cytokinesis) is the normal mode of asexual reproduction in unicellular eukaryotes, and it is the means by which an organism's cells, tissues, and organs develop and are maintained in multicellular eukaryotes. During mitosis and cytokinesis, the parental cell's DNA is divided and passed on to two daughter cells. This process is continuous, but is divided into discrete steps marked by dramatic changes in the cytoskeleton and in the packaging and movement of the chromosomes.

The DNA of eukaryotic cells is organized as chromosomes.

One of the key challenges faced by a dividing eukaryotic cell is ensuring that both daughter cells receive an equal and complete set of chromosomes. The length of DNA contained in the nucleus of an average eukaryotic cell is on the order of 1 to 2 meters, well beyond the diameter of a cell. The DNA therefore needs to be condensed to fit into the nucleus, and then further condensed during cell division so that it does not become tangled as it segregates into daughter cells.

In eukaryotic cells, DNA is organized with histones and other proteins into chromatin, which can be looped and packaged to form the structures we know as chromosomes (Chapter 3). One of the earliest events in mitosis is the condensing of chromosomes from long, thin, threadlike structures typical of interphase to short, dense forms that are identifiable under the microscope during M phase.

FIG. 11.3 A human karyotype showing 22 pairs of chromosomes plus 2 sex chromosomes, or 46 chromosomes in total.

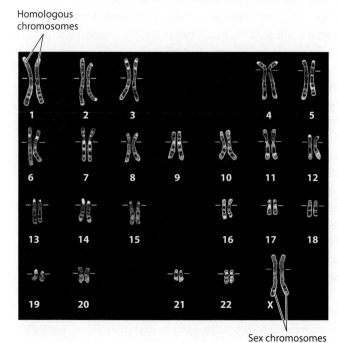

Homologous chromosomes

Sex chromosomes

Every species is characterized by a specific number of chromosomes, and each chromosome contains a single molecule of DNA carrying a specific set of genes. When chromosomes condense and become visible during mitosis, they adopt characteristic shapes and sizes that allow each chromosome to be identified by its appearance in the microscope. The portrait formed by the number and shapes of chromosomes representative of a species is called its **karyotype.** Most of the cells in the human body, with the exception of the gametes, contain 46 chromosomes (**Fig. 11.3**). In contrast, cells from horses have 64 chromosomes, and cells from corn have 20.

FIG. 11.4 Homologous chromosomes and sister chromatids. Sister chromatids result from the duplication of chromosomes. They are held together at the centromere.

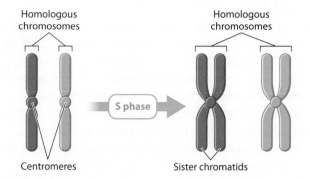

Homologous chromosomes

Homologous chromosomes

S phase

Centromeres

Sister chromatids

In a normal human karyotype, the 46 chromosomes can be arranged into 23 pairs, 22 pairs of **homologous chromosomes** numbered 1 to 22 from the longest to the shortest chromosome and 1 pair of **sex chromosomes** (Fig. 11.3). Each pair of homologous chromosomes represents two of the same type of chromosome (both carrying the same set of genes), one of which was received from the mother and the other from the father. The sex chromosomes are the X and Y chromosomes. Individuals with two X chromosomes are female, and those with an X and a Y chromosome are male.

The number of complete sets of chromosomes in a cell is known as ploidy. A cell with one complete set of chromosomes is **haploid,** and a cell with two complete sets of chromosomes is **diploid.** Some organisms, such as plants, can have four or sometimes more complete sets of chromosomes. Such cells are polyploid.

In order for cell division to proceed normally, every chromosome in the parent cell must be duplicated so that each daughter cell receives a full set of chromosomes. This duplication occurs during S phase. Even though the DNA in each chromosome duplicates, the two identical copies, called **sister chromatids,** do not separate. They stay side by side, physically held together at a constriction called the **centromere.** At the beginning of mitosis, the nucleus of a human cell contains 46 chromosomes, each of which is a pair of identical sister chromatids linked together at the centromere (**Fig. 11.4**). Thus, to count chromosomes, it is simply a matter of counting centromeres.

→ **Quick Check 2** Which DNA sequences are more alike: a pair of sister chromatids or a pair of homologous chromosomes?

Prophase: Chromosomes condense and become visible.

Mitosis takes place in five stages, each of which is easily identified by events that can be observed in the microscope (**Fig. 11.5**). When you look in a microscope at a cell in interphase, specific chromosomes cannot be distinguished because they are long and thin. As the cell moves from G_2 phase to the start of mitosis, the chromosomes condense and become visible in the nucleus. The first stage of mitosis is known

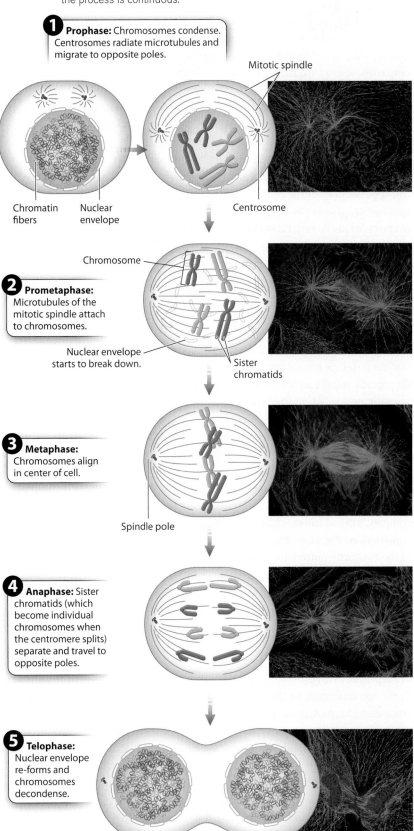

FIG. 11.5 Mitosis, or nuclear division. Mitosis can be divided into separate steps, but the process is continuous.

1 Prophase: Chromosomes condense. Centrosomes radiate microtubules and migrate to opposite poles.

Mitotic spindle

Chromatin fibers

Nuclear envelope

Centrosome

Chromosome

2 Prometaphase: Microtubules of the mitotic spindle attach to chromosomes.

Nuclear envelope starts to break down.

Sister chromatids

3 Metaphase: Chromosomes align in center of cell.

Spindle pole

4 Anaphase: Sister chromatids (which become individual chromosomes when the centromere splits) separate and travel to opposite poles.

5 Telophase: Nuclear envelope re-forms and chromosomes decondense.

as **prophase** and is characterized by the appearance of visible chromosomes.

Outside the nucleus, in the cytosol, the cell begins to assemble the **mitotic spindle,** a structure made up predominantly of microtubules that pull the chromosomes into separate daughter cells. Recall from Chapter 10 that the **centrosome** is a compact structure that is the microtubule organizing center for animal cells. Plant cells also have microtubule-based mitotic spindles, but they lack centrosomes. As part of the preparation for mitosis during S phase in animal cells, the centrosome duplicates and each one begins to migrate around the nucleus, the two ultimately halting at opposite poles in the cell. The final locations of the centrosomes define the opposite ends of the cell that will eventually be separated into two daughter cells. As the centrosomes make their way to the poles of the cell, tubulin dimers assemble around them, forming microtubules that radiate from each centrosome. These radiating filaments form the mitotic spindle and later serve as the guide wires for chromosome movement.

Prometaphase: Chromosomes attach to the mitotic spindle.

In the next stage of mitosis, known as **prometaphase,** the nuclear envelope breaks down and the microtubules of the mitotic spindle attach to chromosomes (Fig. 11.5). The microtubules radiating from the centrosome poles grow and shrink as they explore the region of the cell where the nucleus once was. This process of growing and shrinking depends on the dynamic instability of microtubules, discussed in Chapter 10.

As the ends of the microtubules encounter chromosomes, they attach to the chromosomes at their centromeres. Associated with the centromere of each chromosome are two protein complexes called **kinetochores,** one located on each side of the constriction (**Fig. 11.6**). Each kinetochore is associated with one of the two sister chromatids and forms the site of attachment for a single microtubule. This arrangement ensures that each sister chromatid is attached to a microtubule radiating from one of the poles of the cell. The symmetrical tethering of each chromosome to the two poles of the cell is essential for proper chromosome segregation.

Metaphase: Chromosomes align as a result of dynamic changes in the mitotic spindle.

Once each chromosome is attached to both spindle poles, the microtubules of the mitotic spindle lengthen or shorten to move the chromosomes into position in the middle of the cell. There the chromosomes are lined up in a single plane that is roughly equidistant from both of the spindle poles. This stage of mitosis, when the chromosomes are aligned in the middle of the dividing cell, is called **metaphase** (see Fig. 11.5). It is one of the most visually distinctive stages under the microscope.

FIG. 11.6   **Kinetochores.** Kinetochores, the sites of spindle microtubule attachment, are located on both sides of the centromere.

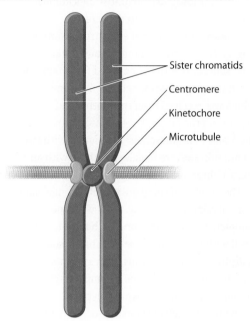

Sister chromatids
Centromere
Kinetochore
Microtubule

Anaphase: Sister chromatids fully separate.

In the next stage of mitosis, called **anaphase,** the sister chromatids separate (see Fig. 11.5). The centromere holding a pair of sister chromatids together divides, allowing the two sister chromatids to separate from each other. After separation, each chromatid is considered to be a full-fledged chromosome. The microtubules attached to the kinetochores gradually shorten, pulling the newly separated chromosomes to the opposite spindle poles of the cell.

This remarkable event is the reason for the equal segregation of chromosomes between the two daughter cells. In chromosome duplication during S phase in a human cell, each of the 46 chromosomes is duplicated to yield 46 pairs of identical sister chromatids. Thus, when the chromatids are separated at anaphase, an identical set of 46 chromosomes arrives at each spindle pole, the complete genetic material for one of the daughter cells.

Telophase: Nuclear envelopes re-form around newly segregated chromosomes.

Once a complete set of chromosomes arrives at a spindle pole, the chromosomes have entered the area that will form the cytosol of a new daughter cell. This event marks the beginning of **telophase**, during which cytosolic changes occur in preparation for the cell's division into two new cells (see Fig. 11.5). The microtubules of the mitotic spindle break down and disappear, while nuclear envelopes begin to re-form around each set of chromosomes, creating two new nuclei. As the nuclei become increasingly distinct in the cell, the chromosomes contained within them decondense, becoming less visible in the microscope. This stage marks the end of mitosis.

The parent cell divides into two daughter cells by cytokinesis.

Usually, as mitosis is nearing its end, cytokinesis begins and the parent cell divides into two daughter cells (**Fig. 11.7**). In animal cells, this stage begins when a ring of actin filaments, called the **contractile ring**, forms against the inner face of the cell membrane at the equator of the cell perpendicular to the axis of what was the spindle (Fig. 11.7a). As if pulled by a drawstring, the ring contracts, pinching the cytoplasm of the cell and dividing

it in two. This process is similar to what occurs in binary fission, though in the case of binary fission, the process is driven by FtsZ protein, a homolog of tubulin, not by actin as in eukaryotic cells. The constriction of the contractile ring is driven by motor proteins that slide bundles of actin filaments in opposite directions. Successful division results in two daughter cells, each with its own nucleus. The daughter cells are now free to enter G_1 phase and start the process anew.

For the most part, mitosis is similar in animal and plant cells, but cytokinesis is different (Fig. 11.7b). Since plant cells have a cell wall, the division of the cell is achieved by constructing a new cell wall. During telophase, dividing plant cells form a structure called the **phragmoplast** in the middle of the cell. The phragmoplast consists of overlapping microtubules that guide vesicles containing cell wall components to the middle of the cell. During late anaphase and telophase, these vesicles fuse to form a new cell wall, called the **cell plate,** in the middle of the dividing cell. Once this developing cell wall is large enough, it fuses with the original cell wall at the perimeter of the cell. Cytokinesis is then complete and the plant cell has divided into two daughter cells.

→ **Quick Check 3** What would be the consequence if a cell underwent mitosis but not cytokinesis?

FIG. 11.7 **Cytokinesis, or cytoplasmic division.** (a) In animal cells, cytokinesis involves a contractile ring made of actin. (b) In plant cells, it involves the growth of a new cell wall called a cell plate.

a.

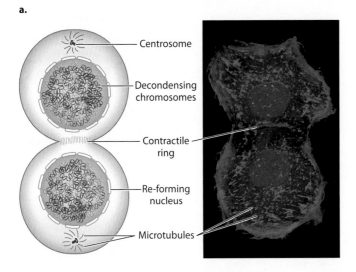

- Centrosome
- Decondensing chromosomes
- Contractile ring
- Re-forming nucleus
- Microtubules

b.

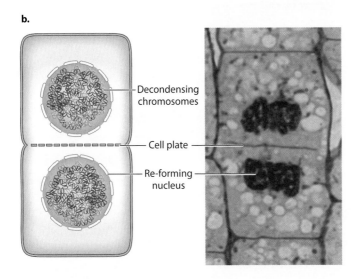

- Decondensing chromosomes
- Cell plate
- Re-forming nucleus

11.3 MEIOTIC CELL DIVISION

As we have seen, mitotic cell division is important in the development of a multicellular organism and in the maintenance and repair of tissues and organs. Mitotic cell division is also the basis of asexual reproduction in unicellular eukaryotes. Sexual reproduction involves the fusion of gametes during fertilization to form a new organism. A new organism produced by sexual reproduction has the same number of chromosomes as its parents because the egg and sperm each have half the number of chromosomes as the diploid parents.

Gametes are produced by **meiotic cell division,** a form of cell division that includes two rounds of nuclear division. Meiotic cell division makes sexual reproduction possible. There are several major differences between meiotic cell division and mitotic cell division. First, meiotic cell division results in four daughter cells instead of two. Second, each of the four daughter cells contains half the number of chromosomes as the parent cell. (The word "meiosis" is from the Greek for "diminish" or "lessen.") Third, the four daughter cells are each genetically unique. In other words, they are genetically different from each other and from the parental cell.

In multicellular animals, the cells produced by meiosis are the haploid eggs and sperm that fuse in sexual reproduction. In other organisms, such as fungi, the products are spores, and in some unicellular eukaryotes, the products are new organisms. In this section, we consider the steps by which meiosis occurs, its role in sexual reproduction, and how it likely evolved.

Pairing of homologous chromosomes is unique to meiosis.

Like mitotic cell division, meiotic cell division follows one round of DNA synthesis, but, unlike mitotic cell division, meiotic cell division consists of two successive cell divisions. The two cell divisions are called **meiosis I** and **meiosis II,** and they occur one after the other. Each cell division results in two cells, so that by the end of meiotic cell division a single parent cell has produced four daughter cells.

Meiosis I begins with **prophase I,** illustrated in **Fig. 11.8.** The beginning of prophase I marks the earliest visible manifestation of chromosome condensation. The chromosomes first appear as long, thin threads present throughout the nucleus. By this time, DNA replication has already taken place, so each chromosome has become two sister chromatids held together at the centromere.

What happens next is an event of enormous importance and is unique to meiosis. The homologous chromosomes pair with each other, coming together to lie side by side, gene for gene, in a process known as **synapsis.** Even the *X* and *Y* chromosomes pair, but only at the tip where their DNA sequences are nearly identical. Because one of each pair of homologs is maternal in origin and the other is paternal in origin, chromosome pairing provides an opportunity for the maternal and paternal chromosomes to exchange genetic information, as described in the next section.

Because each homologous chromosome is a pair of sister chromatids attached to a single centromere, a pair of synapsed chromosomes creates a four-stranded structure: two pairs of sister chromatids aligned along their length. The whole unit is called a **bivalent,** and the chromatids attached to different centromeres are called **non-sister chromatids,** in contrast to sister chromatids, which result from replication of a single chromosome. The important distinction between sister chromatids and non-sister chromatids is that sister chromatids, as replicas of the same chromosome, are genetically identical; non-sister chromatids, which are replicas of different chromosomes, are genetically similar but not identical.

→ **Quick Check 4** In a human cell at the end of prophase I, how many chromatids, centromeres, and bivalents are present?

Crossing over between DNA molecules results in exchange of genetic material.

Within the bivalents are crosslike structures, each called a **chiasma** (from the Greek meaning a "cross piece"; the plural is "chiasmata") (**Fig. 11.9**). Each chiasma is a visible manifestation of a **crossover,** the physical breakage and reunion between non-sister chromatids.

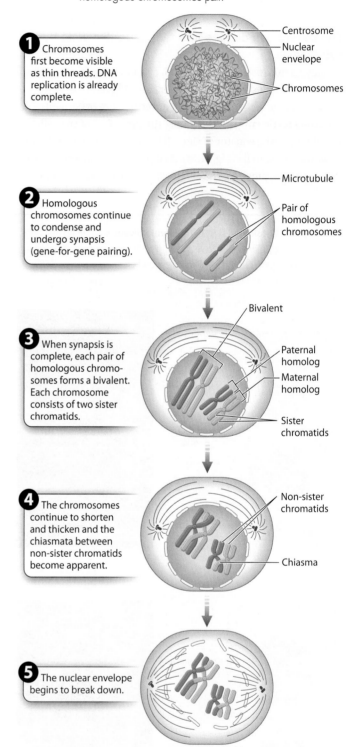

FIG. 11.8 **Prophase I of meiosis.** Chromosomes condense and homologous chromosomes pair.

1 Chromosomes first become visible as thin threads. DNA replication is already complete.

- Centrosome
- Nuclear envelope
- Chromosomes

2 Homologous chromosomes continue to condense and undergo synapsis (gene-for-gene pairing).

- Microtubule
- Pair of homologous chromosomes

3 When synapsis is complete, each pair of homologous chromosomes forms a bivalent. Each chromosome consists of two sister chromatids.

- Bivalent
- Paternal homolog
- Maternal homolog
- Sister chromatids

4 The chromosomes continue to shorten and thicken and the chiasmata between non-sister chromatids become apparent.

- Non-sister chromatids
- Chiasma

5 The nuclear envelope begins to break down.

FIG. 11.9 **Chiasmata.** Crossing over between non-sister chromatids results in recombinant chromatids.

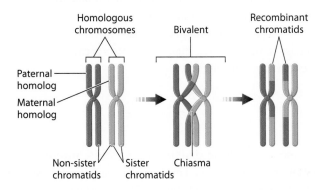

the orientation of these bivalents is random with respect to each other. For some, the maternal homolog is attached to the spindle radiating from a given pole and the paternal homolog is attached to the spindle originating from the other pole. For others, the orientation is reversed. As a result, when the homologous chromosomes separate from each other in the next step (anaphase I), a complete set of chromosomes moves toward each pole, and that chromosome set is a random mix of maternal and paternal homologs. The random alignment of chromosomes on the spindle in metaphase I further increases genetic diversity in the products of meiosis.

Through the process of crossing over, meiosis allows homologous chromosomes of maternal origin and paternal origin to undergo an exchange of DNA segments. The positions of these exchanges along the chromosome are essentially random, and therefore each chromosome that emerges from meiosis is unique, containing some DNA segments from the maternal chromosome and others from the paternal chromosome. The process is very precise: No nucleotides are gained or lost as homologous chromosomes exchange material. Note the results of crossing over as shown in Fig. 11.9: The recombinant chromatids are those that carry partly paternal and partly maternal segments. In this way, crossing over increases genetic diversity.

The number of chiasmata that are formed during meiosis depends on the species. In humans, the usual range is 50–60 chiasmata per meiosis. Most bivalents have at least one chiasma. Even the X and Y chromosomes are joined by a chiasma in the small region where they are paired. In addition to exchanging genetic material, the chiasmata also play a mechanical role in meiosis by holding the bivalents together while they become properly oriented in the center of the cell during metaphase, the stage we turn to next.

The first meiotic division brings about the reduction in chromosome number.

At the end of prophase I, the chromosomes are fully condensed and have formed chiasmata, the nuclear envelope has begun to disappear, and the meiotic spindle is forming. We are now ready to move through the remaining stages of meiosis I, which are illustrated in **Fig. 11.10.**

In **metaphase I,** the meiotic spindle is completed and the bivalents move so that they come to lie on an imaginary plane cutting transversely across the spindle. Each bivalent lines up so that its two centromeres lie on opposite sides of this plane, pointing toward opposite poles of the spindle. Importantly,

FIG. 11.10 **Meiosis I.** Meiosis I is the reductional division: The number of chromosomes is halved.

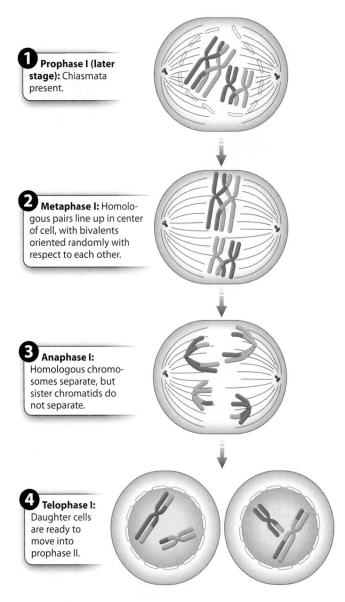

1 **Prophase I (later stage):** Chiasmata present.

2 **Metaphase I:** Homologous pairs line up in center of cell, with bivalents oriented randomly with respect to each other.

3 **Anaphase I:** Homologous chromosomes separate, but sister chromatids do not separate.

4 **Telophase I:** Daughter cells are ready to move into prophase II.

At the beginning of **anaphase I,** the two homologous chromosomes of each bivalent separate as they are pulled in opposite directions. The key feature of anaphase I is that the centromeres do not split, and the two chromatids that make up each chromosome remain together. Anaphase I is thus very different from anaphase of mitosis, in which the centromeres split and each pair of chromatids becomes separated.

The end of anaphase I coincides with the arrival of the chromosomes at the poles of each spindle. Only one of the two homologous chromosomes goes to each pole, so in human cells there are 23 chromosomes at each pole at the end of meiosis I. Each of these chromosomes consists of two chromatids attached to a single centromere. Meiosis I is sometimes called the **reductional division,** since it reduces the number of chromosomes by half.

In **telophase I,** the chromosomes may uncoil slightly, a nuclear envelope briefly reappears, and in many species (including humans) the cytoplasm divides, producing two separate cells. The chromosomes do not completely decondense, however, and so telophase I blends into prophase II. Importantly, there is no DNA synthesis between the two meiotic divisions.

→ **Quick Check 5** List three ways in which meiosis I differs from mitosis.

The second meiotic division resembles mitosis.

Now let's turn to the second meiotic division, meiosis II, shown in **Fig. 11.11.** Starting with **prophase II,** the second meiotic

---

FIG. 11.11 **Meiosis II.** Meiosis II is the equational division: The number of chromosomes stays the same.

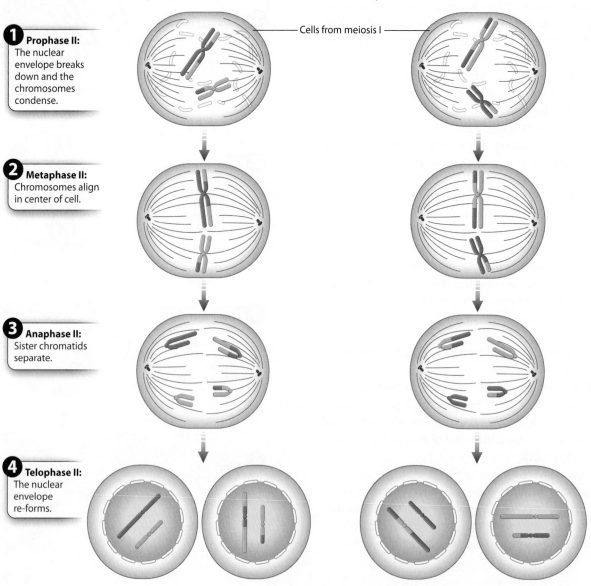

1 **Prophase II:** The nuclear envelope breaks down and the chromosomes condense.

Cells from meiosis I

2 **Metaphase II:** Chromosomes align in center of cell.

3 **Anaphase II:** Sister chromatids separate.

4 **Telophase II:** The nuclear envelope re-forms.

division is in many respects like a conventional mitotic division, except that the nuclei in prophase II have the haploid number of chromosomes (23 in humans), not the diploid number. In prophase II, the chromosomes recondense to their maximum extent. Toward the end of prophase II, the nuclear envelope disappears (in those species in which it has formed), and the spindle begins to be set up.

In **metaphase II,** the chromosomes line up so that their centromeres lie on an imaginary plane cutting across the spindle.

In **anaphase II,** the centromere of each chromosome splits. The separated chromatids, now each regarded as a full-fledged chromosome, are pulled toward opposite poles of the spindle. In this sense, anaphase II resembles anaphase of mitosis.

Finally, in **telophase II,** the chromosomes uncoil and become diffuse, a nuclear envelope re-forms around each set of chromosomes, and the cytoplasm divides by cytokinesis. Each resulting nucleus after telophase II has the haploid number of chromosomes. Because cells in meiosis II have the same number of chromosomes at the beginning and at the end, meiosis II is often called the **equational division.**

→ **Quick Check 6** The genetic constitution of each cell after telophase II is different from the others. What two processes during meiosis result in these differences?

A comparison of mitosis and meiosis gives us hints about how meiosis might have evolved (**Table 11.1** and **Fig. 11.12**). During meiosis I, maternal and paternal homologs separate from each other, whereas during meiosis II, sister chromatids separate from each other, similar to mitosis. The similarity of meiosis II and mitosis suggests that meiosis likely evolved from mitosis. Mitosis occurs in all eukaryotes and was certainly present in the common ancestor of all living eukaryotes. Meiosis is present in most, but not all, eukaryotes. Because the steps of meiosis are the same in all eukaryotes, meiosis is thought to have evolved in the common ancestor of all eukaryotes and has been subsequently lost in some lineages.

Division of the cytoplasm often differs between the sexes.

In multicellular organisms, division of the cytoplasm in meiotic cell division differs between the sexes. In female

TABLE 11.1 Comparison of Mitosis and Meiosis

	MITOSIS	MEIOSIS
Function	Asexual reproduction in unicellular eukaryotes Development in multicellular eukaryotes Tissue regeneration and repair in multicellular eukaryotes	Sexual reproduction Production of gametes and spores
Organisms	All eukaryotes	Most eukaryotes
Number of rounds of DNA synthesis	1	1
Number of cell divisions	1	2
Number of daughter cells	2	4
Chromosome complement of daughter cell compared to parent cell	Same	Half
Pairing of homologous chromosomes	No	Meiosis I—Yes Meiosis II—No
Crossing over	No	Meiosis I—Yes Meiosis II—No
Separation of homologous chromosomes	No	Meiosis I—Yes Meiosis II—No
Centromere division	Yes	Meiosis I—No Meiosis II—Yes
Separation of sister chromatids	Yes	Meiosis I—No Meiosis II—Yes

FIG. 11.12 Comparison of mitosis and meiosis.

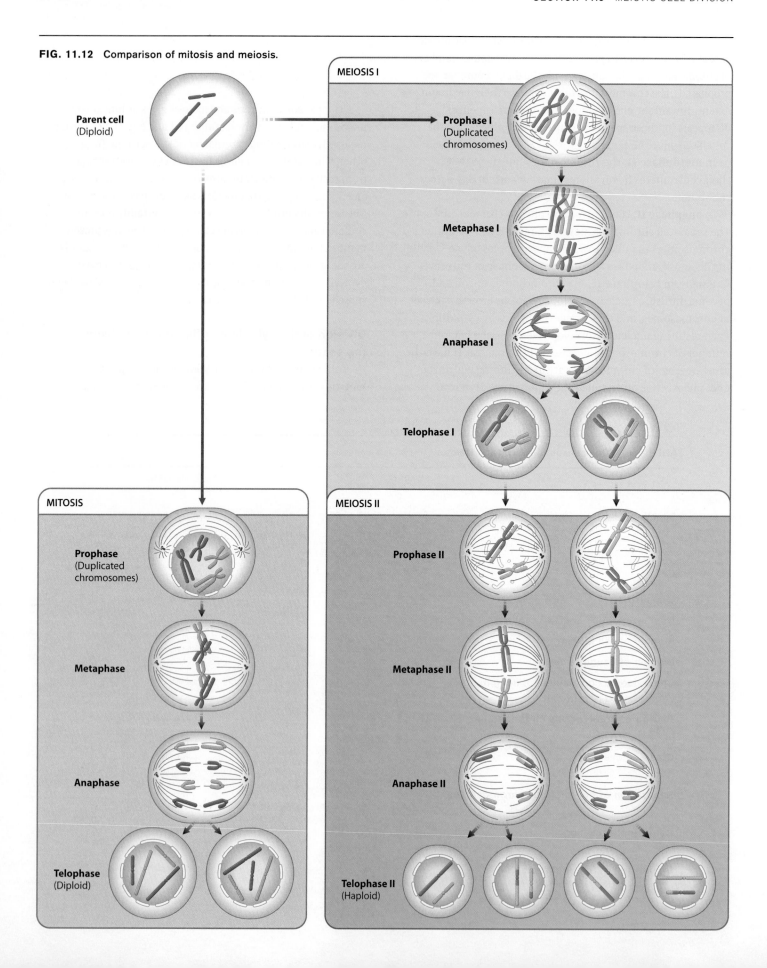

mammals (**Fig. 11.13a**), the cytoplasm is divided very unequally in both meiotic divisions. Most of the cytoplasm is retained in one meiotic product, a very large cell called the oocyte, which can develop into the functional egg cell, and the other meiotic products receive only small amounts of cytoplasm. These smaller cells are called **polar bodies**. In male mammals (**Fig. 11.13b**), the cytoplasm divides about equally in both meiotic divisions, and each of the resulting meiotic products goes on to form a functional sperm. During the development of the sperm, most of the cytoplasm is eliminated, and what is left is essentially a nucleus in the sperm head equipped with a long whiplike flagellum to help propel it toward the egg.

Meiosis is the basis of sexual reproduction.

Sexual reproduction involves two processes: meiotic cell division and fertilization. Meiotic cell division, as we just saw, produces cells with half the number of chromosomes present in the parent cell. In multicellular animals, the products of meiotic cell division are gametes: An egg cell is a gamete and a sperm cell is a gamete. Each gamete is haploid, containing a single set of chromosomes. In humans, meiosis takes place in the ovaries of the female and the testes of the male, and each resulting gamete contains 23 chromosomes, including one each of the 22 numbered chromosomes plus either an X or a Y chromosome.

FIG. 11.13 Cytoplasmic division in (a) females and (b) males. In females, cytoplasmic division results in one oocyte and three polar bodies, and in males it results in four sperm cells.

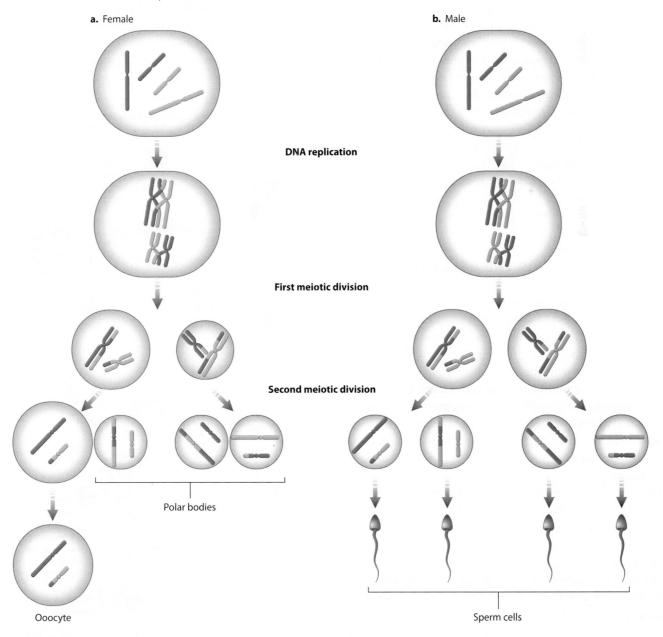

a. Female

b. Male

DNA replication

First meiotic division

Second meiotic division

Polar bodies

Ooocyte

Sperm cells

During fertilization, these gametes fuse to form a single cell called a **zygote.** The zygote is diploid, having two complete sets of chromosomes, one from each parent. Therefore, fertilization restores the original chromosome number.

As we discuss further in Chapters 16 and 42, sexual reproduction plays a key role in increasing genetic diversity. Genetic diversity results from meiotic cell division (the cells that are produced are each genetically different from one another), and from fertilization (different gametes are combined to produce a new, unique individual). The increase in genetic diversity made possible by sexual reproduction allows organisms to evolve and adapt more quickly to their environment than is possible with asexual reproduction.

In the life cycle of multicellular animals like humans, then, the diploid organism produces single-celled gametes that fuse to make a diploid zygote. In this case, the only haploid cells in the life cycle are the gametes, and the products of meiotic cell division do not undergo mitotic cell division but instead fuse to become a diploid zygote. However, there are a number of life cycles in other organisms that differ in the timing of meiotic cell division and fertilization, discussed more fully in Chapter 27. Some organisms, like most fungi, are haploid. These haploid cells can fuse to produce a diploid zygote, but this cell immediately undergoes meiotic cell division to produce haploid cells, so that the only diploid cell in the life cycle is the zygote (Chapter 34). Other organisms, like plants, have both multicellular haploid and diploid phases (Chapter 30). In this case, meiotic cell division produces haploid spores that divide by mitotic cell division to produce a multicellular haploid phase, and subsequently haploid cells fuse to form a diploid zygote that also divides by mitotic cell division to produce a multicellular diploid phase.

11.4 REGULATION OF THE CELL CYCLE

Both mitotic and meiotic cell division must occur only at certain times and places. Mitotic cell division, for example, occurs during growth of a multicellular organism, wound healing, or in the maintenance of actively dividing tissues such as the skin or lining of the intestine. Similarly, meiotic cell division occurs only at certain times during development. Cell division cannot occur all the time because uncontrolled cell proliferation is dangerous—in fact, it is a hallmark of cancer. Even for unicellular organisms, cell division needs to be regulated so that it takes place only when conditions are favorable—for example, when enough nutrients are present in the environment.

Cells do not proceed to cell division until they are ready. Has all of the DNA been accurately replicated during S phase? Has the cell grown to a sufficient size to support division into viable daughter cells? If these and other preparations have not been accomplished, the cell halts its progression through the cell cycle. The cell has regulatory mechanisms for spotting faulty or incomplete preparations and arresting cell division. When these mechanisms fail, the resulting daughter cells are abnormal, and either may not

survive or may run the risk of dividing inappropriately. In this section, we consider how cells control their passage through the cell cycle. Our focus is on control of mitotic cell division. However, many of the same factors also regulate meiotic cell division, a reminder of the close evolutionary connection between these two forms of cell division.

Protein phosphorylation controls passage through the cell cycle.

Early animal embryos, such as those of frogs and sea urchins, are useful models for studying cell cycle control because they are large and undergo many rapid mitotic cell divisions following fertilization. During these rapid cell divisions, mitosis and S phase alternate with virtually no G_1 and G_2 phases in between. Studies of animal embryos revealed two interesting patterns. First, as the cells undergo this rapid series of divisions, several proteins appear and disappear in a cyclical fashion. Researchers interpreted this observation to mean that they might play a role in the control of the progression through the cell cycle. Second, several enzymes become active and inactive in cycles. These enzymes are kinases,

FIG. 11.14 Cyclins and cyclin-dependent kinases (CDKs). Cyclins and CDKs control progression through the cell cycle.

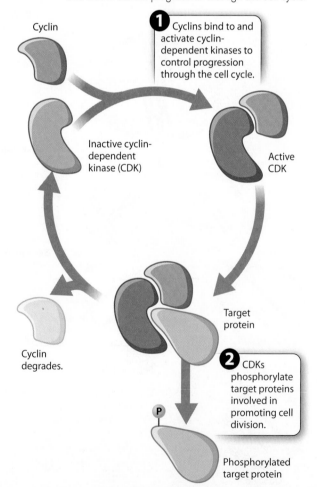

Cyclin

1 Cyclins bind to and activate cyclin-dependent kinases to control progression through the cell cycle.

Inactive cyclin-dependent kinase (CDK)

Active CDK

Cyclin degrades.

Target protein

2 CDKs phosphorylate target proteins involved in promoting cell division.

P

Phosphorylated target protein

proteins that phosphorylate other proteins (Chapter 9). The timing of kinase activity is delayed slightly relative to the appearance of the cyclical proteins.

These and many other observations led to the following view of cell cycle control: Proteins are synthesized that activate the kinases. These regulatory proteins are called **cyclins** because their levels rise and fall with each turn of the cell cycle. Once activated by cyclins, the kinases phosphorylate target proteins involved in promoting cell division (**Fig. 11.14**). These kinases, **cyclin-dependent kinases,** or **CDKs,** are always present within the cell but are active only when bound to the appropriate cyclin. It is the kinase activity of the cyclin–CDK complexes that triggers the required cell cycle events. Therefore, the cyclical change in cyclin–CDK activity depends on the cyclical levels of the cyclins.

These cell cycle control proteins, including cyclins and CDKs, are widely conserved across eukaryotes, reflecting their fundamental role in controlling cell cycle progression, and have been extensively studied in yeast, sea urchins, mice, and humans (**Fig. 11.15**).

HOW DO WE KNOW?

FIG. 11.15

How is progression through the cell cycle controlled?

BACKGROUND The cell cycle is characterized by cyclical changes in many components of the cell: Chromosomes condense and decondense, the mitotic spindle forms and breaks down, the nuclear envelope

breaks down and re-forms. How these regular and cyclical changes are controlled is the subject of active research. First, clues came from studies in yeast in which mutations in certain genes blocked progression through the cell cycle, suggesting that these genes encode proteins that play a role in cell cycle progression. Additional clues came from studies in embryos of the sea urchin *Arbacia punctulata*. These embryos are large and divide rapidly by mitosis, making them a good model system for the study of the control of cell division. In the early 1980s, it was known that inhibition of protein synthesis blocks key steps of cell division in sea urchins. It was also known that an enzyme called MPF, or M-phase promotion factor, is important for the transition from G_2 to M phase.

EXPERIMENT To better understand events in the cell cycle, English biochemist Tim Hunt and colleagues measured protein levels in sea urchin embryos as they divide rapidly by mitosis. He added radioactive methionine (an amino acid) to eggs, which became incorporated into any newly synthesized proteins. The eggs were then fertilized and allowed to develop. Samples of the rapidly dividing embryos were taken every 10 minutes and run on a gel to visualize the levels of different proteins.

RESULTS Most protein bands became darker as cell division proceeded, indicating more and more protein synthesis. However, the level of one protein band oscillated, increasing in intensity and then decreasing with each cell cycle, as shown in the graph.

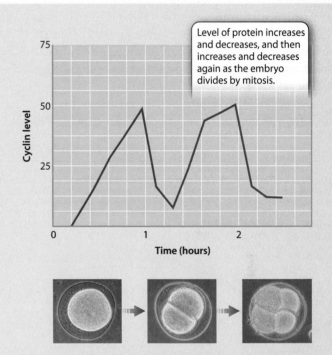

Level of protein increases and decreases, and then increases and decreases again as the embryo divides by mitosis.

CONCLUSION Hunt and colleagues called this new protein "cyclin." Although they did not know its function, its fluctuating level suggested it might play a role in the control of the cell cycle. However, more work was needed to figure out if cyclins actually cause progression through the cell cycle or whether their levels oscillate in response to progression through the cell cycle.

FOLLOW-UP WORK Hunt and colleagues found a similar rise and fall in the levels of certain proteins in the sea urchin *Lytechinus pictus* and surf clam *Spisula solidissima*. MPF was found to consist of a cyclin protein and a cyclin-dependent kinase that play a key role in the G_2–M transition. In other words, cyclins do in fact control progression through the cell cycle by their interactions with cyclin-dependent kinases. Hunt shared the Nobel Prize in Physiology or Medicine in 2001 for his work on cyclins.

SOURCE T. Evans, E. T. Rosenthal, J. Youngblom, D. Distel, and T. Hunt. 1983. "Cyclin: A Protein Specified by Maternal mRNA in Sea Urchin Eggs That Is Destroyed at Each Cleavage Division." *Cell* 33:389–396.

Different cyclin–CDK complexes regulate each stage of the cell cycle.

In mammals, there are several different cyclins and CDKs that act at specific steps of the cell cycle. Three steps in particular are subject to cyclin-CDK regulation in all eukaryotes (**Fig. 11.16**).

The G_1/S cyclin-CDK complex, which is active at the end of the G_1 phase, is necessary for the cell to enter S phase. For example, this cyclin-CDK complex activates a protein that promotes the expression of histone proteins needed for packaging the newly replicated DNA strands.

The S cyclin–CDK complex is involved in the initiation of DNA synthesis. It activates protein complexes involved in DNA replication that contain enzymes necessary for DNA synthesis. Once replication has begun at a particular place on the DNA, S cyclin–CDK activity prevents the replication complex from reassembling at the same place and re-replicating the same DNA sequence. Synthesizing the same sequence repeatedly would be dangerous because cells with too much or not enough DNA could die or become cancerous.

The M cyclin–CDK complex initiates multiple events associated with mitosis. For example, M cyclin–CDK phosphorylates structural proteins in the nucleus, triggering the breakdown of the nuclear envelope in prophase. M cyclin–CDK also phosphorylates proteins that regulate the assembly of tubulin into microtubules, promoting the formation of the mitotic spindle.

Cell cycle progression requires successful passage through multiple checkpoints.

The regulatory system represented by cyclins and CDKs gives the cell opportunities to halt the cell cycle should something go wrong. In other words, if the preparations for the next stage of the cell cycle are incomplete or if there is some kind of damage, regulatory mechanisms block the cyclin–CDK activity required for the next step, pausing cell division until preparations are complete or the damage is repaired. Each regulatory mechanism is called a **checkpoint.**

Cells have many cell cycle checkpoints. Three major checkpoints that have been well studied are illustrated in **Fig. 11.17.** The presence of unreplicated DNA arrests the cell at the end G_2 before the cell enters mitosis, and abnormalities in chromosome attachment to the spindle arrest the cell in early mitosis. By way of illustration, we focus on a key checkpoint that responds to the presence of damaged DNA that occurs at the end of G_1.

DNA can be damaged by environmental insults such as ultraviolet radiation or chemical agents. Typically, damage takes the form of double-stranded breaks in the DNA. If the cell progresses through mitosis with DNA damage, the damage might be inherited by the daughter cells or the chromosomes might not segregate normally. Some checkpoints delay progression through the cell cycle until DNA damage is repaired. An important one occurs in late G_1. This DNA damage checkpoint depends on several regulatory proteins, some of which recognize damaged DNA while others arrest cell cycle progression before S phase (Fig. 11.17).

When DNA is damaged by radiation, a specific protein kinase is activated that phosphorylates a protein called **p53.** Normally, p53 is exported from the nucleus and therefore is at very low levels in the nucleus. Phosphorylation of p53 prevents its export and thereby increases its levels in the nucleus. As p53 levels rise, p53 activates the transcription of a gene that expresses a CDK inhibitor protein. This inhibitor binds to and blocks the activity of the G_1/S cyclin–CDK complex (**Fig. 11.18**). In so doing, p53 arrests the cell at the G_1/S transition, giving the cell time to repair the damaged DNA.

FIG. 11.16 Three cyclin–CDK complexes active at different times in the cell cycle.

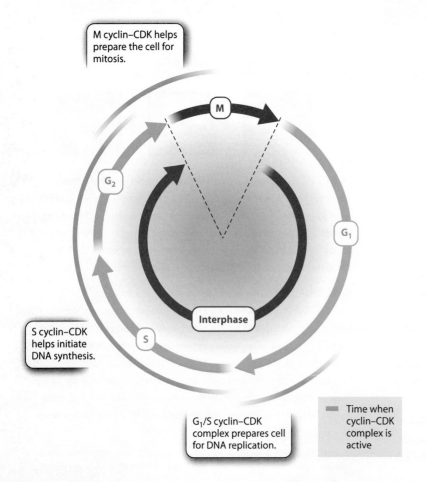

M cyclin–CDK helps prepare the cell for mitosis.

S cyclin–CDK helps initiate DNA synthesis.

G_1/S cyclin–CDK complex prepares cell for DNA replication.

Time when cyclin–CDK complex is active

→ **Quick Check 7** Can you think of two ways in which the function of p53 can be disrupted?

FIG. 11.17 Cell cycle checkpoints. Cell cycle checkpoints monitor key steps in the cell cycle.

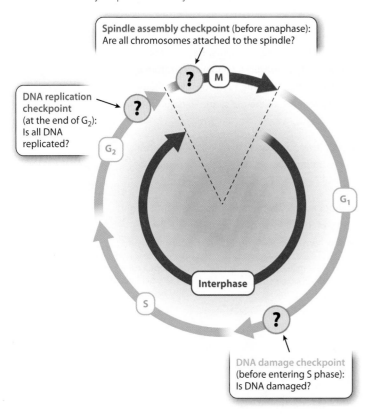

What happens when cell division is not properly regulated? One possibility is that a cell divides rapidly, leading to **cancer**, a group of diseases characterized by uncontrolled cell division. When cells inappropriately activate mechanisms that promote cell division or lose the normal checks that prevent cell division, they can divide rapidly.

In this section, we explore the various ways in which cell cycle control can fail and lead to cancer. We begin with a discussion of a cancer caused by a virus. Although most cancers are not caused by viruses, the study of cancers caused by viruses helped us to understand how cancers develop.

Oncogenes promote cancer.

Our understanding of cancer is based partly on early observations of cancers in animals. In the first decade of the twentieth century, Peyton Rous studied cancers called sarcomas in chickens (**Fig. 11.19**). His work and that of others led to the discovery of the first virus known to cause cancer in animals, named the Rous sarcoma virus.

Viruses are assemblages of protein surrounding a core of either RNA or DNA. They multiply by infecting cells and using the biochemical machinery of their host to synthesize the proteins encoded in their genome and to make more copies of themselves. Viruses typically carry only a handful of genes, facilitating the identification of genes involved in cancer. Their investigation therefore provided a major breakthrough in our understanding of cancer.

As discussed in Chapter 9, growth factors activate several types of signaling proteins inside the cell that promote cell division. The gene from the Rous sarcoma virus that promotes uncontrolled cell division encodes a protein kinase similar to the cellular kinases that function as signaling proteins. This viral gene was named *v-src*, for *viral-src* (pronounced "sarc" and short for "sarcoma," the type of cancer it causes).

? CASE 2 Cancer: When Good Cells Go Bad

11.5 WHAT GENES ARE INVOLVED IN CANCER?

As we have just seen, cells have evolved multiple regulatory mechanisms to ensure that they divide only at the appropriate time and place, and that cell division proceeds without error.

FIG. 11.18 DNA damage checkpoint mediated by p53.

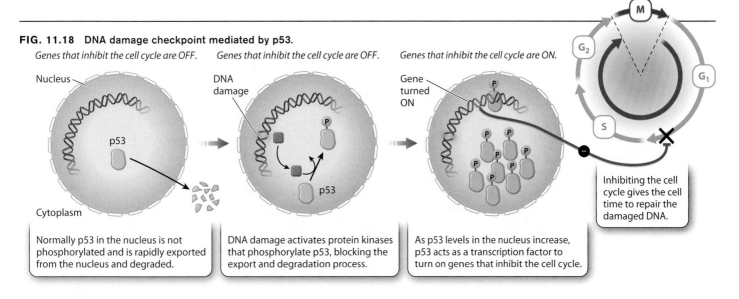

Genes that inhibit the cell cycle are OFF.

Nucleus

Cytoplasm

Normally p53 in the nucleus is not phosphorylated and is rapidly exported from the nucleus and degraded.

Genes that inhibit the cell cycle are OFF.

DNA damage

DNA damage activates protein kinases that phosphorylate p53, blocking the export and degradation process.

Genes that inhibit the cell cycle are ON.

Gene turned ON

As p53 levels in the nucleus increase, p53 acts as a transcription factor to turn on genes that inhibit the cell cycle.

Inhibiting the cell cycle gives the cell time to repair the damaged DNA.

FIG. 11.19

Can a virus cause cancer?

BACKGROUND In the early 1900s, little was known about the cause of cancer or the nature of viruses. Peyton Rous, an American pathologist, studied a form of cancer called a sarcoma in chickens. First, he moved a cancer tumor from a diseased chicken to a healthy chicken, and found that the cancer could be transplanted. Then, he tried to isolate the factor that causes the cancer in chickens. He made an extract of the tumor, filtered it to remove all the cells, and injected the extract into a healthy chicken to see if it could induce cancer.

HYPOTHESIS Experiments in other organisms, such as mice, rats, and dogs, showed that an extract free of cells from a tumor does not cause cancer. Therefore, Rous hypothesized that a cell-free extract of the chicken sarcoma would not induce cancer in healthy chickens.

EXPERIMENT Rous took a sample of the sarcoma from a chicken, ground it up, suspended it in solution, and centrifuged it to remove the debris. In one experiment, he injected this extract into a healthy chicken. In a second experiment, he passed the extract through a filter to remove all cells, including cancer cells and bacterial cells, and then injected this cell-free extract into a healthy chicken.

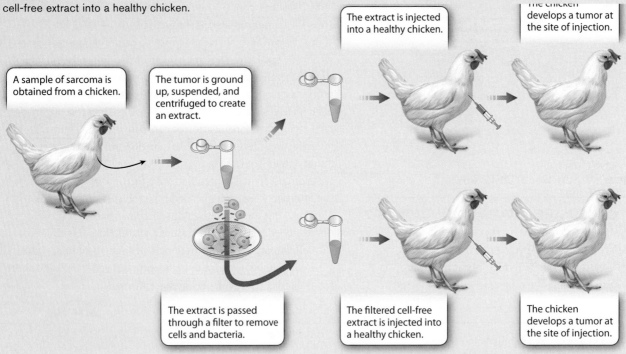

A sample of sarcoma is obtained from a chicken.

The tumor is ground up, suspended, and centrifuged to create an extract.

The extract is injected into a healthy chicken.

The chicken develops a tumor at the site of injection.

The extract is passed through a filter to remove cells and bacteria.

The filtered cell-free extract is injected into a healthy chicken.

The chicken develops a tumor at the site of injection.

RESULTS In both cases, healthy chickens injected with the extract from the sarcoma developed cancer at the site of injection. Microscopic examination of the cancer showed it to be the same type of cancer as the original one.

CONCLUSIONS AND FOLLOW-UP WORK Rous concluded, contrary to his hypothesis, that a small agent—a virus or chemical—is capable of causing cancer. Later experiments confirmed that the cause of the cancer is a virus. This result was surprising, controversial, and dismissed at the time. A second cancer-causing virus was not found until the 1930s. Although most cancers are not caused by viruses, work with cancer-causing viruses helped to identify cellular genes that, when mutant, can lead to cancer. In 1966, Rous shared the Nobel Prize in Physiology or Medicine for his discovery.

SOURCES Rous, P. 1910. "A Transmissable Avian Neoplasm (Sarcoma of the Common Fowl)." *J. Exp. Med.* 12:696–705; Rous, P. 1911. "Transmission of a malignant new growth by means of a cell-free filtrate." *JAMA* 56:198.

Protein kinases are enzymes that activate other proteins by adding phosphate groups. These activation events are usually counterbalanced by other enzymes, called phosphatases, that remove phosphate groups. The viral protein encoded by *v-src* is overactive compared to cellular protein kinases. When the *v-src* gene is introduced into a host cell, it drives the cell to divide uncontrollably.

The *v-src* gene is one of several examples of an **oncogene,** or cancer-causing gene, found in viruses. A real surprise was the discovery that the *v-src* oncogene is found not just in the Rous sarcoma virus. It is in fact an altered version of a gene normally found in the host animal cell, known as *c-src* (*cellular-src*). The *c-src* gene plays a role during embryonic development and is involved in the control of cell division.

Proto-oncogenes are genes that when mutated may cause cancer.

The realization that the *v-src* oncogene has a normal counterpart in the host cell was an important step toward determining the cellular genes that participate in cell growth and division. These normal cellular genes are called **proto-oncogenes** because they are related to viral oncogenes but do not themselves cause cancer. Proto-oncogenes are normal genes important in cell division; only when they are mutated do they have the potential to cause cancer. Today, we know of scores of proto-oncogenes, most of which were identified through the study of cancer-causing viruses in chickens, mice, and cats.

Oncogenes also play a major role in human cancers. Most human cancers are not caused by viruses. Instead, human proto-oncogenes can be mutated into cancer-causing oncogenes by environmental agents such as chemical pollutants. A well-studied environmental factor linked to cancer is the set of aromatic amines present in the smoke of a burning cigarette. Aromatic amines are organic chemicals that can enter cells and associate with DNA, leading to damage or errors during DNA replication. Such changes result in mutations in DNA that can in some cases convert a normal proto-oncogene into an oncogene.

Not all proto-oncogenes encode protein kinases like Src. Nearly every protein that performs a key step in a signaling cascade that promotes cell division can be the product of a proto-oncogene. In other words, normal proto-oncogenes encoding growth factors, cell-surface receptors, G proteins, and protein kinases can be mutated to become oncogenes. Since the outcome of cell division depends on a complex and interconnected cascade of protein activities, any player in this scheme that does not function properly can lead to uncontrolled cell division.

Let's consider an example of a proto-oncogene that codes for a cell-surface receptor. In Chapter 9, we discussed platelet-derived growth factor, or PDGF, which promotes cell division by binding to and dimerizing a receptor kinase in the membrane of the target cell. This action leads to the downstream activation of several signaling pathways,

including the MAP kinase pathway and the promotion of cell division. In one type of leukemia (a cancer of blood cells), a mutation in the PDGF receptor gene results in an altered receptor that is missing the extracellular portion needed to bind the growth factor. Instead, the receptor dimerizes on its own, independent of PDGF binding. As a consequence, the receptor is always turned on.

Just like an overactive Src kinase, the overactive PDGF receptor turns on too many target proteins over too long a time period, leading to uncontrolled proliferation of blood cells. In both cases, mutations that change proto-oncogenes to oncogenes activate the protein inappropriately. That is, the mutant oncogene has more activity than its proto-oncogene counterpart.

Tumor suppressors block specific steps in the development of cancer.

From our discussion so far, you might think that oncogenes are solely responsible for the rampant cell growth that leads to cancer. This is true in some cases such as *v-src* in chickens, but more often something else must also go wrong before cancer can occur. Cells have safeguards that must be overcome before the controls on cell division are totally removed. These safeguards are a family of genes collectively called **tumor suppressors** because they encode proteins whose normal activities inhibit cell division.

Tumor suppressors prevent cell division by acting in opposition to proto-oncogenes. Therefore, whether a cell divides or not depends on the activities of both proto-oncogenes and tumor suppressors: Proto-oncogenes must be turned on and tumor suppressors must be turned off. Given the importance of controlling cell division, it is not surprising that cells have two counterbalancing systems that must be in agreement before division takes place.

We have already introduced a well-known example of a tumor suppressor, namely *p53*, which is defective in a majority of human cancers. As discussed earlier in this chapter and in Case 2: Cancer, the p53 protein normally halts cell division in response to DNA damage. When p53 activity is missing from the cell, excessive cell division is promoted.

→ **Quick Check 8** How do oncogenes differ from tumor suppressor genes?

Most cancers require the accumulation of multiple mutations.

Most human cancers require more than the overactivation of one oncogene or the inactivation of a single tumor suppressor. Given the multitude of different tumor suppressor proteins that are produced in the cell, it is likely that one will compensate for even the complete loss of another. Cells have evolved a redundant arrangement of these control mechanisms to ensure that cell division is properly regulated.

FIG. 11.20 **Multiple-mutation model for the development of cancer.** Cells that become cancerous typically carry mutations in several different genes.

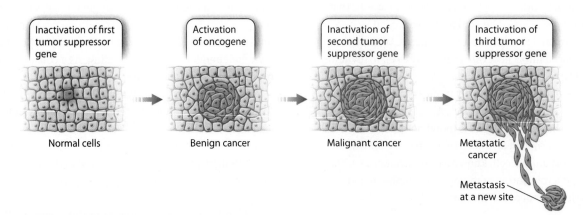

When several different cell cycle regulators fail, leading to both the overactivation of oncogenes and the loss of tumor suppressor activity, it is likely that cancer will develop. The cancer may be benign, which means that it is relatively slow growing and does not invade the surrounding tissue, or it may be malignant, which means that it grows rapidly and invades surrounding tissues. In many cases of malignant colon cancer, for example, tumor cells contain at least one overactive oncogene and several inactive tumor suppressor genes (**Fig. 11.20**). The gradual accumulation of these mutations over a period of years can be correlated with the stepwise progression of the cancer from a benign form to full malignancy.

Taken together, we can now define some of the key characteristics that make a cell cancerous. Uncontrolled cell division is certainly important, but given the communities of cells and extracellular matrix we have discussed over the last few chapters, additional characteristics should also be considered. In 2000, American biologists Douglas Hanahan and Robert Weinberg wrote a paper called "Hallmarks of Cancer," in which they highlighted key features of cancer cells. These include the ability to divide on their own in the absence of growth signals; resistance to signals that inhibit cell division and cell death; the ability to invade local and distant tissues (metastasis); and the production of signals to promote new blood vessel growth for nutrients to support cell division. Considered in this light, a cancer cell is one that no longer plays by the rules of a normal cellular community. Cancer therefore serves to remind us of the normal controls and processes that are required to allow cells to exist in a community. These processes, which work together, are summarized in **Fig. 11.21** on page 11-22.

Core Concepts Summary

11.1 DURING CELL DIVISION, A SINGLE PARENTAL CELL DIVIDES INTO TWO DAUGHTER CELLS.

Prokaryotic cells divide by binary fission, in which a cell replicates its DNA, segregates its DNA, and divides into two cells. page 11-2

Eukaryotic cells divide by mitosis (nuclear division) and cytokinesis (cytoplasmic division). Together, mitosis and cytokinesis are known as mitotic cell division. page 11-3

M phase (mitosis and cytokinesis) alternates with interphase, which consists of G_1, S (synthesis), and G_2 phases. These four stages together constitute the cell cycle. page 11-3

Cells that do not need to divide exit the cell cycle and are in G_0. page 11-4

11.2 MITOTIC CELL DIVISION IS THE BASIS OF ASEXUAL REPRODUCTION IN UNICELLULAR EUKARYOTES AND THE PROCESS BY WHICH CELLS DIVIDE IN MULTICELLULAR EUKARYOTES.

DNA in a eukaryotic cell is packaged as linear chromosomes. page 11-4

Humans have 46 chromosomes: 22 pairs of homologous chromosomes and one pair of sex chromosomes. Each parent contributes one complete set of 23 chromosomes at fertilization. page 11-5

During S phase, chromosomes replicate, resulting in the formation of sister chromatids held together at the centromere. page 11-5

Mitosis involves five steps following DNA replication: (1) prophase—the chromosomes condense and become visible under the light microscope; (2) prometaphase—the microtubule spindles attach to the centromeres; (3)

metaphase—the chromosomes line up in the middle of the cell; (4) anaphase—the centromeres divide and the chromosomes move to opposite poles; and (5) telophase—the nuclear envelope re-forms and chromosomes decondense. page 11-5

Mitosis is followed by cytokinesis, in which one cell divides into two. In animals, a contractile ring of actin pinches the cell in two. In plants, a new cell wall, called the cell plate, is synthesized between the daughter cells. page 11-7

11.3 MEIOTIC CELL DIVISION IS ESSENTIAL FOR SEXUAL REPRODUCTION, THE PRODUCTION OF OFFSPRING THAT COMBINES GENETIC MATERIAL FROM TWO PARENTS.

Sexual reproduction involves meiosis and fertilization, both of which are important in increasing genetic diversity. page 11-7

Meiotic cell division is a form of cell division that reduces the number of chromosomes by half to produce haploid gametes or spores that have one copy of each chromosome. page 11-7

Fertilization involves the fusion of haploid gametes to produce a diploid cell. page 11-7

Meiosis consists of two successive cell divisions: The first is reductional (the chromosome number is halved), and the second is equational (the chromosome number stays the same). Each division consists of prophase, metaphase, anaphase and telophase. page 11-8

In meiosis I, homologous chromosomes pair and exchange genetic material at chiasmata, or regions of crossing over. In contrast to mitosis, centromeres do not divide and sister chromatids do not separate. page 11-8

Genetic diversity is generated by crossing over and random alignment and subsequent segregation of maternal and paternal homologs on the metaphase plate in meiosis I. page 11-9

Meiosis II is similar to mitosis, in which chromosomes align on the metaphase plate, centromeres divide, and sister chromatids separate from each other. page 11-10

The similarity of meiosis II and mitosis suggests that meiosis evolved from mitosis. page 11-11

The division of the cytoplasm differs between the sexes: Male meiotic cell division produces four functional sperm cells, whereas female meiotic cell division produces a single functional egg cell and three polar bodies. page 11-11

11.4 THE CELL CYCLE IS REGULATED SO THAT CELL DIVISION OCCURS ONLY AT APPROPRIATE TIMES.

Levels of proteins called cyclins increase and decrease during the cell cycle. page 11-15

Cyclins form complexes with cyclin-dependent kinases (CDKs), activating the CDKs to phosphorylate target proteins involved in cell division. page 11-15

Different cyclin–CDK complexes control progression through the cell cycle at key steps, including G_1/S phase, S phase, and M phase. page 11-16

These complexes can be inhibited at key checkpoints, halting progression through the cell cycle if something is not right. page 11-16

11.5 CANCER IS UNCONTROLLED CELL DIVISION THAT USUALLY RESULTS FROM MUTATIONS IN GENES THAT CONTROL CELL DIVISION.

Cancers can be caused by certain viruses carrying oncogenes that promote uncontrolled cell division, although most cancers are not caused by viruses. page 11-17

Viral oncogenes have cellular counterparts called proto-oncogenes that play normal roles in cell growth and division and that, when mutated, can cause cancer. page 11-19

Oncogenes and proto-oncogenes often encode proteins involved in signaling pathways that promote cell division. page 11-19

The normal cellular role of tumor suppressor proteins, such as p53, is to block cell division and inhibit cancers. page 11-19

Cancers usually result from several mutations in proto-oncogenes and tumor suppressor genes that have accumulated over time within the same cell. page 11-20

Self-Assessment

1. Compare and contrast the ways in which prokaryotic cells and eukaryotic cells divide.

2. Describe three situations in which mitotic cell division occurs.

3. Name the five steps of mitosis, and draw the changes in the structure and position of the chromosomes at each step.

4. Describe how chromosomes behave in meiosis. Be able to state when chromosomes are duplicated (forming sister chromatids) and when they are not duplicated.

5. Compare and contrast mitotic cell division and meiotic cell division in terms of number of products, number of cell divisions, and processes unique to each.

6. Name two ways in which meiotic cell division creates genetic diversity, and explain how each occurs.

7. Explain how cytokinesis differs between animal and plant cells.

8. Describe the roles of cyclins and cyclin–dependent kinases in the cell cycle.

9. Give three examples of checkpoints that the cell monitors before proceeding through the cell cycle.

10. Describe the differences among a proto-oncogene, an oncogene, and a tumor suppressor gene.

Do you understand the chapter's Core Concepts? Log into BIO**PORTAL** to check your answers to the Self-Assessment questions, then practice what you've learned and reinforce this chapter's concepts by working through the problems and multimedia tutorials provided there.

📶 http://courses.bfwpub.com/yourbioportal/index.php

Cell Division

1 **Prophase:** Chromosomes condense. Centrosomes radiate microtubules and migrate to opposite poles.

2 **Metaphase:** Chromosomes align in center of cell.

3 **Anaphase:** Sister chromatids (individual chromosomes when the centromere splits) separate and travel to opposite poles.

4 **Telophase and cytokinesis:** Nuclear envelope re-forms, chromosomes condense, and the cytoplasm divides.

M phase (Mitosis and cytokinesis)

G₂ phase (Gap 2)

G₁ phase (Gap 1)

S phase (DNA synthesis)

Interphase

Epidermis

Dermis

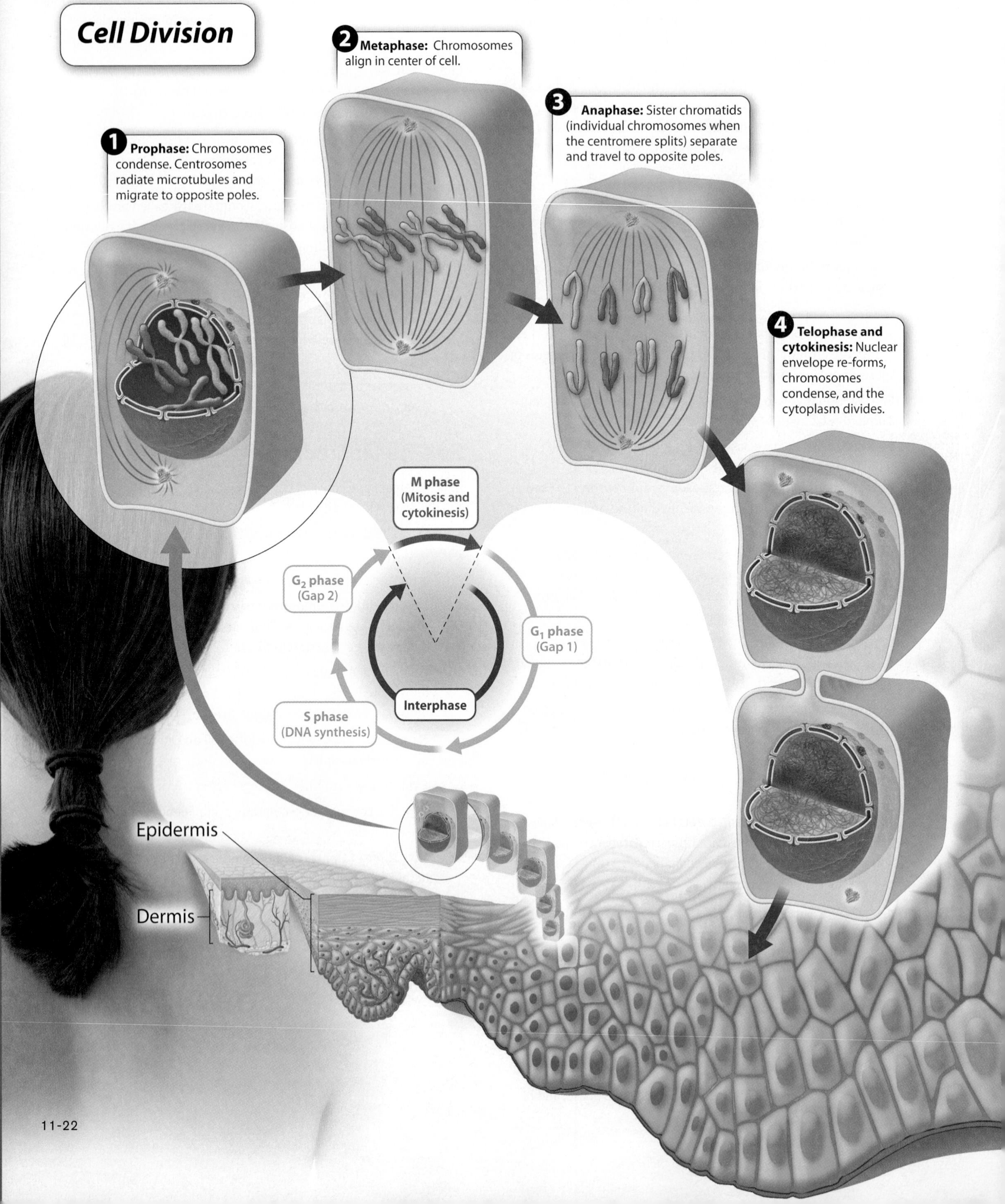

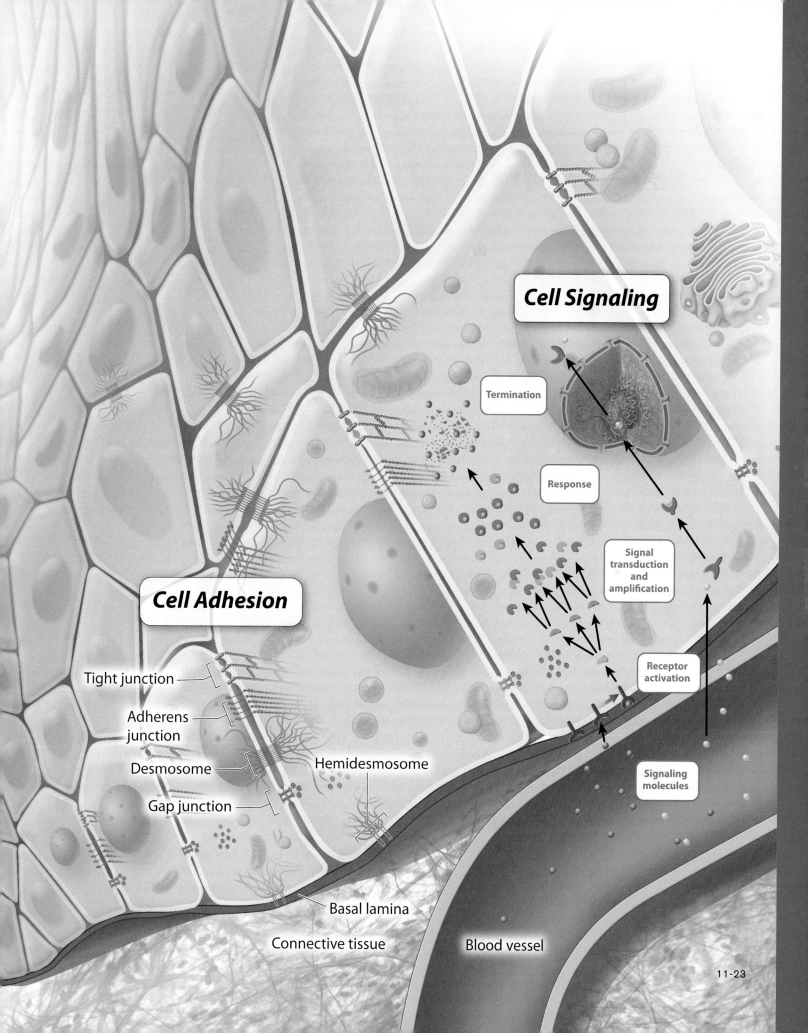

Cell Signaling

Termination

Response

Signal
transduction
and
amplification

Receptor
activation

Signaling
molecules

Cell Adhesion

Tight junction

Adherens
junction

Desmosome

Hemidesmosome

Gap junction

Basal lamina

Connective tissue

Blood vessel

You, From A to T

YOUR PERSONAL GENOME

Answers in the genetic code. Claudia Gilmore found that her genome contains a mutation that can lead to breast cancer.

As an American Studies major at Georgetown University, Claudia Gilmore had plenty of experience taking exams. But at the age of 21, she faced an altogether different kind of test—and no amount of studying could have prepared her for the result.

Gilmore had decided to be tested for a mutation in a gene known as *BRCA1*. Specific mutations in the *BRCA1* and *BRCA2* genes are associated with an increased risk of breast and ovarian cancers.

Gilmore's grandmother had battled breast cancer and later passed away from ovarian cancer. Before she died, she tested positive for the *BRCA1* mutation. Her son, Gilmore's father, was tested and discovered he had inherited the mutation as well. After talking with a genetic counselor to help her understand the implications of the test, Gilmore gave a sample of her own blood and crossed her fingers.

"I had a fifty-fifty chance of inheriting the mutation. I knew there was a great possibility it would be a part of my future," she says. "But I was 21, I was healthy. A part of me also thought this could never really happen to me."

Mutations that increase the risk of developing a particular disease are called risk factors.

Unfortunately, it could. Two weeks after her blood was drawn, she learned that she, too, carried the mutated gene.

Genetic testing is becoming increasingly common— in some cases, even routine. In 2003, after 13 years of painstaking work, scientists published the first draft of the complete human genome. The human genetic code contains about 3 billion base pairs, or structural units of DNA. In the years that followed, much attention has been placed on understanding the genetic differences between individuals.

In reality, there isn't one single human genome. Everyone on Earth (with the exception of identical twins) has his or her own unique genetic sequence. Your personal genome is the blueprint that codes for your hair color, the length of your nose, and your susceptibility to certain diseases. On average, the genomes of two people are 99.9% identical, meaning that they differ at about 3 million sites.

Oftentimes, those individual differences have no impact on health. In some cases, however, a particular genetic signature is associated with disease. Sometimes a gene mutation makes a given illness inevitable. Certain mutations in a gene called *HTT*, for instance, always result in Huntington's disease, a degenerative brain condition that usually appears in middle age.

The link between mutations and disease isn't always so clear-cut, however. Most genetic diseases are complex in origin, and may require multiple genetic mutations, as well as other nongenetic factors, for the disease to develop. Mutations that increase the risk of developing a particular disease are called risk factors.

Certain mutations in the *BRCA1* and *BRCA2* genes are known risk factors for breast and ovarian cancers, for instance. But not everyone with these mutations develops

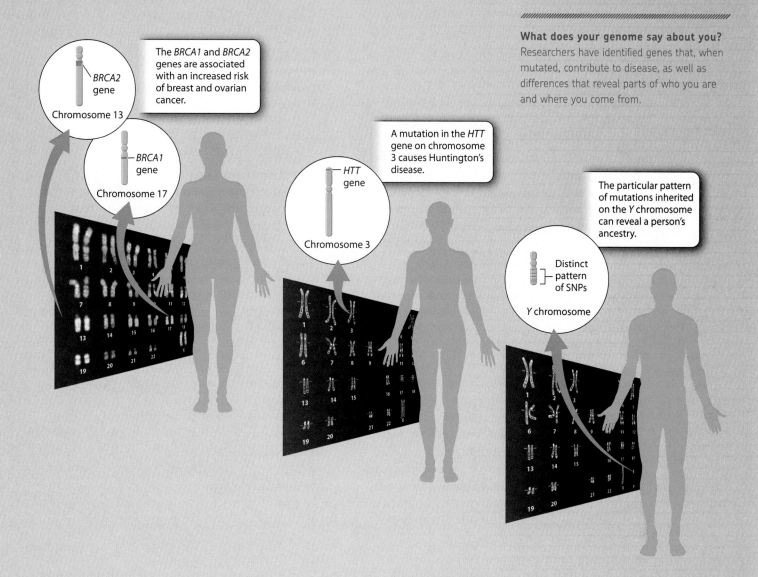

The *BRCA1* and *BRCA2* genes are associated with an increased risk of breast and ovarian cancer.

BRCA2 gene

Chromosome 13

BRCA1 gene

Chromosome 17

A mutation in the *HTT* gene on chromosome 3 causes Huntington's disease.

HTT gene

Chromosome 3

The particular pattern of mutations inherited on the *Y* chromosome can reveal a person's ancestry.

Distinct pattern of SNPs

Y chromosome

cancer. According to the National Cancer Institute, about 60% of women with a harmful *BRCA* mutation will develop breast cancer in her lifetime, compared to about 12% of women in the general population. And 15% to 40% of women with a *BRCA* mutation will be diagnosed with ovarian cancer, versus just 1.4% of women without that genetic signature.

The *BRCA* mutations are just some of the thousands of harmful genetic changes that geneticists have identified so far. Other common mutations have been shown to elevate one's risk of developing heart disease, diabetes, various cancers, and numerous other common illnesses. Often, these mutations involve changes to just a single base pair of DNA. These common single-letter mutations are known as single nucleotide polymorphisms, or SNPs.

Genome-sequencing technology has improved significantly over the last decade, making it easier and less expensive to scan an individual's DNA for potentially harmful SNPs. A number of companies now offer genetic tests directly to the public. Unlike tests such as the *BRCA* blood test that Gilmore was given, these direct-to-consumer (DTC) tests are offered to customers without any involvement from a medical professional, at a cost of a few hundred dollars.

Some of these tests aren't related to health at all. Your personal genome contains many unique features—from the shape of your fingernails to the shade of your skin—that don't impact your health, but make you the person you are. Some DTC testing services aim to tell customers about their heritage, by screening genes to identify mutations that are more common in certain geographical regions or among members of certain ethnic groups. One such company offers genetic tests to African-Americans to determine from what part of the African continent their ancestors originated.

Other popular DTC tests inspect DNA samples for SNPs associated with certain diseases and physical traits—everything from Parkinson's disease and age-related macular degeneration to earwax type and propensity for baldness.

Advocates of the tests say the technology puts the power of genetic information in the hands of consumers. Critics, on the other hand, argue that the information provided by DTC tests isn't always very meaningful. Some SNPs might raise the risk of an already-rare disease by just 2% or 3%, for example. In many cases, the precise link between mutation and disease is still being sorted out. Also, without input from a genetic counselor or medical professional, consumers may not know how to interpret the information revealed by the tests. The American Medical Association has recommended that a doctor always be involved when any genetic testing is performed.

Moreover, knowing your genetic risk factors isn't the whole story. When it comes to your health and well-being, the environment also plays a significant role. Someone might override a genetic predisposition for skin cancer by using sunscreen faithfully everyday. On the other hand, a person might have a relatively low genetic risk for type 2 diabetes, but still boost the odds of developing the disease by eating a poor diet and getting little physical exercise.

Claudia Gilmore is especially careful to exercise regularly and eat a healthy diet. Still, she can only control her environment to a degree. She knew that, given her genetic status, her risk of breast cancer remained high. She made the extraordinary decision to eliminate that risk by undergoing a mastectomy at the age of 23. It wasn't an easy decision, she says, but she feels privileged to have been able to take proactive steps to protect her health. "I'll be a 'previvor' instead of a survivor," she says.

For now, it's still too costly to sequence every individual's entire genome. But each year, many more genetic tests hit the market. Already, doctors are beginning to design medical treatments based on a patient's personal genome. People with a certain genetic profile, for example, are less likely than others to benefit from statins, medications prescribed to lower cholesterol. Doctors are also choosing which cancer drugs to prescribe based on the unique genetic signatures of patients and their tumors.

We've only just entered the era of personal genomics. While there's much left to decipher, it's clear that each of our individual genomes contains a wealth of biological knowledge. And, as Gilmore says, "I've always been taught that knowledge is power."

? CASE 3 QUESTIONS

Answers to Case 3 questions can be found in Chapters 12–20.

1. What new technologies will be required to sequence your personal genome? *See page 12-16.*
2. Why sequence your personal genome? *See page 13-4.*
3. What can your personal genome tell you about your genetic risk factors? *See page 14-4.*
4. How can genetic risk factors be detected? *See page 15-9.*
5. How do genetic tests identify disease risk factors? *See page 16-17.*
6. How can the Y chromosome be used to trace ancestry? *See page 17-14.*
7. How can mitochondrial DNA be used to trace ancestry? *See page 17-16.*
8. Can personalized medicine lead to effective treatments of common diseases? *See page 18-12.*
9. How do lifestyle choices affect expression of your personal genome? *See page 19-10.*
10. Can cells with your personal genome be reprogrammed for new therapies? *See page 20-5.*

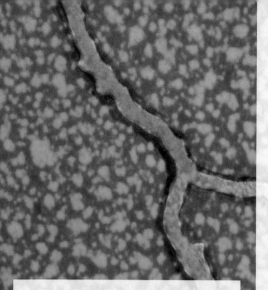

CHAPTER 12

DNA REPLICATION AND MANIPULATION

Core Concepts

12.1 In DNA replication, a single parental molecule of DNA produces two daughter molecules.

12.2 The replication of linear chromosomal DNA requires mechanisms that ensure efficient and complete replication.

12.3 Techniques for manipulating DNA follow from the basics of DNA structure and replication.

12.4 Recombinant DNA technology combines DNA from two or more organisms.

One of the overarching themes of biology discussed in Chapter 1 is that the functional unit of life is the cell, a theme that rests on the fundamental concept that all cells come from preexisting cells. In Chapter 11, we considered the mechanics of cell division and how it is regulated. Prokaryotic cells multiply by binary fission, whereas eukaryotic cells multiply by mitosis and cytokinesis. These processes ensure that cellular reproduction results in daughter cells that are like the parental cell except for any mutations that may have taken place during the cell cycle. In other words, in cell division, like begets like.

The two main processes of cell division—binary fission for prokaryotes and mitosis followed by cytokinesis for eukaryotes—differ primarily because of the way the DNA is organized in the two types of cell. Most prokaryotes have just a single circular DNA molecule, whereas eukaryotes have multiple linear DNA molecules that are typically very long and packaged into chromosomes. The eukaryotic chromosomes must condense during mitosis into compact structures that can be maneuvered properly into the daughter cells by the elaborate spindle apparatus. Concealed in the details that make the two processes different is the fact that in *all* dividing cells a double-stranded DNA molecule gives rise to two double-stranded daughter DNA molecules that are identical to each other except for rare mutations.

The process of duplicating a DNA molecule is called **DNA replication,** and it occurs in virtually the same way in all organisms, reflecting its evolution very early in life's history. The process is conceptually simple—the parental strands separate and new partner strands are made—but the molecular details are more complicated. Once scientists understood the molecular mechanisms of DNA replication, they could devise improved methods for manipulating and studying DNA. An understanding of DNA replication is therefore fundamental not only to understanding how cells and organisms produce offspring like themselves, but also to understanding some of the key experimental methods in modern biology.

12.1 DNA REPLICATION

You may recall from Chapter 3 that double-stranded DNA consists of a pair of deoxyribonucleotide polymers wound around each other in antiparallel helical coils in such a way that, across the center of the double helix, a purine base (A or G) in one strand is paired with a pyrimidine base (T or C, respectively) in the other strand. To say that the strands are antiparallel means that the 3′ hydroxyl of any deoxyribose sugar in the backbone of one strand is opposite the 5′ phosphate group of the corresponding deoxyribose sugar in the backbone across the way. These key elements of DNA structure are the only essential pieces of information needed to understand the mechanism of DNA replication.

During DNA replication, the parental strands separate and new partners are made.

When Watson and Crick published their paper describing the structure of DNA, they also coyly laid claim to another discovery: "It has not escaped our notice that the specific pairing we have postulated [A with T, and G with C] immediately suggests a copying mechanism for the genetic material." The copying mechanism they had in mind is exquisitely simple. The two strands of the parental duplex molecule separate (**Fig. 12.1**), and each individual parental strand serves as a model, or **template strand,** for the synthesis of a **daughter strand.** As each daughter strand is synthesized, the order of the bases in the template strand determines the order of the complementary bases added to the daughter strand. For example, the sequence 5'-ATGC-3' in the template strand specifies the sequence 3'-TACG-5' in the daughter strand because A pairs with T and G pairs with C. (The designations 3' and 5' convey the antiparallel orientation of the strands.)

A key prediction of the model shown in Fig. 12.1 is **semiconservative replication.** That is, after replication, each new DNA duplex will consist of one strand that was originally present in the parental duplex and one newly synthesized strand. An alternative model is conservative replication, which proposes that the original DNA duplex remains intact and the daughter DNA duplex is completely new. The correct model cannot be determined without knowing just how DNA is replicated. If there were a way to distinguish newly synthesized daughter DNA strands ("new strands") from previously synthesized parental strands ("old strands"), the products of replication could be observed and the mode of replication determined.

The American molecular biologists Matthew S. Meselson and Franklin W. Stahl carried out an experiment to determine how DNA replicates. This experiment, described in **Fig. 12.2,** has been called "the most beautiful experiment in biology" because it so elegantly demonstrated the scientific method (Chapter 1) of hypothesis, prediction, and experimental test. They distinguished "old" from "new" DNA strands by labeling them with different isotopes of nitrogen, either the normal form of nitrogen ^{14}N or a heavier form with an extra neutron, denoted ^{15}N.

Meselson and Stahl's finding that DNA replicates semiconservatively (Fig. 12.2) also predicted the results when cells are allowed to undergo two rounds of replication in a medium containing only light ^{14}N nitrogen. The heavy strand and light strand each serve as templates for a new light daughter strand. The result is that half of the DNA molecules will have one heavy old strand and one light new strand and an intermediate

FIG. 12.1 DNA replication. During DNA replication, each parental strand serves as a template for the synthesis of a complementary daughter strand.

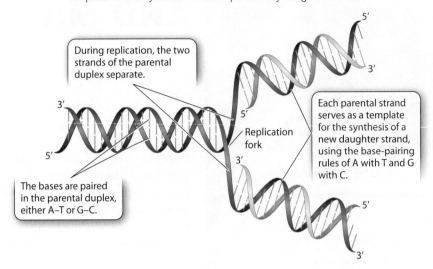

During replication, the two strands of the parental duplex separate.

The bases are paired in the parental duplex, either A–T or G–C.

Replication fork

Each parental strand serves as a template for the synthesis of a new daughter strand, using the base-pairing rules of A with T and G with C.

HOW DO WE KNOW?

FIG. 12.2

How is DNA replicated?

BACKGROUND Watson and Crick's discovery of the structure of DNA in 1953 suggested a mechanism by which DNA is replicated. Experimental evidence came with research by American molecular biologists Matthew Meselson and Franklin Stahl in 1958.

HYPOTHESIS DNA replicates in a semiconservative manner, meaning that each new DNA molecule consists of one parental strand and one newly synthesized strand.

ALTERNATIVE HYPOTHESIS DNA replicates in a conservative manner, meaning that one DNA molecule consists of two parental strands, and the other consists of two newly synthesized strands.

METHOD Meselson and Stahl distinguished parental strands ("old") from newly synthesized strands ("new") using two isotopes of nitrogen atoms. Old strands were labeled with a heavy form of nitrogen with an extra neutron (^{15}N), and new strands were labeled with the normal, lighter form of nitrogen (^{14}N).

EXPERIMENT The researchers first grew bacterial cells on medium containing only the heavy ^{15}N form of nitrogen. As the cells grew, ^{15}N was incorporated into the DNA bases, resulting, after several generations, in DNA containing only ^{15}N. They then transferred the cells into medium containing only light ^{14}N nitrogen. After one round of replication in this medium, cell replication was halted. The researchers could not observe the DNA directly, but instead they measured the density of the DNA by spinning it in a high-speed centrifuge in tubes containing a solution of cesium chloride.

density, and half of the DNA molecules will have one light old strand and one light new strand and a low density. This is precisely what they observed (Fig. 12.2).

→ **Quick Check 1** Suppose Meselson and Stahl had done their experiment the other way around, starting with cells fully labeled with ^{14}N light DNA and then transferring them to medium containing only ^{15}N heavy DNA. What density of DNA molecule would you predict after one and two rounds of replication?

Important as it was in demonstrating semiconservative replication in bacteria, the Meselson–Stahl experiment left open the possibility that DNA replication in eukaryotes might be different. It was only some years after the Meselson–Stahl experiment that methods for labeling DNA with fluorescent nucleotides were developed. These methods allowed researchers to visualize entire strands of eukaryotic DNA and follow each strand through replication. **Fig. 12.3** shows a human

FIG. 12.3 Eukaryotic DNA replication. Further evidence that DNA replication is semiconservative came from observing the uptake of fluorescent nucleotides into chromosomal DNA.

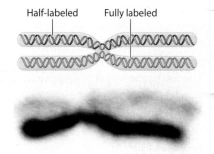

Half-labeled   Fully labeled

After two rounds of DNA replication in a labeled medium, one daughter molecule is half-labeled, and the other is fully labeled (compare with Figure 12.2).

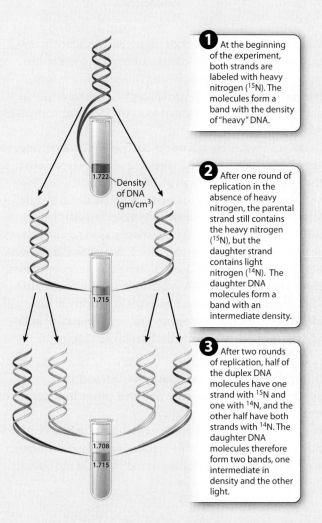

1 At the beginning of the experiment, both strands are labeled with heavy nitrogen (^{15}N). The molecules form a band with the density of "heavy" DNA.

1.722 — Density of DNA (gm/cm^3)

2 After one round of replication in the absence of heavy nitrogen, the parental strand still contains the heavy nitrogen (^{15}N), but the daughter strand contains light nitrogen (^{14}N). The daughter DNA molecules form a band with an intermediate density.

1.715

3 After two rounds of replication, half of the duplex DNA molecules have one strand with ^{15}N and one with ^{14}N, and the other half have both strands with ^{14}N. The daughter DNA molecules therefore form two bands, one intermediate in density and the other light.

1.708
1.715

PREDICTION If DNA replicated conservatively, half of the DNA in the cells should be composed of two heavy parental strands containing ^{15}N, and half should be composed of two light daughter strands containing ^{14}N. If DNA replicated semiconservatively, the daughter DNA molecules should each consist of one heavy strand and one light strand.

RESULTS When the fully ^{15}N-labeled parental DNA was spun, it concentrated in a single heavy band with a density of 1.722 gm/cm^3. After one round of replication, the DNA formed a band at a density of 1.715 gm/cm^3, which is the density expected of a duplex molecule containing one heavy (^{15}N-labeled) strand and one light (^{14}N-labeled) strand. DNA composed only of ^{14}N would have a density of 1.708 gm/cm^3. After two rounds of replication, half the molecules exhibited a density of 1.715 gm/cm^3, indicating a duplex molecule with one heavy strand and one light strand, and the other half exhibited a density of 1.708 gm/cm^3, indicating a duplex molecule containing two light strands.

CONCLUSION DNA replicates semiconservatively, supporting the first hypothesis.

SOURCE Meselson, M., and F. W. Stahl. 1958. "The Replication of DNA in *Escherichia coli*." *PNAS* 44:671–82.

two rounds of replication in medium containing a fluorescent nucleotide. The chromosome was photographed at metaphase of mitosis, after chromosome duplication but before the separation of the chromatids into the daughter cells. Notice that one chromatid contains hybrid DNA with one labeled strand and one unlabeled strand, which fluoresces faintly (light); the other chromatid contains two strands of labeled DNA, which fluoresces strongly (dark). This result is conceptually the same as what was seen by Meselson and Stahl after two rounds of replication and exactly as predicted by the semiconservative replication model. The result also demonstrates that each eukaryotic chromosome contains a single DNA molecule that runs continuously all along its length.

New DNA strands grow by the addition of nucleotides to the 3′ end.

Although replication is semiconservative, as predicted by the model in Fig. 12.1, the model alone does not tell us the details of replication. For example, the model implies that both daughter strands should grow in length by the addition of nucleotides near the site where the parental strands separate, a site called the **replication fork.** As more and more parental DNA is unwound and the replication fork moves forward (to the left in Fig. 12.1), both new strands would also grow in the direction of replication fork movement. But it turns out that this scenario is impossible.

We have seen that the two DNA strands in a double helix run in an antiparallel fashion: One of the template strands (the bottom one in Fig. 12.1) has a left-to-right 5′-to-3′ orientation, whereas the other template strand (the top one in Fig. 12.1) has a left-to-right 3′-to-5′ orientation. Therefore, the new daughter strands will also have opposite orientations, so that near the replication fork the daughter strand in the bottom duplex terminates in a 3′ hydroxyl, whereas that in the top duplex terminates in a 5′ phosphate. There's the rub: The strand that terminates in the 5′ phosphate cannot grow in the direction of the replication fork because new DNA strands can grow only by the addition of successive nucleotides to the 3′ end. That is, DNA always grows in the 5′-to-3′ direction.

DNA polymerization occurs only in the 5′-to-3′ direction because of the chemistry of DNA synthesis, discussed in Chapter 3. The building blocks of DNA (Chapter 2) are nucleotides, each consisting of a deoxyribose sugar with three phosphate groups attached to the 5′ carbon, a nitrogenous base (A, T, G, or C) attached to the 1′ carbon, and a free hydroxyl (OH) group attached to the 3′ carbon. DNA polymerization occurs when the 3′ hydroxyl at the growing end of the polynucleotide chain attacks the triphosphate at the 5′ end of an incoming nucleotide (**Fig. 12.4**). Each of these incoming nucleotides is a triphosphate (three phosphate groups attached to the 5′ carbon of the deoxyribose).

FIG. 12.4 DNA synthesis by nucleotide addition to the 3′ end of a growing DNA strand.

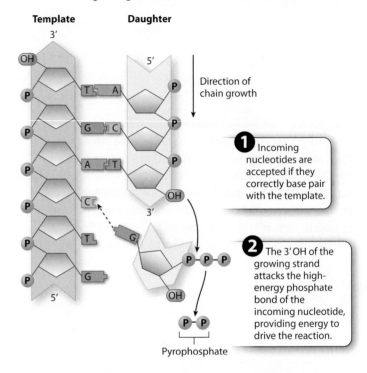

When the incoming nucleotide triphosphate is added to the growing DNA strand, the outermost two phosphates (called pyrophosphate) are cleaved off and diffuse away. The energy released by cleaving off the pyrophosphate is what drives the polymerization reaction that attaches the incoming nucleotide to the growing strand.

The polymerization reaction is catalyzed by **DNA polymerase,** an enzyme that is a critical component of a large protein complex that carries out DNA replication. DNA polymerases exist in all organisms and are highly conserved, meaning that they vary little from one species to another because they carry out an essential function. A cell typically contains several different DNA polymerase enzymes, each specialized for a particular situation. But all DNA polymerases share the same basic function in that they synthesize a new DNA strand from an existing template. Most, but not all, also correct mistakes in replication, as we will see. DNA polymerases have many practical applications in the laboratory, which we will discuss later in this chapter.

In replicating DNA, one daughter strand is synthesized continuously and the other in a series of short pieces.

Because a new DNA strand can be elongated only at the 3′ end, the two daughter strands are synthesized in quite different ways (**Fig. 12.5**). The daughter strand shown at the bottom of Fig. 12.5 has its 3′ end pointed toward the replication fork, so that as the parental double helix unwinds, this daughter strand can be synthesized as one long, continuous polymer. This daughter strand is called the **leading strand.**

The situation is different for the daughter strand shown at the top in Fig. 12.5. Its 5′ end is pointed toward the replication fork, but the strand cannot grow in that direction. Instead, as the replication fork unwinds, it forms a stretch of single-stranded DNA of a few hundred to a few thousand nucleotides, depending on the species. Then a new daughter strand is initiated with its 5′ end near the replication fork, and this strand is elongated at the 3′ end as usual. The result is that the daughter strand shown at the top in Fig. 12.5 is actually synthesized in short, discontinuous pieces. As the parental double helix unwinds, a new piece is initiated at intervals, and each new piece is elongated at its 3′ end until it reaches the piece in front of it. This daughter strand is called the

lagging strand. The short pieces in the lagging strand are sometimes called **Okazaki fragments** after their discoverer, Japanese molecular biologist Reiji Okazaki.

The presence of leading and lagging strands during DNA replication is a consequence of the antiparallel nature of the two strands in a DNA double helix, and the fact that DNA polymerase can synthesize DNA in only one direction.

A small stretch of RNA is needed to begin synthesis of a new DNA strand.

Each new DNA strand must begin with a short stretch of RNA that serves as a **primer,** or starter, for DNA synthesis. The primer is needed because the DNA polymerase complex cannot begin a new strand on its own; it can only elongate the end of an existing piece of DNA or RNA. The primer is made by an RNA polymerase called **RNA primase,** which synthesizes a short piece of RNA complementary to the DNA template

---

FIG. 12.5 **Leading and lagging strand synthesis.** In DNA replication, one daughter strand (the leading strand) is synthesized continuously and the other (the lagging strand) is synthesized in smaller pieces.

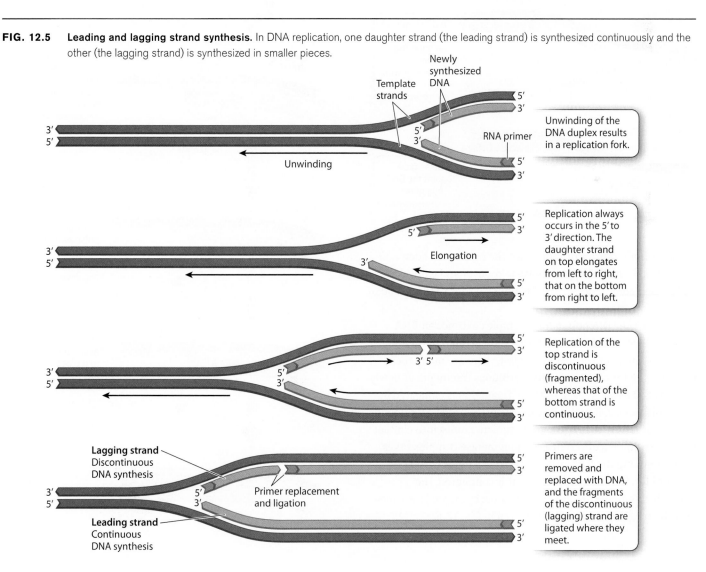

FIG. 12.6   Synthesis and removal of RNA primers.

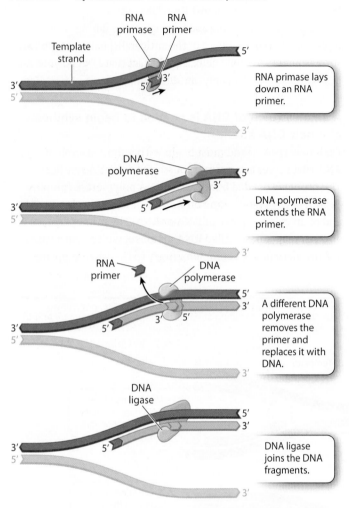

RNA primase lays down an RNA primer.

DNA polymerase extends the RNA primer.

A different DNA polymerase removes the primer and replaces it with DNA.

DNA ligase joins the DNA fragments.

and does not require a primer. Once the primer has been synthesized, the DNA polymerase takes over and elongates the primer, adding successive DNA nucleotides to the 3′ end of the growing strand.

Because the DNA polymerase complex extends an RNA primer, all new DNA strands have a short stretch of RNA at their 5′ end. For the lagging strand, there are many such primers, one for each of the discontinuous fragments of newly synthesized DNA. As each of these fragments is elongated by DNA polymerase, it grows toward the primer of the fragment in front of it. When the growing fragment comes into contact with the primer, a different DNA polymerase complex takes over, removing the RNA primer, and replacing it with DNA nucleotides. When the replacement is completed, the adjacent fragments are joined, or ligated, by an enzyme called **DNA ligase.** This process is illustrated in **Fig. 12.6**.

DNA polymerase is self-correcting because of its proofreading function.

Most DNA polymerases can correct their own errors in a process called **proofreading,** which is a separate enzymatic activity from strand-elongation (synthesis) (**Fig. 12.7**).

When each new nucleotide comes into line in preparation for attachment to the growing DNA strand, the nucleotide is

FIG. 12.7   Proofreading, the process by which an incorrect nucleotide is removed immediately after it is incorporated.

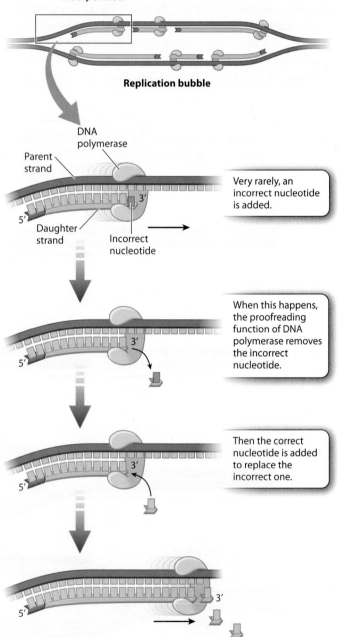

Very rarely, an incorrect nucleotide is added.

When this happens, the proofreading function of DNA polymerase removes the incorrect nucleotide.

Then the correct nucleotide is added to replace the incorrect one.

temporarily held in place by hydrogen bonds that form between the base in the new nucleotide and the base across the way in the template strand. The strand being synthesized and the template strand therefore have complementary bases—A paired with T, or G paired with C. However, on rare occasions, improper hydrogen bonds form, with the result that an incorrect nucleotide is attached to the new DNA strand. DNA polymerase can correct errors because it detects mispairing between the template and the most recently added nucleotide. Mispairing between a base in the parental strand and a newly added base in the daughter strand activates a DNA-cleavage function of DNA polymerase that removes the incorrect nucleotide, and inserts the correct one in its place.

Mutations resulting from errors in nucleotide incorporation still occur, but proofreading reduces their number. In the bacterium *E. coli,* for example, about 99% of the incorrect nucleotides that are incorporated during replication are removed and repaired by the proofreading function of DNA polymerase. Those that slip past proofreading and other repair systems (Chapter 14) lead to mutations, which are then faithfully copied and passed on to daughter cells. Some of these mutations may be harmful, but others are neutral and a rare few may be beneficial. These mutations are the ultimate source of genetic variation that we see among individuals of the same species and among species, as we explore in Chapter 15.

Many proteins participate in DNA replication.

We have seen that DNA replication requires the DNA polymerase complex that elongates each strand at the 3′ end, the RNA primase that makes the primer, the DNA polymerase complex that replaces the RNA primer with DNA, and the DNA ligase that joins the DNA fragments in the lagging strand. Many other proteins are also involved (**Fig. 12.8**). One of these, **helicase,** unwinds the parental double helix at the replication fork. **Single-stranded binding proteins** then bind the resulting single-stranded regions of DNA to prevent the template strands from coming back together. **Topoisomerase II** works upstream from the replication fork to relieve the stress on the double helix that results from its unwinding at the replication fork.

Although many evolutionarily conserved proteins are required for DNA replication, the underlying process is quite simple and the same in all organisms. The two strands of the parental DNA duplex separate, and each serves as a template for the synthesis of a daughter strand according to the base-pairing rules of A–T and G–C, with each successive nucleotide being added to the 3′ end of the growing strand.

FIG. 12.8 Major proteins involved in DNA replication.

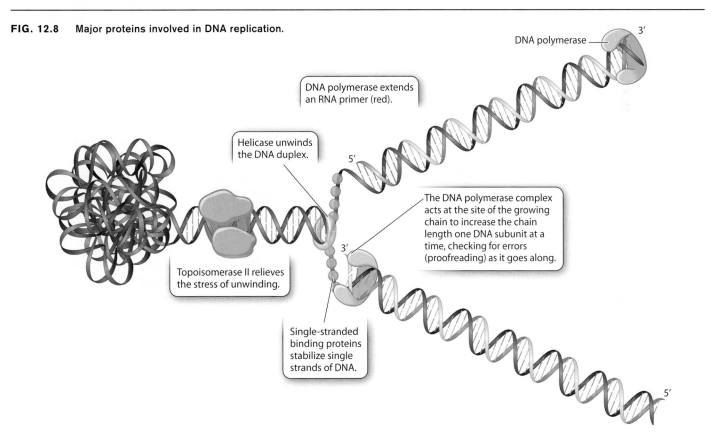

DNA polymerase — 3′

DNA polymerase extends an RNA primer (red).

Helicase unwinds the DNA duplex.

5′

The DNA polymerase complex acts at the site of the growing chain to increase the chain length one DNA subunit at a time, checking for errors (proofreading) as it goes along.

3′

Topoisomerase II relieves the stress of unwinding.

Single-stranded binding proteins stabilize single strands of DNA.

5′

12.2 REPLICATION OF CHROMOSOMES

The steps involved in DNA replication are universal, suggesting that they evolved in the common ancestor of all living organisms. In addition, they are the same whether they occur in a test tube or in a cell, or whether the segment of DNA being replicated is short or long. However, the replication of an entire linear chromosome poses particular challenges. Here, we consider two such challenges encountered by cells in replicating their chromosomes: how replication starts, and how it ends.

Replication of DNA in chromosomes starts at many places almost simultaneously.

DNA replication is relatively slow. In eukaryotes, it occurs at a rate of about 50 nucleotides per second. At this rate, replication from end to end of the DNA molecule in the largest human chromosome would take almost two months. In fact, it takes only a few hours. This fast pace is possible because, in a long DNA molecule, replication begins almost simultaneously at many places. Each point at which DNA synthesis is initiated is called an **origin of replication.** The opening of the double helix at each origin of replication forms a **replication bubble** with a replication fork

FIG. 12.9   Origins of replication. The replication of chromosomal DNA is initiated at many different places on the chromosome.

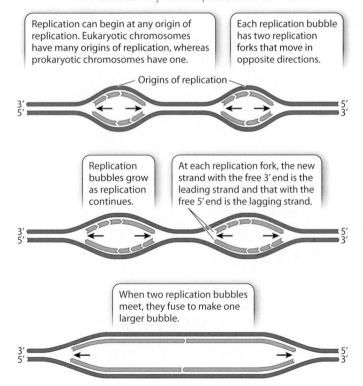

FIG. 12.10   Replication of a circular bacterial chromosome.

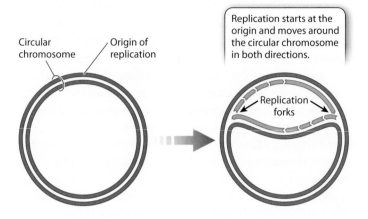

on each side, each with a leading strand and a lagging strand (**Fig. 12.9**). DNA synthesis takes place at each replication fork, and as the replication forks move in opposite directions the replication bubble increases in size. When two replication bubbles meet, they fuse to form one larger replication bubble.

Note in Fig. 12.9 that within a single replication bubble, the same daughter strand is the leading strand at one replication fork and the lagging strand at the other replication fork. This situation results from the fact that the replication forks in each replication bubble move away from each other. When two replication bubbles fuse and the leading strand from one meets the lagging strand from the other, the ends of the strands that meet are joined by DNA ligase, just as happens when the discontinuous fragments within the lagging strand meet (see Fig. 12.6).

Some DNA molecules, including most of the DNA molecules in bacterial cells and the DNA in mitochondria and chloroplasts (Chapter 3) are small circles, not long linear molecules. Such circular DNA molecules typically have only one origin of replication (**Fig. 12.10**). Replication takes place at both replication forks, and the replication forks proceed in opposite directions around the circle until they meet and fuse on the opposite side, completing one round of replication.

Telomerase restores tips of linear chromosomes shortened during DNA replication.

A circular DNA molecule can be replicated completely because it has no ends, and the replication forks can move completely around the circle (Fig. 12.10). Linear DNA molecules have ends, however, and at each round of DNA replication the ends become slightly shorter. The reason for the shortening is illustrated in **Fig. 12.11**. Recall that each fragment of newly synthesized DNA starts with an RNA primer. On the leading strand, the only primer required is at the origin of replication when synthesis begins. The leading strand is elongated in the same direction as the moving replication fork and is able to replicate the template strand all the way to the end. But on the lagging strand, which grows away from the replication fork, many primers are required, and the

---

FIG. 12.11 Shortening of linear DNA at the ends. Because an RNA primer cannot be synthesized precisely at the 3′ end of a DNA strand, its partner strand becomes a little shorter in each round of replication.

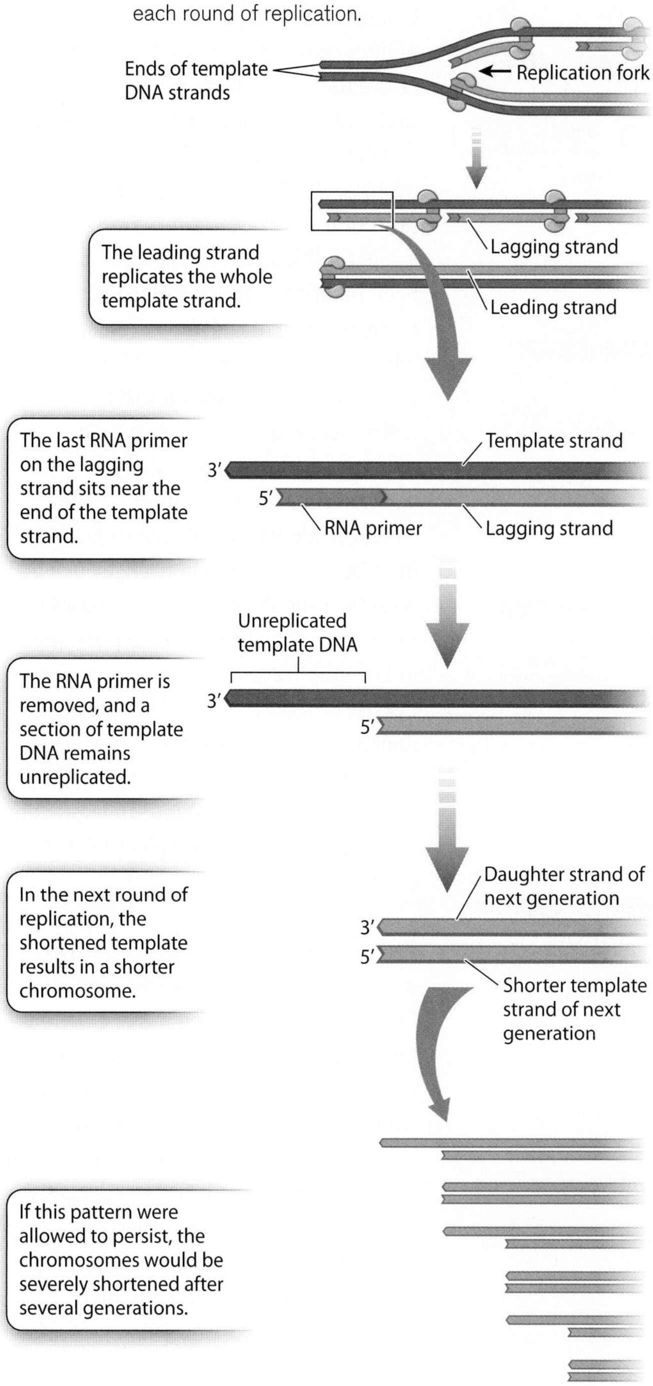

Ends of template DNA strands

Replication fork

The leading strand replicates the whole template strand.

Lagging strand

Leading strand

The last RNA primer on the lagging strand sits near the end of the template strand.

Template strand

3′

5′

RNA primer   Lagging strand

Unreplicated template DNA

The RNA primer is removed, and a section of template DNA remains unreplicated.

3′

5′

In the next round of replication, the shortened template results in a shorter chromosome.

Daughter strand of next generation

3′

5′

Shorter template strand of next generation

If this pattern were allowed to persist, the chromosomes would be severely shortened after several generations.

---

last RNA primer is synthesized on the end of the template strand about 100 nucleotides from the 3′ end of the template. When DNA replication is complete, this new daughter DNA strand (light blue in Fig. 12.11) is therefore missing about 100 base pairs from the tip. When the daughter strand is itself replicated, the newly synthesized strand must terminate at the shortened end of the template strand, and so the new duplex molecule is shortened by about 100 base pairs from the original parental molecule. The strand shortening in each round of DNA replication is a problem because without some mechanism to restore the tips, the DNA in the chromosome would eventually be nibbled away to nothing.

Fig. 12.12 illustrates the mechanism that eukaryotic organisms have evolved to solve the problem of shortened ends. Each end of a eukaryotic chromosome is capped by a repeating sequence called the **telomere,** shown in purple in Fig. 12.12. In human chromosomes, the telomere consists of the sequence 5′-TTAGGG-3′ repeated over and over again in about 1500–3000 copies. The telomere is slightly shortened in each round of DNA replication, as shown in Fig. 12.11, but before the next round of replication the shortened end is restored by an enzyme known as **telomerase,** which replaces the lost telomere repeats. Because there are no genes in the telomere, the slight shortening and subsequent restoration that take place have no harmful consequences.

Telomerase activity differs from one cell type to the next. It is fully active in **germ cells,** which produce sperm or eggs, and also in **stem cells,** which are undifferentiated cells that can undergo an unlimited number of mitotic divisions and can differentiate into any of a large number of specialized cell types. Stem cells are found in embryos, where they differentiate into all the various cell types. Stem cells are also found in some tissues of the body after embryonic development, where they replenish cells with a high rate of turnover, such as blood and intestinal cells, and play a role in tissue repair.

In contrast to the high activity of telomerase in germ cells and stem cells, telomerase is almost inactive in most cells in the adult body, the **somatic cells.** In these cells, the telomeres are actually shortened by about 100 base pairs in each mitotic division. Telomere shortening limits the number of mitotic divisions that the cells can undergo because human cells stop dividing when their chromosomes have telomeres with fewer than about 100 copies of the telomere repeat. Adult somatic cells can therefore undergo only about 50 mitotic divisions until the telomeres are so short that the cells stop dividing.

Many biologists believe that the limit on the number of cell divisions explains in part why our tissues become less youthful and wounds heal more slowly with age. The telomere hypothesis of aging is still controversial, but increasing evidence suggests that it is one of several factors that lead to aging. The flip side of the coin is observed in cancer cells, in which telomerase is reactivated and helps support the uncontrolled growth and division of abnormal cells.

FIG. 12.12 Telomerase. Telomerase prevents successive shortening of chromosomes.

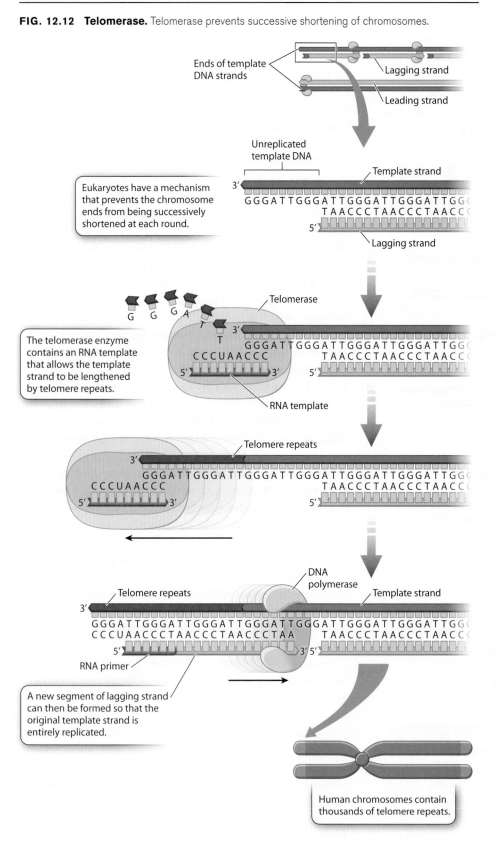

Ends of template DNA strands

Lagging strand

Leading strand

Unreplicated template DNA

Template strand

Eukaryotes have a mechanism that prevents the chromosome ends from being successively shortened at each round.

Lagging strand

Telomerase

The telomerase enzyme contains an RNA template that allows the template strand to be lengthened by telomere repeats.

RNA template

Telomere repeats

DNA polymerase

Telomere repeats

Template strand

RNA primer

A new segment of lagging strand can then be formed so that the original template strand is entirely replicated.

Human chromosomes contain thousands of telomere repeats.

12.3 ISOLATION, IDENTIFICATION, AND SEQUENCING OF DNA FRAGMENTS

Watson and Crick's discovery of the structure of DNA and knowledge of the mechanism of replication allowed biologists not only to understand some of life's central processes, but also to create tools to study how life works. Biologists often need to isolate, identify, and determine the nucleotide sequence of particular DNA fragments. Such procedures can determine whether a genetic risk factor for diabetes has been inherited, whether blood at a crime scene matches that of a suspect, whether a variety of rice or wheat carries a genetic factor for insect resistance, and how closely two species of organisms are related. Many of the experimental procedures for the isolation, identification, and sequencing of DNA are based on knowledge of DNA structure and the physical properties of DNA. Others make use of the principles of DNA replication. In this section, we discuss how particular fragments of double-stranded DNA can be produced, how DNA fragments of different sizes can be physically separated, and how the nucleotide sequence of a piece of DNA can be determined.

The polymerase chain reaction selectively amplifies regions of DNA.

DNA that exists in the nuclei of your cells is present in just one copy per cell (in the case of the *X* or *Y* chromosome in males) or two copies per cell (in the case of the two *X* chromosomes in females and chromosomes other than the sex chromosomes). In the laboratory, it is very difficult to manipulate or visualize a sample containing just one or two copies of a DNA molecule. Instead, researchers typically work with many identical copies of the DNA molecule they are interested in. A common method for making copies of a piece of DNA is the **polymerase chain reaction (PCR),** which allows a targeted region of a DNA molecule to be replicated (or **amplified**) into as many copies as desired. PCR is both selective and highly sensitive, so it is used to amplify and detect small quantities of nucleic acids, such as HIV in blood-bank supplies, or to study DNA samples as minuscule as those left by a smoker's lips on a cigarette butt dropped at the scene of a crime. The starting sample can be as small as a single molecule of DNA.

The principles of PCR are illustrated in **Fig. 12.13**. Because the PCR reaction is essentially a DNA synthesis reaction, it requires the same basic components used by the cell to replicate its DNA. In this case, the procedure takes place in a small plastic tube containing a solution that includes four essential components:

1. Template DNA. At least one molecule of double-stranded DNA containing the region to be amplified serves as the template for amplification.

2. DNA polymerase. The enzyme DNA polymerase is used to replicate the DNA.

3. All four deoxynucleoside triphosphates. Deoxynucleoside triphosphates with the bases A, T, G, or C are needed as building blocks for the synthesis of new DNA strands.

4. Two primers. Two short sequences of single-stranded DNA are required for the DNA polymerase to start synthesis. Enough primer is added so that the number of primer DNA molecules is much greater than the number of template DNA molecules.

The primer sequences are **oligonucleotides** (*oligos* is the Greek word for "few") produced by chemical synthesis and are typically 20–30 nucleotides long. Their base sequences are chosen to be complementary to the ends of the region of template DNA to be amplified. In other words, the primers flank the specific region of DNA to be amplified. The 3′ end of each primer must be oriented toward the region to be amplified, so that when DNA polymerase extends the primer, it creates a new DNA strand complementary to the targeted region. Because the 3′ ends of the primers both point toward the targeted region, one of the primers pairs with one of the template strands and the other pairs with the other template strand.

PCR creates new DNA fragments in a cycle of three steps, as shown in Fig. 12.13a. The first step, **denaturation,** involves heating the solution in the plastic tube to a temperature just short of boiling so that the individual DNA strands of the template duplex separate (or "denature") as a result of the breaking of hydrogen bonds between the complementary bases. The second step, **annealing,** begins as the solution is cooled. Because of the great excess of primer molecules, the two primers bind (or "anneal") to their complementary sequence on the DNA template (rather than two molecules of template coming back together). In the final step, **extension,** the solution is heated to the optimal temperature for DNA polymerase, and each primer is elongated (or "extended") by means of the deoxynucleoside triphosphates.

After sufficient time to allow new DNA synthesis, the solution is heated again, and the cycle of denaturation, annealing, and extension is repeated over and over, as indicated in Fig. 12.13b, usually for 25–35 cycles. In each PCR cycle, the number of copies of the targeted fragment is doubled. The first round of PCR amplifies the targeted region into 2 copies, the next into 4, the next into 8, then 16, 32, 64, 128, 256, 512, 1024, and so forth. The doubling in the number of amplified fragments in each cycle justifies the term "chain reaction."

Although PCR is elegant in its simplicity, the DNA polymerase enzymes from many species (including humans) irreversibly lose both structure and function at the high temperature required to separate the DNA strands. At each cycle, you would have to open the tube and add fresh DNA polymerase. This is possible, and in fact it was how PCR was done when the technique was first developed, but the procedure is time consuming and tedious. To solve this problem, we now use DNA polymerase from a bacterial species, *Thermus aquaticus,* that lives at the near–boiling point of water in natural hot springs such as those at Yellowstone National Park. This polymerase, called *Taq* polymerase, remains active at high temperatures. Once the reaction mixtures are set up, the entire procedure is carried out in a fully automated machine. The time of each cycle, temperatures, number of cycles, and other variables can all be programmed. The fact that DNA polymerase from a bacterium that lives in hot springs can be used to amplify DNA from any organism is further evidence for the conserved function and evolution early in the history of life of this enzyme.

Electrophoresis separates DNA fragments by size.

PCR amplification does not always work as theory says it should. Sometimes the primers are defective; sometimes they fail to anneal properly; sometimes they anneal to multiple sites and several different fragments are amplified. To determine whether or not PCR has yielded the expected product, a researcher must determine the size of the amplified DNA molecules. Usually, the researcher knows what the size of the correctly amplified fragment should be, making it possible to compare the expected size to the actual size.

FIG. 12.13 The polymerase chain reaction (PCR). PCR results in amplification of the DNA sequence flanked by the two primers.

a. Each cycle of amplification includes three steps.

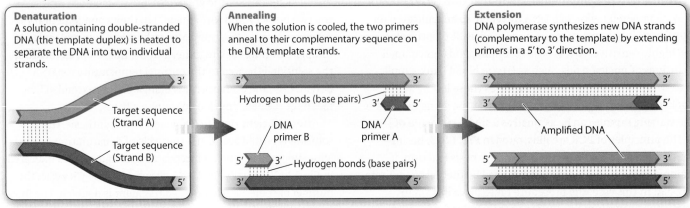

Denaturation
A solution containing double-stranded DNA (the template duplex) is heated to separate the DNA into two individual strands.

Target sequence (Strand A)

Target sequence (Strand B)

Annealing
When the solution is cooled, the two primers anneal to their complementary sequence on the DNA template strands.

Hydrogen bonds (base pairs)

DNA primer B

DNA primer A

Hydrogen bonds (base pairs)

Extension
DNA polymerase synthesizes new DNA strands (complementary to the template) by extending primers in a 5′ to 3′ direction.

Amplified DNA

b. PCR repeats the cycle of amplification.

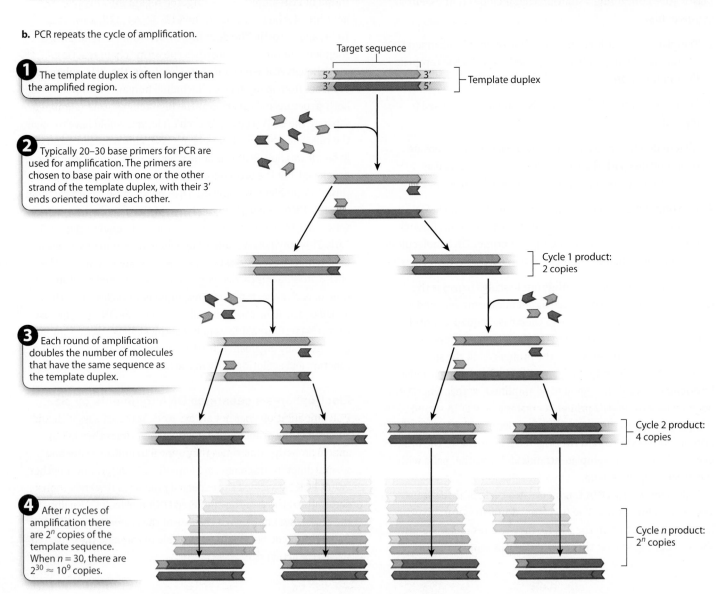

1 The template duplex is often longer than the amplified region.

Target sequence

Template duplex

2 Typically 20–30 base primers for PCR are used for amplification. The primers are chosen to base pair with one or the other strand of the template duplex, with their 3′ ends oriented toward each other.

Cycle 1 product: 2 copies

3 Each round of amplification doubles the number of molecules that have the same sequence as the template duplex.

Cycle 2 product: 4 copies

4 After n cycles of amplification there are 2^n copies of the template sequence. When $n = 30$, there are $2^{30} \approx 10^9$ copies.

Cycle n product: 2^n copies

One way to determine the actual size of a DNA fragment is by **gel electrophoresis** (**Fig. 12.14**), a procedure in which DNA samples are inserted into slots or wells near the edge of a rectangular slab of porous material resembling solidified agar (the "gel"). The gel is then inserted into an apparatus and immersed in a solution that allows an electric current to be passed through it (Fig. 12.14a). Since fragments of double-stranded DNA are negatively charged because of the ionized phosphate groups along the backbone, the molecules move toward the positive pole of the electric field. The DNA molecules move according to their size. Short fragments pass through the pores of the gel more readily than large fragments, and so in a given interval of time short fragments move a greater distance in the gel than large fragments. The rate of migration is dependent only on size, not on sequence, and so all fragments of a given size move together at the same rate in a discrete band, which can be made visible by dyes that bind to DNA and fluoresce under ultraviolet light (Fig. 12.14b). A solution of DNA fragments of known sizes is usually placed in one of the wells, resulting in a series of bands, called a ladder, that can be used for size comparison.

Consider a PCR experiment with primers flanking a 250-base-pair (bp) length of DNA. PCR amplifies this region, theoretically creating many millions of copies of the 250-bp DNA fragment. To determine if the experiment worked

as expected, a sample of the product is checked by gel electrophoresis. This sample is loaded into the well of the gel, a current is applied, and DNA fragments migrate to a position in the gel corresponding to their size, creating bands of DNA that are visualized with a dye. If a single band of 250 bp is seen on the gel, then the experiment worked as expected. Sometimes, however, the reaction might yield no bands, a single band of the incorrect size, or multiple bands. The researcher would then need to go back and investigate why the experiment did not work as expected.

→ **Quick Check 2** You do a PCR reaction, run a sample of the product on a gel, and use dyes to visualize the bands. You expect a single product of 250 bp, but you don't see any bands on the gel. Can you suggest a reason why?

Gel electrophoresis can separate DNA fragments produced by any means, not only PCR. Genomic DNA can be cut with certain enzymes and the resulting fragments separated by gel electrophoresis, as described in the next section. Similar procedures can also be used to separate protein molecules.

Restriction enzymes cleave DNA at particular short sequences.

In addition to amplifying segments of DNA, it is often useful to cut DNA at specific sites. Cutting DNA molecules allows pieces from the same or different organisms to be brought together in recombinant DNA technology, which is discussed in the next section. It also is a way to determine whether or not specific sequences are present in a segment of DNA, as techniques for cutting DNA depend on specific DNA sequences. Finally, cutting DNA allows whole genomes to be broken up into smaller pieces for further analysis, such as DNA sequencing.

The method for cutting DNA makes use of a class of enzyme that recognizes specific, short nucleotide sequences in double-stranded DNA and cleaves the DNA at these sites. The enzymes are known as **restriction enzymes,** of which about 1000 different kinds have been isolated from bacteria and other microorganisms. The recognition sequences, called **restriction sites,** are typically four or six base pairs long, and most enzymes cleave double-stranded

---

FIG. 12.14 Gel electrophoresis. (a) A typical electrophoresis apparatus consists of a plastic tray, gel, and solution. (b) DNA bands can be visualized after staining with a dye that fluoresces under ultraviolet light.

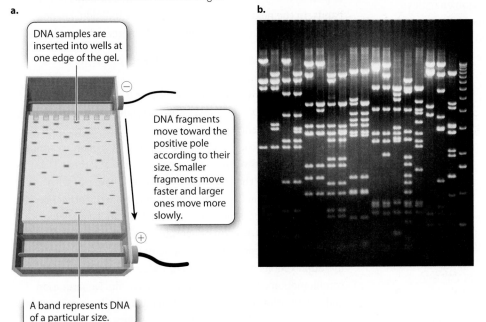

a.

DNA samples are inserted into wells at one edge of the gel.

DNA fragments move toward the positive pole according to their size. Smaller fragments move faster and larger ones move more slowly.

A band represents DNA of a particular size.

b.

DNA at or near the restriction site. For example, the enzyme *Eco*RI has the following restriction site:

$$\downarrow$$
5′-GAATTC-3′
3′-CTTAAG-5′
$$\uparrow$$

Wherever the enzyme finds this site in a DNA molecule, it cleaves each strand exactly at the position indicated by the vertical arrows. Note that the *Eco*RI restriction site is symmetrical: Reading from the 5′ end to the 3′ end, the sequence of the top strand is exactly the same as the sequence of the bottom strand. This kind of symmetry is called **palindromic** (that is, it reads the same in both directions) and is typical of restriction sites. Note also that the site of cleavage is not in the center of the recognition sequence. The cleaved double-stranded molecules therefore each terminate in a short single-stranded overhang. In this case the overhang is at the 5′ end, as shown below:

$$\downarrow \qquad\qquad \downarrow$$
5′-G   -3′   5′- AATTC-3′
                 +
3′-CTTAA -5′   3′-   G-5′
$$\uparrow \qquad\qquad \uparrow$$

Table 12.1 shows more examples of restriction enzymes. Some cleave their restriction site to produce a 5′ overhang, others produce a 3′ overhang, and still others cleave exactly in the middle of their restriction site and leave blunt ends with no overhang. The standard symbols for restriction enzymes include both italic and roman letters. The italic letters stand for the species from which the enzyme is derived (*E. coli* in the case of *Eco*RI, *Bacillus amyloliquefaciens* in the case of *Bam*HI), and the Roman letters designate the particular restriction enzyme isolated from that species.

FIG. 12.15   *Eco*RI restriction fragments (a) on a circular DNA plasmid and (b) separated on a gel.

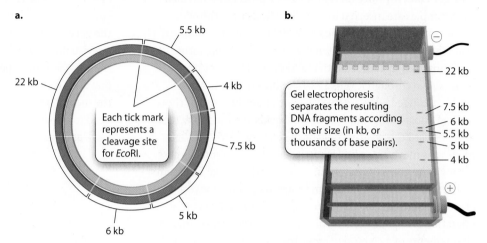

When a particular restriction enzyme is used to break up a whole genome into smaller fragments, the specificity of restriction enzymes ensures that the DNA from each cell in an individual organism will yield the same set of fragments and that any particular DNA sequence will be present in a fragment of a particular size. If the genome is small enough that the number and sizes of the fragments are limited, the individual fragments can be visualized directly in a gel (**Fig. 12.15**). These fragments can then be extracted from the gel for further analysis or manipulation. For instance, the extracted fragments can be sequenced or ligated to other fragments.

But most genomes are too large to give such a simple picture. For example, the human genome is cleaved into more than a million different fragments by *Eco*RI, and these fragments would appear as one big smear in a gel rather than as a series of discrete bands. In the next section, we discuss how individual bands containing a sequence of interest can be detected in such a gel.

DNA strands can be separated and brought back together again.

A researcher may wish to know whether a gene in one species is present in the DNA of a related species, but the nucleotide sequence of the gene is unknown. In such a case, techniques like PCR that require knowledge of the target DNA sequence cannot be used. Instead, the researcher can determine whether a DNA strand containing the gene in one species can base pair with a complementary sequence in a DNA strand from the other species. The base pairing of complementary single-stranded nucleic acids is known as **renaturation** or hybridization, and the process is the opposite of denaturation. In denaturation, the DNA strands in a duplex molecule are separated, and renaturation allows complementary strands to come together again. Denaturation and renaturation are also opposites in regard to the experimental conditions in which they occur. When a solution containing duplex DNA molecules is gradually heated to a sufficiently high temperature, the strands denature. When the solution is allowed to cool, the complementary strands renature.

TABLE 12.1   Examples of Restriction Enzymes with Six-Base Cleavage Sites

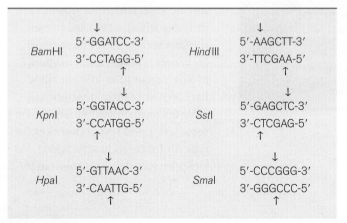

Denatured DNA strands from one source can renature with DNA strands from a different source if their sequences are mostly complementary. Two very closely related sequences will have more perfectly matched bases, and thus more hydrogen bonds holding them together, than two sequences that are less closely related. The degree of base pairing between two sequences affects the temperature at which they renature—very closely related sequences renature at a higher temperature than less closely related sequences. Evolutionary biologists have used this principle to estimate the proportion of perfectly matched bases present in the DNA of different species, which is used as a measure of how closely species are related. In general, the more closely two species are related, the more similar their DNA sequences. Knowledge of species relatedness is important in many applications, including conservation, identifying endangered species, and tracing the evolutionary history of organisms.

Renaturation makes it possible to use a small DNA fragment as a **probe.** This fragment is usually attached to a light-emitting or radioactive chemical that serves as a label. The probe can be used to determine whether or not a sample of double-stranded DNA molecules contains sequences that are complementary to it. Any DNA fragment can be used as a probe, and a probe can be obtained in any number of ways, such as by chemical isolation of a DNA fragment, amplification by PCR, or nucleotide synthesis.

Let's say you are interested in determining the number of copies of a particular DNA sequence or determining whether a given gene in human genomic DNA is intact. Recall that human and other genomic DNA cut with a restriction enzyme will yield a large number of DNA fragments that will look like a smear following gel electrophoresis. A labeled probe can be used to determine the size and number of a DNA sequence of interest in such a gel. The method is known as a **Southern blot** (**Fig. 12.16**) after its inventor, the British molecular biologist Edwin M. Southern.

In a Southern blot, the DNA sample of interest is first digested with a restriction enzyme, and the resulting fragments are separated by size using gel electrophoresis. The DNA fragments within the gel are then denatured and transferred, or blotted, onto filter paper to which the DNA strands adhere. Each DNA fragment is transferred to the filter paper in the same position as it was in the gel. In the next step, the filter paper is covered with a solution containing the labeled probe DNA, and renaturation is allowed to proceed. The filter paper is then washed. Any probe DNA that has renatured with the strands stuck on the filter paper will remain in place, and any unbound probe DNA will be washed away. The final step is to overlay the filter paper with a sheet of X-ray film. Light emission or radioactivity from the labeled probe will cause the film to darken over the location of any fragment to which the probe binds.

The presence of a band or bands on the film therefore indicates the number and size of DNA fragments that are complementary to the probe. This information in turn tells you the sizes and the number of copies of a particular DNA sequence present in the starting sample.

DNA sequencing makes use of the principles of DNA replication.

The ability to determine the nucleotide sequence of DNA molecules has given a tremendous boost to progress in biological research. Techniques used to sequence DNA follow from our understanding of DNA replication. Consider a solution containing identical single-stranded template molecules of DNA, each in the process of directing the synthesis of a complementary daughter strand originating at a short primer sequence. The problem is to determine the nucleotide sequence of the template strand. A brilliant answer to this problem was developed by the English geneticist Frederick Sanger, an achievement rewarded with a share

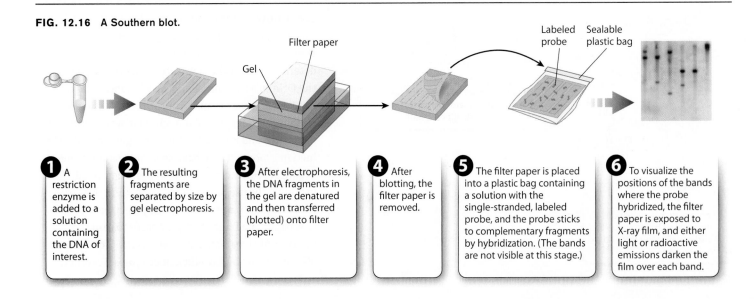

FIG. 12.16 A Southern blot.

1 A restriction enzyme is added to a solution containing the DNA of interest.

2 The resulting fragments are separated by size by gel electrophoresis.

3 After electrophoresis, the DNA fragments in the gel are denatured and then transferred (blotted) onto filter paper.

4 After blotting, the filter paper is removed.

5 The filter paper is placed into a plastic bag containing a solution with the single-stranded, labeled probe, and the probe sticks to complementary fragments by hybridization. (The bands are not visible at this stage.)

6 To visualize the positions of the bands where the probe hybridized, the filter paper is exposed to X-ray film, and either light or radioactive emissions darken the film over each band.

in the Nobel Prize in Chemistry in 1980. (It was his second Nobel; he had also been honored with the award in 1958 for his discovery of a method for determining the sequence of amino acids in a polypeptide chain.)

Recall that a free 3′ hydroxyl group is essential for each step in elongation because that is where the incoming nucleotide is attached (**Fig. 12.17a**). Making use of this fact, Sanger synthesized **dideoxynucleotides,** in which the 3′ hydroxyl group on the sugar ring is absent (**Fig. 12.17b**). Whenever a dideoxynucleotide is incorporated into a growing daughter strand, there is no hydroxyl group to attack the incoming nucleotide, and strand growth is stopped dead in its tracks (**Fig. 12.18a**). For this reason, a dideoxynucleotide is known as a **chain terminator.** By including a small amount of each of the chain terminators in a reaction tube along with all four normal nucleotides, a DNA primer, a DNA template, and DNA polymerase, Sanger was able to produce a series of interrupted daughter strands, each terminating at the site at which a dideoxynucleotide was incorporated.

Fig. 12.18b shows how the interrupted daughter strands help us to determine the DNA sequence by the procedure now called **Sanger sequencing.** In a tube containing dideoxy-A and all the other elements required for DNA replication, a strand of DNA is synthesized complementary to the template until, when it reaches a T in the template strand, it incorporates an A. Only a small fraction of the A nucleotides in the sequencing reaction are in the dideoxy form, so only a fraction of the daughter strands incorporate a dideoxy-A at that point, resulting in termination. The rest of the strands incorporate a normal deoxy-A and continue synthesis, although most of these will be stopped at some point farther along the line. Similarly, in a reaction containing dideoxy-C, DNA fragments will be produced whose sizes correspond to the positions of the Cs, and likewise for dideoxy-T and dideoxy-G.

Each of the four dideoxynucleotides is chemically labeled with a different fluorescent dye, as indicated by the different colors of A, C, T, and G in Fig. 12.18b, and so all four terminators can be present in a single reaction and still be distinguished. After DNA synthesis is complete, the daughter strands are separated by size using gel electrophoresis. The smallest daughter molecules migrate most quickly and therefore are the first to reach the bottom of the gel, followed by the others in order of increasing size. A fluorescence detector at the bottom of the gel "reads" the colors of the fragments as they exit the gel. What the scientist sees is a trace (or graph) of the fluorescence intensities, such as the one shown in **Fig. 12.18c.** The differently colored peaks, from left to right, represent the order of fluorescently tagged DNA fragments emerging from the gel. Thus, a trace showing peaks colored green-purple-red-green-purple-purple-blue-green-blue-red corresponds to a daughter strand having the sequence 5′-ACTACCGAGT-3′ (Fig. 12.18c). By use of the Sanger sequencing method, each sequencing reaction can determine the sequence of about 1000 nucleotides in the template DNA molecule.

→   **Quick Check 3** We have determined that the newly synthesized strand of DNA in our sequencing reaction has the sequence 5′-ACTACCGAGT-3′. What is the sequence of the template strand?

? CASE 3 You, From A to T: Your Personal Genome
What new technologies will be required to sequence your personal genome?

One of the high points of modern biology has been the determination of the complete nucleotide sequence of the DNA in a large number of species, including ours. The human genome and many others were sequenced by Sanger sequencing. This technique works well, but it takes time and is expensive for large genomes like the human genome. There have been many improvements in Sanger sequencing since it was first described, including the use of four-color fluorescent dyes to label the DNA fragments, capillary electrophoresis to separate the fragments, photocells to read the fluorescent signals automatically as the products run off the gel, and highly efficient enzymes. Together,

---

FIG. 12.17   **(a) A deoxynucleotide and (b) a dideoxynucleotide.** Incorporation of a dideoxynucleotide prevents strand elongation.

a.

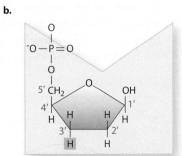

A normal deoxynucleotide has a hydroxyl (–OH) group on the 3′ carbon, allowing this end to be elongated.

b.

A dideoxynucleotide lacks the 3′ hydroxyl group, and it cannot be elongated because there is no hydroxyl group to attack an incoming nucleotide triphosphate.

FIG. 12.18 Sanger sequencing. (a) The incorporation of an incoming dideoxynucleotide stops the elongation of a new strand. (b) Dideoxynucleotides are incorporated into growing DNA strands, terminating their growth. (c) Separation of interrupted daughter strands by size shows where each terminator was incorporated and hence the identity of the corresponding nucleotide in the template strand.

a.

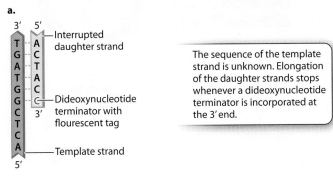

Interrupted daughter strand

Dideoxynucleotide terminator with flourescent tag

Template strand

The sequence of the template strand is unknown. Elongation of the daughter strands stops whenever a dideoxynucleotide terminator is incorporated at the 3′ end.

b.

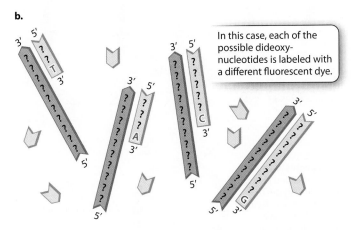

In this case, each of the possible dideoxy-nucleotides is labeled with a different fluorescent dye.

c.

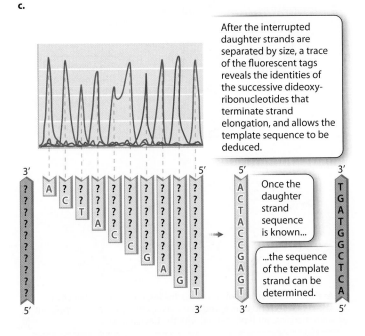

After the interrupted daughter strands are separated by size, a trace of the fluorescent tags reveals the identities of the successive dideoxy-ribonucleotides that terminate strand elongation, and allows the template sequence to be deduced.

Once the daughter strand sequence is known...

...the sequence of the template strand can be determined.

these methods have increased the speed and decreased the cost of DNA sequencing considerably.

However, to be able to sequence everyone's genome, including yours, we will require new technologies to bring down the cost further and to increase the speed of sequencing. Currently, there is a prize for anyone who can sequence a complete human genome for less than $1000. This $1000 genome will rely on next-generation sequencing technologies that get around some of the slower or more expensive steps of Sanger sequencing. For example, in a technique called pyrosequencing, the incorporation of a nucleotide into a growing DNA strand results in a pulse of light, allowing each base that is incorporated to be identified without having to separate DNA fragments on a gel. Another technique, called nanopore sequencing, passes individual DNA molecules through a pore in a membrane with a charge across it. As each nucleotide passes through the pore, it changes the charge across the membrane in a characteristic way, allowing identification.

Interest in large-scale DNA sequencing has stimulated the development of devices that increase scale and decrease cost. As in the development of computer hardware, emphasis is on making the sequencing devices smaller while increasing their capacity through automation. These miniaturized and automated approaches carry out what is often called massively parallel sequencing that can determine the sequence of hundreds of millions of base pairs in a few hours. These technologies will likely enable your own personal genome to be sequenced quickly and cheaply in the coming years.

12.4 RECOMBINANT DNA AND GENETICALLY MODIFIED ORGANISMS

Along with methods to manipulate DNA fragments came the capability of isolating genes from one species and introducing them into another. This type of genetic engineering is called **recombinant DNA** technology because it literally recombines DNA molecules from two (or more) different sources into a single molecule. Recombinant DNA technology involves cutting DNA by restriction enzymes, isolating them by gel electrophoresis, and ligating them with enzymes used in DNA replication. This technology is possible because the DNA of all organisms is the same, differing only in sequence but not in chemical or physical structure. When DNA fragments from two different sources are combined into a single molecule and incorporated into a cell, they are replicated and transcribed just like any other DNA molecule.

Recombinant DNA technology can combine DNA from any two sources, including two different species. DNA from one species of bacteria can be combined with another, or a human gene can be combined with bacterial DNA, or the DNA from a plant and a fungus can be combined into a single molecule.

These new sequences may be unlike any found in nature, raising questions about their possible effects on human health and the environment.

This section discusses one of the basic methods for producing recombinant DNA and also some of the important (and controversial) applications of recombinant DNA technology, such as genetically modified food.

Recombinant DNA combines DNA molecules from two sources.

The first application of recombinant DNA technology was the introduction of foreign DNA fragments into the cells of bacteria in the early 1970s. The method is simple and straightforward, and remains one of the mainstays of modern molecular research. It can be used to generate a large quantity of a protein for study or therapeutic use.

The method requires a fragment of double-stranded DNA that serves as the **donor.** The donor fragment may be a protein-coding gene, a regulatory part of a gene, or any DNA segment of interest. If you were interested in generating bacteria that could produce human insulin, you might use the coding region of the human insulin gene as your donor DNA molecule. Also required is a **vector** sequence into which the donor fragment is to be inserted. The vector is the carrier of the donor fragment, and it must have the ability to be maintained in bacterial cells. A frequently used vector is a bacterial **plasmid,** a small circular molecule of DNA found naturally in certain bacteria that can replicate when the bacterial genomic DNA replicates and be transmitted to the daughter bacterial cells when the parental cell divides. Many naturally occurring plasmids have been modified by genetic engineering to make them suitable for use as vectors in recombinant DNA technology.

A common method for producing recombinant DNA is shown in **Fig. 12.19.** In order to make sure donor DNA can be fused with vector DNA, both pieces are cut with the same restriction enzyme so they will both have the same overhangs. In the example shown in Fig. 12.19, the donor DNA is a fragment produced by digestion of genomic DNA with the restriction enzyme *Eco*RI, resulting in four-nucleotide 5′ overhangs at the fragment ends. The vector is a circular plasmid that contains a single *Eco*RI cleavage site, so digestion of the vector with *Eco*RI opens the circle with a single cut that also has four-nucleotide 5′ overhangs. Note that the overhangs on the donor fragment and the vector are complementary in sequence, which allows the ends of the donor fragment to renature with the ends of the opened vector when the two types of molecule are mixed. Once this renaturation has taken place, the ends of the donor fragment and the vector are covalently joined by DNA ligase. The joining of the donor DNA to the vector creates the recombinant DNA molecule.

The next step in the procedure is **transformation,** in which the recombinant DNA is mixed with bacteria that have been

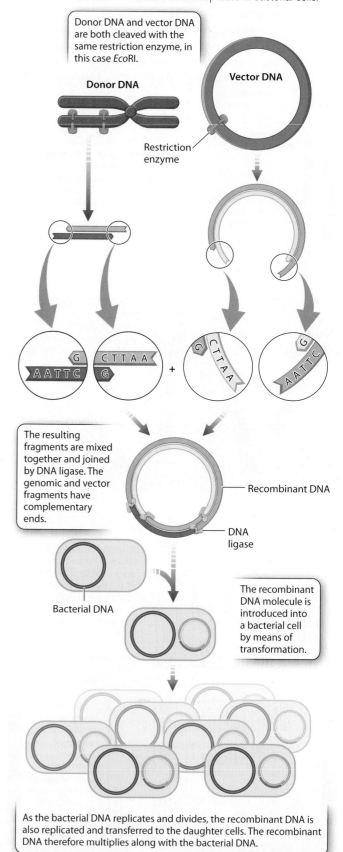

FIG. 12.19 Recombinant DNA. Donor DNA fragments are joined with a vector molecule that can replicate in bacterial cells.

Donor DNA and vector DNA are both cleaved with the same restriction enzyme, in this case *Eco*RI.

Donor DNA

Vector DNA

Restriction enzyme

G
AATTC
CTTAA
G

+

G
CTTAA

G
AATTC

The resulting fragments are mixed together and joined by DNA ligase. The genomic and vector fragments have complementary ends.

Recombinant DNA

DNA ligase

Bacterial DNA

The recombinant DNA molecule is introduced into a bacterial cell by means of transformation.

As the bacterial DNA replicates and divides, the recombinant DNA is also replicated and transferred to the daughter cells. The recombinant DNA therefore multiplies along with the bacterial DNA.

chemically coaxed into a physiological state in which they take up DNA from outside the cell. Having taken up the recombinant DNA, the bacterial cells are transferred into growth medium, where they multiply. Since the vector part of the recombinant DNA molecule contains all the DNA sequences needed for its replication and partition into the daughter cells, the recombinant DNA multiplies as the bacterial cell multiplies. If the recombinant DNA functions inside the bacterial cell, then new genetic characteristics may be expressed by the bacteria. For example, the recombinant DNA may allow the bacterial cells to produce a human protein, such as insulin or growth hormone.

→ **Quick Check 4** In making recombinant DNA molecules that combine restriction fragments from different organisms, researchers usually prefer restriction enzymes like *Bam*HI or *Hind*III that generate fragments with "sticky ends" (ends with overhangs) rather than enzymes like *Hpa*I or *Sma*I (Table 12.1) that generate fragments with "blunt ends" (ends without overhangs). Can you think of a reason for this preference?

Recombinant DNA is the basis of genetically modified organisms.

Applications of recombinant DNA have gone far beyond genetically engineered bacteria. Using methods that are conceptually similar to those described for bacteria but differing in many details, scientists have been able to produce varieties of genetically engineered viruses and bacteria, laboratory organisms, agricultural crops, and domesticated animals (**Fig. 12.20**). Examples include sheep that produce a human protein in their milk used to treat emphysema, chickens that produce eggs containing human antibodies to help fight bacteria, and salmon with increased growth hormone for rapid growth.

FIG. 12.20 Genetically modified organisms (GMOs): (a) wheat, (b) soybean, (c) sheep, (d) chicken, (e) salmon, (f) pig.

Plants such as corn, canola, cotton, and many others have been engineered to resist insect pests, and other engineered products are rice with a high content of vitamin A, tomatoes with delayed fruit softening, potatoes with waxy starch, and sugarcane with increased sugar content. To model disease, researchers have used recombinant DNA to produce organisms such as laboratory mice that have been engineered to develop heart disease and diabetes. By studying these organisms, researchers can better understand human diseases and begin to find new treatments for them.

Genetically engineered organisms are known as **transgenic organisms** or **genetically modified organisms (GMOs).** Transgenic laboratory organisms are indispensable in the study of gene function and regulation and to identify genetic risk factors for disease. In crop plants and domesticated animals, GMOs promise enhanced resistance to disease, faster growth and higher yields, more efficient utilization of fertilizer or nutrients, and improved taste and quality. But there are concerns about unexpected effects on human health or the environment, the increasing power and influence of agribusiness conglomerates, and ethical objections to tampering with the genetic makeup of animals and plants. Nevertheless, more than 250 million acres of GMO crops are grown annually in more than 20 countries. The majority of this acreage is in the United States and South America. Resistance to the use of GMOs in Europe remains strong and vocal.

Core Concepts Summary

12.1 IN DNA REPLICATION, A SINGLE PARENTAL MOLECULE OF DNA PRODUCES TWO DAUGHTER MOLECULES.

DNA replication involves the separation of the two strands of the double helix at a replication fork and the use of these strands as templates to direct the synthesis of new strands. page 12-2

DNA replication is semiconservative, meaning that each daughter DNA molecule consists of a newly synthesized strand and a strand that was present in the parental DNA molecule. page 12-2

Nucleotides are added to the 3′ end of the growing strand. Therefore, synthesis proceeds in a 5′-to-3′ direction. page 12-4

At the replication fork, one new strand is synthesized continuously (the leading strand) and the other is synthesized in small pieces (the lagging strand). page 12-5

An RNA primer is required to begin DNA synthesis. page 12-5

DNA polymerase can correct its own mistakes by detecting a pairing mismatch between a template base and an incorrect new base. page 12-6

12.2 THE REPLICATION OF LINEAR CHROMOSOMAL DNA REQUIRES MECHANISMS THAT ENSURE EFFICIENT AND COMPLETE REPLICATION.

Chromosomal DNA has many origins of replication and replication proceeds from all of these almost simultaneously. page 12-8

Telomerase prevents chromosomes from shortening after each round of replication by adding a short stretch of DNA to the ends of chromosomes. page 12-8

12.3 TECHNIQUES FOR MANIPULATING DNA FOLLOW FROM THE BASICS OF DNA STRUCTURE AND REPLICATION.

The polymerase chain reaction (PCR) is a technique for amplifying a segment of DNA. page 12-10

PCR requires a DNA template, DNA polymerase, the four nucleoside triphosphates, and two primers. It is a repeated cycle of denaturation, annealing, and extension. page 12-11

Gel electrophoresis allows DNA to be separated according to size, with small fragments running farther than big fragments in a gel. page 12-11

Restriction enzymes cut DNA at specific recognition sequences called restriction sites. page 12-13

Restriction sites are usually palindromic, meaning that the recognition sequence is the same on each strand when read in a given direction. Restriction enzymes cut DNA leaving a single-stranded overhang or a blunt end. page 12-14

In DNA denaturation, the two strands of a single DNA molecule separate from each other. In DNA renaturation or hybridization, two complementary strands come back together again. page 12-14

A Southern blot involves cutting up DNA molecules using restriction enzymes, separating the resulting DNA fragments by size using gel electrophoresis, denaturing the DNA fragments in the gel, transferring the DNA fragments to filter paper, and detecting fragments of interest by allowing renaturation with a labeled probe. page 12-15

In Sanger sequencing of DNA, chain terminators are used to stop the DNA synthesis reaction and produce a series of short DNA fragments from which the DNA sequence can be determined. page 12-15

New DNA sequencing technologies are being developed to increase the speed and decrease the cost of sequencing, perhaps making it possible to sequence everyone's personal genomes. page 12-16

12.4 RECOMBINANT DNA TECHNOLOGY COMBINES DNA FROM TWO OR MORE ORGANISMS.

A recombinant DNA molecule can be made by cutting DNA from two organisms with the same restriction enzyme and then using DNA ligase to join them. page 12-18

Recombinant DNA is the basis for genetically modified organisms (GMOs), which offer both potential benefits and risks. page 12-19

Self-Assessment

1. Explain how DNA structure relates to DNA replication.

2. Describe the orientation of the two DNA strands and the direction of DNA synthesis.

3. List the differences and similarities in synthesis of the two daughter strands of DNA.

4. Explain why replicating the tips of linear chromosomes is problematic and how the cell overcomes this challenge.

5. Name the three steps of PCR and at least two uses for the PCR technique.

6. Explain how the properties of DNA determine how it moves through a gel, is cut by restriction enzymes, and hybridizes to other DNA strands.

7. Describe how DNA molecules are sequenced.

8. Describe how recombinant DNA techniques can be used to express a mammalian gene in bacteria.

Do you understand the chapter's Core Concepts? Log into BIOPORTAL to check your answers to the Self-Assessment questions, then practice what you've learned and reinforce this chapter's concepts by working through the problems and multimedia tutorials provided there.

📶 http://courses.bfwpub.com/yourbioportal/index.php

CHAPTER 13

GENOMES

Core Concepts

13.1 A genome is all the genetic material of an organism transmitted from parents to offspring, and its sequence is the order of bases along a DNA molecule.

13.2 Researchers annotate genome sequences to identify genes and other functional elements.

13.3 The number of genes in a genome and the size of a genome do not correlate well with the complexity of an organism.

13.4 The orderly packaging of DNA allows it to carry out its functions and fit inside the cell.

In Chapter 12, we saw how small pieces of DNA are isolated, identified, and sequenced. This technology has advanced to the point where the complete genome sequences for thousands of species have been determined, including those of humans and our closest primate relatives, as well as dozens of other mammals. The term **genome** refers to all the genetic material of an organism that is transmitted from parents to their offspring. Some genomes, like that of HIV, are small, whereas others, like the human genome, are large. In fact, the human genome sequence is so long that printing it in the size of the type used in this book would require 1.5 million pages. As we will see, however, the human genome is far from the largest among organisms.

The sequence of a genome is merely a long string of A's, T's, G's, and C's, which represent the order of bases present in successive nucleotides along the DNA molecules in the genome. But a genome sequence, on its own, is not very useful to scientists. Additional research is required to understand what proteins and other molecules are encoded in the genome sequence, and to learn when these molecules are produced during an organism's lifetime and what they do.

In this chapter, we discuss how the sequence of a genome is determined and analyzed to reveal its key biological features, such as the protein-coding genes. We also examine what other kinds of DNA sequences are present in genomes and how these sequences are organized, with special emphasis on the human genome.

13.1 GENOME SEQUENCING

What exactly is a genome? Originally, the term referred to the complete set of chromosomes present in a reproductive cell, like a sperm or an egg, which in the human genome is 23 chromosomes. The word "genome" is almost as old as the word "gene," and it was coined at a time when chromosomes were thought to consist of densely packed genes lined up one after another.

We know now, however, that chromosomes consist primarily of DNA and associated proteins, and that the genetic information in the chromosomes resides in the DNA. One might therefore define the genome as the DNA molecules that are transmitted from parents to offspring. This definition has the advantage of including the DNA in organisms that lack true chromosomes, such as bacteria and archaeons, as well as eukaryotic organelles that contain their own DNA, such as mitochondria and chloroplasts. But a definition restricted to DNA is too narrow because it excludes viruses, like HIV, whose genetic material consists of RNA. Defining a genome as the genetic material transmitted from parents to offspring therefore embraces all known cellular forms of life, all known organelles, and all viruses.

In this first section, we focus on how genomes are sequenced, building on the DNA sequencing technology introduced in Chapter 12.

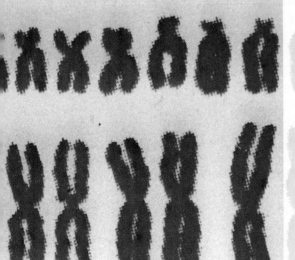

Complete genome sequences are assembled from smaller pieces.

In Chapter 12, we discussed a method of DNA sequencing known as Sanger sequencing. Such methods are now automated to the point where specialized machines can determine the sequence of billions of DNA nucleotides in a single day. However, even with recent advances, the data are obtained in the form of short sequences, typically less than a few hundred nucleotides long. If you are interested in sequencing a short DNA fragment, these technologies work well. However, let's say you are interested in the sequence of human chromosome 1, which is a DNA molecule approximately 250 million nucleotides long. How can you sequence a DNA molecule as long as that?

In one approach, the single long DNA molecule is first broken up into small fragments, each of which is short enough to be sequenced by existing technologies. Even though the sequence data obtained from a small DNA fragment is only a minuscule fraction of the length of the DNA molecules in most genomes, each run of an automated sequencing machine yields hundreds of millions of these short sequences from random locations throughout the genome. To sequence a whole genome, researchers typically sequence such a large number of random DNA fragments that, on average, any particular small region of the genome is sequenced 10–50 times. This redundancy is necessary to minimize the number of errors present in the final genome sequence and to minimize the number and size of gaps where the genome sequence is incomplete.

When a sufficient number of short sequences has been obtained, the next step is **sequence assembly:** The short sequences are put together in the correct order to generate the long, continuous sequence of nucleotides in the DNA molecule present in each chromosome.

Assembly is accomplished by complex computer programs, but the principle is simple. The short sequences are assembled according to their overlaps, as illustrated in **Fig. 13.1**, using a sentence to represent the nucleotide sequence. When assembly is complete, the overlapping fragments yield the famous sentence from Watson and Crick's original paper on the chemical structure of DNA, in which, referring to the pairing of bases A with T and of G with C, they write, "It has not escaped our notice that the specific pairing we have postulated immediately suggests a plausible copying mechanism for the genetic material." This approach is called **shotgun sequencing** because the sequenced fragments do not originate from a particular gene or region but from sites scattered randomly across the chromosome.

→ **Quick Check 1** DNA sequencing technology has been around since the late 1970s. Why did sequencing whole genomes present a challenge?

FIG. 13.1

How are whole genomes sequenced?

BACKGROUND DNA sequencing technologies can only determine the sequence of DNA fragments far smaller than the genome itself. How can the sequences of these small fragments be used to determine the sequence of an entire genome? In the early years of genome sequencing, many researchers thought that it would be necessary to know first where in the genome each fragment originated before sequencing it. A group at Celera Genomics reasoned that, if so many fragments were sequenced that the ends of one would almost always overlap with those of others, then a computer program with sufficient power might be able to assemble the short sequences to reveal the sequence of the entire genome.

HYPOTHESIS A genome sequence can be determined by sequencing small, randomly generated DNA fragments and assembling them into a complete sequence by matching regions of overlap between the fragments.

EXPERIMENT Hundreds of millions of short sequences from the genome of the fruit fly, *Drosophila melanogaster*, were sequenced. Fig. 13.1a shows examples of overlapping fragments, using an English sentence as an analogy.

Sequences that are repeated complicate sequence assembly.

Sequence assembly is not quite as straightforward as Fig. 13.1 might suggest. Real sequences are composed of nucleotides with only the four bases designated by the four letters A, T, G, and C, and any given short sequence could come from either strand of the double-stranded DNA molecule. Therefore, the overlaps between fragments must be long enough both to ensure that the assembly is correct, and to determine from which strand of DNA the short sequence originated.

Some features of genomes present additional challenges to sequence assembly, and the limitations of the computer programs for handling such features require hands-on assembly. Chief among these complicating features is the problem of repeated sequences.

There are a variety of types of repeated sequence in eukaryotic genomes, and some are shown in **Fig. 13.2**. The repeated sequence may be several thousand nucleotides long and present in multiple identical or nearly identical copies. These long repeated sequences may be tandem, meaning that they are next to each other (Fig. 13.2a), or they may be dispersed throughout the genome (Fig. 13.2b).

RESULTS The computer program the group had written to assemble the fragments worked. The researchers were able to sequence the entire *Drosophila* genome by piecing together the fragments according to their overlaps. In the sentence analogy, the fragments (Fig. 13.1a) can be assembled into the complete sentence (Fig. 13.1b) by matching the overlaps between the fragments.

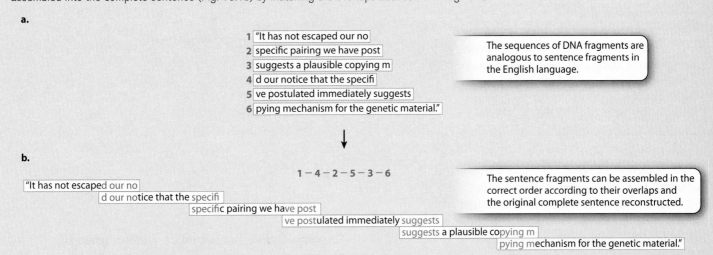

a.

1 "It has not escaped our no
2 specific pairing we have post
3 suggests a plausible copying m
4 d our notice that the specifi
5 ve postulated immediately suggests
6 pying mechanism for the genetic material."

The sequences of DNA fragments are analogous to sentence fragments in the English language.

b.

1 − 4 − 2 − 5 − 3 − 6

The sentence fragments can be assembled in the correct order according to their overlaps and the original complete sentence reconstructed.

"It has not escaped our no
d our notice that the specifi
specific pairing we have post
ve postulated immediately suggests
suggests a plausible copying m
pying mechanism for the genetic material."

CONCLUSION The hypothesis was supported: Celera Genomics could determine the entire genomic sequence of an organism by sequencing small, random fragments and piecing them together at their overlapping ends.

FOLLOW-UP WORK Today, the computer assembly method is routinely used to determine genome sequences. This method is also used to infer the genome sequences of hundreds of bacterial species simultaneously—for example, in bacterial communities sampled from seawater or from the human gut.

SOURCE Adams, M. D., et al. 2000. "The Genome Sequence of *Drosophila melanogaster*." *Science* 287:2185–2195.

FIG. 13.2 **Principal types of sequence repeats found in eukaryotic genomes (not drawn to scale).** Repeats often pose problems in DNA sequencing.

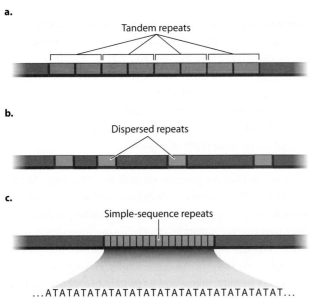

a.

Tandem repeats

b.

Dispersed repeats

c.

Simple-sequence repeats

...ATATATATATATATATATATATATATATATAT...
...TATATATATATATATATATATATATATATATA...

The difficulty with long repeated sequences is that they typically are much longer than the short sequences obtained by automated sequencing. As a result, the repeat may not be detected at all. And if the repeat is detected, there is no easy way of knowing the number of copies of the repeat, that is, whether the segment includes two, three, four, or any number of copies of the repeat. Sometimes, researchers can use the ends of repeats, where the fragments overlap with an adjacent, nonrepeating sequence, as a guide to the position and number of repeats.

In another type of repeat, the repeating sequence is short, even as short as two nucleotides, such as AT, repeated over and over again in a stretch of DNA (Fig. 13.2c). Short repeating sequences of this kind are troublesome for sequencing machines because any single-stranded fragment consisting of alternating AT can fold back upon itself to form a double-stranded structure in which A is paired with T. Such structures are more stable than the unfolded single-stranded structures and are not easily sequenced.

→ **Quick Check 2** Let's say that a stretch of repeated AT is successfully sequenced. From what you know of the difficulties of sequencing long repeated sequences, what other problems might you encounter in assembling these fragments?

? CASE 3 You, from A To T: Your Personal Genome
Why sequence your personal genome?

The Human Genome Project, which began in 1990, had the goal of sequencing the human genome as well as the genomes of certain key organisms used as models in genetic research. The model organisms chosen are the mainstays of laboratory biology— a species each of bacteria, yeast, nematode worm, fruit fly, and mouse. By 2003, the genome sequences of these model organisms had been completed, as well as the human genome. By then, the cost of sequencing had become so low and the sequence output so high that many more genomes were sequenced than originally planned. Large-scale genome sequencing is still done today, and soon you could choose to have your personal genome sequenced.

Why sequence more genomes? And if the human genome is sequenced, why sequence yours? As we saw in Case 3: You, from A to T, there is really no such thing as *the* human genome, any more than there is *the* fruit fly genome or *the* mouse genome. With the exception of identical twins, every person's genome is unique, the product of a fusion of a unique egg with a unique sperm. The sequence that is called "the human genome" is actually a composite of sequences from different individuals. This sequence is nevertheless useful because most of us share the same genes and regulatory regions, organized the same way on chromosomes.

Detailed knowledge of your own personal genome can be valuable. Our individual DNA sequences differ at millions of nucleotide sites from one person to the next. Some of these differences account in part for the physical differences we see among us; others have the potential to predict susceptibility to disease and response to medication. For Claudia Gilmore, knowledge of the sequence of her *BRCA1* gene had a significant impact on her life (Case 3: You, from A to T).

Determining these differences is a step toward **personalized medicine,** in which an individual's genome sequence, by revealing his or her disease susceptibilities and drug sensitivities, allows treatments to be tailored to the individual. There may come a time, perhaps within your lifetime, when personal genome sequencing becomes part of routine medical testing. Information about a patient's genome will bring benefits but also raises ethical concerns and poses risks to confidentiality and insurability.

13.2 GENOME ANNOTATION

A goal of biology is to identify all the component macromolecules in biological systems and to understand their individual functions and the ways in which they interact—their cellular organization, metabolism, growth, adaptation, reproduction, and other aspects of how life works. This research has practical applications: Increased understanding of the molecular and cellular basis of disease, for example, can lead to improved diagnosis and treatment.

The value of genome sequencing in identifying macromolecules is that the genome sequence contains, in coded form, the nucleotide sequence of all RNA molecules transcribed from the DNA as well as the amino acid sequence of all proteins. There is a catch, however. A genome sequence is merely an extremely long list of A's, T's, G's, and C's that represent the order in which nucleotides occur along the DNA in one strand of the double helix. (Because A in one strand is paired with T in the other and G is paired with C, knowing the sequence of one strand specifies the other.) The catch is that in multicellular organisms, not all of the DNA is transcribed into RNA, and not all of the RNA that is transcribed is translated into protein. Therefore, genome sequencing is just the first step in understanding the function of any particular DNA sequence. Following genome sequencing, the next step is to identify the locations and functions of the various types of sequence present in the genome.

Genome annotation identifies various types of sequence.

Genomes contain many different types of sequence, among them protein-coding genes. Protein-coding genes are themselves composed of different regions, including regulatory elements that specify when and where an RNA transcript will be produced, noncoding introns that are removed from the RNA transcript during RNA processing (Chapter 3), and protein-coding exons that contain the codons that specify the amino acid sequence of a polypeptide chain (Chapter 4). Genomes also contain coding sequences for RNAs that are not translated into protein (noncoding RNAs), such as ribosomal RNA, transfer RNA, and other types of small RNA molecule. Finally, much of the DNA in the genomes of multicellular organisms does not code for proteins or RNA at all, nor has it any other known function in the metabolism, physiology, development, or behavior of the organism.

Genome annotation is the process by which researchers identify the various types of sequence present in genomes. Genome annotation is essentially an exercise in adding commentary to a genome sequence that identifies which types of sequence are present and where they are located. It can be thought of as a form of pattern recognition, where the patterns are regularities in sequence that are characteristic of protein-coding genes or other types of sequence.

An example of genome annotation is shown in **Fig. 13.3.** Genes present in one copy per genome are indicated in orange. Most of these single-copy genes are protein-coding genes. The annotation of a single-copy gene typically specifies any nearby regulatory regions that control transcription, the intron–exon boundaries in the gene, and any known or predicted alternative forms in which the introns and exons are spliced (Chapter 3). Each single-copy gene is given a unique name and its protein product identified. Note in Fig. 13.3 that single-copy genes can differ in size from

FIG. 13.3 **Genome annotation.** Given the DNA sequence of a genome, researchers can pinpoint locations of various types of sequence.

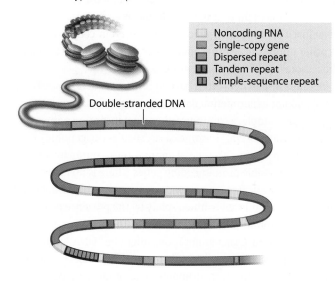

one gene to the next. The annotations in Fig. 13.3 also specify the locations of sequences that encode RNAs that are not translated into proteins, as well as various types of repeated sequence.

Small genomes such as that of HIV and other viruses can be annotated by hand, but for large genomes like the human genome, computers are essential. In the human genome, some protein-coding genes extend for more than a million nucleotides. A comparison helps convey the challenge of genome annotation. Roughly speaking, if the sequence of the approximately 3 billion nucleotides in a human egg or sperm was printed in normal-sized type, the length of the ribbon would stretch 4000 miles (6440 kilometers), about the distance from Fairbanks, Alaska, to Miami, Florida. By contrast, for the approximately 10,000 nucleotides in the HIV genome, the ribbon would extend a mere 70 feet (21 meters).

Genome annotation is an ongoing process because, as macromolecules and their functions and interactions become better understood, the annotations to the genome must be updated. A sequence that is annotated as nonfunctional today may be found to have a function tomorrow. For this reason, the annotation of certain genomes—including the human genome—will certainly continue to change.

Genome annotation includes searching for sequence motifs.

Because genome annotation is essentially pattern recognition, it begins with the identification of a **sequence motif,** a telltale sequence that indicates what type of sequence it is (**Fig. 13.4**). This sequence pattern can be found in the DNA itself, or in the RNA sequence inferred from the DNA sequence. Once identified, sequence motifs are typically confirmed by experimental methods.

An example of a sequence motif is an **open reading frame (ORF)** (Fig. 13.4a). The motif for an open reading frame is a long string of codons for amino acids with no stop codon. The presence of such a motif by itself is enough to annotate the DNA segment as potentially protein coding.

Fig. 13.4b shows another type of sequence motif, this one also present in a hypothetical RNA transcript inferred from the DNA sequence. The nucleotide sequence in one part of the RNA is complementary to that in another part, so the single-stranded molecule is able to fold back on itself and undergo base pairing to form a hairpin-shaped structure. Such hairpin structures are characteristic of certain types of RNA that function in gene regulation (Chapter 19). The DNA from which this RNA is transcribed would have complementary sequences on either end as well.

FIG. 13.4 **Some common sequence motifs useful in genome annotation.** (a) An open reading frame; (b) a noncoding RNA molecule; (c) transcription factor binding sites.

a.

RNA from a protein-coding region contains an open reading frame consisting of triplets of nucleotides that can specify amino acids.

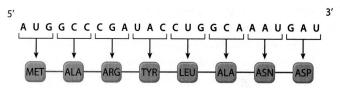

b.

Regions of some RNA molecules, such as those in transfer RNA, form hairpin structures in which the molecule folds back on itself.

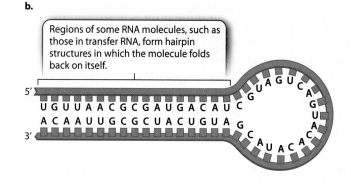

c.

DNA sequences that bind transcription factors are often short sequences present in multiple copies near a protein-coding gene.

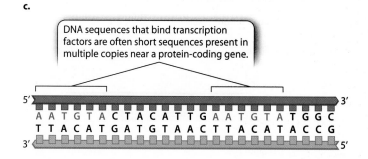

Some sequence motifs are detected directly in the double-stranded DNA. Fig. 13.4c shows two copies of a short sequence that are known binding sites for DNA-binding proteins called transcription factors (Chapter 3), whose binding to DNA initiates transcription. Transcription factor binding sites are often present in multiple copies and in either strand of the DNA. Sometimes they are located near the region of a gene where transcription is initiated because the transcription factor helps determine when the gene will be transcribed. However, they can also be located far upstream of the gene, downstream of the gene, or in introns, and so their identification is difficult.

Comparison of genomic DNA with messenger RNA reveals the intron–exon structure of genes.

In annotating an entire genome, researchers typically make use of information beyond the genome sequence itself. This information may include sequences of messenger RNA molecules that are isolated from various tissues or from various stages of development of the organism. Recall from Chapter 3 that messenger RNA (mRNA) molecules undergo processing and are therefore usually simpler than the DNA sequences from which they are transcribed—for example, introns are removed and exons are spliced together. The resulting mature mRNA therefore contains a long sequence of codons uninterrupted by a stop codon—in other words, an open reading frame. The open reading frame in an mRNA is the region that is actually translated into protein on the ribosome.

One aspect of genome annotation is the determination of which portions of the genome sequence correspond to sequences in mRNA transcripts. An example is shown in **Fig. 13.5**, which compares the DNA and mRNA for the β (beta) chain of hemoglobin, the oxygen-carrying protein in red blood cells. Note that the genomic DNA contains some sequences present in the mRNA, which correspond to exons, and some sequences that are not present in the mRNA, which correspond to introns. Comparison of mRNA with genomic DNA therefore reveals the intron–exon structure of protein-coding genes. In fact, introns were first discovered by comparing β-globin mRNA with genomic DNA.

An annotated genome summarizes knowledge, guides research, and reveals evolutionary relationships among organisms.

Genome annotation, which aims to identify all the functional and repeat sequences present in the genome, is an imperfect science. Even in a well-annotated genome, some protein-coding sequences or other important features may be overlooked, and occasionally the annotation of a sequence motif is incorrect.

Because researchers often have to rely on sequence motifs alone and not experimental data, their descriptions may be vague. For example, a common annotation in large genomes is "hypothetical protein." In some cases, such as the genome of the malaria parasite, this type of annotation accounts for about 50% of the possible protein-coding genes. There is no hint of what a hypothetical protein may do or even whether it is actually produced, since it is determined solely by the presence of an ORF in the genomic sequence, and not by the presence of actual mRNA or protein. Other annotations might be "DNA-binding protein," "possible hairpin RNA," or "tyrosine kinase"—with no additional detail. In short, although some genome annotations summarize experimentally verified facts, many others are hypotheses and guides to future research.

Genome sequences contain information about ancestry and evolution, and so comparisons among genomes can reveal how different species are related. For example, the sequence of the human genome is significantly more similar to that of the chimpanzee than to that of the gorilla, indicating a more recent common ancestry of humans and chimpanzees (Chapter 1).

Analysis of the similarities and differences in protein-coding genes and other types of sequence in the genomes of different species is an area of study called **comparative genomics.** Such studies help us understand how genes and genomes evolve. They can also guide genome annotation because the sequences of important functional elements are often very similar among genomes of different organisms. Sequences that are similar in different organisms are said to be **conserved.** A sequence motif that is conserved is likely to be important even if its function is unknown, since it has changed very little over evolutionary time.

The HIV genome illustrates the utility of genome annotation and comparison.

HIV and related viruses provide an example of how genomes are annotated and how comparisons among genome sequences can reveal evolutionary relationships. A **virus** is a small infectious agent that contains a nucleic acid genome packaged inside a protein coat called a capsid. In some viruses, a lipid envelope surrounds the capsid. Viruses can bind to surface receptor molecules on cells of the host organism, enabling the viral genome to enter the cell. Infection of a host cell is essential to viral reproduction because viruses use cellular ATP and hijack cellular machinery to replicate, transcribe, and translate their genome in order to make more viruses.

FIG. 13.5 Identification of exons and introns by comparison of genomic DNA with mRNA sequence.

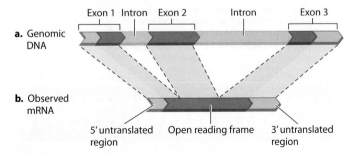

FIG. 13.6 Evolutionary relationships among viruses related to HIV.

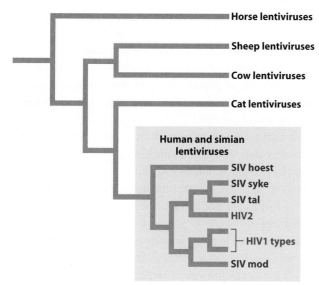

Whereas the genome of all cells consists of double-stranded DNA, the genomes of viruses may be double-stranded DNA, single-stranded DNA, double-stranded RNA, or single-stranded RNA. The genome of HIV is single-stranded RNA. The sequence of the HIV genome identifies it as a retrovirus that replicates via a DNA intermediate that can be incorporated into the host genome. More narrowly, the sequence of the HIV genome groups it among the mammalian lentiviruses, so named because of the long lag between the initial time of infection and the appearance of symptoms (*lenti-* means "slow").

Fig. 13.6 shows the evolutionary relationships among a sample of lentiviruses, grouped according to the similarity of their genome sequences. The evolutionary tree shows that closely related viruses have closely related hosts. For example, cat lentiviruses are more closely related to one another than they are to cow lentiviruses. This observation implies that the genomes of the viruses evolve along with the genomes of their hosts. A second feature shown by the evolutionary tree is that human HIV originated from at least two separate simian viruses that switched hosts from simians (most likely chimpanzees) to humans.

The annotated sequence of the HIV genome tells us a lot about the biology of this virus (**Fig. 13.7**). Many details are left out here, but the main point is to show the functional elements of HIV in the form of an annotated genome. The open reading frame denoted *gag* encodes protein

components of the capsid, *pol* encodes proteins needed for reverse transcription of the viral RNA into DNA and incorporation into the host genome, and *env* encodes proteins that are embedded in the lipid envelope. The annotation in Fig. 13.7 also includes the genes *tat* and *rev*, encoding proteins essential for the HIV life cycle, as well as the genes *vif, vpr, vpu,* and *nef,* which encode accessory proteins that enhance virulence in organisms. Identification of the genes necessary to complete the HIV cycle is the first step to finding drugs that can interfere with the cycle and prevent infection.

→ **Quick Check 3** Fig. 13.6 shows that closely related lentiviruses have closely related host organisms. Given this pattern, how many different kinds of organisms would you expect one lentivirus to be capable of infecting?

13.3 GENE NUMBER, GENOME SIZE, AND ORGANISMAL COMPLEXITY

Before whole-genome sequencing, molecular biology and evolution research tended to focus on single genes. Researchers studied how individual genes are turned on and off, and how a gene in one organism is related to a gene in another organism. Now, with the availability of genome sequences from multiple species, it is possible to make comparisons across full genomes. Some of the results have been striking.

Gene number is not a good predictor of biological complexity.

The complete genome sequences of many organisms allow us to make comparisons among them. One of the surprising results is the relatively low number of genes in humans relative to the

FIG. 13.7 The annotated genome of HIV.

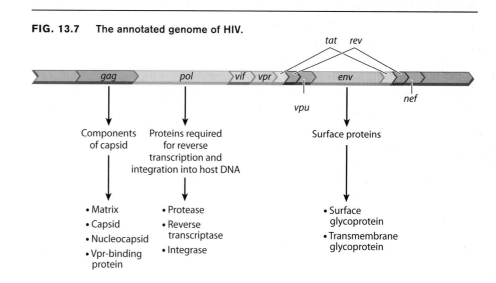

TABLE 13.1 Gene Numbers of Several Organisms.
Humans have more genes than fruit flies and nematode worms, but not as many as might be expected on the basis of complexity.

COMMON NAME	SPECIES NAME	APPROXIMATE NUMBER OF GENES
Mustard plant	*Arabidopsis thaliana*	27,000
Human	*Homo sapiens*	25,000
Nematode worm	*Caenorhabditis elegans*	20,000
Fruit fly	*Drosophila melanogaster*	14,000
Baker's yeast	*Saccharomyces cerevisiae*	6000
Gut bacterium	*Escherichia coli*	4000

number in other species sequenced (**Table 13.1**). Because humans are so much more complex in cell number and type, and in behavior, it was expected that we would have many more genes than we do.

Humans have about 25,000 genes. Surprisingly, the mustard plant *Arabidopsis*, a common weed and model organism in plant biology, has 27,000, about the same number. Perhaps the most sobering comparison is with the nematode worm *Caenorhabditis elegans*, another model organism, which has only 959 cells (we have an estimated 100 trillion), of which 302 are nerve cells that form the worm's brain (our brain has 100 billion nerve cells). Despite having 100 million times as many cells, we have roughly the same number of genes as the worm. How can we account for the disconnect between levels of complexity and gene number?

One hypothesis is that human cells are able to do many more things with the genes they have. A number of mechanisms are likely to be important. The expression of our relatively few genes can be regulated in many subtle ways, causing different gene products to be made in different amounts in different cells at different times (Chapters 19 and 20). This differential gene expression contributes to the large number of different cell types. Human proteins interact with one another so that, even though there are relatively few actual proteins, they are capable of combining in many different ways to perform different functions. And we know that a single gene may yield multiple proteins, either because different exons are spliced together to make different proteins (Chapter 3) or because the proteins undergo biochemical changes after they have been translated.

Overall, the discovery of the relatively low human gene number poses many tantalizing evolutionary questions and suggests that major evolutionary changes can be accomplished not only by the acquisition of whole new genes, but also by modifying existing genes and their regulation in subtle ways.

Viruses, bacteria, and archaeons have small, compact genomes.

As well as comparing numbers of genes, we can also compare sizes of genomes in different organisms. Before making such comparisons, we need to understand how genome size is measured. Genomes are measured in numbers of base pairs, and the yardsticks of genome size are a thousand base pairs (a kilobase, kb), a million base pairs (a megabase, Mb), and a billion base pairs (a gigabase, Gb).

Most viral genomes range in size from 3 kb to 300 kb, but a few are very large. The largest viral genome, found in a virus that infects the amoeba *Acanthamoeba polyphaga*, is 1.2 Mb. This viral genome contains almost 1000 protein-coding genes, including some for sugar, lipid, and amino acid metabolism not found in any other viruses.

The largest viral genome is twice as large as that of the bacterium *Mycoplasma genitalium*. At 580 kb and encoding only 471 genes, the genome of *M. genitalium* is the smallest known among free-living bacteria, those capable of living entirely on their own. The complete sequence of small bacterial genomes has allowed researchers to define the smallest, or minimal, genome (and therefore the minimal set of proteins) necessary to sustain life. Current findings suggest that the small *M. genitalium* is about two times larger than the minimal genome size thought to be necessary to encode all the functions essential to life.

The genomes of bacteria and archaeons are information dense, meaning that most of the genome has a defined function. Roughly speaking, 90% or more of their genomes consists of

TABLE 13.2 Genome Sizes of Several Organisms
Genome size varies tremendously among eukaryotic organisms, and there is no correlation between genome size and the complexity of an organism.

COMMON NAME	SPECIES NAME	APPROXIMATE GENOME SIZE (MB)
Fruit fly	*Drosophila melanogaster*	180
Fugu fish	*Fugu rubripes*	400
Boa constrictor	*Boa constrictor*	2100
Human	*Homo sapiens*	3100
Locust	*Schistocerca gregaria*	9300
Onion	*Allium cepa*	18,000
Newt	*Amphiuma means*	84,000
Lungfish	*Protopterus aethiopicus*	140,000
Fern	*Ophioglossum petiolatum*	160,000
Amoeba	*Amoeba dubia*	670,000

protein-coding genes. Bacterial genomes range in size from 0.5 to 10 Mb. The bigger genomes have more genes, allowing these bacteria to synthesize small molecules that other bacteria have to scrounge for, or to use chemical energy in the covalent bonds of substances that other bacteria cannot. Archaeons, whose genomes range in size from 0.5 to 5.7 Mb, have similar capabilities.

Among eukaryotes, there is no relationship between genome size and organismal complexity.

In eukaryotes, just as the number of genes does not correlate well with organismal complexity, the size of the genome is unrelated to the metabolic, developmental, and behavioral complexity of the organism (**Table 13.2**). The range of genome sizes is huge, even among similar organisms (**Fig. 13.8**). The largest eukaryotic genome exceeds the size of the smallest by a factor of more than 500,000—and both the smallest and the largest are found among protozoa. The range among flowering plants (angiosperms) is about three orders of magnitude, and the range among animals is about seven orders of magnitude. One species of lungfish has a genome size more than 45 times larger than the human genome (Table 13.2). Clearly, there is no relationship between the size of the genome and the complexity of the organism.

The disconnect between genome size and organismal complexity is called the **C-value paradox.** The C-value is the amount of DNA in a reproductive cell, and the "paradox" is the apparent contradiction between genome size and organismal complexity, and hence the difficulty of predicting one from the other.

If organismal complexity is not a good predictor of genome size, what is? In eukaryotic organisms, large genomes can differ from small ones for a number of reasons. One reason

is **polyploidy,** or having more than two sets of chromosomes in the genome. Polyploidy is especially prominent in many groups of plants. Humans have two sets of 23 chromosomes, giving us 46 chromosomes in total. But the polyploid bread wheat *Triticum aestivum,* for example, has six sets of seven chromosomes.

Polyploidy, which is widespread, has played an important role in plant evolution. Many agricultural crops are polyploid, including wheat, potato, olive, banana, sugarcane, and coffee. Among flowering plants, it is estimated that 30% to 80% of existing species have polyploidy in their evolutionary history, either because of the duplication of the complete set of chromosomes in a single species, or because of hybridization, or crossing, between related species followed by duplication

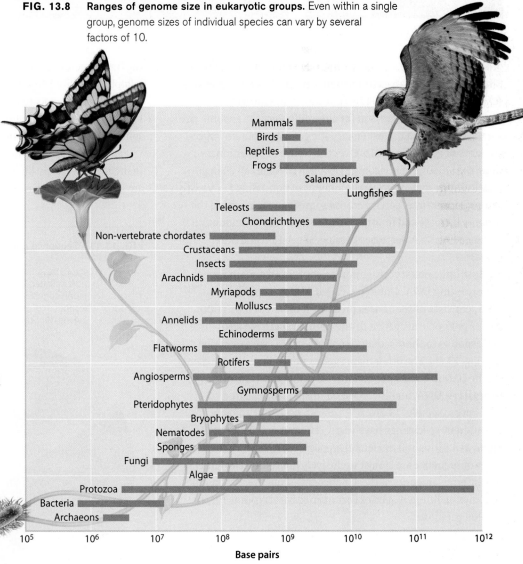

FIG. 13.8 **Ranges of genome size in eukaryotic groups.** Even within a single group, genome sizes of individual species can vary by several factors of 10.

FIG. 13.9   Polyploidy in plants. This species was formed by hybridization between two different species, and it contains a full set of chromosomes from each parent (colored yellow and green).

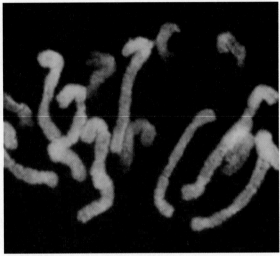

of the chromosome sets in the hybrid (**Fig. 13.9**). Some ferns take polyploidy to an extreme: One species has 84 copies of a set of 15 chromosomes—1260 chromosomes altogether.

Another important reason for large differences in genome size among species is that most eukaryotic genomes contain large amounts of noncoding DNA. Over the course of evolutionary time, the amount of noncoding DNA in a genome can change drastically. In some species, the amount of noncoding DNA vastly increases over time, partly because some sequences within the genome increase and multiply. In other species the amount of noncoding DNA decreases because of deletion and other processes.

Most large eukaryotic genomes contain two main types of noncoding DNA. One type, called **highly repetitive DNA,** consists of sequences present in more than 100,000 copies per genome. Much of the highly repetitive DNA corresponds to short sequence repeats such as we saw earlier (see Fig. 13.2c). The other main type of noncoding DNA, present in 100–10,000 copies per genome, is called **moderately repetitive DNA,** and it consists of dispersed repeated sequences (see Fig. 13.2b).

Different species can have vastly different quantities of highly repetitive and moderately repetitive DNA. Since these types of sequence are almost exclusively noncoding DNA, it is the differing amounts of these noncoding sequences among the genomes of different species that in large part accounts for the C-value paradox.

→   **Quick Check 4** Given our knowledge of genome sizes in different organisms, would you predict that humans or amoebas (a single-celled eukaryote) have a larger genome?

About half of the human genome consists of repetitive DNA and transposable elements.
Complete genome sequencing has allowed the different types of noncoding DNA to be specified more precisely in a variety of organisms. It came as a great surprise to learn that in the human genome only about 2.5% of the genome actually codes for proteins. The other 97.5% includes sequences we have encountered earlier, including sequences that specify noncoding RNA, repetitive DNA, and noncoding regions of genes, such as introns.

In **Fig. 13.10**, we see the principal repetitive sequences in the human genome. Among the highly repetitive sequences is α (alpha) satellite DNA, which consists of tandem copies of a 171-bp sequence repeated near each centromere an average of 18,000 times. The α satellite DNA is essential for attachment of spindle fibers to the centromeres during cell division (Chapter 11).

Fig. 13.10 also shows the proportions of several types of sequence collectively known as **transposable elements,** which are DNA sequences that can replicate and insert themselves

FIG. 13.10   Sequence composition of the human genome.

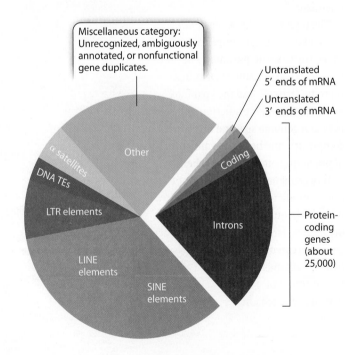

into new positions in the genome. As a result, they have the potential to increase their copy number in the genome over time. Transposable elements are sometimes referred to as "selfish" DNA because it seems that their only function is to duplicate themselves and proliferate in the genome, making them the ultimate parasite.

Transposable elements make up about 45% of the DNA in the human genome. They can be classified into two groups based on the way they replicate. One class consists of **DNA transposable elements (DNA TEs),** which replicate and transpose via DNA replication and repair. The other class consists of elements that transpose by means of an RNA intermediate. Among these are **LTR elements,** which are characterized by long repeated sequences, called long terminal repeats (LTRs), at their ends. Also in this class are two types that are distinguished by their length: the **LINEs** (long interspersed nuclear elements), of about 1000 base pairs, and the **SINEs** (short interspersed nuclear elements), with about 300 base pairs.

13.4 ORGANIZATION OF GENOMES

The genomes of all organisms are large relative to the size of the cell. For example, if the circular genome of the intestinal bacterium *Escherichia coli* were fully extended, its length would be 200 times greater than the diameter of the cell itself. The fully extended length of DNA in human chromosome 1, our longest chromosome, would be 10,000 times greater than the diameter of the average human cell. There is consequently a need to package an enormous length of DNA into a form that will fit inside the cell while still allowing the DNA to replicate and carry out its coding functions. The mechanism of packaging differs substantially in bacteria, archaeons, and eukaryotes. We focus here on bacteria and eukaryotes, primarily because less is known about how DNA is packaged in archaeons.

Bacterial cells package their DNA as a nucleoid composed of many loops.

Bacterial genomes are circular, and the DNA double helix is underwound, which means that it makes fewer turns in going around the circle than would allow every base in one strand to pair with its partner base in the other strand. Underwinding is caused by an enzyme, **topoisomerase II**, that breaks the double helix, rotates the ends, and then seals the break. Underwinding creates strain on the DNA molecule, which is relieved by the formation of **supercoils**, in which the DNA molecule coils on itself. Supercoiling allows all the base pairs to form, even though the molecule is underwound. (You can make your own supercoil by stretching and twirling the ends of a rubber band, then relaxing the stress slightly to allow the twisted part to form coils around itself.) Supercoils that result from underwinding

are called negative supercoils, and those that result from overwinding are positive supercoils. In most organisms, DNA is negatively supercoiled.

In bacteria, the supercoils of DNA form a structure with multiple loops called a **nucleoid** (**Fig. 13.11**). The supercoil loops are bound together by proteins. In *E. coli*, the nucleoid has about 100 loops, each containing about 50 kb of DNA. In addition to the protein binding that forms the loops, the negative supercoiling of the DNA serves to compress the molecule into a compact volume.

The supercoils in the loops of the nucleoid can be relaxed by introducing nicks, or interruptions, in the DNA backbones by means of enzymes or chemicals. The nicks allow the strands to rotate around each another to remove the supercoils, and the

FIG. 13.11 Bacterial nucleoid. The circular bacterial chromosome twists on itself to form supercoils, which are anchored by proteins.

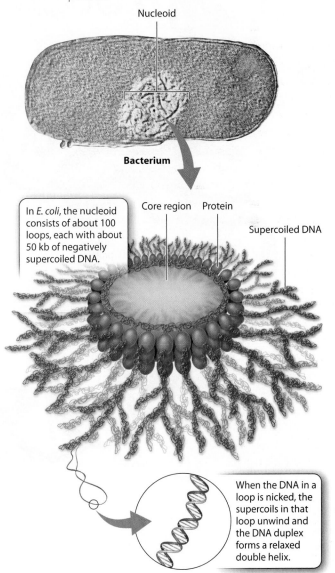

Nucleoid

Bacterium

In *E. coli*, the nucleoid consists of about 100 loops, each with about 50 kb of negatively supercoiled DNA.

Core region   Protein

Supercoiled DNA

When the DNA in a loop is nicked, the supercoils in that loop unwind and the DNA duplex forms a relaxed double helix.

FIG. 13.12 Levels of chromosome condensation.

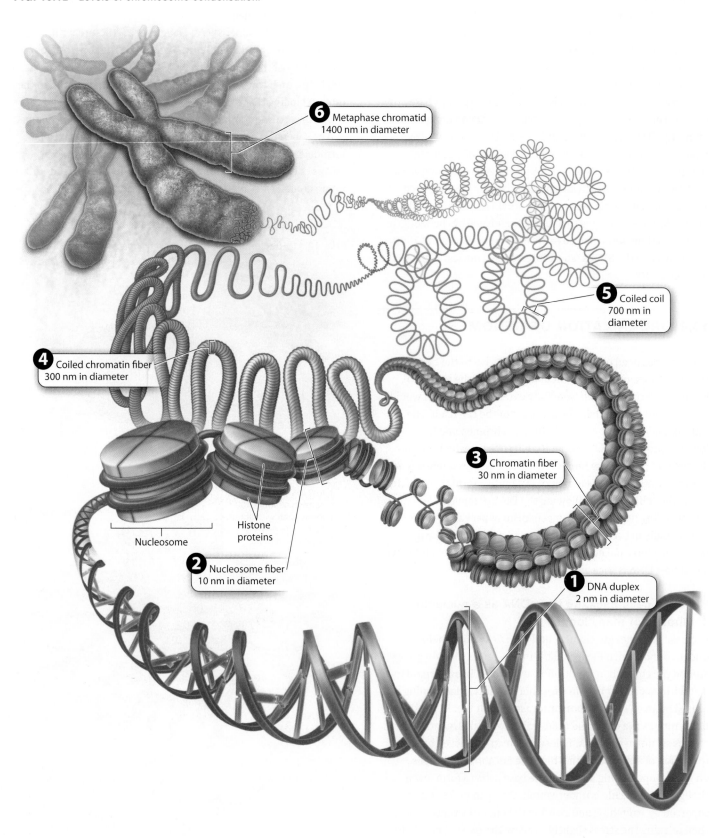

6 Metaphase chromatid
1400 nm in diameter

5 Coiled coil
700 nm in
diameter

4 Coiled chromatin fiber
300 nm in diameter

3 Chromatin fiber
30 nm in diameter

Histone
proteins

Nucleosome

2 Nucleosome fiber
10 nm in diameter

1 DNA duplex
2 nm in diameter

DNA molecule relaxes into the standard double helix. Any nick will relieve the supercoils in a loop, but only in the loop that is nicked. This means that each loop is supercoiled independently of the others (because of the proteins that hold the loops together).

Eukaryotic cells package their DNA as one molecule per chromosome.

In eukaryotic cells, DNA in the nucleus is packaged differently from that in bacteria (**Fig. 13.12**). Eukaryotic DNA is first wrapped around a group of histone proteins called a **nucleosome** (Chapter 3). Each nucleosome consists of two molecules, and each molecule consists of four different histone proteins. The histone proteins are rich in the amino acids lysine and arginine, whose positive charges neutralize the negative charges of the phosphates along the backbone of each DNA strand. This first level of packaging of the DNA is sometimes referred to as "beads on a string," with the nucleosomes the beads, and the DNA the string.

The nucleosomes and associated DNA are then coiled to form a structure called the **30-nm chromatin fiber** (Fig. 13.12). When the chromosomes in the nucleus condense in preparation for cell division, each chromosome becomes progressively shorter and thicker as the 30-nm fiber coils in a manner that is still not fully understood. The progressive coiling constitutes **chromosome condensation,** an active, energy-consuming process requiring the participation of several types of proteins.

Greater detail of the structure of a fully condensed chromosome is revealed when the histones are chemically removed (**Fig. 13.13**). Without histones to coil around, the DNA

FIG. 13.13 (a) A chromosome with histones and (b) a chromosome depleted of histones, showing the underlying scaffold.

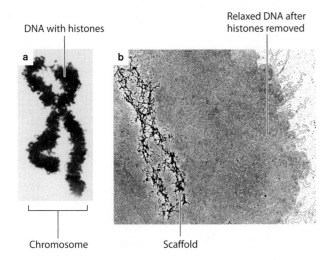

DNA with histones

Relaxed DNA after histones removed

a

b

Chromosome

Scaffold

spreads out in loops around a supporting protein structure called the chromosome **scaffold.** Each loop of relaxed DNA is 30 to 90 kb long and anchored to the scaffold at its base. Before removal of the histones, the loops are compact and supercoiled. Each human chromosome contains 2000–8000 such loops, depending on its size.

Despite intriguing similarities between the nucleoid model in Fig. 13.11 and the chromosome scaffold model in Fig. 13.13, the structures evolved independently and make use of different types of protein to bind the DNA and to form the folded structure of DNA and protein. Furthermore, the similarities are misleading, in part because the size of the eukaryotic chromosome is vastly greater than the size of the bacterial nucleoid. To appreciate the difference in scale, keep in mind that the volume of a fully condensed human *chromosome* is five times larger than the volume of a bacterial *cell*.

The human genome consists of 22 pairs of chromosomes and two sex chromosomes.

As emphasized in Chapter 11, the orderly process of meiosis is possible because chromosomes occur in pairs. The pairs usually match in size, general appearance, and position of the centromere, but there are exceptions, such as the X and Y sex chromosomes. The pairs of chromosomes that match in size and appearance are called **homologous chromosomes**. The members of each pair of homologous chromosomes have the same genes arranged in the same order along their length. If the DNA duplexes in each pair of homologs were denatured, each DNA strand could form a duplex with its complementary strand from the other homolog. There would be some differences in DNA sequence due to genetic variation, but not so many differences as to prevent DNA hybridization.

Chromosome painting illustrates the nearly identical nature of the DNA molecules in each pair of homologs. In this technique, individual chromosomes are isolated from cells in metaphase of mitosis. Metaphase of mitosis is the easiest stage in which to isolate chromosomes because of the availability of chemicals that prevent the spindle from forming. These chemicals block the cell cycle at metaphase, so cells progress to metaphase and then stop.

Once the chromosomes have been isolated, the DNA from each chromosome is fragmented, denatured, and labeled with a unique combination of fluorescent dyes. Under fluorescent light, the dyes give the DNA in each type of chromosome a different color. The fluorescently labeled DNA fragments are then mixed and hybridized to intact metaphase chromosomes from another cell. Each labeled fragment hybridizes to its complementary sequence in the metaphase chromosomes, "painting" each metaphase chromosome with dye-labeled DNA fragments.

FIG. 13.14 **A chromosome paint of chromosomes from a human male.** (a) Condensed chromosomes are "painted" with fluorescent dyes. (b) Chromosomes are arranged in the standard form of a karyotype. The colors in (a) and (b) do not match exactly because the "paints" are different.

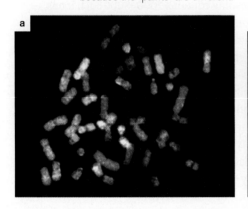

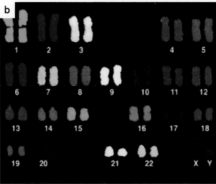

A chromosome paint of the chromosomes in a human male is shown in **Fig. 13.14**. Fig. 13.14a shows the chromosomes in the random orientation in which they were found in the metaphase cell, and Fig. 13.14b shows them arranged in a standard form called a **karyotype** (Chapter 11). To make a karyotype, the images of the homologous chromosomes are arranged in pairs from longest to shortest, with the sex chromosomes placed at the lower right. In this case, the sex chromosomes are XY (one X chromosome and one Y chromosome), indicating that the individual is male, whereas in a female the sex chromosomes would be XX (a pair of X chromosomes). Including the sex chromosomes, humans have 23 pairs of chromosomes.

An important observation from the chromosome paint shown in Fig. 13.14 is that the two members of each pair of homologous chromosomes show the same pattern of fluorescent color. This means that a particular labeled DNA fragment only hybridized with the two homologs of one chromosome. Hence, the DNA in each pair of homologous chromosomes is different from that in any other pair of homologous chromosomes.

Higher resolution of human chromosomes can be obtained by the use of stains that bind preferentially to certain chromosomal regions and produce a visible pattern of **bands,** or crosswise striations, in the chromosomes. One such stain is the Giemsa stain; a Giemsa-stained karyotype is shown in **Fig. 13.15**. Note that each chromosome has a unique pattern of bands and that homologous chromosomes can readily be identified by their identical banding patterns. Procedures using the Giemsa stain yield about 300 bands that are used as landmarks for describing the location of genes along the chromosome.

Every species of eukaryote has its characteristic number of chromosomes. The number differs from one species to the next, with little relation between number and genome size. Despite variation in number, the rule that chromosomes come in pairs holds up pretty well, with the exception of the sex chromosomes.

Polyploids, too, are an exception, but even in polyploids the number of copies of each homologous chromosome is usually an even number, so there are pairs of homologs after all.

The occurrence of chromosomes in pairs allows eukaryotes to reproduce sexually. When reproductive cells are formed during meiotic cell division, each cell receives one and only one copy of each of the pairs of homologous chromosomes (Chapter 11). When reproductive cells from two individuals fuse to form an offspring cell, the chromosome number characteristic of the species is reconstituted.

Organelle DNA forms nucleoids that differ from those in bacteria.

Most eukaryotic cells contain mitochondria, and many contain chloroplasts. Each type of organelle has its own DNA, meaning that eukaryotic cells have multiple genomes. Each has a **nuclear genome** consisting of the DNA in the chromosomes. Cells with mitochondria also have a **mitochondrial genome**, and those with chloroplasts also have a **chloroplast genome**.

Because the genome organization and mechanisms of protein synthesis in these organelles resemble those of bacteria, most biologists subscribe to the theory that the organelles originated as free-living bacterial cells that were engulfed by primitive eukaryotic cells billions of years ago (Chapter 27). In Chapters 7

FIG. 13.15 **Giemsa bands in a karyotype of a human male.** Each dashed line marks the position of the centromere.

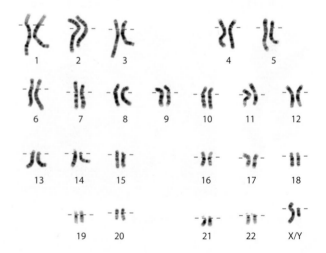

and 8, we saw that the likely ancestor of mitochondria resembled a group of today's non-photosynthetic bacteria (a group that includes *E. coli*), and the likely ancestor of chloroplasts resembled today's photosynthetic cyanobacteria. In both cases, the DNA of the organelles became smaller during the course of evolution because most of the genes were transferred to the DNA in the nucleus. If the products of these transferred genes are needed in the organelles, they are synthesized in the cytoplasm and targeted for entry into the organelles by signal peptides (Chapter 5).

DNA in mitochondria and chloroplasts is often but not always circular, and there are usually multiple copies per organelle. Among animals, the size of a mitochondrial DNA molecule ranges

from 14 kb to 18 kb. Mitochondrial DNA in plants is generally much larger, up to 100 kb. Plant chloroplast DNA is more uniform in size than mitochondrial DNA, with a range of 130 to 200 kb.

On the basis of size alone, some kind of packaging of organelle DNA is necessary. For example, the mitochondrial DNA in human cells is a circular molecule of 16 kb. Fully extended, it would have a circumference about as large as that of the mitochodrion itself. From their bacterial origin, you might expect organelle DNA to be packaged as a nucleoid rather than as a chromosome, and indeed it is. But the structures of the nucleoid in mitochondria and chloroplasts differ from each other, and also differ from those in free-living bacteria.

Core Concepts Summary

13.1 A GENOME IS ALL THE GENETIC MATERIAL OF AN ORGANISM TRANSMITTED FROM PARENTS TO OFFSPRING, AND ITS SEQUENCE IS THE ORDER OF BASES ALONG A DNA MOLECULE.

The sequence of an organism's genome can be determined by breaking up the genome into small fragments, sequencing these fragments, and then putting the sequences together at their overlaps. page 13-2

Sequences that are repeated in the genome can make sequence assembly difficult. page 13-2

13.2 RESEARCHERS ANNOTATE GENOME SEQUENCES TO IDENTIFY GENES AND OTHER FUNCTIONAL ELEMENTS.

Genome annotation is the process by which the types and locations of the different types of sequences, such as protein-coding genes, are identified. page 13-4

Genome annotation sometimes involves scanning the DNA sequence for characteristic sequence motifs. page 13-5

Comparison of DNA sequences with messenger RNA sequences reveals the intron–exon structure of protein-coding genes. page 13-6

By comparing annotated genomes of different organisms, we can gain insight into their ancestry and evolution. page 13-6

The annotated HIV genome shows it is a retrovirus, and it contains the genes *gag*, *pol*, and *env*. page 13-7

13.3 THE NUMBER OF GENES IN A GENOME AND THE SIZE OF A GENOME DO NOT CORRELATE WELL WITH THE COMPLEXITY OF AN ORGANISM.

Humans have just 25,000 protein-coding genes, a smaller

number than was predicted on the basis of number of cells or overall complexity. page 13-8

Viruses, bacteria, and archaeons have small, compact genomes. page 13-8

The C-value paradox describes the observation that the size of a genome (measured by its C-value) does not correlate with an organism's complexity. page 13-9

In eukaryotes, the C-value paradox can be explained by differences in the amount of noncoding DNA. Some genomes have a lot of noncoding DNA; others do not. page 13-10

13.4 THE ORDERLY PACKAGING OF DNA ALLOWS IT TO CARRY OUT ITS FUNCTIONS AND FIT INSIDE THE CELL.

Bacteria package their circular DNA in a structure called a nucleoid. page 13-11

Eukaryotic cells package their DNA into linear chromosomes. page 13-13

DNA in eukaryotes is wound around groups of histone proteins called nucleosomes, which in turn coil to form higher-order structures, such as the 30-nm fiber. page 13-13

Diploid organisms have two copies of each chromosome, and these two copies are called homologous chromosomes. page 13-13

Humans have 23 pairs of chromosomes, including the X and Y sex-chromosome pair. Females are XX, and males are XY. page 13-14

The genomes of mitochondria and chloroplasts are organized into nucleoids that resemble, but are distinct from, those of bacteria. page 13-14

Self-Assessment

1. Define the term "genome."

2. Describe a method for determining the complete genome sequence of an organism.

3. Given that the human genome has been sequenced, why might it be useful to sequence your own genome?

4. Describe several types of sequence present in many genomes.

5. Explain the purpose of genome annotation.

6. Describe how the comparison of genomic DNA to messenger RNA can identify the exons and introns in a gene.

7. Explain how comparing the sequences of two genomes can help to infer evolutionary relationships.

8. Define the C-value paradox and explain why it is a paradox.

9. Compare and contrast the mechanisms by which bacterial cells and eukaryotic cells package their DNA.

10. Define "homologous chromosomes" and describe a technique that you could use to show their similarity.

Do you understand the chapter's Core Concepts? Log into BIO*PORTAL* to check your answers to the Self-Assessment questions, then practice what you've learned and reinforce this chapter's concepts by working through the problems and multimedia tutorials provided there.

📶 http://courses.bfwpub.com/yourbioportal/index.php

CHAPTER 14

MUTATION AND DNA REPAIR

Core Concepts

14.1 Mutations are very rare for any given nucleotide and occur randomly without regard to the needs of an organism.

14.2 Small-scale mutations include point mutations, insertions and deletions, and movement of transposable elements.

14.3 Chromosomal mutations involve large regions of one or more chromosomes.

14.4 DNA can be damaged by mutagens, but most DNA damage is repaired.

The sequencing of the human genome was a great step forward. However, as we saw in the previous chapter, it is a simplification to speak of *the* human genome. Virtually all species have abundant amounts of genetic variation, that is, different nucleotides at the same site. Hence the accepted human genome sequence is actually a composite, displaying the most common nucleotide at most sites.

Differences among genomes arise from **mutations.** Any heritable change in the genetic material is a mutation, and by "heritable" we mean that the mutation is stable and therefore passed on through cell division (meiotic cell division, mitotic cell division, or binary fission). The process by which mutations occur is fundamental in biology because mutation is the ultimate source of genetic variation, which accounts in part for the physical differences we see among individuals, such as differences in hair color, eye color, and height. And, on a much larger scale, genetic variation results in the diversity of organisms on this planet, from bacteria to blue whales.

There are many different types of mutation, from small changes affecting a single base to larger alterations, such as the duplication or deletion of a segment of a chromosome, that affect one or more chromosomes. In this chapter, we examine some of the basic principles of mutation: the different types of mutation, how and when they occur, and how they are repaired. In Chapter 15, we look at common types of mutation, or genetic variation, present in populations, and, in Chapter 16, at how this variation is inherited from one generation to the next.

14.1 THE RATE AND NATURE OF MUTATIONS

Most mutations are **spontaneous,** occurring by chance in the absence of any assignable cause. They also occur randomly, unconnected to an organism's needs—it makes no difference whether or not a given mutation would benefit the organism. Whether a favorable mutation does or does not occur is purely a matter of chance. This key principle, that mutations are spontaneous and random, as well as other basic features of mutation, are discussed in this section.

For individual nucleotides, mutation is a rare event.

For any individual nucleotide, mutation is a very rare event, and the rate of mutation varies among organisms. **Fig. 14.1** compares the probability of the occurrence of a new mutation in a given base pair in a single round of replication in different organisms. As seen in the graph, the mutation rates for different organisms range across almost eight orders of magnitude.

The highest rates of mutation per nucleotide per replication are found among RNA viruses and retroviruses, including HIV. Lower rates occur in DNA viruses, and even lower rates in unicellular organisms such as bacteria and yeast. The rates of mutation

FIG. 14.1   Mutation rate. The rate of mutation per nucleotide per replication varies among organisms.

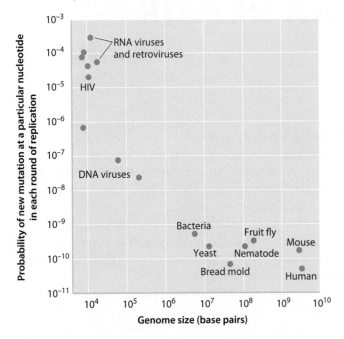

mutations that occur in **germ cells** (the reproductive cells and the cells that give rise to them) and mutations that occur in **somatic cells** (the other cells of the body). In mammals, the rate of mutation per nucleotide per replication is greater in somatic cells than in germ-line cells.

Across the genome as a whole, mutation is common.

So far, we have considered the mutation rate for any given nucleotide, which varies from organism to organism, but in all cases is relatively small. For a particular cell, the overall mutation rate depends on the number of times DNA replication occurs and the size of the genome. In multicellular organisms, there are sometimes many cycles of DNA replication and cell division that take place in the germ line before meiosis and the formation of reproductive cells. In a human male at age 30, for example, about 400 cycles of DNA replication and cell division take place before meiosis. Therefore, the overall rate of mutation per nucleotide in sperm is 400 times greater than the rate per single cycle of replication plotted in Fig. 14.1. Furthermore, some genomes are much larger than others (Chapter 13), and across a genome as a whole, there will be a greater number of mutations per genome in large genomes than in small ones.

Fig. 14.2 shows the average number of mutations for a genome in an organismal generation for the same organisms

per nucleotide per DNA replication are nearly the same for all multicellular animals, including mice and humans.

It is unclear why the rates vary over such a large range. RNA viruses and retroviruses might be expected to have a relatively high rate of mutation, first because the backbone of an RNA strand is more prone to spontaneous breakage than that of a DNA strand, and second because the replication of these genomes lacks a proofreading function. For the other genomes, the rate of mutation per nucleotide per DNA replication might simply reflect the limits of proofreading and other repair mechanisms. Some mutations must inevitably occur because of chemical errors such as base mispairing and DNA-strand breakage.

For the cellular organisms plotted in Fig. 14.1, the average probability of a new mutation per DNA replication is about 10^{-10}, which means that, on average, only 1 nucleotide in every 10 billion is mistakenly substituted for another.

But averaging conceals many details. First, certain nucleotides are especially prone to mutation and can exhibit rates of mutation that are greater than the average by a factor of 10 or more. Sites in the genome that are especially mutable are called **hotspots.** Second, in some multicellular organisms, the rates of mutation differ between the sexes. In humans, for example, the rate of mutation is substantially greater in males than in females. Finally, the rates for the multicellular animals plotted in Fig. 14.1 depend on the type of cell: A distinction must be made between

FIG. 14.2   The average number of new mutations per genome per organismal generation.

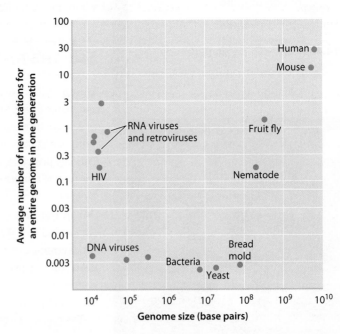

as shown in Fig. 14.1, but in this case taking into account the number of germ-line cell divisions as well as genome size. The picture is now quite different. For the DNA viruses, bacteria, and fungi (the bread mold), the average number of new mutations per genome per generation is remarkably similar, about 0.003. This number indicates that, in bacteria and fungi, roughly one cell division in every eight yields a daughter cell with a new mutation somewhere in the genome.

For RNA viruses and retroviruses, the average number of new mutations per genome reflects the high rate of mutation per nucleotide seen in Fig. 14.1. Among multicellular animals, the average number of new mutations per genome reflects the effects of multiple germ-line cell divisions per generation of organisms as well as larger genome size. It is these mutations, accumulated through many generations and shuffled by recombination and independent assortment (Chapter 11), that account for the genetic diversity of most populations and the genetic uniqueness of each individual.

Such a large number of new mutations as occurs in the human genome would be intolerable in organisms with a high density of protein-coding genes, such as bacteria or fungi. It is tolerable in humans and other mammals only because a mere 2.5% of the genome codes for protein (Chapter 13). The vast majority of new mutations therefore occur in noncoding DNA and are neutral or very nearly neutral in their effects.

Only germ-line mutations are transmitted to progeny.

Which is more important—the rate of mutation per cycle of DNA replication or the rate of mutation per organismal generation? That depends on context. Mutations can take place in any type of cell. Those that occur in eggs and sperm and the cells that give rise to these reproductive cells are called **germ-line mutations,** and those in nonreproductive cells are called **somatic mutations.** This distinction is important because somatic mutations affect only the individual in which they occur. In other words, they are not transmitted to future generations. In contrast, germ-line mutations are transmitted to future generations because they occur in reproductive cells.

For germ-line mutations, it is the rate of mutation per organismal generation that matters most. Germ-line mutations are important to the evolutionary process because, through transmission between generations, they may eventually come to be present in many individuals descended from the original carrier.

For somatic mutations, the mutation rate that matters is the rate of mutation per cycle of DNA replication. Although somatic mutations are not transmitted to future generations,

FIG. 14.3 **Somatic mutation.** Somatic mutations in the Japanese morning glory (*Ipomoea nil*) in cell lineages that differ in their ability to make purple pigment cause sectors of different pigmentation in the flower.

they are transmitted to progeny cells in mitotic cell divisions (Chapter 11). Hence, a somatic mutation affects not only the cell in which it occurs, but also all the cells that descend from it. The areas of different color or pattern that appear in "sectored" flowers, valued as ornamental plants (**Fig. 14.3**), are usually due to somatic mutations in flower-color genes. A mutation in a flower-color gene occurs in one cell, and as it replicates during development of the flower, all its descendants in the cell lineage—the generations of cells that originate from a single ancestral cell—carry that mutation, producing a sector with altered coloration.

Most cancers result from mutations in somatic cells (Chapter 11). In some cases, the mutation increases the activity of a gene that promotes cell growth and division, while in other cases, it decreases the activity of a gene that restrains cell growth and division. In either event, the mutant cell and its descendants escape from one of the normal control processes. Fortunately, a single somatic mutation is usually not sufficient to cause cancer—usually two or three or more mutations in different genes are required to derail control of normal cell division so extensively that cancer results.

To cause cancer, the mutations must all be present in the same cell lineage, which means that they all must have occurred

FIG. 14.4 Three somatic mutations implicated in the origin of invasive colon cancer. These mutations must occur in the same cell lineage for cancer to develop.

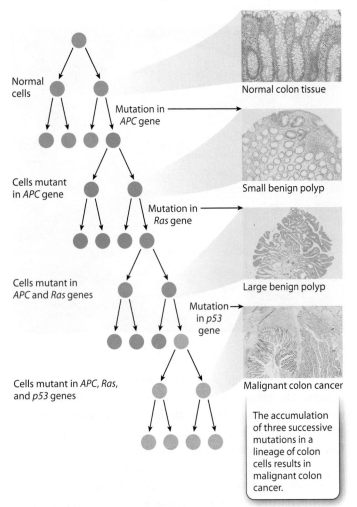

Normal cells

Mutation in *APC* gene

Normal colon tissue

Cells mutant in *APC* gene

Small benign polyp

Mutation in *Ras* gene

Cells mutant in *APC* and *Ras* genes

Large benign polyp

Mutation in *p53* gene

Cells mutant in *APC*, *Ras*, and *p53* genes

Malignant colon cancer

The accumulation of three successive mutations in a lineage of colon cells results in malignant colon cancer.

in the same original cell. **Fig. 14.4** shows three key mutations that have been implicated in the origin of invasive colon cancer: *p53*, *Ras*, and *APC*. Each mutation occurs randomly, but if, by chance, a mutation in the *Ras* gene occurs in a cell that is derived from one in which the *APC* gene has been mutated, that cell's progeny forms a polyp. Another chance mutation in the same cell line, which now carries mutations in both the *APC* and *Ras* genes, could lead to malignant cancer. Normally, the occurrence of multiple mutations in a single cell lineage is rare, but in people exposed to chemicals that cause mutations or who carry mutations in DNA repair processes, multiple mutations in a single cell lineage are more likely to occur and so the risk of cancer is increased.

? CASE 3 You, From A To T: Your Personal Genome
What can your personal genome tell you about your genetic risk factors?

Cancer is usually due to a series of mutations that occur sequentially in a single lineage of somatic cells, as illustrated for colon cancer in Fig. 14.4. Each type of cancer is caused by its own particular sequence of mutations, although some genes are implicated in several different types of cancer. An example is the *p53* gene, the product of which detects DNA damage and slows the cell cycle to allow time for DNA repair (Chapter 11). Mutations in *p53* are one step in the mutational progression of many different types of cancer, including colon cancer and breast cancer.

In most individuals with cancer, all the sequential mutations that cause the cancer are spontaneous mutations that take place in somatic cells. They are not transmitted through the germ line, and so there is little or no increased risk of cancer in the offspring. In some families, however, there is a germ-line mutation in one of the genes implicated in cancer that is transmitted from parents to their children. In any child who inherits the mutation, all cells in the body contain the defective gene, and hence the cells already have taken one of the mutational steps that lead to cancer. The effect of such a germ-line mutation is therefore to reduce the number of additional mutations that would otherwise be necessary to produce cancer cells.

Any mutation that increases the risk of disease in an individual is known as a **genetic risk factor** for that disease. For colon cancer, the major genetic risk factors are mutations in *APC*, *Ras*, and *p53*. For breast cancer, the major genetic risk factors are mutations in the *BRCA1* and *BRCA2* genes (Case 3: You, From A to T). A risk factor does not cause the disease, but it makes the disease more likely to occur. For the genes implicated in colon cancer, each is a risk factor because, when a mutation is present, only two more mutations are needed for the cancer to form, whereas in its absence three mutations are required. Because a cell lineage is much more likely to undergo two mutations than three, a mutation in each of the genes implicated in colon cancer is a risk factor that substantially increases the likelihood of the disease.

The DNA sequence of each of our personal genomes can reveal the genetic risk factors that each of us carries, not only for cancer but for many other diseases as well. Not all genetic risk factors are known for all diseases, and a great deal of current research aims to identify new ones. But many genetic risk factors are already known for a large number of common diseases, including high blood pressure, diabetes, inflammatory bowel disease, age-related macular degeneration, Alzheimer's disease, and many forms of cancer. Therefore, your personal genome can be of great value in identifying diseases for which you carry risk factors, as was the case for Claudia Gilmore (Case 3: You, From A to T).

Our personal genomes can identify only *genetic* risk factors, however. In many cases, disease risk is substantially increased by environmental risk factors as well, especially lifestyle choices. While there are genetic risk factors for lung cancer, for example, the single biggest environmental risk factor is cigarette smoking. For skin cancer, the greatest environmental risk factor is exposure to the damaging ultraviolet rays in sunlight. For heart disease, it is smoking, lack of physical activity, and obesity. For diabetes, it is an unhealthy diet.

For breast cancer, the environmental risk factors include certain forms of hormone therapy, lack of physical activity, and alcohol. While we may not be able to do much about the genetic risk factors for any of these conditions, knowing that we have them may make us more careful about the lifestyle choices that we make.

Mutations are random with regard to an organism's needs.

How do mutations arise? Consider the following example: If an antibiotic is added to a liquid culture of bacterial cells that are growing and dividing, most of the cells are killed, but a few survivors continue to grow and divide. These survivors are found to contain mutations that confer resistance to the antibiotic. This simple observation raises a profound question. Does this experiment reveal the presence of individual bacteria with mutations that had arisen spontaneously and were already present? Or do the antibiotic-resistant mutants arise in response to the presence of the antibiotic?

These alternative hypotheses had deep implications for all of biology because they suggested two very different ways in which mutations might arise. The first suggested that mutations occur without regard to the needs of an organism. According to this hypothesis, the presence of the antibiotic in the experiment with bacterial cells would not direct or induce antibiotic resistance in the cells, but instead would allow the small number of preexisting antibiotic-resistant mutants to flourish at the expense of the antibiotic-sensitive cells. The second hypothesis suggested that there is some sort of feedback between the needs of an organism and the process of mutation, and the environment directs specific mutations that would be beneficial to the organism.

To distinguish between these two hypotheses, in 1952 Joshua and Esther Lederberg carried out a now-famous experiment, described in **Fig. 14.5.** Bacterial cells were grown and formed

colonies on agar plates in the absence of antibiotic. Then, using a technique they invented called replica plating, the Lederbergs transferred these colonies to new plates containing antibiotic. Only bacteria that were resistant to the antibiotic grew on the new plates. Because replica plating preserved the arrangement of the colonies, the Lederbergs were able to go back to the original plate and identify the colony that produced the antibiotic-resistant colony on the replica plate. From that original colony, they were then able to isolate a pure culture of antibiotic-resistant bacteria.

Replica plating allowed the Lederbergs to isolate a pure culture of antibiotic-resistant bacteria, even though the original bacteria actually never were exposed to antibiotic. This result supported the first hypothesis: Mutations occur randomly, and without regard to the needs of the organisms. The role of the environment is not to create specific mutations, but instead to select them. The principle the Lederbergs demonstrated is true of all organisms so far examined.

→ **Quick Check 1** If mutations occur at random with respect to an organism's needs, then how does a species become more adapted to its environment over time?

14.2 SMALL-SCALE MUTATIONS

At the molecular level, a mutation is a change in the nucleotide sequence of a genome. Such changes can be small, affecting one or a few bases, or large, affecting entire chromosomes. We begin by considering the origin and effects of small-scale changes to the DNA sequence. While mutation provides the raw material that allows evolution to take place, it can play this role only because of an important feature of living systems: Once a mutation has taken place in a gene, the mutant genome is replicated as faithfully as the nonmutant genome.

Point mutations are changes in a single nucleotide.

Most DNA damage or errors in replication are immediately removed or corrected by specialized enzymes in the cell. (Some examples of DNA repair will be discussed in section 14.4.) We have already seen one example of DNA repair, the proofreading function of DNA polymerase, which acts to remove an incorrect nucleotide from the 3′ end of growing DNA strand (see Fig. 12.7). Damage that is corrected is not regarded as a mutation because the DNA sequence is immediately restored to its original state.

If a change in DNA is to become stable and subsequently inherited through mitotic or meiotic cell divisions, it must escape correction by the DNA repair systems. The example in

FIG. 14.5

Do mutations occur randomly, or are they directed by the environment?

BACKGROUND Researchers have long observed that beneficial mutations tend to persist in environments where they are useful— in the presence of antibiotic, bacteria become antibiotic resistant; in the presence of insecticides, insects become insecticide resistant.

HYPOTHESES These observations lead to two hypotheses about how a mutation, such as one that confers antibiotic resistance on bacteria, might arise. The first suggests that mutations occur randomly in bacterial populations and over time become more common in the population in the presence of antibiotic (which destroys those bacteria without the mutation). In other words, they occur randomly with respect to the needs of an organism. The second hypothesis suggests that the environment, in this case the application of antibiotic, induces or directs antibiotic resistance.

METHOD To distinguish between these two hypotheses, Joshua and Esther Lederberg developed replica plating. In this technique, bacteria are grown on agar plates, where they form colonies (Fig. 14.5a). The cells in any one colony result from the division of a single original cell, and thus they constitute a group of cells that are genetically identical except for rare mutations that occur in the course of growth and division. Then a disk of sterilized velvet is pressed onto the plate. Cells from each colony stick to the velvet disk (in mirror image, but the relative positions of the colonies are preserved). The disk is then pressed onto the surface of a fresh plate, transferring to the new plate a few cells that originate from each colony on the first agar plate, in their initial positions.

EXPERIMENT First, the Lederbergs grew bacterial colonies on medium without antibiotic, called a nonselective medium because all cells are able to grow and form colonies on it. Then, by replica plating, they transferred some cells from each colony to a plate containing antibiotic, so only antibiotic-resistant cells could multiply and form colonies. (Medium containing antibiotic is a selective medium because it "selects" for a particular attribute or element, in this case antibiotic-resistant cells.) Because replica plating preserves the arrangement of the colonies, the location of an antibiotic-resistant colony on the selective medium reveals the location of its parental colony on the nonselective plate (Fig. 14.5b). Finally, the Lederbergs were able to go back to the original colony and isolate a pure culture of antibiotic-resistant bacteria (Fig. 14.5c).

CONCLUSION The Lederbergs' replica-plating experiments demonstrated that antibiotic-resistant mutants can arise in the absence of antibiotic because at no time in the experiments did the cells on nonselective medium come into contact with the antibiotic. Only the successive generations of daughter cells carried over to selective medium by replica plating were exposed to the antibiotic. Nevertheless, by their procedure the Lederbergs were able to isolate pure colonies of antibiotic-resistant cells.

FOLLOW-UP WORK These results have been extended to other types of mutation and other organisms, suggesting that mutations are random and not directed by the environment.

SOURCE Lederberg, J., and E. M. Lederberg. 1952. "Replica Plating and Indirect Selection of Bacterial Mutants." *Journal of Bacteriology* 63:399–406.

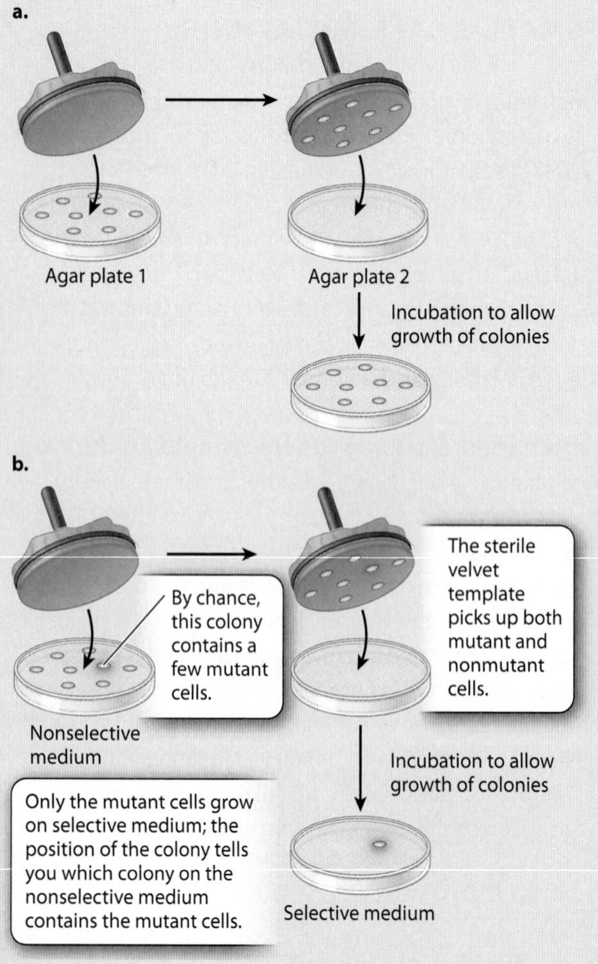

a.

Agar plate 1

Agar plate 2

Incubation to allow growth of colonies

b.

By chance, this colony contains a few mutant cells.

The sterile velvet template picks up both mutant and nonmutant cells.

Nonselective medium

Incubation to allow growth of colonies

Only the mutant cells grow on selective medium; the position of the colony tells you which colony on the nonselective medium contains the mutant cells.

Selective medium

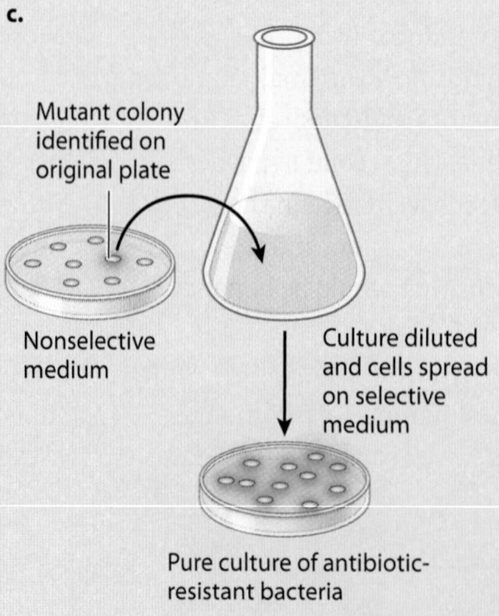

c.

Mutant colony identified on original plate

Nonselective medium

Culture diluted and cells spread on selective medium

Pure culture of antibiotic-resistant bacteria

FIG. 14.6 **A point mutation.** A point mutation is a change in a single nucleotide.

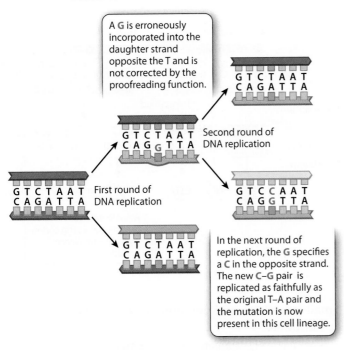

A **G** is erroneously incorporated into the daughter strand opposite the T and is not corrected by the proofreading function.

G T C T A A T
C A G A T T A

Second round of DNA replication

G T C T A A T
C A G G T T A

G T C T A A T
C A G A T T A

First round of DNA replication

G T C C A A T
C A G G T T A

G T C T A A T
C A G A T T A

In the next round of replication, the **G** specifies a **C** in the opposite strand. The new **C–G** pair is replicated as faithfully as the original T–A pair and the mutation is now present in this cell lineage.

Fig. 14.6 shows how a mutation incorporated during replication can become a permanent change to the genome. The figure shows the replication of a DNA molecule in which a T–A base pair temporarily becomes a mismatched T–G base pair because DNA polymerase misincorporates a G into the daughter strand opposite the T in the template strand. Ordinarily, this G would be removed immediately after incorporation by the proofreading function of DNA polymerase and replaced with an A. In this example, we assume that the proofreading function failed to catch the mistake. This leaves the T–G mismatch in the double-stranded DNA, and at the next replication the G in the new template strand specifies a C in the daughter strand, with the result that the daughter DNA duplex has a perfectly matched C–G base pair. From this point forward, the DNA molecule containing the mutant C–G base pair will replicate as faithfully as the original molecule

bearing the nonmutant T–A base pair. A mutation in which one base pair (in this example, T–A) is replaced by a different base pair (in this example, C–G) is called a **nucleotide substitution** or **point mutation.** This is the most frequent type of mutation.

The effect of a point mutation depends in part on where in the genome it occurs. In many multicellular eukaryotes, including humans, the vast majority of DNA in the genome does not code for protein or RNA (Chapter 13). Most of the sequences in noncoding DNA have no known function, which may explain why many mutations in noncoding DNA have no detectable effects on the organism.

On the other hand, mutations in coding sequences do have predictable consequences in an organism. **Fig. 14.7** shows an example in the human DNA sequence coding for the amino acid chain of β- (beta-) globin, a subunit of the protein hemoglobin, which carries oxygen in red blood cells. Fig. 14.7a shows a small part of the nonmutant DNA sequence, transcription and translation of which results in incorporation of the amino acids Pro-Glu-Glu in the β-globin polypeptide.

Fig. 14.7b shows an example of a harmless nucleotide substitution in this coding sequence. The mutation consists of the substitution of an A–T base pair for the normal G–C base pair. In the mRNA, the mutation changes the normal GAG codon into the mutant GAA codon. But GAG and GAA both code for the same amino acid, glutamic acid (Glu). In other words, they are synonymous codons, and so the resulting amino acid sequences are the same: Pro-Glu-Glu. Such mutations are called **synonymous (silent) mutations.** This example is typical in that the synonymous codons differ at their third position (the 3′ end of the codon).

FIG. 14.7 **Synonymous and nonsynonymous mutations.** Synonymous mutations do not change the amino acid sequence. Nonsynonymous mutations change the amino acid sequence.

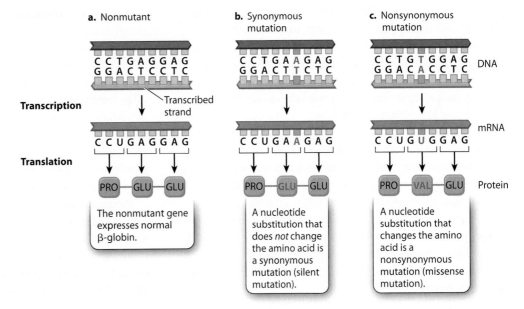

a. Nonmutant

C C T G A G G A G
G G A C T C C T C

Transcription

Transcribed strand

C C U G A G G A G

Translation

PRO — GLU — GLU

The nonmutant gene expresses normal β-globin.

b. Synonymous mutation

C C T G A A G A G
G G A C T T C T C

C C U G A A G A G

PRO — GLU — GLU

A nucleotide substitution that does *not* change the amino acid is a synonymous mutation (silent mutation).

c. Nonsynonymous mutation

C C T G T G G A G
G G A C A C C T C   DNA

C C U G U G G A G   mRNA

PRO — VAL — GLU   Protein

A nucleotide substitution that changes the amino acid is a nonsynonymous mutation (missense mutation).

A quick look at the genetic code (see Table 4.1) shows that most amino acids can be specified by synonymous codons, and that in most cases the synonymous codons differ in the identity of the nucleotide at the third position.

On the other hand, a point mutation in coding sequences can sometimes have a drastic effect on an organism. Fig. 14.7c shows such an example. In this case, a point mutation substitutes the first A–T base pair for a T–A base pair. The result is a change in the mRNA from GAG, which specifies Glu (glutamic acid), into GUG, which specifies Val (valine). The resulting protein therefore contains the amino acids Pro–Val–Glu instead of Pro–Glu–Glu. In other words, the nucleotide substitution results in an **amino acid replacement.** Point mutations that cause amino acid replacements are called **nonsynonymous (missense) mutations.**

Since the complete β-globin chain consists of 146 amino acids, it may seem that a change in only one amino acid would have little effect. But the change in even a single amino acid can affect the three-dimensional structure of a protein, and therefore change its ability to function. Individuals who inherit two copies of the mutant β-globin gene that specifies the Glu-to-Val replacement have a disease known as **sickle-cell anemia.** In this condition, the hemoglobin molecules tend to crystallize when exposed to lower-than-normal levels of oxygen. The crystallization of hemoglobin causes the cell to collapse from its normal ellipsoidal shape into the shape of a half-moon, or "sickle." In this form, the red blood cell is unable to carry the normal amount of oxygen. More important, the sickled cells tend to block tiny capillary vessels, interrupting the blood supply to vital tissues and organs.

Children with sickle-cell anemia tire easily, may be slow in their physical development, and tend to be susceptible to infections as a result of their general weakened condition brought on by the reduced amount of normal hemoglobin. Occasionally, those affected experience sickle-cell crises marked by fever and severe, incapacitating pains in the joints, particularly in the extremities, and in the chest, back, and abdomen. The pains are caused by the clogging of the blood supply to these vital areas. The painful episodes may last from hours to days to weeks and may be provoked by anything that lowers the oxygen supply: overexertion, high altitude, or respiratory ailments.

Fig. 14.8 shows a third way that a point mutation can affect a protein, one that nearly always has severe effects. This is a **nonsense mutation,** which creates a stop codon that terminates translation. In the example in Fig. 14.8, the mutation creates a UAG codon in the mRNA. Because UAG is a translational stop codon, the resulting polypeptide terminates after Pro. Polypeptides that are truncated are nearly always nonfunctional. They are also unstable and are quickly destroyed. Eukaryotic cells have mechanisms to destroy mRNA molecules that contain premature stop codons.

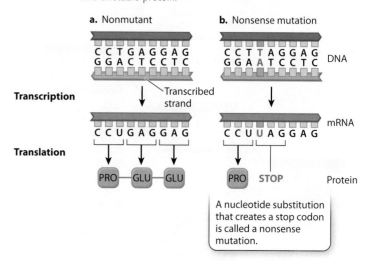

FIG. 14.8   **A nonsense mutation.** A nonsense mutation can change an amino acid to a stop codon, resulting in a shortened and unstable protein.

A nucleotide substitution that creates a stop codon is called a nonsense mutation.

Small insertions and deletions involve several nucleotides.

Another relatively common type of mutation is the deletion or insertion of a small number of nucleotides. In noncoding DNA, such mutations have little or no effect. In protein-coding regions, their effects depend on their size. A small deletion or insertion that is an exact multiple of three nucleotides results in a polypeptide with as many fewer (in the case of a deletion) or more (in the case of an insertion) amino acids as there are codons deleted or inserted. Thus, a deletion of three nucleotides eliminates one amino acid, and an insertion of six adds two amino acids.

The effects of a deletion of three nucleotides can be seen in cystic fibrosis. This disease is characterized by the production of abnormal secretions in the lungs, liver, and pancreas and other glands. Its chief symptoms are recurrent respiratory infections, malnutrition resulting from incomplete digestion and absorption of fats and proteins, and liver disease. Patients with cystic fibrosis have an accumulation of thick, sticky mucus in their lungs, which often leads to respiratory complications, including recurrent bacterial infections. Untreated, 95% of affected children die before age 5. With proper medical care, including regular physical therapy to clear the lungs, antibiotics, pancreatic enzyme supplements, and good nutrition, the average life expectancy is currently 30 to 40 years.

The mutations responsible for cystic fibrosis are in the gene encoding the cystic fibrosis transmembrane conductance regulator (CFTR) (**Fig. 14.9**). The CFTR protein is a chloride channel, which acts as a transporter to pump chloride ions out of the cell. Malfunction of CFTR causes ion imbalances that result in abnormal secretions from the many cell types in

FIG. 14.9 CFTR, the cystic fibrosis transmembrane conductance regulator.

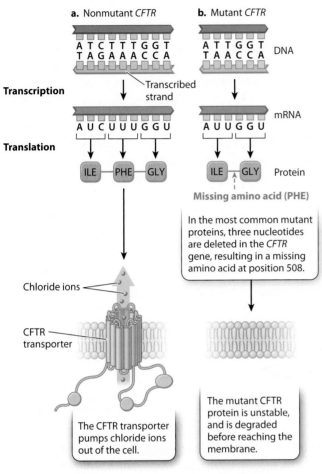

a. Nonmutant *CFTR*

b. Mutant *CFTR*

In the most common mutant proteins, three nucleotides are deleted in the *CFTR* gene, resulting in a missing amino acid at position 508.

The CFTR transporter pumps chloride ions out of the cell.

The mutant CFTR protein is unstable, and is degraded before reaching the membrane.

which the *CFTR* gene is expressed. About 70% of the mutations associated with cystic fibrosis have a specific mutation known as Δ508 (*delta 508*), which is a deletion of three nucleotides that eliminates a phenylalanine normally present at position 508 in the protein. The missing amino acid results in a CFTR protein that does not fold properly and is degraded before reaching the membrane. Some researchers hope that future therapy will include drugs that stabilize the mutant protein or even treatments that repair the defective gene in affected cells.

Small deletions or insertions that are not exact multiples of 3 can cause changes in amino acid sequence because they do not insert or delete entire codons. The effect of such a mutation can be appreciated by seeing how deletion of a single letter turns a perfectly sensible sentence of three-letter words into gibberish. Consider the sentence:

THE BIG BOY SAW THE CAT EAT THE BUG

If the red E is deleted, the new reading frame for three-letter words is as follows:

THB IGB OYS AWT HEC ATE ATT HEB UG

The result is unintelligible. Similarly, an insertion of a single nucleotide causes a one-nucleotide shift in the reading frame of the mRNA, and it changes all codons following the site of insertion. For this reason, such mutations are called **frameshift mutations.**

Fig. 14.10 shows the consequences of a frameshift mutation in the β-globin gene. The normal sequence in Fig. 14.10a corresponds to amino acids 5–10. The frameshift mutation in Fig. 14.10b is caused by the insertion of a C–G base pair. The mRNA transcript of the DNA therefore also has a single-base insertion. When this mRNA is translated, the one-nucleotide shift in the reading frame results in an amino acid sequence that has no resemblance to the original protein. All amino acids downstream of the site of insertion are changed, resulting in loss of protein function.

→ **Quick Check 2** The coding sequence of genes that specify proteins with the same function in related species sometimes include an insertion or deletion of contiguous nucleotides. The number of nucleotides that are inserted or deleted is almost always an exact multiple of 3. Why is this expected?

FIG. 14.10 A frameshift mutation. A frameshift mutation changes the translational reading frame.

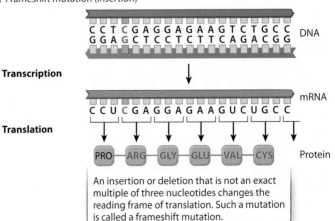

a. Nonmutant

b. Frameshift mutation (insertion)

An insertion or deletion that is not an exact multiple of three nucleotides changes the reading frame of translation. Such a mutation is called a frameshift mutation.

FIG. 14.11

What causes sectoring in corn kernels?

BACKGROUND In the late 1940s, Barbara McClintock discovered what are now called transposable elements, DNA sequences that can move from one position to another in the genome. She studied corn (*Zea mays*). Wild-type corn has purple kernels, resulting from expression of purple anthocyanin pigment (Fig. 14.11a). A mutant with yellow kernels results from lack of purple anthocyanin pigment. McClintock noticed that streaks of purple pigmentation could be seen in many yellow kernels (Fig. 14.11b). This observation indicated that the mutation causing yellow color was unstable and could revert to the normal purple color.

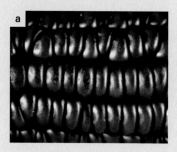

HYPOTHESIS McClintock hypothesized that the yellow mutant color resulted from a transposable element, which she called *Dissociator* (*Ds*), jumping into a site near or in the anthocyanin gene and disrupting its function. She attributed the purple streaks to cell lineages in which the transposable element had jumped out again, restoring the anthocyanin gene.

EXPERIMENT AND RESULTS By a series of genetic crosses, McClintock showed that the genetic instability of *Ds* was due to something on another chromosome that she called *Activator* (*Ac*). She set up crosses in which she could track the *Ac*-bearing chromosome. She observed that in the presence of *Ac*, mutant yellow kernels

reverted to normal purple, resulting in purple sectors in an otherwise yellow kernel. From this observation, she inferred that the *Ds* element had jumped out of the anthocyanin gene, restoring its function. She also demonstrated that restoration of the original purple color was associated with mutations elsewhere in the genome. From this observation, she inferred that the *Ds* element had integrated elsewhere in the genome, where it disrupted the function of another gene.

CONCLUSION McClintock's conclusion is illustrated in Fig. 14.11c: Transposable elements can be excised from their original position in the genome and inserted into another position.

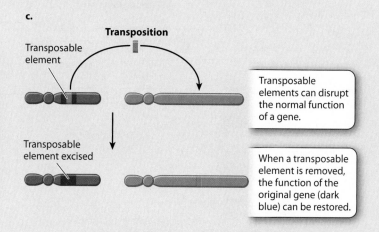

FOLLOW-UP WORK McClintock won the Nobel Prize in Physiology or Medicine in 1983. Later experiments showed that *Ds* is a transposable element that lacks a functional gene for transposase, the protein needed for the element to move, and *Ac* is a transposable element that encodes transposase. Presence of *Ac* produces active transposase that allows *Ds* to move. Much additional work showed that there are many different types of transposable element and that they are ubiquitous among organisms.

SOURCE McClintock, B. 1950. "The Origin and Behavior of Mutable Loci in Maize." *Proceedings of the National Academy of Sciences of the United States of America.* 36:344–355.

Some mutations are due to the insertion of a transposable element.

An important source of new mutations in many organisms is the insertion of movable DNA sequences into or near a gene. Such movable DNA sequences are called **transposable elements.** As we saw in Chapter 13, the genomes of virtually all organisms contain several types of transposable element, each present in multiple copies per genome.

Transposable elements were discovered by American geneticist Barbara McClintock in the 1940s (**Fig. 14.11**).

She studied corn (maize) because genetic changes that affect pigment formation can be observed directly in the kernels. The normal color of maize kernels is purple. Each kernel consists of many cells, and if no mutations affecting pigmentation occur in a kernel, it will be uniformly purple. The kernel pigments are synthesized by enzymes in a metabolic pathway, and any of these enzymes can be rendered nonfunctional if a transposable element jumps into the gene that codes for them. Since her work, we have learned that most transposable elements are segments of DNA a thousand or more base pairs long. When such a large piece of DNA inserts into a gene, it can interfere with transcription, cause errors in RNA processing, or disrupt the open reading frame. The result in the case of maize is that the cell is unable to produce pigment, and so the kernels will be yellow.

McClintock observed that, while the kernels in the mutant corn were mostly yellow, most of them had purple sectors. Each colored sector consists of a lineage of progeny cells from a single progenitor cell in which pigment synthesis had been restored. McClintock realized that, just as the inability of the kernel cells to produce pigment was caused by a transposable element jumping into a gene, restoration of that ability could be caused by the transposable element jumping out again. Her hypothesis that transposable elements are responsible for the pigment mutations was confirmed when she found that in cells where pigment had been restored, mutations affecting other genes had also occurred. She deduced that these other mutations were due to a transposable element jumping out of a pigment gene and into a different gene in the same cell.

The movement or **transposition** of transposable elements, including those McClintock studied, requires specialized enzymes, different for each type of element, which are often encoded in the sequence of the element itself. These enzymes recognize specific sequences in the ends of the transposable element, cut it out of the DNA molecule it is in, and insert it somewhere else in the genome. In some cases, the excised transposable element leaves a copy of itself in its original position, resulting in multiple identical sequences throughout the genome as the transposable element jumps around. In other cases, the transposable element is removed entirely, leading to restoration of gene function, and the sectoring shown in Fig. 14.11b. Unstable mutations due to transposable elements can occur in almost any organism, including the Japanese morning glory, whose sectored flowers are shown in Fig. 14.3.

14.3 CHROMOSOMAL MUTATIONS

Whereas some mutations involve only one or a few nucleotides, some affect larger regions extending over thousands or millions of nucleotides, and a few have effects on chromosome structure that are large enough to be visible through a microscope. In this section, we briefly consider some of the major chromosome abnormalities. The most important are those in which the mutation affects the **centromere,** the site associated with attachment of the spindle fibers that move the chromosome during cell division (Chapter 11). An abnormal chromosome without a centromere or one with two centromeres is usually lost within a few cell divisions because it cannot be directed properly into the daughter cells during cell division.

Duplications and deletions result in gain or loss of DNA.

Among the most common chromosomal abnormalities are those in which a segment of the chromosome is either present in two copies or is missing altogether (**Fig. 14.12**). A chromosome in which a region is present twice instead of once is said to contain a **duplication** (Fig. 14.12a). Although large duplications that include hundreds or thousands of genes are usually harmful and quickly eliminated from the population, small duplications including only one or a few genes can be maintained over many generations. Usually, duplication of a region of the genome is less harmful than deletion of the same region.

An example of a **deletion,** in which a region of the chromosome is missing, is shown in Fig. 14.12b. A deletion can result from an error in replication or from the joining of breaks in a chromosome that occur on either side of the deleted region. Even though a deletion may eliminate a gene that is essential for survival, the deletion can persist in the population because chromosomes usually occur in homologous pairs. If one member of a homologous pair has a deletion of an essential gene but the gene is present in the other member of the pair, that one copy of the gene is often sufficient for survival and reproduction. In these cases, the deletion can be transmitted from generation to generation and persist harmlessly, as long as the chromosome is present along with a normal chromosome.

But some deletions decrease the chance of survival or reproduction of an organism even when the homologous chromosome is normal. In general, the larger the deletion, the smaller the chance of survival. In the fruit fly *Drosophila,* individuals with deletions of more than 100–150 genes rarely survive even when the homologous chromosome is normal. The interpretation of the reduced survival is that organisms are sensitive to the **dosage,** or number of copies, of each gene. Normal embryonic development requires that genes be present in a particular dosage. Although small deviations from normal gene dosage can be tolerated, as indicated by the survival of individuals containing small duplications or deletions, the cumulative effects of large deviations from normal gene dosage are incompatible with life. It is usually not the total number of

---

FIG. 14.12 Duplication and deletion. (a) In a duplication, a segment of chromosome is repeated. (b) In a deletion, a segment of chromosome is missing.

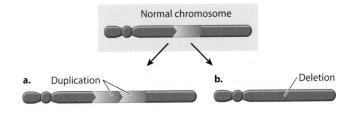

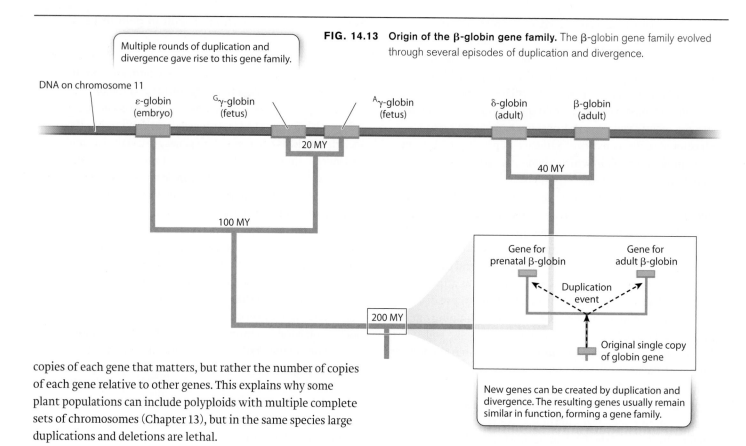

Multiple rounds of duplication and divergence gave rise to this gene family.

FIG. 14.13 **Origin of the β-globin gene family.** The β-globin gene family evolved through several episodes of duplication and divergence.

New genes can be created by duplication and divergence. The resulting genes usually remain similar in function, forming a gene family.

copies of each gene that matters, but rather the number of copies of each gene relative to other genes. This explains why some plant populations can include polyploids with multiple complete sets of chromosomes (Chapter 13), but in the same species large duplications and deletions are lethal.

Gene families arise from gene duplication and evolutionary divergence.

Small duplications play an important role in the origin of new genes in the course of evolution. In most cases, when a gene is duplicated, one of the copies is free to change without causing harm to the organism because the other copy continues to carry out the normal function of the gene. Occasionally, a mutation in the "extra" copy of the gene may result in a beneficial effect on survival or reproduction, and gradually a new gene is formed from the duplicate. These new genes usually have a function similar to that of the original gene.

This process of creating new genes from duplicates of old ones is known as **duplication and divergence.** Multiple rounds of duplication and divergence can give rise to a group of genes with related functions known as a **gene family.** The largest gene family in the human genome has about 400 genes and encodes for proteins that detect odors. These proteins are structurally very similar, but differ in the region that binds small odor molecules. It is the diversity of the odorant binding sites that allows us to identify so many different smells.

Most gene families are not as large and diverse as that for odor detection. **Fig. 14.13** shows the evolutionary origin of the family of globin genes, which in humans are spread across about 50 kb of chromosome 11. The globin gene family consists of five different genes that are expressed at various times during

development (embryo, fetus, or adult). The two γ- (gamma-) globin polypeptides are nearly identical in amino acid sequence but expressed at different levels in the fetus, whereas the adult δ- and β-polypeptides differ somewhat more and are expressed at very different levels. The sequences are all similar enough to imply that the genes arose through duplication and divergence.

Globin sequences have changed through evolutionary time at a relatively constant rate, and so the fraction of differences between any two sequences is proportional to the time since they were created by duplication. The relative constancy of rates of evolutionary change in a DNA nucleotide sequence or a protein amino acid sequence is known as a **molecular clock,** and it allows molecular differences among genomes to be correlated with the fossil record and dated accordingly (Chapter 21). For example, the earliest duplication event in the tree in **Fig. 14.13**, which produced distinct genes for fetal and adult hemoglobin, took place at about the same time (200 million years ago) that the common ancestor of today's placental mammals became a distinct species from the common ancestor of today's marsupial mammals.

An inversion has a chromosomal region reversed in orientation.

Chromosomes in which the normal order of a block of genes is reversed contain an **inversion** (**Fig. 14.14**). An inversion is typically produced when the region between two breaks in

FIG. 14.14   Inversion. A chromosome with an inversion has a segment of chromosome present in reverse orientation.

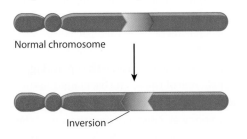

Normal chromosome

Inversion

FIG. 14.15   Reciprocal translocation. A reciprocal translocation results from an interchange of parts between nonhomologous chromosomes.

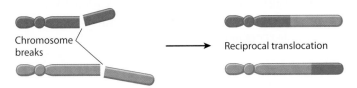

Chromosome breaks

Reciprocal translocation

a chromosome is flipped in orientation before the breaks are repaired. Especially in large genomes, the breaks are likely to occur in noncoding DNA rather than within a gene. Whereas large inversions can cause problems in meiosis, small inversions are common in many populations and play an important role in chromosome evolution. The accumulation of inversions over evolutionary time explains in part why the order of genes along a chromosome can differ even among closely related species.

A reciprocal translocation joins segments from nonhomologous chromosomes.

A **reciprocal translocation** (**Fig. 14.15**) is said to have occurred when two different (nonhomologous) chromosomes undergo an exchange of parts. In the formation of a reciprocal translocation, both chromosomes are broken and the terminal segments are exchanged before the breaks are repaired. In large genomes,

the breaks are likely to occur in noncoding DNA, so the breaks themselves do not usually disrupt gene function.

Since reciprocal translocations change only the arrangement of genes and not their number, most reciprocal translocations do not affect the survival of organisms. Proper gene dosage requires the presence of both parts of the reciprocal translocation, however, as well as one copy of each of the normal homologous chromosomes. Problems can arise in meiosis because both chromosomes involved in the reciprocal translocation may not move together into the same daughter cells, resulting in gametes with only one part of the reciprocal translocation. This inequality does upset gene dosage, because these gametes have extra copies of genes in one of the chromosomes and are missing copies of genes in the other. In the next chapter, we will see that such abnormalities are observed in a significant number of human embryos.

14.4 DNA DAMAGE AND REPAIR

DNA is a fragile molecule, prone to damage of many different kinds. Every day, in each cell in our bodies, the DNA is damaged in some way at tens of thousands of places along the molecule. Fortunately, cells have evolved mechanisms for repairing various types of damage and restoring the DNA to its original condition. In this section, we examine some of the major types of DNA damage and some of the ways in which it is repaired.

DNA damage can affect both DNA backbone and bases.

Most mutations are spontaneous, occurring without an assignable cause. However, mutations can also be induced by radiation or chemicals. **Mutagens** are agents that increase the probability of mutation. The presence of a mutagen can increase the probability of mutation by a factor of 100 or more.

Some of the most important types of DNA damage induced by mutagens are illustrated in **Fig. 14.16**, which shows a highly mutated DNA molecule. Some types of damage affect DNA structure. These include breaks in the sugar–phosphate backbone,

FIG. 14.16   Major types of DNA damage. Most types of DNA damage can be repaired by specialized enzymes.

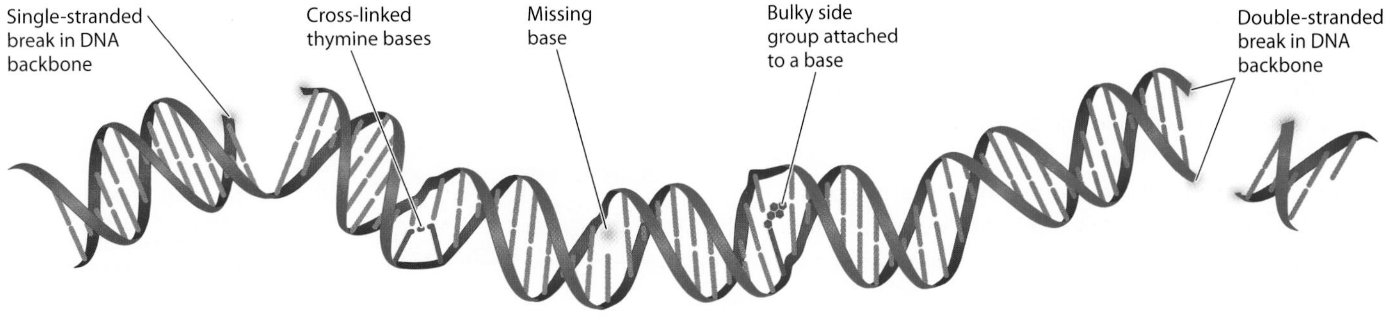

Single-stranded break in DNA backbone

Cross-linked thymine bases

Missing base

Bulky side group attached to a base

Double-stranded break in DNA backbone

one of the main mutagenic effects of X-rays. Breaks can occur in just one strand of the DNA or both. Ultraviolet light can cause cross-links between adjacent pyrimidine bases, especially thymine, resulting in the formation of thymine dimers.

Yet another type of structural damage is loss of a base from one of the deoxyribose sugars, resulting in a gap in one strand where no base is present. Spontaneous loss of a purine base is one of the most common types of DNA damage, occurring at the rate of about 13,000 purines lost per human cell per day. The rate increases with age, and it can also be increased by exposure to oxidizing agents such as household bleach or hydrogen peroxide.

Other types of damage affect the bases themselves. Bases that are chemically damaged tend to mispair. Some bases are damaged spontaneously when reaction with a water molecule replaces an amino group $(-NH_2)$ with an atom of oxygen $(=O)$. Some naturally occurring molecules mimic bases and can be incorporated into DNA and cause nucleotide substitutions. Caffeine mimics a purine base, for example (although to be mutagenic, the amount of caffeine required is far more than any normal person could possibly consume).

Chemicals that are highly reactive tend to be mutagenic, often because they add bulky side groups to the bases that hinder proper base pairing. The main environmental source of such chemicals is tobacco smoke. Other chemicals can perturb the DNA replication complex and cause the insertion or deletion of one or occasionally several nucleotides.

→   **Quick Check 3** Earlier, we described the Lederbergs' experiment, which demonstrated that mutations are not directed by the environment. But mutagens, which are environmental, can lead to mutations. What's the difference?

Most DNA damage is corrected by specialized repair enzymes.

Cells contain many specialized DNA-repair enzymes that correct specific kinds of damage, and in this section we examine a few examples. Perhaps the simplest is the repair of breaks in the sugar–phosphate backbone, which are sealed by **DNA ligase,** an enzyme that can repair the break by using the energy in ATP to join the 3′ hydroxyl of one end to the 5′ phosphate of the other end. Most organisms have multiple different types of DNA ligase, some of which participate in DNA replication (Chapter 12) and others in DNA repair. One type of ligase seals single-stranded breaks in DNA, and a different type seals double-stranded breaks. Double-stranded breaks often result in point mutations or chromosomal rearrangements because they are less likely to be repaired than single-stranded breaks. In addition to their importance in DNA replication and repair, ligases are an important tool in research in molecular biology because they allow DNA molecules from different sources to be joined to produce recombinant DNA (Chapter 12).

As we saw earlier in this chapter, mispairing of bases during DNA replication leads to the incorporation of incorrect nucleotides and potentially to nucleotide substitutions. Although 99% of the mispaired bases are corrected immediately by the proofreading function of DNA polymerase, another mechanism also scans the DNA for mismatches to afford a second level of quality control. This process is called **mismatch repair** (**Fig. 14.17**). In mismatch repair, one of the strand backbones in the vicinity of the mismatch is cleaved and then degraded nucleotide by nucleotide to a point at a distance past the site of the mismatch. Then the gap is filled by new synthesis, which corrects the mismatch.

Fig. 14.18 shows an example of a more specialized repair system called **base excision repair.** Fig. 14.18a depicts a molecule in which uracil was mistakenly incorporated into a new DNA strand instead of cytosine. Recall that uracil is normally found in mRNA, but not in DNA. Most organisms have an enzyme called DNA uracil glycosylase that cleaves the uracil from

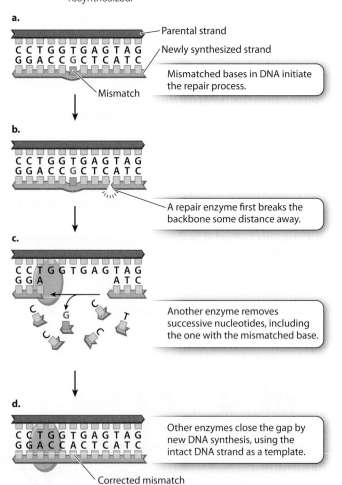

FIG. 14.17   Mismatch repair. In mismatch repair, the segment of a DNA strand containing the mismatch is removed and then resynthesized.

a.

C C T G G T G A G T A G
G G A C C G C T C A T C

Parental strand

Newly synthesized strand

Mismatched bases in DNA initiate the repair process.

Mismatch

b.

C C T G G T G A G T A G
G G A C C G C T C A T C

A repair enzyme first breaks the backbone some distance away.

c.

C C T G G T G A G T A G
G G A   A T C

Another enzyme removes successive nucleotides, including the one with the mismatched base.

d.

C C T G G T G A G T A G
G G A C C A C T C A T C

Other enzymes close the gap by new DNA synthesis, using the intact DNA strand as a template.

Corrected mismatch

FIG. 14.18 Base excision repair. In base excision repair, an improper base in DNA and its deoxyribose sugar are both removed, and the resulting gap is then repaired.

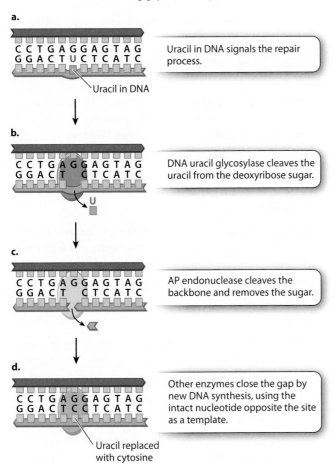

a.

Uracil in DNA signals the repair process.

Uracil in DNA

b.

DNA uracil glycosylase cleaves the uracil from the deoxyribose sugar.

c.

AP endonuclease cleaves the backbone and removes the sugar.

d.

Other enzymes close the gap by new DNA synthesis, using the intact nucleotide opposite the site as a template.

Uracil replaced with cytosine

FIG. 14.19 Nucleotide excision repair. In nucleotide excision repair, a damaged segment of a DNA strand is removed and resynthesized using the undamaged partner strand as a template.

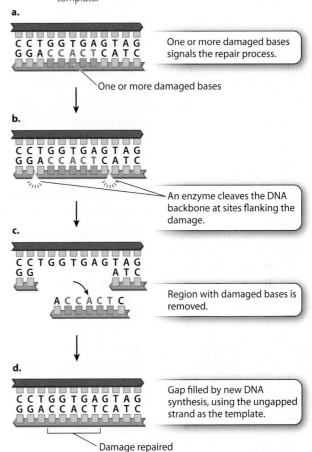

a.

One or more damaged bases signals the repair process.

One or more damaged bases

b.

An enzyme cleaves the DNA backbone at sites flanking the damage.

c.

Region with damaged bases is removed.

d.

Gap filled by new DNA synthesis, using the ungapped strand as the template.

Damage repaired

its deoxyribose sugar, resulting in a sugar in the DNA backbone lacking a base (Fig. 14.18b). Such sites are recognized by an enzyme called AP endonuclease (Fig. 14.18c), which cleaves the backbone on both sides of the sugar that lacks a base. This cleavage results in a one-nucleotide gap, which is filled by new synthesis using the intact DNA strand as a template. The result is that uracil is removed and replaced with cytosine. Fig. 14.18 shows DNA repair systems that work in tandem, in this case DNA uracyl glycosylase acting with the AP endonuclease. Other types of glycosylases remove abnormal or damaged bases from the DNA, and these enzymes are also coupled with the AP endonuclease.

Nucleotide excision repair, which is similar in some ways to mismatch repair, is illustrated in **Fig. 14.19.** The major difference is that mismatch repair operates on single mispaired bases, whereas nucleotide excision repair recognizes multiple mismatched or damaged bases across a region. The region excised in mismatch repair is small, but that in nucleotide excision repair can extend for thousands of nucleotides. Nucleotide excision

repair is also used to remove nucleotides with some types of bulky side group, as well as thymine dimers resulting from ultraviolet light.

The importance of DNA repair mechanisms is illustrated by considering what happens when they do not function properly. Xeroderma pigmentosum (XP) is a disease in which nucleotide excision repair is defective. People with XP are exquisitely sensitive to the UV radiation in sunlight. Because of the defect in nucleotide excision repair, damage to DNA resulting from UV light is not corrected, leading to the accumulation of mutations in skin cells. The result is high rates of skin cancer. People with XP must minimize their exposure to sunlight and in extreme cases stay out of the sun altogether.

When DNA repair mechanisms function properly, they reduce the rate of mutation to a level that is compatible with life. But they are not perfect, and they do not catch all the mistakes. The result is genetic variation, the raw material of evolution.

Core Concepts Summary

14.1 MUTATIONS ARE VERY RARE FOR ANY GIVEN NUCLEOTIDE AND OCCUR RANDOMLY WITHOUT REGARD TO THE NEEDS OF AN ORGANISM.

For an individual nucleotide, the frequency of mutation is very rare, though it differs among species. page 14-1

Mutations are common across an entire genome and across many cell divisions. page 14-2

Germ-line mutations occur in reproductive cells, and somatic mutations occur in nonreproductive cells. Only mutations in germ cells are transmitted to progeny and play a role in evolution. page 14-3

Mutations are random in that they occur without regard to the needs of an organism. This principle can be demonstrated by replica plating bacterial colonies in the absence and presence of antibiotic. page 14-5

14.2 SMALL-SCALE MUTATIONS INCLUDE POINT MUTATIONS, INSERTIONS AND DELETIONS, AND MOVEMENT OF TRANSPOSABLE ELEMENTS.

A point mutation, or nucleotide substitution, is a change of one base for another. page 14-5

The effect of a point mutation depends on where it occurs. If it occurs in noncoding DNA, it will likely have no effect on an organism. If it occurs in a protein-coding gene, it can result in a change of the amino acid sequence (nonsynonymous mutation), no change of the amino acid sequence (synonymous mutation), or the introduction of a stop codon (nonsense mutation). page 14-7

Small insertions or deletions in DNA add or remove one base or a few contiguous bases. Their effect depends on where in the genome they occur and on their size. An insertion of a single nucleotide in a protein-coding gene results in a frameshift mutation, in which all the codons downstream of the insertion or deletion are changed. page 14-8

Transposable elements are DNA sequences that can jump from one place in a genome to another. They can affect the expression of a gene if they insert into or near a gene. page 14-10

14.3 CHROMOSOMAL MUTATIONS INVOLVE LARGE REGIONS OF ONE OR MORE CHROMOSOMES.

A duplication is a region of the chromosome that is present two times, and a deletion is the loss of part of a chromosome. page 14-11

Duplications and deletions both affect gene dosage, which can have important effects on a cell or organism. page 14-11

Gene duplication followed by evolutionary divergence results in gene families made up of genes with related but not identical functions. page 14-12

An inversion is a segment of a chromosome in reverse orientation. page 14-12

A reciprocal translocation involves the exchange of a part of one chromosome with another. Reciprocal translocations do not affect gene dosage, but can lead to problems during meiosis. page 14-13

14.4 DNA CAN BE DAMAGED BY MUTAGENS, BUT MOST DNA DAMAGE IS REPAIRED.

Some types of damage alter the structure of DNA, such as single-stranded or double-stranded breaks, cross-linked thymine dimers, or missing bases. page 14-13

Other types of DNA damage, such as changes in the side groups that form hydrogen bonds or the addition of side groups that interfere with base pairing, affect the bases themselves. page 14-14

Common mutagens are X-rays, which cause single-stranded and double-stranded breaks, ultraviolet light, which creates thymine dimers, and reactive chemicals in cigarette smoke, which damage the bases. page 14-14

Many specialized DNA repair enzymes can correct DNA damage. page 14-14

DNA ligase seals breaks in DNA and is an important tool for molecular biologists. page 14-14

Mismatch repair provides a backup mechanism for mistakes not caught by the proofreading function of DNA polymerase. page 14-14

Base excision repair corrects individual nucleotides and involves several DNA repair enzymes working together. page 14-14

Nucleotide excision repair functions similarly to mismatch repair but excises longer stretches of damaged nucleotides. page 14-15

Self-Assessment

1. Describe different effects a mutation can have on an organism.

2. Explain the difference between the mutation rate for a given nucleotide and the mutation rate for a given cell.

3. Explain what it means to say that mutations are random.

4. Describe several types of small-scale mutation and their likely effect on an organism.

5. Explain why the location of a small-scale mutation in the genome can make a difference in the phenotype.

6. Describe the differences among silent, missense, nonsense, and frameshift mutations.

7. Describe several types of large-scale mutation and their likely effect on an organism.

8. Explain how a gene family, such as the odorant receptor gene family, is thought to have evolved.

9. Name several common mutagens and their effect on DNA.

10. Describe a DNA repair mechanism.

Do you understand the chapter's Core Concepts? Log into BIO PORTAL to check your answers to the Self-Assessment questions, then practice what you've learned and reinforce this chapter's concepts by working through the problems and multimedia tutorials provided there.

http://courses.bfwpub.com/yourbioportal/index.php

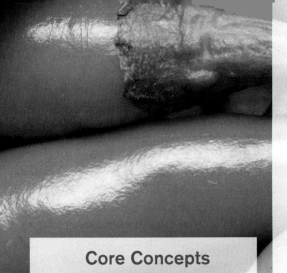

CHAPTER 15

GENETIC VARIATION

Core Concepts

15.1 Genetic variation describes common genetic differences (polymorphisms) among the individuals in a population at any given time.

15.2 Human genetic variation can be detected by DNA typing, which can uniquely identify each individual.

15.3 Two common types of genetic variation are single-nucleotide polymorphisms (SNPs) and copy-number variation (CNV).

15.4 Chromosomal variants can also occur but are usually harmful.

In the last chapter, we saw how mutations arise and what common types of mutation occur. What is the fate of all these mutations? Some, as we have seen, are corrected by DNA repair mechanisms. In this case, the DNA sequence is not changed. Some mutations escape these repair mechanisms and are replicated as faithfully as the original DNA sequence. If such mutations occur in somatic (body) cells, they can be passed on in the individual's cells through mitotic cell divisions, but they will not be passed on to progeny. If they occur in the germ line, they can be passed on to progeny. Over time, through evolution (Chapter 21), these mutations may increase or decrease in frequency. Therefore, if we look at any present-day population of organisms, such as the human population, we will find that it harbors lots of genetic differences, all of which result from mutations that occurred sometime in the past. **Genetic variation** refers to genetic differences that exist among individuals in a population at a particular point in time.

In the human population, you can observe the effects of common genetic differences or mutations by looking at the people around you. They differ in height, weight, facial features, skin color, eye color, hair color, hair texture, and in many other ways. These traits differ in part because of genetic variation, and in part because of the environment. Weight is affected by diet, for example, and skin color by exposure to sunlight.

In this chapter, we consider examples of major types of DNA and chromosomal variation in populations today and examine their consequences for the organism. We also describe key molecular techniques that allow genetic variation to be studied directly in DNA molecules. The emphasis here is primarily, but not exclusively, on human populations.

15.1 GENOTYPE AND PHENOTYPE

We tend to think of mutations as something negative or harmful; the term "mutant" ordinarily connotes something unpleasantly abnormal. But because mutations result in genetic variation among individuals and organisms, we are in fact all mutants, different from one another genetically because of mutations, that is, differences in our DNA. Whereas some mutations are harmful, some have no effect on an organism, and some indeed are beneficial. Without mutations, evolution would not be possible. Mutations generate the occasional favorable variants that allow organisms to evolve and become adapted to their environment over time (Chapter 21).

Genotype is the genetic makeup of a cell or organism; phenotype is its observed characteristics.

The genetic makeup of a cell or organism constitutes its **genotype.** A population with a gene pool that has many variants in many different genes will consist of organisms with numerous different genotypes. For example, any two human genomes are likely to differ at about 3 million nucleotide sites. Most humans have the same genes as one another, organized in the same way along the same set of chromosomes. We differ primarily from one person to the next in a very small fraction of nucleotides.

Mutations, as we have seen, are the ultimate source of differences among genotypes. If we consider any present-day population of organisms, we find that some mutations are very common. Geneticists use the term **polymorphism** to refer to any genetic difference among individuals that is sufficiently common that it would almost certainly be present in a group of 50 randomly chosen individuals. For example, if many people have an A–T pair at a particular site in the genome, but many others have a G–C pair at the same site, this difference is a polymorphism. Of course, the polymorphism is the result of a mutation. All individuals once had the same genotype at this site, but a mutation in one or a few individuals made different genotypes possible. In this example, the mutation that made either A–T or G–C possible occurred sometime in the past, and is now commonly found in the population.

Phenotype is an individual's observable characteristics or traits, such as a person's height, weight, eye color, and so forth. The phenotype may be visible, as in these characteristics, or may be seen in the development, physiology, or behavior of a cell or organism. For example, color blindness and lactose intolerance are phenotypes. The phenotype results in part from the genotype: A genotype with a mutated gene for an enzyme that would normally metabolize lactose can lead to the phenotype of lactose intolerance. However, the environment also commonly plays an important role, so it is most accurate to say that a phenotype results from an interaction between the genotype and environment. These genotype–environment interactions are discussed in Chapter 18.

The effect of a genotype often depends on several factors.

Let's examine how genotype influences phenotype with an example of a genetic polymorphism that we introduced in the previous chapter. **Fig. 15.1** shows genetic variation in the gene for β- (beta-) globin, one of the subunits of hemoglobin that carries oxygen in red blood cells. Three forms of the β-globin gene are shown in the figure: *A, S,* and *C*. These three forms of the gene are relatively common in certain African populations and in people of African descent (the mutations originated in Africa). The different forms of any gene are called **alleles,** and they correspond to different DNA sequences (polymorphisms) in the genes. In this case, the most common allele is the *A* allele, which has a GAG codon in the position indicated. This codon translates to glutamic acid in the resulting polypeptide.

The allele denoted *S* in Fig. 15.1 is associated with sickle-cell anemia (Chapter 14). In this allele, the GAG codon seen in the *A* allele is instead a GTG codon, with the result that the glutamic acid in the protein is replaced with valine (Val). The third allele in Fig. 15.1 is the *C* allele. It has a variation in exactly the same codon as the *S* allele, but in this case the change is from the normal GAG to AAG, which results in glutamic acid being replaced with lysine (Lys). Although in each case only one amino acid of the β-globin protein is affected, this change can have a dramatic effect on the function of the protein, since the amino acid sequence determines how a protein folds, and protein folding in turn determines the protein's function (Chapter 4).

An individual who inherits an allele of the same type from each parent is said to be **homozygous.** For the hemoglobin *A, S,* and *C* alleles, there are three possible homozygous genotypes, *AA, SS,* and *CC.* (The first letter or symbol indicates the allele inherited from one parent, and the second indicates the allele inherited from the other parent. By convention, alleles and genotypes are designated by italic letters.)

By contrast, individuals who inherit different types of alleles from their parents are **heterozygous.** For the hemoglobin *A, S,* and *C* alleles, there are three possible heterozygous genotypes: *AS, AC,* and *SC.* Note that while each individual can have only two alleles of a gene, many more alleles can exist in an entire population. In the hemoglobin example, a person can have two identical alleles (homozygous) or two different alleles (heterozygous), but there are three different alleles available in the population to mix and match in each individual. How those alleles are inherited is explored in Chapter 16.

FIG. 15.1 **Three alleles of the gene encoding β-globin, a subunit of hemoglobin.** Adult hemoglobin is made up of 2 α-globin and 2 β-globin subunits.

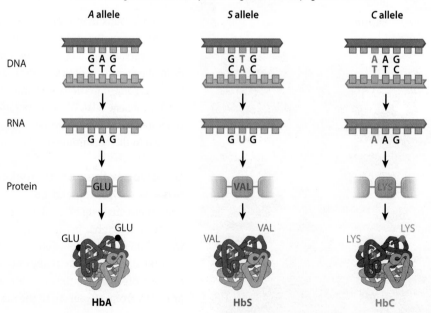

What are the effects of these mutations? Are they beneficial, harmful, or neutral? The short answer is, it depends. Let's consider the *S* allele. When it is inherited from both parents, the individual is homozygous *SS* and has sickle-cell anemia. In the absence of proper medical care, patients with sickle-cell anemia usually die before adulthood. However, when the *S* allele is inherited from one parent and the *A* allele is inherited from the other parent, the individual is heterozygous (*AS*) and the mutant allele causes only a mild form of blood disease. Furthermore, in Africa, where malaria is widespread, the mutation is actually beneficial because it affords partial protection against severe malaria.

Whether the effects of an allele, in this case the *S* allele, are beneficial or harmful illustrates two important principles about the connection between genotype and phenotype. First, the answer often depends on whether the mutation is homozygous or heterozygous. In areas with malaria, the *S* allele is harmful as a homozygote but beneficial as a heterozygote. Second, the effect of a particular genotype may depend on the environment. The *S* allele, as a heterozygote, is beneficial only in malarial-prone regions, where it offers protection from the disease that outweighs its other effects. In areas without malaria, it is harmful.

What about the *C* allele? Individuals who inherit a *C* allele from one parent and an *A* allele from the other parent (genotype *AC*) are partially protected against severe malaria, and those who inherit a *C* allele from both parents (genotype *CC*) are not only more protected from malaria but also have at worst a mild anemia that usually needs no medical treatment. As with the *S* allele, the phenotype of an allele may depend on whether the allele was inherited from one or both parents.

→ **Quick Check 1** A mutation arises in a bacterium that confers antibiotic resistance. Is this mutation harmful, beneficial, or neutral?

Some genetic differences are major risk factors for disease.

As we saw in the last chapter, when a mutation occurs in the coding sequence of a gene, it may have no effect on the amino acid sequence, or it may result in a change in the amino acid sequence, introduce a stop codon, or shift the reading frame. Many of these latter mutations are harmful. Harmful mutations are often eliminated in one or a few generations because they decrease the survival and reproduction of the individuals that carry them.

Sometimes, however, harmful mutations persist in a population. For example, many polymorphisms increase susceptibility to particular diseases. One such polymorphism increases the risk of emphysema, a condition marked by overinflation of the air sacs in the lungs. Emphysema patients suffer from shortness of breath even when at rest, a wheezy

cough, and increased blood pressure in the arteries of the lungs. Without proper treatment, the disease progresses to respiratory failure or congestive heart failure, and eventual death. Onset of the disease usually occurs in middle age, and the lifespan of affected individuals is shortened by 10 to 30 years depending on the effect of treatment.

About 80% of all cases of emphysema are associated with cigarette smoking, which affects the action of the enzyme alpha-1 antitrypsin (α1AT). The main function of α1AT is to inhibit another enzyme, known as elastase (**Fig. 15.2a**). The elasticity of the lung, which allows normal breathing, requires a balance between the production and the breakdown of the connective-tissue protein elastin. Breakdown of elastin results from the action of elastase. Too-rapid breakdown is normally prevented by the inhibition of elastase by α1AT, but cigarette smoke reduces the activity of α1AT (**Fig. 15.2b**). The result is excessive destruction of elastin, loss of lung elasticity, and emphysema.

While most cases of emphysema are due to smoking, not everyone who smokes will get emphysema. A smoker's chance of getting emphysema is significantly increased by inheriting a mutation in the gene that encodes α1AT. Among the many different alleles of this gene, a defective allele denoted *PiZ* is particularly common in populations of European descent. Among Caucasians in the United States, about 1 person in 30 is heterozygous for the *PiZ* allele, and about 1 in 3000 is homozygous *PiZ/PiZ*. Individuals with the homozygous genotype produce α1AT with reduced activity and hence have reduced elastase inhibition, leading to severe emphysema and death in more than 70% of affected individuals (**Fig. 15.2c**). Smoking markedly increases both the severity of the disease and the rapidity of its progression in *PiZ/PiZ* individuals. The life expectancy of *PiZ/PiZ* nonsmokers is 65 years, whereas that of *PiZ/PiZ* smokers is only 40 years.

This is an example of **genotype-by-environment interaction,** in which a phenotype is the result of an interplay between genes and the environment. In this case, a particular combination of genetic and environmental risk factors is much worse than either risk factor acting alone. Chapter 18 includes a detailed discussion of genotype-by-environment interaction.

Not all genetic differences are harmful.

Some mutations have no effect on the organism, or have effects that are not associated with differences in survival or reproduction. Such mutations are considered **neutral.** Neutral mutations are often found in noncoding DNA, and so occur especially in organisms with large genomes and abundant noncoding DNA (Chapter 13).

→ **Quick Check 2** Given what you read about the human genome in Chapter 13, would you predict that most mutations in humans are harmful, beneficial, or neutral?

FIG. 15.2   A harmful mutation. (a) The enzyme alpha-1 antitrypsin (α1AT) normally inhibits the activity of elastase, which breaks down elastin in the lung. (b) Cigarette smoke inhibits α1AT activity and increases the risk of emphysema. (c) A mutation in *α1AT* called *PiZ* is harmful because it reduces α1AT activity and also leads to increased risk of emphysema.

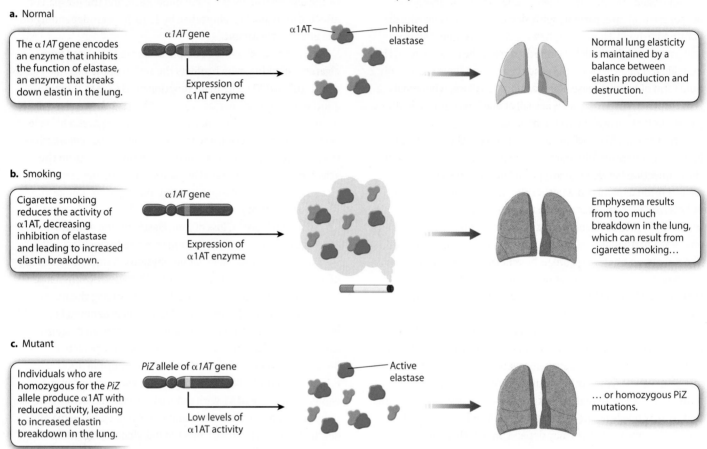

a. Normal

The *α1AT* gene encodes an enzyme that inhibits the function of elastase, an enzyme that breaks down elastin in the lung.

α1AT gene

Expression of α1AT enzyme

α1AT — Inhibited elastase

Normal lung elasticity is maintained by a balance between elastin production and destruction.

b. Smoking

Cigarette smoking reduces the activity of α1AT, decreasing inhibition of elastase and leading to increased elastin breakdown.

α1AT gene

Expression of α1AT enzyme

Emphysema results from too much breakdown in the lung, which can result from cigarette smoking…

c. Mutant

Individuals who are homozygous for the *PiZ* allele produce α1AT with reduced activity, leading to increased elastin breakdown in the lung.

PiZ allele of *α1AT* gene

Low levels of α1AT activity

Active elastase

… or homozygous PiZ mutations.

Sometimes common, harmless genetic variations occur in coding sequences. One example in human populations is the taster phenotype associated with perception of a bitter taste from certain chemicals, including phenylthiocarbamide (PTC). The taster polymorphism was discovered in 1931 when a commercial chemist seeking a new artificial sweetener accidentally released a cloud of fine crystalline PTC and heard his colleague working nearby complain about its bitter taste. The chemist himself tasted nothing. He began testing his own and other families, and set the stage for future genetic studies.

The minimal concentration for PTC tasting varies almost continuously among individuals, but being able to taste a concentration of 0.5 millimolar or less is often taken as the cutoff between the taster and nontaster phentoypes. In a sample from Utah, the frequency of nontasters is about 30%. This is typical for people of European descent, but the frequency of nontasters differs among populations, from as low as 3% in West Africa to as high as 40% in India.

The ability or inability to taste PTC is due largely, but not exclusively, to alleles of a single gene that encodes a taste receptor in the tongue. Nonhuman primates are homozygous for an allele of this gene known as the *PAV* allele, so called because the protein it encodes has the amino acids proline (P), alanine (A), and valine (V) at specific positions. Humans also have the *PAV* allele, and *PAV/PAV* homozygous genotypes are almost all tasters.

The most common allele associated with the nontaster phenotype is *AVI*, in which the amino acids in the taste receptor are alanine (A), valine (V), and isoleucine (I) instead of proline, alanine, and valine. About 80% of homozygous *AVI/AVI* genotypes are nontasters. One copy of the *PAV* allele is usually sufficient for the taster phenotype; about 98% of *PAV/AVI* heterozygous genotypes are tasters.

The factors contributing to the taster phenotype are more complex than a genotype at a single gene, however. The *AVI/AVI* genotype tips the balance toward the nontaster phenotype, but not completely. Other genes and the environment also play a role.

Why is this strange variation present in the human population? One hypothesis is that an aversion to compounds that contain a thiourea group (N–C=S), as PTC does, may discourage eating certain plants that produce poisonous defense compounds. One class of such compounds is the glycosinolates, which are present in many wild plants and some cultivated vegetables, including broccoli, watercress, turnip, and horseradish. Sure enough, *PAV/PAV* tasters rate such vegetables as significantly more bitter than *AVI/AVI* nontasters, whereas *PAV/AVI* heterozygous genotypes are intermediate in their perception of bitterness.

We hasten to add, however, that the low level of glycosinolates in broccoli and other cultivated vegetables is nontoxic, so you should still eat your vegetables! But if you find broccoli and its relatives somewhat bitter, you may well be a taster.

A few genetic differences are beneficial.

While many mutations are neutral, or nearly so, and many others are harmful, some mutations are beneficial. In human populations, beneficial mutations are often discovered through their effects in protecting against infectious disease. The most widely known example is probably the sickle-cell allele in the gene encoding the β chain of hemoglobin, which when heterozygous protects against malaria (see Fig. 15.1). In this section, we consider another example that protects against AIDS, which is caused by the human immunodeficiency virus (HIV).

By means of its surface glycoprotein (a product of the *env* region in the annotated HIV genome shown in Fig. 13.7), HIV combines with a cell-surface receptor called CD4 to gain entry into T cells. Interaction with CD4 alone, however, does not enable the virus to infect the T cell. The surface glycoprotein must also interact with another receptor, which is denoted CCR5, in the

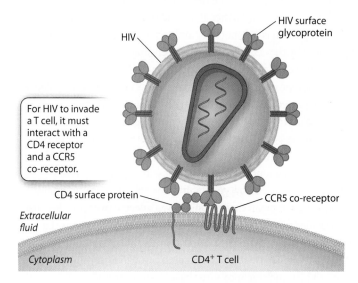

FIG. 15.3 **HIV infection of T cells.** HIV gains entry into a T cell by interacting with a CD4 protein and a CCR5 receptor on the surface of T cells.

HIV

HIV surface glycoprotein

For HIV to invade a T cell, it must interact with a CD4 receptor and a CCR5 co-receptor.

CD4 surface protein

CCR5 co-receptor

Extracellular fluid

Cytoplasm

CD4⁺ T cell

early stages of infection (**Fig. 15.3**). The normal function of CCR5 is to bind certain small secreted proteins that promote tissue inflammation in response to infection. But because CCR5 is also an HIV receptor, cells lacking CCR5 are more difficult to invade.

A beneficial effect of a particular mutation in the *CCR5* gene was discovered in studies focusing on HIV patients whose infection had not progressed to full-blown AIDS for 10 years or more. The protective allele is denoted the *Δ32* allele because the mutation is a 32-base-pair deletion in the coding sequence of the *CCR5* gene (**Fig. 15.4**). Because the 32 is not a multiple of 3, the reading frame

FIG. 15.4 **A beneficial mutation in the human population.** Mutant *CCR5* has a 32-nucleotide deletion that results in defective CCR5 protein and therefore slows the progression of HIV to AIDS.

a. Nonmutant *CCR5* allele

HIS–PHE–PRO–TYR–SER–GLN–TYR–GLN–PHE–TRP–LYS–ASN–PHE–GLN–THR–LEU–LYS–ILE–VAL–ILE

. . . C A T T T T C C A T A C AGTCAGTATCAATTCTGGAAGAATTTCCAGAC A T T A A A G A T A G T C A T C . . .

b. *Δ32* mutant *CCR5* allele

The deletion causes a shift in the translational reading frame, and all downstream amino acids are incorrect.

HIS–PHE–PRO–TYR–ILE–LYS–ASP–SER–HIS

. . . C A T T T T C C A T A C A T T A A A G A T A G T C A T C . . .

Translation continues for another 26 amino acids, at which point the shifted reading frame encounters a termination codon.

AGTCAGTATCAATTCTGGAAGAATTTCCAGAC

for translation is shifted at the site of the deletion, and instead of the normal amino acid sequence Ser–Gln–Tyr–Gln–Phe···, the mutant sequence is Ile–Lys–Asp–Ser–His···. Not only is the amino acid sequence incorrect, the ribosome encounters a stop codon a mere 26 amino acids farther along and translation terminates. The mutant protein is 215, not 352, amino acids long. The CCR5 protein produced by the Δ32 allele is completely inactive.

The effect of the Δ32 allele is pronounced. In homozygous Δ32/Δ32 genotypes, HIV progression to AIDS is rarely observed. There is some protection even in heterozygous Δ32 genotypes, where progression to AIDS is delayed by an average of about 2 years.

Much has been written about the evolutionary history of the Δ32 allele. It is found almost exclusively in European populations, where the frequency of heterozygous genotypes ranges from 10% to 25%. The narrow geographical distribution was originally interpreted to mean that the allele was selected over time because it provided protection against some other infectious agent that also interacted with the CCR5 protein. Both the bacterium that caused the Black Death, which roared through Europe beginning in about 1350, and smallpox virus have been suggested.

Beneficial mutations not only provide protection against disease; in rare cases, they permit organisms to become adapted to their environment. For example, certain birds, such as Rüppell's vulture, commonly fly at altitudes of 20,000 feet and sometimes much higher. This feat is possible because of mutations in the structure of hemoglobin that allow hemoglobin to bind oxygen with high affinity, even at the low pressure of oxygen high in the atmosphere. These mutations were selected and passed on generation after generation, allowing the birds to be well adapted to flying at high altitudes.

as restriction sites, typically four or six nucleotides long, were among the first tools used to study genetic variation in DNA. These enzymes are useful because DNA from different individuals can differ in the distance between adjacent restriction sites or in the presence or absence of a particular restriction site at some location in the genome. Such differences among individuals are the basis of **DNA typing,** in which the analysis of a small quantity of DNA can uniquely identify an individual. DNA typing can be as reliable as fingerprints for identifying individuals.

Areas of the genome with variable numbers of tandem repeats are useful in DNA typing.

Polymorphisms do not always result from the replacement of one nucleotide or sequence of nucleotides with another. In many cases, as we saw with *CCR5,* polymorphisms can be differences in the amount of DNA present. When PCR (Chapter 12) is used to amplify a region of the genome from different individuals or from maternal and paternal homologs of the same individual, the lengths of the resulting DNA fragments may be different. They differ because the number of short repeated sequences of DNA varies from one chromosome to the next. This genetic difference is called a **variable number tandem repeat,** or **VNTR (Fig. 15.5).** Just as an individual has two copies of each gene, possibly with two different alleles, so each individual has two copies of these polymorphic tandem repeats, each copy representing an allele of the region. The total number of alleles of variable repeats present in a population can be very large. An example with only five alleles is shown in Fig. 15.5a.

No matter how many alleles exist in the population as a whole, any one diploid individual can have only two alleles, present at

15.2 GENETIC VARIATION AND INDIVIDUAL UNIQUENESS

While examples like sickle-cell anemia, emphysema, and HIV susceptibility show that genetic variation in some genes has important effects on phenotypes, most of the genetic variation in populations is neutral or has no obvious effects. Much of the neutral variation consists of differences in noncoding DNA. Nonetheless, this variation can be revealed by direct studies of DNA that make use of many of the techniques for DNA manipulation described in Chapter 12.

Restriction enzymes, which cleave double-stranded DNA at the positions of specific sequences known

FIG. 15.5   **Variable number of tandem repeats (VNTR).** (a) The number of short, repeated sequences at a given site in a human chromosome can vary. (b) These differences can be visualized using PCR followed by gel electrophoresis.

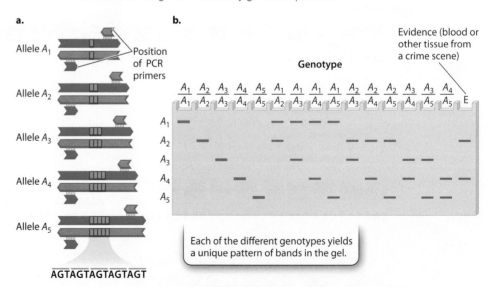

Each of the different genotypes yields a unique pattern of bands in the gel.

AGTAGTAGTAGTAGT

the same positions in the homologous chromosomes inherited from the mother and the father. With five alleles there are 5 possible homozygous genotypes and 10 possible heterozygous genotypes. These can be visualized using PCR, in which primers are used to amplify a specific region of DNA and the resulting fragments are separated by size on a gel and then visualized with a dye. The pattern of bands expected from the DNA in each genotype is shown in Fig. 15.5b. Note that each genotype yields a distinct pattern of bands, and so these patterns can be used to identify the genotype of any individual for a particular region of DNA.

With as few as 10 equally frequent alleles, the chance that any two individuals would have the same genotype by chance alone is about 1 in 50, and with 20 equally frequent alleles the chance of identity is about 1 in 200. These numbers suggest why DNA typing can yield a sort of genetic fingerprint that can uniquely match DNA samples.

The lane labeled "E" at the far right in Fig. 15.5b shows the DNA bands for this same polymorphism from biological material collected at the scene of a crime. In this case, the bands in lane E imply that the source of the evidence is an individual of

genotype A_2/A_4 because this is the only genotype with bands with vertical positions in the gel that match those of the evidence sample exactly. A single polymorphism of the type shown in Fig. 15.5 is not enough to say for sure that two pieces of DNA come from the same person, but because the human genome has such polymorphisms scattered throughout, many multiple-allele polymorphisms can be examined. If six or eight of these polymorphisms match between two samples, it is very likely that the samples come from the same individual (or from identical twins). On the other hand, if any of the polymorphisms fails to match band for band, then it is almost certain that the samples come from different individuals (barring such technical mishaps as samples whose DNA is contaminated, degraded, or mislabeled).

One of the advantages of DNA typing is that a large amount of DNA is not needed. Even minuscule amounts of DNA can be typed, so tiny spots of blood, semen, or saliva are sufficient samples. A cotton swab wiped across the inside of your cheek will contain enough DNA for typing; so will a discarded paper cup or a cigarette butt. One enterprising researcher in England used PCR to type the dog feces on his lawn and matched it to the DNA from hair he obtained from neighborhood dogs, much to the chagrin of the guilty dog's owner.

→ **Quick Check 3** In typing DNA from a sample found at a crime scene, how can a DNA mismatch prove that a suspect is not the source of that sample, whereas a DNA match does not necessarily prove that a suspect is the source?

Some polymorphisms add or remove restriction sites in the DNA.

Researchers can use restriction enzymes to detect another type of polymorphism commonly present in genomes and useful in DNA typing. Sometimes, because of common polymorphisms or sequence differences, a restriction site will be present along a stretch of DNA in some chromosomes but not in others.

Fig. 15.6 shows an example. Here, a restriction enzyme cleaves DNA near the sequence GAGGAG. The three sites shown are in and flanking the β-globin gene from the sickle-cell example we

---

FIG. 15.6 Restriction fragment length polymorphism between the *A* and *S* alleles of the β-globin gene.

a.

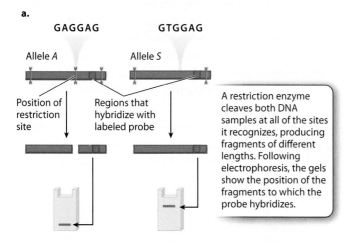

GAGGAG   GTGGAG

Allele *A*   Allele *S*

Position of restriction site

Regions that hybridize with labeled probe

A restriction enzyme cleaves both DNA samples at all of the sites it recognizes, producing fragments of different lengths. Following electrophoresis, the gels show the position of the fragments to which the probe hybridizes.

b.

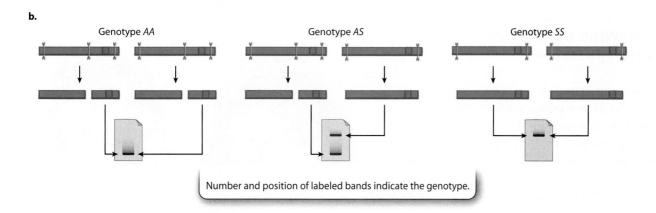

Genotype *AA*   Genotype *AS*   Genotype *SS*

Number and position of labeled bands indicate the genotype.

explored earlier in the chapter. The restriction site in the middle includes the GAG that is mutated to GTG in the *S* allele (see Fig. 15.1). Note that whereas the DNA of the *A* allele is cleaved at three sites, the DNA of the *S* allele is cleaved at only two sites because the *S* mutation changes the GAGGAG restriction site into GTGGAG.

These differences can be visualized by a Southern blot (Chapter 12), in which DNA is isolated from different individuals, cut with restriction enzymes, separated by size on a gel, transferred to a blot, and hybridized to a probe to detect the bands of interest. In this case, we would use a restriction enzyme that recognizes the GAGGAG sequence. The *A* allele produces two fragments: a short fragment that moves rapidly through the gel and ends up near the bottom, and a longer fragment that ends up near the top. Since the probe hybridizes only where indicated in Fig. 15.6a, the longer restriction fragment produced by digestion of the *A* allele is not detected. The band produced by the *S* allele is larger because there is no restriction site in the middle. This larger fragment moves more slowly in gel electrophoresis and ends up forming a band near the top of the gel. This kind of polymorphism is called a **restriction fragment length polymorphism**, or **RFLP,** because the length of the restriction fragments is polymorphic—that is, different—in the two alleles.

As seen in the restriction fragment length polymorphism in Fig. 15.6b, DNA from homozygous *AA* individuals yields only the small fragment, and that from homozygous *SS* individuals yields only the large fragment. DNA from heterozygous *AS* individuals yields *both* the small fragment and the large fragment. Therefore, each of the three genotypes *AA*, *AS*, and *SS* yields a unique pattern of bands, allowing each of the possible genotypes to be identified.

How many restriction fragment length polymorphisms are there in the human genome? As in the case of VNTRs, the human genome is littered with restriction sites, so there are numerous RFLPs in the human population, making it another good individual "fingerprint."

→ **Quick Check 4** VNTRs and RFLPs both result in restriction fragments of different lengths. How, then, are they different?

15.3 GENOMEWIDE STUDIES OF GENETIC VARIATION

Restriction enzymes are extremely useful for some purposes, but their utility as a tool for studying genomewide genetic variation is limited because they reveal only sequence variation in restriction sites or differences in the distances between adjacent restriction sites. In this section, we examine methods by which genetic differences in any individual nucleotide can be studied.

Single-nucleotide polymorphisms (SNPs) are single base changes in the genome.

One of the most common types of genetic variation is a difference in a nucleotide at a specific site. A **single-nucleotide polymorphism (SNP)** is a site in the genome where there is a base-pair difference among chromosomes that is common enough to be present in a random sample of 50 diploid individuals. The differences among the hemoglobin alleles are SNPs. The *A*, *S*, and *C* alleles differ from each other at just one nucleotide site (see Fig. 15.1).

Eye color is also associated with a SNP. The blue-eyed phenotype results from reduced expression of a gene called *OCA2*, which encodes a membrane protein involved in the transport of small molecules including the amino acid tyrosine, which is a precursor of the melanin pigment associated with brown eyes. Although more than a dozen alleles of *OCA2* are known that have an amino acid replacement in the protein, none of these results in blue eyes.

The SNP nucleotide implicated in blue eyes is a C–G base pair in one allele. The other common variant is a T–A, which is not associated with blue eyes (**Fig. 15.7**). In one study, the homozygous *C–G* genotype was found in 94% of 183 individuals with blue eyes and in only 2% of 176 individuals with brown eyes. This strong association is quite unexpected because the SNP associated with blue eyes is a noncoding SNP present in an intron of a neighboring gene. The proposed mechanism for the association is that the *C–G* allele makes the adjacent *OCA2* gene less accessible to transcription factors, thereby reducing the amount of the transporter protein and consequently the production of melanin

FIG. 15.7 **Single-nucleotide polymorphisms (SNPs).** A SNP in the region neighboring *OCA2* is strongly associated with blue eyes.

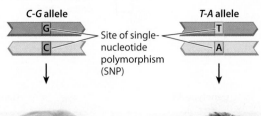

in the iris. The proposed mechanism may be right or wrong; this example emphasizes that scientists have much to learn about the possible phenotypic effects of noncoding DNA.

The *C–G* versus *T–A* SNP is typical of most SNPs in that only two of the four possible base pairs are present in the population at any appreciable frequency.

→ **Quick Check 5** What's the difference between a point mutation and a SNP?

❓ CASE 3 You, From A To T: Your Personal Genome
How can genetic risk factors be detected?

SNPs result from point mutations, the most frequent type of mutation. A point mutation is the substitution of one base pair for another in double-stranded DNA (Chapter 14). Each of us is genetically unique partly because of the abundance of SNPs in the human genome. There are approximately 3 million SNPs that distinguish any one human genome from any other. SNPs are abundant in the genomes of most species; some are thought to be the main source of evolutionary innovation, and others are major contributors to inherited disease. Practically speaking, SNPs are important because they can be used to detect the presence of a genetic risk factor for a disease before the onset of the disease. For example, the ability to detect the β-globin SNPs shown in Fig. 15.1 allows prenatal identification of the β-globin genotype of a fetus.

While there is great interest in developing ultrafast DNA sequencing machines that can determine anyone's personal genome quickly at relatively low cost, between any two genomes 99.9% of the nucleotides are identical. An alternative is to focus on genotyping just SNPs. As many as one million SNPs at different positions in the genome can be genotyped simultaneously, and the genotyping can be carried out on thousands or tens of thousands of individuals. Such massive genotyping allows any SNP associated with a disease to be identified, which is especially important for complex diseases affected by many different genetic risk factors (Chapter 18).

What does it mean to say that a SNP is associated with a disease? It means that individuals carrying one of the SNP alleles are more likely to develop the disease than those carrying the other allele. The increased risk depends on the disease and can differ from one SNP to the next. Sickle-cell anemia affords an example at one extreme of the spectrum of effects. In this case, the *T–A* base pair in the *S* allele of the β-globin gene is the SNP that results in the amino acid replacement of glutamic acid with valine in the protein. Because *SS* individuals always have sickle-cell anemia, it would be fair to say that homozygous *S* "causes" sickle-cell anemia.

But except for inherited diseases due to single mutant genes, which are usually rare, the vast majority of SNPs implicated in disease increase the risk only moderately, typically by 10% to 50% as compared with individuals lacking the risk factor. We then say that the SNP is "associated" with the disease, since the SNP alone does not cause the disease but only increases the risk. For heart disease, diabetes, and some other diseases, many SNPS at different places in the genome, as well as environmental risk factors, can be associated with the disease. Usually, genetic and environmental risk factors act cumulatively: the more you have, the greater the risk.

As emphasized in the case of Claudia Gilmore's genome, certain SNPs in the *BRCA1* and *BRCA2* genes are associated with an increased risk of breast and ovarian cancers. Women who carry a mutation in either of these genes can minimize their risk by frequent mammograms and other tests. Both genes are large—*BRCA1* codes for a protein of 1863 amino acids and *BRCA2* for one of 3418 amino acids—and many different mutations in these genes can predispose to breast or ovarian cancer. In certain high-risk populations, however, such as Ashkenazi Jews, only a few mutations predominate, and the SNPs associated with these mutations can be detected easily and efficiently.

SNPs can be detected by DNA microarrays.

A widely used method for SNP genotyping is shown in **Fig. 15.8.** The technique involves a **DNA microarray,** which consists of a waferlike supporting surface about the size of a postage stamp to which are attached millions of different **oligonucleotides,** short, single-stranded DNA molecules of known sequence. Microarrays have many applications in biology, one of which is the detection of SNPs. For each SNP, researchers design oligonucleotides that contain a base in the middle that is complementary to one or the other of the SNP alleles. In the example shown in Fig. 15.8a, the bases on the oligonucleotide are G and C, which complement one SNP allele, and A and T, which complement the other. The flanking bases are complementary to those in both SNP alleles, which are the same. Although for clarity each oligonucleotide is shown as a single strand in Fig. 15.8a, there are actually millions of identical copies of each oligonucleotide deposited at each spot on the microarray.

Once a microarray with oligonucleotides complementary to both SNP alleles has been constructed, researchers add single-stranded DNA taken from an individual. Recall that DNA hybridization involves two single-stranded DNA molecules forming a double-stranded DNA molecule (Chapter 12). Under suitable conditions of hybridization, DNA fragments from individuals homozygous for the *C–G* allele will hybridize only with the oligonucleotides that contain G or C (Fig. 15.8b) and those from individuals homozygous for the *T–A* allele will hybridize with the oligonucleotides that contain A or T (Fig. 15.8d). The DNA fragments from heterozygous *C–G/T–A* individuals will hybridize with all the complementary oligonucleotides (Fig. 15.8c). The DNA fragments are usually labeled with a fluorescent dye,

FIG. 15.8   SNP genotyping. SNPs can be genotyped by observing their pattern of hybridization with oligonucleotides on a microarray.

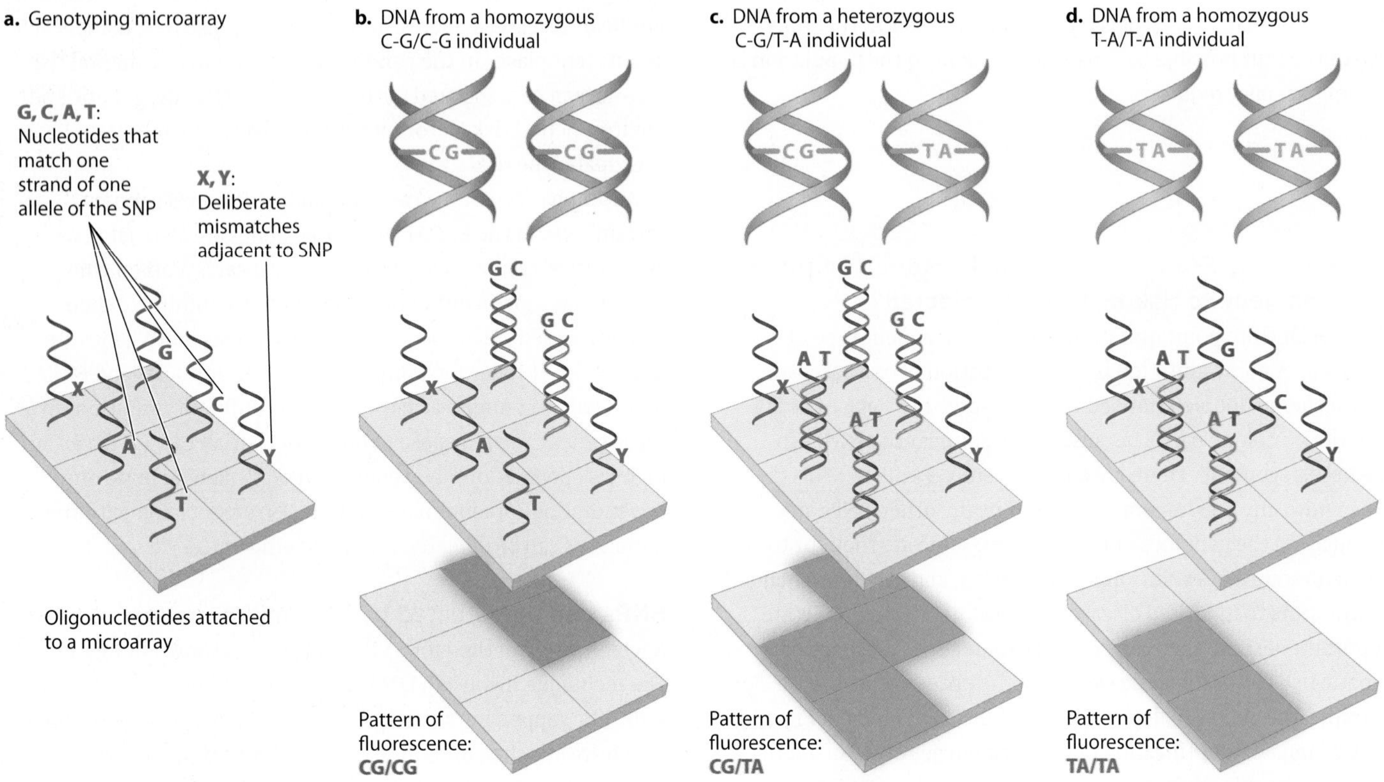

a. Genotyping microarray

G, C, A, T:
Nucleotides that
match one
strand of one
allele of the SNP

X, Y:
Deliberate
mismatches
adjacent to SNP

Oligonucleotides attached
to a microarray

b. DNA from a homozygous
C-G/C-G individual

Pattern of
fluorescence:
CG/CG

c. DNA from a heterozygous
C-G/T-A individual

Pattern of
fluorescence:
CG/TA

d. DNA from a homozygous
T-A/T-A individual

Pattern of
fluorescence:
TA/TA

and any fragment that hybridizes with an oligonucleotide will fluoresce at that site.

The patterns of fluorescence are shown beneath the microarrays in Fig. 15.8. The key point is that each SNP genotype yields a unique pattern of fluorescence. DNA microarrays also include oligonucleotides that serve as experimental controls (important in any experiment) to ensure that the correct SNP has been identified. These contain deliberate mismatches adjacent to the site of the SNP. The control oligonucleotides in Fig. 15.8 are denoted X and Y; and they are expected not to show any fluorescence.

Copy-number variation constitutes a significant proportion of genetic variation.

Genotyping microarrays are useful for detecting **copy-number variation (CNV),** the differences among individuals in the number of copies of a region of the genome. In contrast to the short repeats characteristic of VNTRs, the regions involved in CNVs are large and may include one or more complete genes. An example is shown in **Fig. 15.9.** In this case, a region of the genome that is normally present in only one copy per chromosome (Fig. 15.9a) may in some chromosomes be duplicated (Fig. 15.9b) or deleted (Fig. 15.9c). As in the figure, the multiple copies of the CNV region are usually adjacent to one another along the chromosome.

One of the surprises that emerged from sequencing the human genome was that CNV is quite common in the human population. Any two individuals' genomes differ in copy number at about five different regions, each with an average length of 200 to 300 kb. Across the genome as a whole, about 10% to 15% of the genome is subject to copy-number variation.

FIG. 15.9   Copy-number variation in a region of a chromosome.

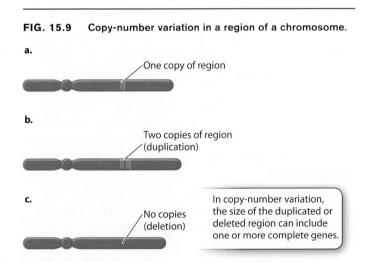

a.

One copy of region

b.

Two copies of region
(duplication)

c.

No copies
(deletion)

In copy-number variation,
the size of the duplicated or
deleted region can include
one or more complete genes.

FIG. 15.10 Copy-number variation. Copy numbers of *AMY1* vary between societies with high-starch and with low-starch diets.

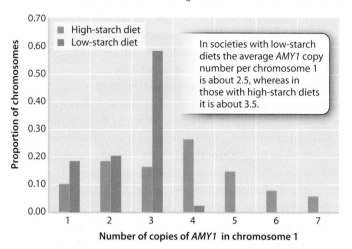

In societies with low-starch diets the average *AMY1* copy number per chromosome 1 is about 2.5, whereas in those with high-starch diets it is about 3.5.

Some CNVs occur in noncoding regions, but others consist of genes that are present in multiple tandem copies along the chromosome. An example is the human gene *AMY1* for the salivary-gland enzyme amylase, which aids in the digestion of starch. This gene is located in chromosome 1, and the *AMY1* copy number differs from one chromosome 1 to the next. **Fig. 15.10** shows the distribution of *AMY1* copy number along chromosome 1 in two groups of people: societies with a long history of a high-starch diet, and societies with a long history of a low-starch diet. There is a clear tendency for chromosomes from the latter group to have fewer copies of *AMY1* than those from the former group. On average, a chromosome 1 from the low-starch group has a copy number of about

FIG. 15.11 CNV genotyping. Copy-number variation can be detected by the intensity of hybridization on a DNA microarray.

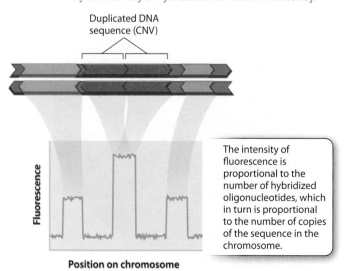

Duplicated DNA sequence (CNV)

The intensity of fluorescence is proportional to the number of hybridized oligonucleotides, which in turn is proportional to the number of copies of the sequence in the chromosome.

2.5, whereas one from the high-starch group has an average of about 3.5. Because each individual has two copies of chromosome 1, this difference means that the average individual in the low-starch group has about 5 copies of *AMY1*, whereas the average individual in the high-starch group has about 7 copies. A plausible hypothesis is that extra copies were selected in groups with a high-starch diet because of the advantage extra copies conferred in digesting starch.

The detection of CNV is based on the relative intensity of hybridization of spots in a DNA microarray. Recall that each tiny spot on a DNA microarray holds millions of identical copies of a particular oligonucleotide sequence. In this case, the researcher chooses oligonucleotides in regions of the genome of interest, where CNV is likely. The greater the number of copies of a sequence in the genome, the more hybridization will occur when total genomic DNA is hybridized with complementary oligonucleotides on the microarray. Extra copies of a region result in greater intensity of fluorescence, and missing copies result in decreased fluorescence compared to the level of fluorescence observed for single-copy regions (**Fig. 15.11**).

15.4 GENETIC VARIATION IN CHROMOSOMES

Copy-number variation usually involves only one or a small number of genes, and the size of the duplicated or deleted region is physically so small that the differences are undetectable with conventional microscopy. In the human genome, some common variants involve large regions of the chromosome and are big enough to be visible through a microscope. Most of these variations involve regions of the genome with an extremely low density of genes, such as regions around the centromere or the long arm of the Y chromosome.

It may come as a surprise to learn that major chromosomal differences occur quite commonly. They are infrequently observed, however, because most of them are lethal. Nevertheless, a few major chromosomal differences are found in the general population. Some are common enough that their phenotypic effects are familiar. Others are less common, and a few have no major phenotypic effects at all. In this section, we focus on the types of difference that are observed, what causes them, and their phenotypic effects.

Nondisjunction in meiosis results in extra or missing chromosomes.

Nondisjunction is the failure of a pair of chromosomes to separate during anaphase of cell division (Chapter 11). The result is that one daughter cell receives an extra copy of one chromosome, and the other daughter cell receives no copy of that chromosome. Nondisjunction can take place in mitosis, and it leads to cell lineages with extra or missing chromosomes—which is often observed in cancer cells.

FIG. 15.12   Nondisjunction. (a) Chromosomes separate evenly into gametes in normal meiotic cell division. (b) Homologous chromosomes fail to separate in first-division nondisjunction. (c) Sister chromatids fail to separate in second-division nondisjunction.

a. Normal meiosis

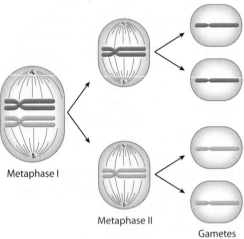

Metaphase I

Metaphase II

Gametes

b. First-division nondisjunction

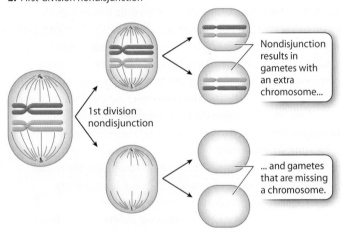

1st division nondisjunction

Nondisjunction results in gametes with an extra chromosome...

... and gametes that are missing a chromosome.

c. Second-division nondisjunction

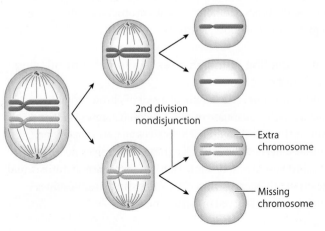

2nd division nondisjunction

Extra chromosome

Missing chromosome

When nondisjunction takes place in meiosis, the result is reproductive cells (gametes) that have either an extra or a missing chromosome. **Fig. 15.12** illustrates nondisjunction in meiosis. Fig. 15.12a shows key stages in a normal meiosis, in which chromosome separation (disjunction) takes place in both meiotic divisions, with the result that each gamete receives one and only one copy of each chromosome.

When failure of chromosome separation occurs, it can take place in either of the two meiotic divisions. Both types of nondisjunction result in gametes with an extra chromosome or a missing chromosome, but there is an important difference. In **first-division nondisjunction** (Fig. 15.12b), the homologous chromosomes fail to separate and so the chromosomes that move together are not genetically identical. On the other hand, in **second-division nondisjunction** (Fig. 15.12c), the sister chromatids of a chromosome fail to separate and therefore the two copies of the chromosome that end up in the same gamete are genetically identical. (In this discussion, we are ignoring the process of crossing over discussed in Chapter 11.)

Some human disorders result from nondisjunction.

Approximately 1 out of 155 live-born children (0.6%) has a major chromosome abnormality of some kind. About half of these have a major abnormality in chromosome structure, such as an inversion or translocation (Chapter 14). The others have a chromosome that is present in an extra copy or a chromosome that is missing because of nondisjunction—a parent has produced an egg or a sperm with an extra or a missing chromosome (**Fig. 15.13**).

Perhaps the most familiar of the conditions resulting from nondisjunction is **Down syndrome,** which results from the

FIG. 15.13   Incidence of extra and missing chromosomes in human live births.

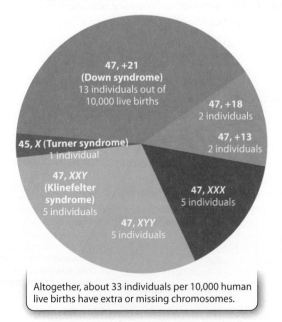

47, +21 (Down syndrome) 13 individuals out of 10,000 live births

47, +18 2 individuals

47, +13 2 individuals

45, X (Turner syndrome) 1 individual

47, XXY (Klinefelter syndrome) 5 individuals

47, XYY 5 individuals

47, XXX 5 individuals

Altogether, about 33 individuals per 10,000 human live births have extra or missing chromosomes.

FIG. 15.14

What is the genetic basis of Down syndrome?

BACKGROUND The detailed images of cells and chromosomes available today are produced by microscopic and imaging techniques not available during most of the history of genetics and cell biology. Techniques for observing human chromosomes were originally so unreliable that the correct number of human chromosomes was firmly established only in the mid-1950s. Mistakes were common, such as counting two nearby chromosomes as one or by including chromosomes in the count of one nucleus when they actually belonged to a nearby nucleus. Despite these limitations, in 1959 French scientists Jérôme Lejeune, Marthe Gautier, and Raymond Turpin decided to investigate whether any common birth abnormalities were associated with chromosomal abnormalities. They chose Down syndrome, one of the most common birth abnormalities, because its genetic basis was an enigma.

HYPOTHESIS Down syndrome is associated with extra or missing chromosomes.

EXPERIMENT The chromosomes of five boys and four girls with Down syndrome were studied. A small patch of skin was taken from each child and placed in growth medium. In this medium, fibroblast cells, which synthesize the extracellular matrix that provides the structural framework of the skin, readily undergo DNA synthesis and divide. After a period allowing cellular growth and division, the fibroblast cells were prepared in a way that allowed the researchers to count the number of chromosomes under a microscope.

RESULTS Chromosomes were counted in 103 cells, yielding counts of 46 chromosomes (10 cells), 47 chromosomes (84 cells), and 48 chromosomes (9 cells). For each cell examined, the researchers noted whether the count was "doubtful" or "absolutely certain." The researchers marked cells as "doubtful" if the chromosomes or nuclei were not well separated from one another. They encountered 57 cells of which they felt "absolutely certain," and in each of these they counted 47 chromosomes. The extra chromosome was always one of the smallest chromosomes in the set.

CONCLUSION The researchers concluded that Down syndrome is the result of a chromosomal abnormality, an extra copy of one of the smallest chromosomes. The discovery helped resolve many of the questions surrounding the genetics of Down syndrome.

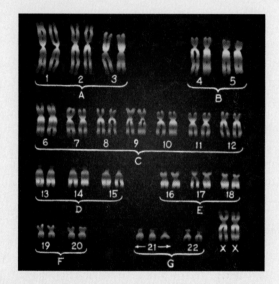

FOLLOW-UP WORK Improved techniques including chromosome banding (shown in Fig. 13.15) later indicated that the extra chromosome was chromosome 21. The finding stimulated many other chromosome studies. Today it is clear that, except for the sex chromosomes, the vast majority of fetuses with extra or missing chromosomes undergo spontaneous abortion. Furthermore, the Human Genome Project has indicated that genes on chromosome 21 have direct roles in many of the signs and symptoms of Down syndrome.

SOURCE J. Lejeune, Gautier, M., and Turpin, R. 1959. "Premier exemple d'aberration autosomique humaine." *Comptes rendus des séances de l'Académie des Sciences.* 248:1721–1722. Translated from the French in *Landmarks in Medical Genetics*, edited by P. S. Harper. Oxford, New York, 2004.

---

presence of an extra copy of chromosome 21. Down syndrome is also known as **trisomy 21** because affected individuals have three copies of chromosome 21. The extra chromosome can be seen in a chromosome layout called a **karyotype.** French researchers Jérôme Lejeune, Marthe Gautier, and Raymond Turpin first saw the extra chromosome when they developed a technique to visualize a patient's chromosomes (**Fig. 15.14**). The shorthand for the condition is 47,+21, meaning that the individual has 47 chromosomes with an extra copy of chromosome 21.

The presence of an extra chromosome 21 leads to a set of traits that, taken together, constitute a syndrome. These traits presumably result from an increase in dosage of the genes and other elements present on chromosome 21, although the specific genes or genetic elements have not been identified. Children with Down syndrome are mentally disabled to varying degrees; most are in the mild to moderate range and with special education and support they can acquire basic communication, self-help, and social skills. People with Down syndrome are short because of delayed maturation of the skeletal system; their muscle tone is low; and they have a characteristic facial appearance. About 40% of children with Down syndrome have major heart defects, and life expectancy is currently about 55 years. Among adults with Down syndrome, the risk of dementia is about 15% to 50%, which is about five times greater than the risk in the general population.

Although Down syndrome affects approximately 1 in 750 live-born children overall, there is a pronounced effect of mother's age on the risk of Down syndrome. For mothers of ages 45–50, the risk of having a baby with Down syndrome is approximately 50 times greater than it is for mothers of ages 15–20. The increased risk is the reason why many physicians recommend tests to determine abnormalities in the fetus for pregnant women over the age of 35.

Two other trisomies of autosomes (that is, chromosomes other than the X and Y chromosomes), are sometimes found in live births. These are trisomy 13 and trisomy 18. Both are much rarer than Down syndrome and also much more severe. In both cases, the developmental abnormalities are so profound that newborns with these conditions usually do not survive the first year of life. Other trisomies occur, but they are not compatible with life.

Extra sex chromosomes have fewer effects than extra autosomes.

Extra or missing **sex chromosomes** (X or Y) are also quite common. In most mammals, females have two X chromosomes (XX), and males have one X and one Y chromosome (XY). The presence of the Y chromosome, not the number of X chromosomes, leads to male development. The female karyotype 47, XXX (47 chromosomes, including three X chromosomes) and the male karyotype 47, XYY (47 chromosomes, including one X and two Y chromosomes) are found among healthy females and males. These persons are in the normal range of physical development and mental capability and usually their extra sex chromosome remains undiscovered until their chromosomes are examined for some other reason.

The reason that 47, XYY males show no detectable phenotypic effects is because of the unusual nature of the Y chromosome.

The Y contains only a few functional genes other than the gene that stimulates the embryo to take the male developmental pathway. The absence of detectable phenotypic effects in 47, XXX females has a completely different explanation that has to do with the manner in which the activity of genes in the X chromosome is regulated. In the cells of female mammals, all X chromosomes except one are inactivated and gene expression is largely repressed. (This process, called X-inactivation, is discussed in Chapter 20.) Because of X-inactivation, a 47, XXX female has one active X chromosome per cell, the same number as in a normal 46, XX female.

→ **Quick Check 6** A male baby is born with the sex-chromosome constitution *XYY*. Both parents have normal sex chromosomes (*XY* in the father, *XX* in the mother). In which meiotic division of which parent did the nondisjunction take place that produced the *XYY* baby?

Two other sex-chromosomal abnormalities do have phenotypic effects, especially on sexual development. The more frequent is 47, XXY (47 chromosomes, including two X chromosomes and one Y chromosome). Individuals with this karyotype are male because of the presence of the Y chromosome, but they have a distinctive group of symptoms known as **Klinefelter syndrome** (**Fig. 15.15a**). Characteristics of the syndrome are very small testes but normal penis and scrotum. Growth and physical development are, for the most part, normal, although affected individuals tend to be tall for their age. About half of the individuals have some degree of mental impairment. When a person with Klinefelter syndrome reaches puberty, the testes fail to enlarge, the voice remains high pitched, pubic and facial hair remains sparse, and there is some enlargement of the breasts. Affected males do not produce sperm and hence are sterile; up to 10% of men who seek aid at infertility clinics turn out to be XXY.

Much rarer than all the other sex-chromosome abnormalities is 45, X (45 chromosomes, with just one X chromosome), the karyotype associated with characteristics known as **Turner syndrome** (**Fig. 15.15b**). Affected females are short and often have a distinctive webbing of the skin between the neck and shoulders. There is no sexual maturation. The external sex organs remain immature, the breasts fail to develop, and pubic hair fails to grow. Internally, the ovaries are small or absent, and menstruation does not occur. Although the mental abilities of affected females are very nearly normal, they have specific defects in spatial abilities and arithmetical skills.

Earlier, we saw that in XX females one X chromosome undergoes inactivation. Why, then, do individuals with just one X chromosome show any symptoms at all? The explanation is that some genes on the inactive X chromosome in XX females are not completely inactivated. Evidently, for normal development to take place, both copies of some genes that escape complete inactivation must be expressed.

45, *X* is one of the rarest karyotypes seen in live-born babies. The reason is that more than 99% of the fetuses that are 45, *X* undergo spontaneous abortion—the subject of the next section.

Nondisjunction is a major cause of spontaneous abortion.

Trisomies and the sex-chromosome abnormalities discussed in the previous section account for most of the simpler chromosomal abnormalities that are found among babies born alive. However, these chromosomal abnormalities represent only a minority of those that actually occur. Most fertilized eggs with chromosome abnormalities fail to complete embryonic development. At some time during pregnancy— in some cases very early, in other cases relatively late—the chromosomally abnormal embryo or fetus undergoes spontaneous abortion.

The relative proportions of some of the major chromosomal abnormalities in spontaneous abortion are shown in **Fig. 15.16**. The bars in red represent recognized pregnancies

FIG. 15.16 Chromosomal abnormalities in spontaneous abortion.

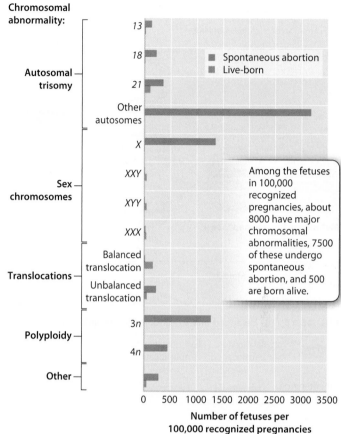

that terminate in spontaneous abortion, and those in blue represent those in which the fetus develops to term and is born alive. Note the large number of autosomal trisomies, none of which (with the exception of trisomies 13, 18, and 21) permit live births. Even among these, about 75% of fetuses with trisomy 21 undergo spontaneous abortion, and the proportions are even greater for trisomies 13 and 18. The 45, *X* karyotype is also very frequent among spontaneous abortions.

A surprisingly large number of fetuses that undergo spontaneous abortion are **triploid** (with three complete sets of chromosomes, 69 altogether) or **tetraploid** (four complete sets, 92 altogether). These karyotypes usually result from a defective spindle apparatus and failure of cell division in anaphase. When this occurs in meiosis, the result is a diploid gamete and a triploid fertilized egg, and when it occurs

FIG. 15.15 Symptoms associated with (a) Klinefelter syndrome and (b) Turner syndrome.

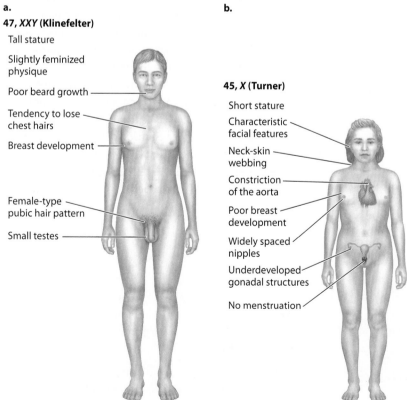

a.

47, *XXY* (Klinefelter)

Tall stature

Slightly feminized physique

Poor beard growth

Tendency to lose chest hairs

Breast development

Female-type pubic hair pattern

Small testes

b.

45, *X* (Turner)

Short stature

Characteristic facial features

Neck-skin webbing

Constriction of the aorta

Poor breast development

Widely spaced nipples

Underdeveloped gonadal structures

No menstruation

FIG. 15.17 Formation of polyploid organisms. (a) A triploid organism can result from failure of division in meiosis. (b) A tetraploid organism can result from failure of cell division in mitosis.

a. Formation of triploid organisms

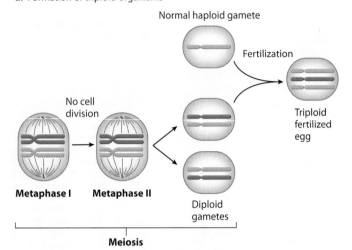

b. Formation of tetraploid organisms

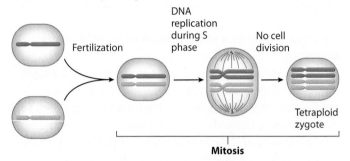

FIG. 15.18 (a) Balanced and (b) unbalanced translocations.

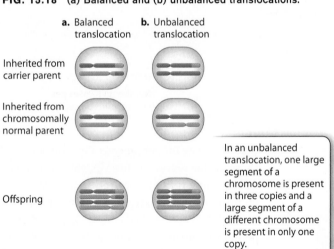

In an unbalanced translocation, one large segment of a chromosome is present in three copies and a large segment of a different chromosome is present in only one copy.

in the first mitosis in a normal fertilized egg, the result is a tetraploid (**Fig. 15.17**). Many spontaneous abortions result from an **unbalanced translocation** (Chapter 14), in which only part of a reciprocal translocation (along with one of the nontranslocated chromosomes) is inherited from one of the parents (**Fig. 15.18**).

Altogether, about 15% of all recognized pregnancies terminate with spontaneous abortion of the fetus, and roughly half of these are due to major chromosomal abnormalities. This number tells only part of the story because embryos with a missing autosome are not found among spontaneously aborted fetuses. These must occur at least as frequently as those with an extra autosome because both are created by the same event of nondisjunction (see Fig. 15.12). The explanation seems to be that in fertilized eggs with a missing autosome the abortion occurs shortly after fertilization, and most cases are not recognized.

Core Concepts Summary

15.1 GENETIC VARIATION DESCRIBES COMMON GENETIC DIFFERENCES (POLYMORPHISMS) AMONG THE INDIVIDUALS IN A POPULATION AT ANY GIVEN TIME.

The genotype of an organism is its genetic makeup. page 15-1

The phenotype of an organism is any observable characteristic of that organism, such as its appearance, physiology, or behavior. The phenotype results from a complex interplay of the genotype and environment. page 15-2

A person's genotype can be homozygous, in which he or she has two alleles of the same type (one from each parent), or heterozygous, in which he or she has inherited different types of alleles from each parent. page 15-2

Genetic variation can be neutral (no effect on survival or reproduction), harmful (associated with decreased survival or reproduction), or beneficial (associated with increased survival or reproduction). page 15-3

15.2 HUMAN GENETIC VARIATION CAN BE DETECTED BY DNA TYPING, WHICH CAN UNIQUELY IDENTIFY EACH INDIVIDUAL.

DNA typing analyzes genetic polymorphisms at multiple genes with multiple alleles. Because there are so many possible genotypes in the population, this procedure can uniquely identify an individual with high probability. page 15-6

A variable number tandem repeat (VNTR) results from differences in the number of small-sequence repeats in a given area of the genome. page 15-6

A restriction fragment length polymorphism (RFLP) results from small changes in the DNA sequence between chromosomes, such as point mutations, that create or destroy restriction sites. page 15-8

15.3 TWO COMMON TYPES OF GENETIC POLYMORPHISM ARE SINGLE-NUCLEOTIDE POLYMORPHISMS (SNPs) AND COPY-NUMBER VARIATION (CNV).

The DNA in any two human genomes differs at about 3 million individual nucleotide sites; these are called SNPs. page 15-8

SNP genotyping allows many SNPs to be identified simultaneously in many individuals. It is carried out by the hybridization of genomic DNA onto a microarray containing millions of different DNA fragments of known sequence corresponding to places in the genome where SNPs are present. page 15-9

CNV is a difference in the number of copies of a particular DNA sequence among chromosomes. CNVs are detected in a similar way to SNPs, except that the readout is signal intensity, which depends on number of copies. page 15-10

15.4 CHROMOSOMAL VARIANTS CAN ALSO OCCUR BUT ARE USUALLY HARMFUL.

Nondisjunction is the failure of a pair of chromosomes to separate during anaphase of cell division. It can occur in mitosis or meiosis and results in daughter cells with extra or missing chromosomes. page 15-11

Nondisjunction in meiosis leads to gametes with extra or missing chromosomes. page 15-12

Most human fetuses with extra or missing chromosomes spontaneously abort, but some are viable and exhibit characteristic syndromes. page 15-13

Trisomy 21 (Down syndrome) is usually characterized by three copies of chromosome 21. page 15-13

Extra or missing sex chromosomes (X or Y) are common and result in syndromes such as Klinefelter syndrome (47, XXY) and Turner syndrome (45, X). page 15-14

Self-Assessment

1. Differentiate between a genotype and a phenotype.

2. Describe common effects of mutations on an organism, and provide an example of each.

3. Explain why it is sometimes an oversimplification to consider a mutation harmful, beneficial, or neutral.

4. Describe two types of genetic polymorphism that are useful in DNA typing.

5. Define the term "SNP" and explain why researchers are interested in detecting SNPs.

6. Explain how SNPs and CNVs are detected in a population of individuals.

7. Diagram how nondisjunction in meiosis I or II can result in extra or missing chromosomes in reproductive cells (gametes).

8. Describe the consequences of an extra copy of chromosome 21 (Down syndrome).

Do you understand the chapter's Core Concepts? Log into BIOPORTAL to check your answers to the Self-Assessment questions, then practice what you've learned and reinforce this chapter's concepts by working through the problems and multimedia tutorials provided there.

📶 http://courses.bfwpub.com/yourbioportal/index.php

CHAPTER 16

MENDELIAN INHERITANCE

Core Concepts

16.1 Early theories of heredity incorrectly assumed the inheritance of acquired characteristics and blending of parental traits in the offspring.

16.2 Modern transmission genetics began with Gregor Mendel, who used the garden pea as his experimental organism and studied traits with contrasting characteristics.

16.3 Mendel's first key discovery was the principle of segregation, which states that members of a gene pair separate equally into gametes.

16.4 Mendel's second key finding was the principle of independent assortment, which states that different gene pairs segregate independently of one another.

16.5 The patterns of inheritance that Mendel observed in peas can also be seen in humans.

From differences in appearances to differences in the ways our bodies work, we have focused so far on how genetic variation leads to our individuality. Examples of genetic variation in the human population range from harmless curiosities like the genetic difference in taste receptors that determine whether or not broccoli is perceived as having an unpleasantly bitter taste, to mutant forms of genes resulting in serious diseases like sickle-cell anemia or emphysema.

This chapter focuses on how that genetic variation is inherited. **Transmission genetics** deals with the manner in which genetic differences among individuals are passed from generation to generation. We are all aware of genetics. We know that children resemble their parents and that there are sometimes uncanny similarities among even distant relatives. But some patterns are more difficult to discern. Traits such as eye color, nose shape, or risk for a particular disease may be passed down faithfully generation after generation, but sometimes they are not, and sometimes they appear and disappear in seemingly random ways.

As a modern science, transmission genetics began with pea-breeding experiments carried out by the monk Gregor Mendel in the 1860s. However, even before then, people understood enough about inheritance that they were able to select crops and livestock with particular characteristics.

16.1 EARLY THEORIES OF INHERITANCE

Thousands of years before Mendel, many societies carried out practical plant and animal breeding. The ancient practices were based on experience rather than on a full understanding of the rules of genetic transmission, but they were nevertheless highly successful. In Mesoamerica, for example, Native Americans chose corn (maize) plants for cultivation that had the biggest ears and softest kernels. Over many generations of such selection, their cultivated corn came to have less and less physical resemblance to its wild ancestral species. Similarly, people in the Eurasian steppes selected their horses for a docile temperament suitable for riding or for hitching to carts or sleds. Practical breeding of this kind provided the crops and livestock from which most of our modern domesticated animals and plants derive.

Early theories of heredity predicted the transmission of acquired characteristics.

The first written speculations about mechanisms of heredity were made by the ancient Greeks. Hippocrates (460–377 BCE), considered the founder of Western medicine, proposed that each part of the body in a sexually mature adult produces a substance that collects in the reproductive organs and that determines the inherited characteristics of the offspring. An implication of this theory is that any **trait,** or characteristic, of an individual can be transmitted from parent to offspring. Even traits that are acquired during the lifetime of an individual, such as muscle strength or bodily injury, were thought to be heritable because of the substance supposedly passed from each body part to the reproductive organs.

The theory that acquired characteristics can be inherited was invoked to explain such traits as the webbed feet of ducks, which were thought to result from many successive generations in which adult ducks stretched the skin between their toes while swimming and passed this trait to offspring. A few decades later, however, Aristotle (384–322 BCE) emphasized several observations that the theory of inheritance of acquired characteristics cannot account for:

- Traits such as hair color can be inherited, but it is difficult to see how hair—a nonliving tissue—could send substances to the reproductive organs.

- Traits that are not yet present in an individual can be transmitted to the offspring. For example, a father and his adult son can both be bald, even though the son was born before the father became bald.

- Parts of the body that are lost as a result of surgery or accident are not missing in the offspring.

From these and other observations, Aristotle concluded that the process of heredity transmits only the *potential* for producing traits present in the parents, and not the traits themselves. Nevertheless, Hippocrates' theory influenced biology until well into the 1800s. It was incorporated into an early theory of evolution proposed by the French biologist Jean-Baptiste Lamarck around 1800, and was also accepted by Charles Darwin, who developed an alternative theory—the theory of evolution by natural selection (Chapter 21).

Belief in blending inheritance discouraged studies of hereditary transmission.

Darwin also subscribed to the now-discredited model of **blending inheritance,** in which traits in the offspring resemble the average of those in the parents. For example, the offspring of plants with blue flowers and those with red flowers should have purple flowers. While traits of offspring are sometimes the average of those of the parents (think of certain cases of human height, for example), the idea of blending inheritance—which implies the blending of the genetic material—as a general rule presents problems. For example, it cannot explain the reappearance of a trait several generations after it apparently "disappeared" in a family, such as red hair or blue eyes.

Another difficulty with the concept of blending inheritance is that variation will be lost over time. Consider an example where black rabbits are rare and white rabbits are common (**Fig. 16.1**).

FIG. 16.1 **Blending inheritance.** This model predicts loss of variation over time and blending of genetic material, which is not observed.

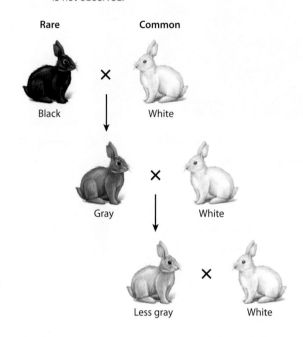

Black rabbits, being rare, are most likely to mate with the much more common white rabbits. If blending inheritance occurs, the result will be gray rabbits. These will also mate with white rabbits, producing even lighter gray rabbits. Over time, the population will end up being all white, or very close to white, and there will be less variation. The only way that black rabbits will be present is if they are re-introduced into the population through mutation or migration. Inheritance will tend to be a homogenizing force, producing in each generation a blend of the original phenotypes. But we know from common experience that variation in most populations is plentiful.

It is ironic that Darwin believed in blending inheritance because this mechanism of inheritance is incompatible with his theory of evolution by means of natural selection. The incompatibility was pointed out by some of Darwin's contemporaries, and Darwin himself recognized it as a serious problem. The problem with blending inheritance is that rare variants, such as black rabbits in the above example, will have no opportunity to increase in frequency even if they survive and reproduce more than white rabbits, since they gradually disappear over time.

Although Darwin was convinced that he was right about natural selection, he was never able to reconcile his theory with the concept of blending inheritance. Unknown to him, the solution had already been discovered in experiments carried out by Gregor Mendel (1822–1884), an Augustinian monk in a monastery in the city of Brno in what is now the Czech Republic. Mendel's key discovery was this: It is not *traits* that are transmitted in inheritance—it is *genes* that are transmitted.

16.2 THE FOUNDATIONS OF MODERN TRANSMISSION GENETICS

Mendel's scientific fame rests on the pea-breeding experiments that he carried out in the years 1856 to 1864 (**Fig. 16.2**), in which he demonstrated the basic principles of transmission genetics. His experiments were so simple and presented with such clarity that they still serve as examples of the scientific method at its best (Chapter 1).

Mendel's experimental organism was the garden pea.
For his experimental material, Mendel used several strains of ordinary garden peas (*Pisum sativum*) that he obtained from a local seed supplier. His experimental approach was similar to that of a few botanists of the eighteenth and nineteenth centuries who studied the results of **hybridization**, or interbreeding between two different varieties or species of an organism. Where Mendel differed from his predecessors was in paying close attention to a small number of easily classified traits with contrasting characteristics. For example, where one strain of peas

had yellow seeds, another had green seeds; and where one had round seeds, the other had wrinkled seeds (**Fig. 16.3**). Altogether Mendel studied seven physical features expressed in contrasting fashion among the strains: seed color, seed shape, pod color, pod shape, flower color, flower position, and plant height.

The expression of each trait in each strain was **true breeding,** which means that the physical appearance of the offspring in each successive generation is identical to the previous one. In other words, plants of the strain with yellow seeds produced only

FIG. 16.2 Gregor Mendel and his experimental organism, the pea plant.

FIG. 16.3 Contrasting traits. Mendel focused on seven contrasting traits.

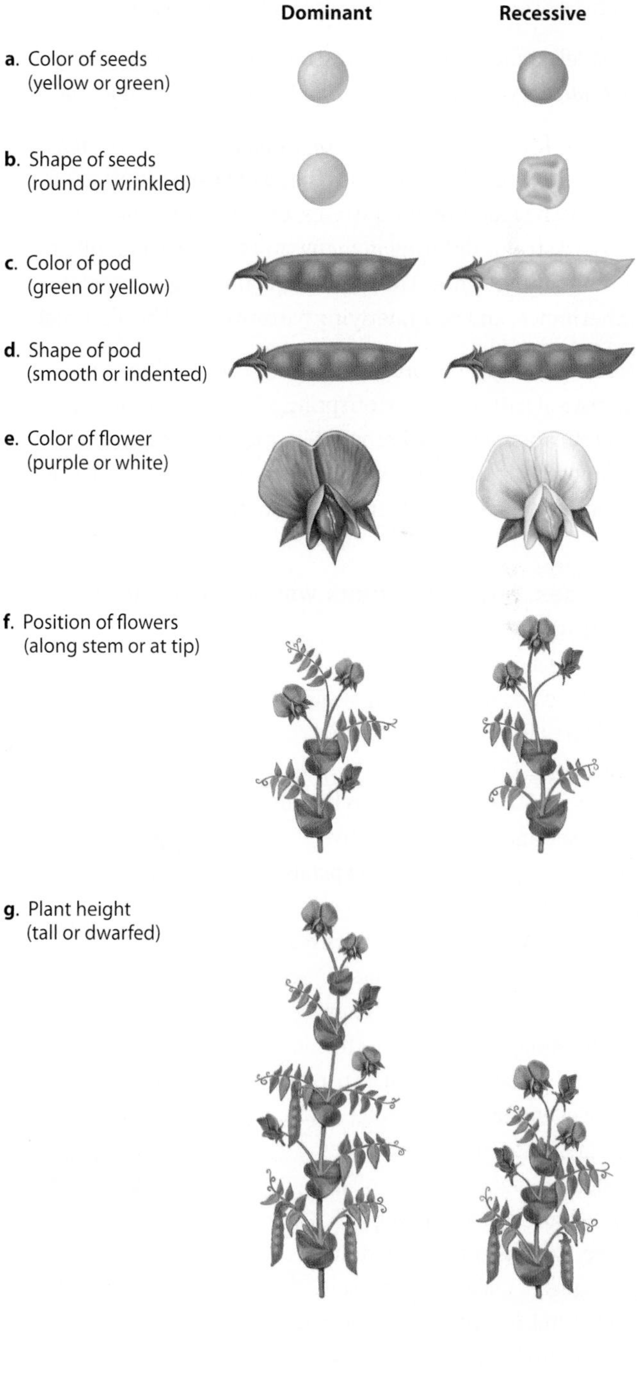

	Dominant	Recessive
a. Color of seeds (yellow or green)		
b. Shape of seeds (round or wrinkled)		
c. Color of pod (green or yellow)		
d. Shape of pod (smooth or indented)		
e. Color of flower (purple or white)		
f. Position of flowers (along stem or at tip)		
g. Plant height (tall or dwarfed)		

yellow seeds, and those of the strain with green seeds produced only green seeds. Likewise, plants of the strain with round seeds produced only round seeds, and those of the strain with wrinkled seeds produced only wrinkled seeds.

The objective of Mendel's experiments was simple. By means of crosses between the true-breeding strains and crosses among their progeny, Mendel hoped to determine whether there are statistical patterns in the occurrence of the contrasting traits, such as yellow seeds or green seeds. If such patterns could be found, he would seek to devise a hypothesis to explain them and then use his hypothesis to predict the outcome of further crosses.

In designing his experiments, Mendel departed from other plant hybridizers of the time in three important ways:

1. Mendel studied true breeding strains, unlike many other plant hybridizers who used complex and poorly defined material.

2. Mendel focused on one trait, or a small number of traits, at a time, with characteristics that were easily contrasted among the true-breeding strains. Other plant hybridizers crossed strains differing in many traits and tried to follow all the traits at once. This resulted in amazingly complex inheritance, and no underlying patterns could be discerned.

3. Mendel counted the progeny of his crosses, looking for statistical patterns in the offspring of his crosses. Others typically noted only whether offspring with a particular characteristic were present or absent, but did not keep track of and count all the progeny of a particular cross.

In crosses, one of the traits was dominant in the offspring.

Mendel began his studies with crosses between true-breeding strains that differed in a single contrasting characteristic. Crossing peas is not as easy as it may sound. Pea flowers include both female and male reproductive organs enclosed together within petals (**Fig. 16.4**). Because of this arrangement, pea plants usually fertilize themselves (self-fertilize). Performing crosses between different plants is a tedious and painstaking process. First, the flower of the designated female parent must be opened at an early stage, and the immature anthers (plant male reproductive organs) clipped off and discarded so the plant cannot self-fertilize. Then mature pollen from the designated male parent must be collected and deposited on the stigma (female reproductive organ) of the

female parent, from where it travels to the reproductive cells in the ovule at the base of the flower. And finally, a cloth bag must be tied around the female flower to prevent stray pollen from entering. No wonder Mendel complained that his eyes hurt!

For each of the seven pairs of contrasting traits, true-breeding strains differing in the trait were crossed. **Fig. 16.5** illustrates a typical result, in this case for yellow versus green seeds. In these kinds of crosses, the parental generation is referred to as the **P_1 generation,** and the first offspring, or filial, generation, is referred to as the **F_1 generation.** In the cross of P_1 yellow $\times$ P_1 green, Mendel observed that all the F_1 progeny were yellow. This result was shown to be independent of the seed color, yellow or green, of the pollen donor because both of the crosses shown below yielded progeny plants with yellow seeds:

Crosses like these, in which the expressions of the trait in the female and male parents are interchanged, are known as **reciprocal crosses.** Mendel showed that reciprocal crosses yielded the same result for each of his seven pairs of contrasting traits.

Moreover, for each pair of contrasting traits, only one of the traits appeared in t he F_1 generation. For these simple crosses, the trait that appears in the F_1 generation is said to be **dominant,** and the contrasting trait that does not appear is said to be **recessive.** For each pair of traits illustrated in Fig. 16.3, the dominant trait is shown on the left, and the recessive on the

FIG. 16.4   Crossing pea plants. Crossing plants in a way that isolated either the ovules or the pollen controlled what genetic material each parent contributed to the offspring.

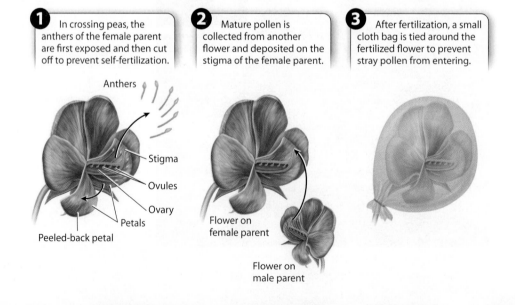

❶ In crossing peas, the anthers of the female parent are first exposed and then cut off to prevent self-fertilization.

❷ Mature pollen is collected from another flower and deposited on the stigma of the female parent.

❸ After fertilization, a small cloth bag is tied around the fertilized flower to prevent stray pollen from entering.

Anthers

Stigma

Ovules

Ovary

Petals

Peeled-back petal

Flower on female parent

Flower on male parent

FIG. 16.5 The first-generation hybrid (F₁). A cross between two of Mendel's true-breeding plants (the parental, or P₁, generation) yielded first-generation hybrids displaying the dominant trait.

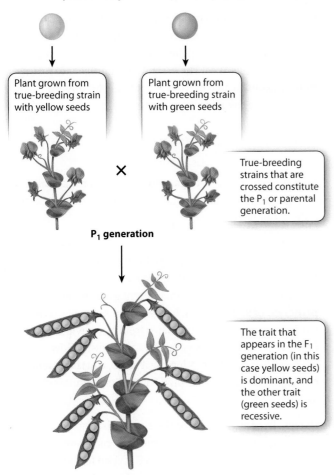

Plant grown from true-breeding strain with yellow seeds

Plant grown from true-breeding strain with green seeds

True-breeding strains that are crossed constitute the P₁ or parental generation.

P₁ generation

The trait that appears in the F₁ generation (in this case yellow seeds) is dominant, and the other trait (green seeds) is recessive.

F₁ generation

the normal function of the gene. For example, yellow pea seeds result from an enzyme that breaks down green chlorophyll, allowing yellow pigments to show through. Green seeds result from a mutation in this gene that inactivates the enzyme, and so the green chlorophyll is retained. In an F₁ hybrid, such as that in Fig. 16.5, which receives a nonmutant gene from one parent and a mutant gene from the other, the seeds are yellow because one copy of the nonmutant gene produces enough of the enzyme to break down the chlorophyll to yield a yellow seed.

16.3 SEGREGATION: MENDEL'S KEY DISCOVERY

Mendel's most important discovery was that the F₁ progeny of a cross between plants with different traits did *not* breed true. In the **F₂ generation**, produced by allowing the F₁ flowers to undergo self-fertilization, the recessive trait reappeared (**Fig. 16.6**). Not only did the recessive trait reappear, it reappeared in a definite numerical proportion. Among a large number of F₂ progeny,

FIG. 16.6 Self-fertilization of the F₁ hybrid, resulting in seeds of the F₂ generation. The recessive trait appeared again in the F₂ generation.

Seeds from F₁ plants produced from a cross of true-breeding yellow-seed and green-seed plants are yellow because yellow is dominant and green is recessive in seed color.

F₁ generation

Peas are normally self-fertilizing, and so if they are left alone, the pollen produced in each flower fertilizes the ovules.

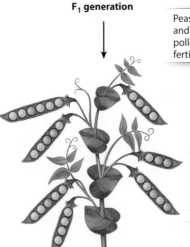

Because fertilization takes place at random, any individual pod can have a ratio of dominant:recessive that deviates from 3:1.

F₂ generation
(ratio 3 yellow seeds:1 green seed)

right. Thus, yellow seed is dominant to green seed, round seed is dominant to wrinkled seed, and so forth. Mendel explained these findings by supposing that there is a hereditary factor for yellow seeds and a different hereditary factor for green seeds, likewise a hereditary factor for round seeds and a different one for wrinkled seeds, and so on. We now know that the hereditary factors that result in contrasting traits are different forms of a gene that affect the trait. The different forms of a gene are called **alleles.** The particular combination of alleles present in an individual constitutes its **genotype,** and the expression of the trait in the individual constitutes its **phenotype.**

In the cross between true-breeding plants with yellow seeds and true-breeding plants with green seeds, the genotype of each F₁ seed includes an allele for yellow from the yellow parent and an allele for green from the green parent. The phenotype of each F₁ seed is nevertheless yellow, because yellow is dominant to green.

The molecular basis of dominance is the fact that, in diploid organisms, only one copy of most genes is needed to carry out

TABLE 16.1　Observed F$_2$ Ratios in Mendel's Experiments

TRAIT	DOMINANT TRAIT	RECESSIVE TRAIT	RATIO
Seed color	6,022	2,001	3.01:1
Seed shape	5,474	1,850	2.96:1
Pod color	428	152	2.82:1
Pod shape	882	299	2.95:1
Flower color	705	224	3.15:1
Flower position	651	207	3.14:1
Plant height	787	277	2.84:1

Mendel found that the dominant:recessive ratio was very close to 3:1. The results he observed among the F$_2$ progeny for each of the seven pairs of traits are given in **Table 16.1.** Across experiments for all seven traits, the ratio of dominant:recessive F$_2$ offspring was 14,949:5,010. Although there is variation from one experiment to the next, the overall ratio of 14,949:5,010 equals 2.98:1, which is a very close approximation to 3:1.

Genes come in pairs that segregate in the formation of reproductive cells.

The explanation for the 3:1 ratio in the F$_2$ and Mendel's observations in general can be summarized with reference to **Fig. 16.7:**

FIG. 16.7　The principle of segregation.

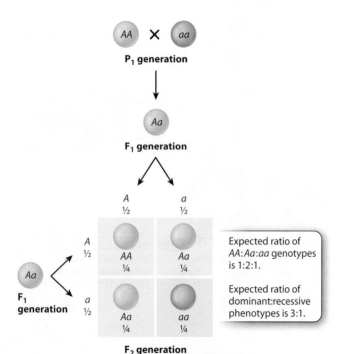

F$_2$ generation

1. Except for cells involved in reproduction, each cell of a pea plant contains two alleles of each gene. In each true-breeding strain constituting the P$_1$ generation, the two alleles are identical. In Fig. 16.7, we designate the allele associated with yellow seeds as *A* and that associated with green seeds as *a*. The genotype of the true-breeding strain with yellow seeds can therefore be written as *AA*, and that of the true-breeding strain with green seeds as *aa*. The *AA* and *aa* genotypes are said to be **homozygous,** which means that both alleles present in an individual are the same.

→　**Quick Check 1**　What are the genotypes and phenotypes for Mendel's true-breeding parent plants?

2. Each reproductive cell, or **gamete,** contains only one allele of each gene. In this case, a gamete can contain the *A* allele or the *a* allele, but not both.

3. In the formation of gametes, the two members of a gene pair **segregate** (or separate) equally into gametes, so that half the gametes get one allele and half get the other allele. This separation of alleles into different gametes defines the **principle of segregation.** In the case of homozygous plants (such as *AA* or *aa*), all the gametes from an individual are the same. That is, the homozygous *AA* strain with yellow seeds produces gametes containing the *A* allele, and the homozygous *aa* strain with green seeds produces gametes containing the *a* allele.

4. The fertilized egg cell, called the **zygote,** is formed from the random union of two gametes, one from each parent. For the cross *AA* × *aa*, the zygote is an F$_1$ hybrid formed from the union of an *A*-bearing gamete with an *a*-bearing gamete. Each F$_1$ hybrid therefore has the genotype *Aa* (Fig. 16.7). The *Aa* genotype is **heterozygous,** which means that the two alleles for a given gene are different. The F$_1$ seeds are yellow because yellow is dominant to green. Note that each F$_1$ progeny contains an *a* allele because its genotype is *Aa*, but the phenotype of the seed is yellow and indistinguishable from that of an *AA* genotype.

→　**Quick Check 2**　Is it possible for two individuals to have the same phenotype but different genotypes? The same genotype, but different phenotypes? How?

5. When the F$_1$ progeny (genotype *Aa*) form gametes, by the principle of segregation the *A* and *a* alleles again separate, so that half the gametes contain only the *A* allele and the other half contain only the *a* allele (Fig. 16.7).

6. In the formation of the F$_2$ generation, the gametes from the F$_1$ parents again combine at random. The consequences of random union of gametes can be worked out by means of

a checkerboard of the sort shown in Fig. 16.7. This kind of square is called a **Punnett square** after its inventor, Reginald Punnett, a British geneticist.

Across the top of a Punnett square are the gametes from one parent, each with its respective frequency; and down the side are the gametes from the other parent, again each with its respective frequency. These frequencies are the probabilities of each type of gamete occurring. In the case illustrated in Fig. 16.7, both parents are F_1 hybrids with the genotype Aa, and because the A and a alleles undergo segregation in the formation of gametes, half of the gametes from each parent are A and half are a.

Inside the Punnett square, each box contains the genotype of a possible zygote formed by random union of the gametes. The genotype of the zygote in each cell corresponds to the alleles in the gametes in the corresponding row and column, and the relative frequency of each zygote is obtained by multiplication of the gametic frequencies in the corresponding row and column. For example, the zygote in the top left corner in the Punnett square in Fig. 16.7 is formed by the union of an A-bearing gamete from the top and an A-bearing gamete from the side. The zygote genotype is therefore AA, and because each of the gametic types has a relative frequency of ½, the relative frequency of the AA zygote is ½ × ½ = ¼. It is the multiplication of the gametic frequencies that corresponds to the random union of gametes.

For the cross in Fig. 16.7, the boxes of the Punnett square correspond to all of the possible individuals in the F_2 generation. The expected *genotypes* of the progeny are therefore ¼ AA, ½ Aa, and ¼ aa (or 1:2:1). When there is dominance, however, as there is in this case, the AA and Aa genotypes have the same phenotype, and so the ratio of dominant:recessive *phenotypes* is 3:1. The Punnett square in Fig. 16.7 illustrates the biological basis of the 3:1 ratio of phenotypes that Mendel observed in the F_2 generation. Nevertheless, the underlying ratio of AA:Aa:aa genotypes is 1:2:1.

→ **Quick Check 3** What are the expected progeny (genotypes and phenotypes) from a cross of an AA plant with an Aa plant?

The principle of segregation was tested by predicting the outcome of crosses.

The model of segregation of gene pairs (alleles) and their random combination in the formation of a zygote depicted in Fig. 16.7 was Mendel's hypothesis, an explanation he put forward to explain an observed result. But without further experiments, he could not know if his hypothesis was right or wrong. The true test of a hypothesis is whether it can predict the results of experiments that have not yet been carried out (Chapter 1). If the predictions are correct, one's confidence in the hypothesis is strengthened. Mendel appreciated this intuitively, even though the scientific method as understood today had not been formalized.

The Punnett square in Fig. 16.7 makes two strong predictions. The first is that the seeds in the F_2 generation showing the recessive green phenotype should be homozygous aa. If the green F_2 seeds have the genotype aa, then they should breed true. That is, when the seeds are grown into mature plants and self-fertilization is allowed to take place, the self-fertilized aa plants should produce only green seeds (aa). This prediction was confirmed by examining seeds actually produced by plants grown from the F_2 green seeds.

The second prediction from the Punnett square in Fig. 16.7 is more complex. It has to do with the seeds in the F_2 generation that show the dominant yellow phenotype. Note that although these seeds have the same phenotype, they have two different genotypes (AA and Aa). Among just the yellow seeds, ⅓ should have the genotype AA and ⅔ should have the genotype Aa, for a ratio of 1 AA:2 Aa. (The proportions are ⅓:⅔ because we are considering *only* the seeds that are yellow.) The AA and Aa genotypes can be distinguished by the types of seeds they produce when self-fertilized. The AA plants produce only seeds with the dominant yellow phenotype (that is, they are true breeding), whereas the Aa plants yield dominant yellow and recessive green seeds in the ratio 3:1. Mendel did such experiments, and the prediction turned out to be correct. His data confirming the 1:2 ratio of AA:Aa among F_2 individuals with the dominant phenotype are shown in **Table 16.2**.

A testcross is a mating to an individual with the homozygous recessive genotype.

A more direct test of segregation is to cross the F_1 progeny with the true-breeding recessive strain instead of allowing them to self-fertilize. Any cross of an unknown genotype with a homozygous recessive genotype is known as a **testcross.**

The F_1 progeny show the dominant yellow seed phenotype. A yellow seed phenotype can result from either of two possible genotypes, Aa or AA. A testcross with plants of the homozygous

TABLE 16.2 Genetic ratios from self-fertilization of plants showing the dominant phenotype

TRAIT	HOMOZYGOUS DOMINANT	HETERO-ZYGOUS	RATIO
Yellow seeds	166	353	0.94:2
Round seeds	193	372	1.04:2
Green pods	40	60	1.33:2
Smooth pods	29	71	0.82:2
Purple flowers	36	64	1.13:2
Flowers along stem	33	67	0.99:2
Tall plants	28	72	0.78:2

recessive genotype (*aa*) can distinguish between these two possibilities (**Fig. 16.8**). The testcross is highly informative because the homozygous recessive parent produces only gametes carrying the recessive allele (*a*). In Fig. 16.8, the gametes from the homozygous recessive parent are shown across the top, and they consist only of *a*-bearing gametes. Down the side are gametes from the individual with the unknown genotype.

Let's first consider what happens in a testcross to an *Aa* individual (Fig. 16.8a). An *Aa* individual produces both *A*-bearing gametes and *a*-bearing gametes. Inside the Punnett square are the predicted offspring from the testcross, which consist of ½ *Aa* zygotes, which yield yellow seeds, and ½ *aa* zygotes, which yield green seeds. By contrast, an *AA* individual produces only *A*-bearing gametes, so all the zygotes have the *Aa* genotype, which yields yellow seeds (Fig. 16.8b). In other words, the testcross gives different results depending on whether the parent is heterozygous (*Aa*) or homozygous (*AA*).

Note that in a testcross the *phenotypes* of the progeny reveal the *alleles* present in the gametes from the tested parent. An *Aa* individual yields ½ *Aa* (yellow seeds) and ½ *aa* (green seeds), since the *Aa* parent produces ½ *A*-bearing and ½ *a*-bearing gametes. An *AA* individual yields only *Aa* (yellow seeds), since the *AA* parent produces only *A*-bearing gametes. These results are a direct demonstration of the principle of segregation, since the ratio of the phenotypes of progeny reflect the equal segregation of alleles into gametes. Some of Mendel's testcross data indicating 1:1 segregation in heterozygous genotypes are shown in **Table 16.3**.

Segregation of alleles reflects the separation of chromosomes in meiosis.

The principles of transmission genetics have a physical basis in the process of meiosis (Chapter 11). During meiosis I, maternal and paternal chromosomes (homologous chromosomes) align on the metaphase plate. Then, during anaphase I, the homologous

FIG. 16.8   A testcross. A cross with a homozygous recessive individual reveals the genotype of the other parent.

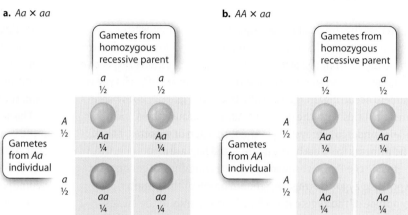

chromosomes separate, and each chromosome goes to a different pole. Because gene pairs are carried on homologous chromosomes, segregation of alleles observed by Mendel corresponds to the separation of chromosomes that takes place in anaphase I.

Fig. 16.9 illustrates the separation of a pair of homologous chromosomes in anaphase I. In the configuration shown, the copies of the *A* allele (dark blue) separate from the copies of the *a* allele (light blue) in anaphase I. The separation of chromosomes is the physical basis of the segregation of alleles.

Dominance is not universally observed.

Many traits do not show complete dominance such as Mendel observed with pea plants. Instead, they show **incomplete dominance,** in which the phenotype of the heterozygous

TABLE 16.3   Phenotype of progeny from testcrosses of heterozygotes

TRAIT	DOMINANT TRAIT	RECESSIVE TRAIT	RATIO
Seed color	196	189	1.04:1
Seed shape	193	192	1.01:1
Flower color	85	81	1.05:1
Plant height	87	79	1.10:1

FIG. 16.9   Segregation of alleles of a single gene. Homologous chromosomes separate during meiosis, leading to segregation of alleles.

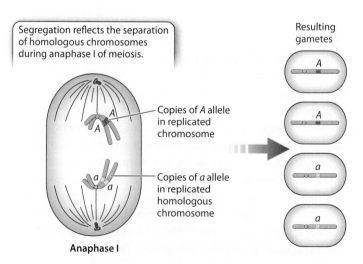

genotype is intermediate between those of the homozygous genotypes. In such cases, the result of segregation can be observed directly because each genotype has a distinct phenotype. An example is flower color in the snapdragon (*Antirrhinum majus*), in which the homozygous genotypes have red ($C^R\,C^R$) or white ($C^W\,C^W$) flowers, and the heterozygous genotype $C^R\,C^W$ has pink flowers (**Fig. 16.10**). In notating incomplete dominance, we use superscripts to indicate the alleles, rather than upper-case and lower-case letters, because neither allele is dominant to the other. A cross of homozygous $C^R\,C^R$ and $C^W\,C^W$ strains results in hybrid F_1 progeny that are pink (C^RC^W), and when these are crossed the resulting F_2 generation consists of ¼ red ($C^R\,C^R$), ½ pink ($C^R\,C^W$), and ¼ white ($C^W\,C^W$).

FIG. 16.10 **Incomplete dominance for flower color in snapdragons.** In incomplete dominance, an intermediate phenotype is seen.

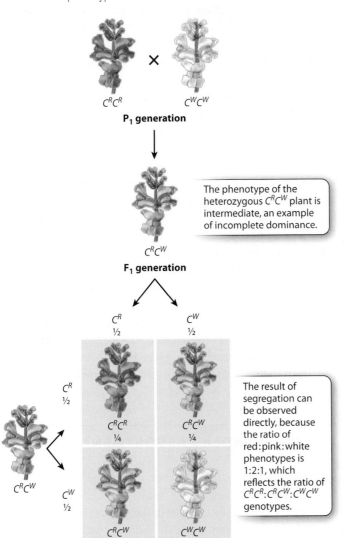

The phenotype of the heterozygous C^RC^W plant is intermediate, an example of incomplete dominance.

The result of segregation can be observed directly, because the ratio of red:pink:white phenotypes is 1:2:1, which reflects the ratio of C^RC^R:C^RC^W:C^WC^W genotypes.

F_2 generation

Note that in this case the genotype ratio and the phenotype ratio are both 1:2:1, since each genotype has a distinct phenotype. Such a direct demonstration of segregation makes one wonder whether Mendel's work might have been appreciated more readily if his traits had shown incomplete dominance!

The principles of transmission genetics are statistical and stated in terms of probabilities.

The element of chance in fertilization implies that the genotype of any particular progeny cannot be determined in advance. However, one can deduce the likelihood, or **probability,** that a specified genotype will occur. The probability of occurrence of a genotype must always lie between 0 and 1; a probability of 0 means that the genotype cannot occur, and a probability of 1 means that the occurrence of the genotype is certain. For example, in the cross $Aa \times AA$, no offspring can have the genotype *aa*, so in this mating the probability of *aa* is 0. Similarly, in the mating $AA \times aa$, all offspring must have the genotype *Aa*, so in this mating the probability of *Aa* is 1.

In many cases, the probability of a particular genotype is neither 0 nor 1, but some intermediate value. For one gene, the probabilities for a single individual can be deduced from the parental genotypes in the mating and the principle of segregation. For example, the probability of producing a homozygous recessive individual from the cross $Aa \times Aa$ is ¼ (see Fig. 16.7), and that from the cross $Aa \times aa$ is ½ (see Fig. 16.8a).

The probabilities for a single individual can also be inferred from observed data because the overall proportions of two (or more) genotypes among a large number of observations approximates the probability of each of the genotypes for a single observation. For example, in Mendel's F_2 data (see Table 16.1), the overall ratio of dominant:recessive is 2.98:1, or very nearly 3:1. This result implies that the probability that an individual F_2 plant has the homozygous recessive phenotype is very close to ¼, which is the value inferred from the principle of segregation.

Sometimes it becomes necessary to combine the probabilities of two or more possible outcomes of a cross, and in such cases either of two rules may be helpful.

1. **Addition rule.** This principle applies when the possible outcomes being considered cannot occur simultaneously. For example, suppose that a single offspring is chosen at random from the progeny of the mating $Aa \times Aa$, and we wish to know the probability that the offspring is either *AA* or *Aa*. The key words here are "either" and "or." Each of these outcomes is possible, but both cannot occur simultaneously in a single individual; the outcomes are mutually exclusive. When the possibilities are mutually exclusive, the addition rule states that the probability of either event occurring is given by the sum of their individual probabilities. In this example, the chosen offspring could either have genotype *AA* (with probability ¼,

according to Fig. 16.7), or the offspring could have genotype *Aa* (with probability ½). Therefore, the probability that the chosen individual has either the *AA* or the *Aa* genotype is given by ¼ + ½ = ¾ (see Fig. 16.7). Alternatively, the ¾ could be interpreted to mean that, among a large number of offspring from the mating *Aa* × *Aa*, the proportion exhibiting the dominant phenotype will be very close to ¾. This interpretation is verified by the data in Table 16.1.

2. **Multiplication rule**. This principle applies when outcomes can occur simultaneously, and the occurrence of one has no effect upon the likelihood of the other. Events that do not influence one another are independent, and the multiplication rule states that the probability of two independent events occurring together is the product of their respective probabilities. This rule is widely used to determine the probabilities of successive offspring of a cross, because each event of fertilization is independent of any other. For example, in the mating *Aa* × *Aa*, one may wish to determine the probability that, among four peas in a pod, the one nearest the stem is green and the others yellow. Here, the word "and" is a simple indicator that the multiplication rule should be used. Because each seed results from an independent fertilization, this probability is given by the product of the probability that the seed nearest the stem is *aa* and the probability that each of the other seeds is either *AA* or *Aa*, and hence the probability is ¼ × ¾ × ¾ × ¾ = 27/256, as shown for the top pod in **Fig. 16.11.**

The addition and multiplication rules are very powerful when used in combination. Consider the following question: In the mating *Aa* × *Aa*, what is the probability that, among four seeds in a pod, exactly one is green? We have already seen in Fig. 16.11 that the multiplication rule gives the probability of the seed nearest the stem being green as 27/256. As illustrated in Fig. 16.11, there are only four possible ways in which exactly one seed can be green, each of which has a probability of 27/256, and these outcomes are mutually exclusive. Therefore, by the addition rule, the probability of there being exactly one green and three yellow seeds in a pod, occurring in any order, is given by 27/256 + 27/256 + 27/256 + 27/256 = 108/256, or approximately 42%.

→   **Quick Check 4** What is the probability that *any* two peas are green and two are yellow in a pea pod with exactly four seeds?

Mendelian segregation preserves genetic variation.
As noted earlier, Darwin was befuddled because blending inheritance would make genetic variation disappear so rapidly that evolution by means of natural selection could not occur. Although Darwin was completely unaware of Mendel's findings, segregation was the answer to his problem.

The importance of segregation is that it demonstrates that the alleles encoding a trait do not alter or influence one another when they are present together in a heterozygous genotype (except in very rare instances). The recessive trait, masked in one generation, can appear in the next, looking exactly as it did in the true-breeding strains. Mendel fully appreciated the significance of this discovery. In one of his letters, he emphasized that "the two parental traits appear, separated and unchanged, and there is nothing to indicate that one of them has either inherited or taken over anything from the other." In other words, no hint of any sort of blending between the parental genetic material takes place. Because the individual genes maintain their identity down through the generations (except for rare mutations), genetic variation in a population also tends to be maintained through time. The maintenance of genetic variation is discussed further in Chapter 21.

FIG. 16.11 Application of the multiplication and addition rules.

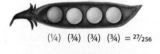

(¼) (¾) (¾) (¾) = 27/256

Probability that the seed closest to the stem is green *and* the others are yellow is determined by the multiplication rule.

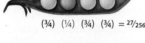

(¾) (¼) (¾) (¾) = 27/256

(¾) (¾) (¼) (¾) = 27/256

(¾) (¾) (¾) (¼) = 27/256

————
108/256 = 42%

Probability that *any* seed is green and the others are yellow is determined by first using the multiplication rule to determine the probability that a particular seed is green, then the addition rule to determine that any seed is green.

16.4 INDEPENDENT ASSORTMENT

We have seen that segregation of dominant and recessive alleles of a single gene results in a 3:1 ratio of dominant:recessive phenotypes in the F$_2$ generation. What happens when the parental strains differ in two traits, for example when a strain having yellow and wrinkled seeds is crossed with a strain having green and round seeds? The results of these kinds of experiments constitute Mendel's second key discovery, the **principle of independent assortment.** This principle states that segregation of one set of alleles of a gene pair is independent of the segregation of another set of alleles of a different gene pair. That is, different gene pairs assort (segregate) independently of one another.

Independent assortment is observed when genes segregate independently of one another.

In the cross between a strain with yellow and wrinkled seeds and a strain with green and round seeds, the phenotype of the F_1 seeds is easily predicted. Because yellow is dominant to green, and round is dominant to wrinkled, the F_1 seeds are expected to be yellow and round, and in fact they are (**Fig. 16.12**). When these seeds are grown and the F_1 plants are allowed to undergo self-fertilization, the result is as shown in Fig. 16.12. Among 639 seeds from this cross, Mendel observed the following:

yellow round	367
green round	122
yellow wrinkled	113
green wrinkled	37

The ratio of these phenotypes is 9.9 : 3.3 : 3.1 : 1.0, which Mendel realized is close to 9 : 3 : 3 : 1. The latter ratio is that expected if the *A* and *a* alleles for seed color undergo segregation and form gametes independently of the *B* and *b* alleles for seed shape. For seed color alone we expect a ratio of ¾ yellow : ¼ green, and for seed shape alone we expect a ratio of ¾ round : ¼ wrinkled. If the traits are independent, then we can use the multiplication rule to predict the outcomes for both traits:

yellow round	$(3/4) \times (3/4) = 9/16$
green round	$(1/4) \times (3/4) = 3/16$
yellow wrinkled	$(3/4) \times (1/4) = 3/16$
green wrinkled	$(1/4) \times (1/4) = 1/16$

Note that 9/16 : 3/16 : 3 /16 : 1/16 is equivalent to 9 : 3 : 3 : 1.

The underlying reason for the 9 : 3 : 3 : 1 ratio of phenotypes in the F_2 generation is that the alleles for yellow versus green and those for round versus wrinkled are assorted into gametes independently of each other. In other words, the hereditary transmission of either gene has no effect on the hereditary transmission of the other. A Punnett square depicting

FIG. 16.12 Mendel's crosses with two traits. Plants homozygous for two traits produce offspring with a phenotypic ratio of 9:3:3:1.

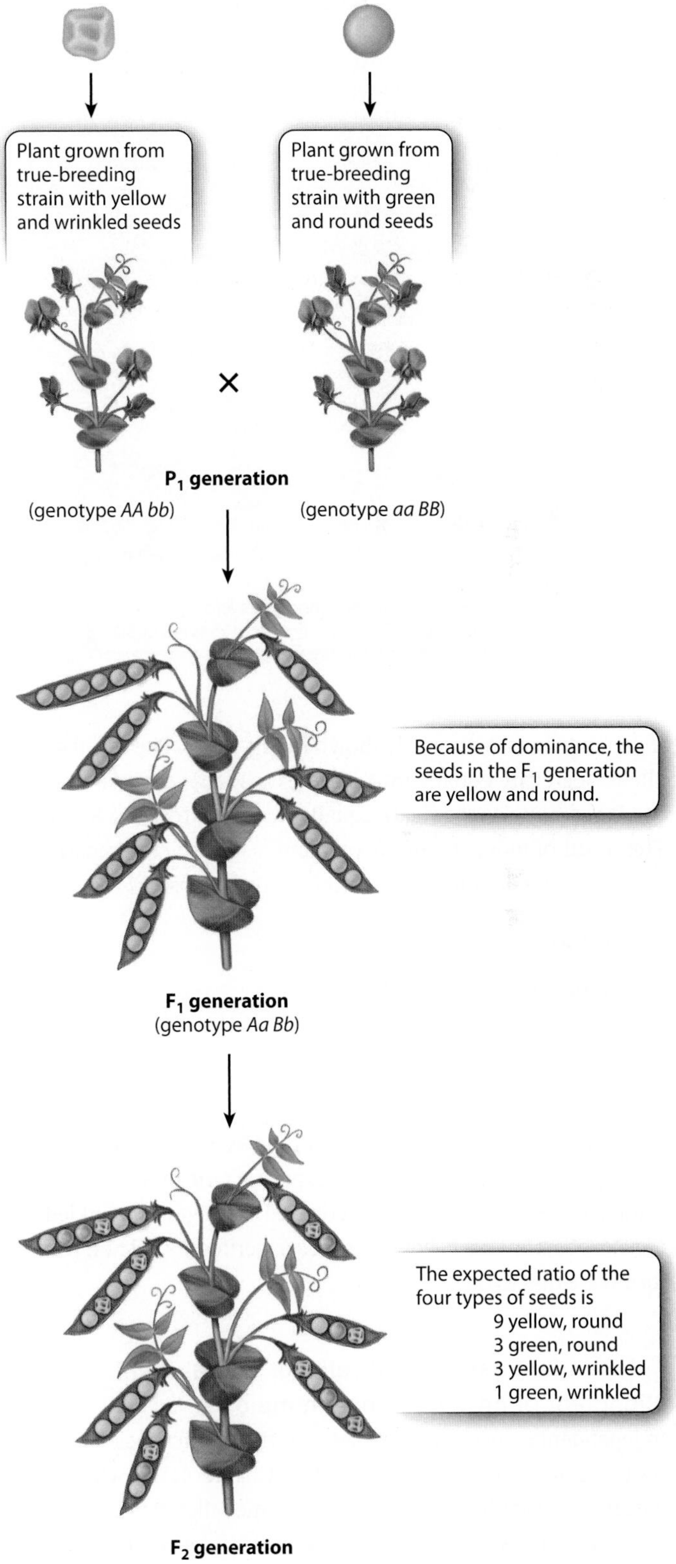
Plant grown from true-breeding strain with yellow and wrinkled seeds
Plant grown from true-breeding strain with green and round seeds
×
P_1 generation
(genotype *AA bb*)
(genotype *aa BB*)
Because of dominance, the seeds in the F_1 generation are yellow and round.
F_1 generation
(genotype *Aa Bb*)
The expected ratio of the four types of seeds is
9 yellow, round
3 green, round
3 yellow, wrinkled
1 green, wrinkled
F_2 generation

FIG. 16.13 **Independent assortment of two gene pairs.** The Punnett square reveals the underlying phenotypic ratio of 9:3:3:1.

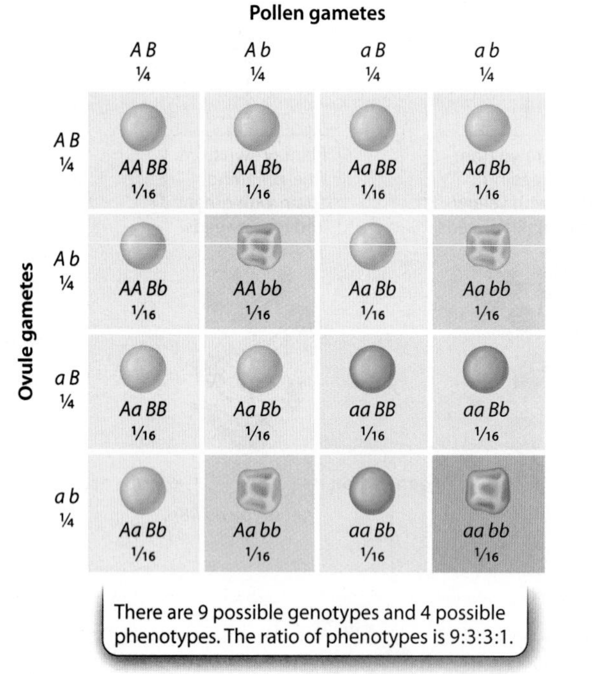

Pollen gametes

	A B ¼	A b ¼	a B ¼	a b ¼
A B ¼	AA BB ¹⁄₁₆	AA Bb ¹⁄₁₆	Aa BB ¹⁄₁₆	Aa Bb ¹⁄₁₆
A b ¼	AA Bb ¹⁄₁₆	AA bb ¹⁄₁₆	Aa Bb ¹⁄₁₆	Aa bb ¹⁄₁₆
a B ¼	Aa BB ¹⁄₁₆	Aa Bb ¹⁄₁₆	aa BB ¹⁄₁₆	aa Bb ¹⁄₁₆
a b ¼	Aa Bb ¹⁄₁₆	Aa bb ¹⁄₁₆	aa Bb ¹⁄₁₆	aa bb ¹⁄₁₆

(Ovule gametes, left axis)

There are 9 possible genotypes and 4 possible phenotypes. The ratio of phenotypes is 9:3:3:1.

independent assortment is shown in **Fig. 16.13.** The *A* and *a* alleles segregate equally into gametes as ½ *A* : ½ *a*, and likewise the *B* and *b* alleles segregate equally into gametes as ½ *B* : ½ *b*. The result of independent assortment is that the four possible gametic types are produced in equal proportions:

AB gametes $(\frac{1}{2}) \times (\frac{1}{2}) = \frac{1}{4}$

Ab gametes $(\frac{1}{2}) \times (\frac{1}{2}) = \frac{1}{4}$

aB gametes $(\frac{1}{2}) \times (\frac{1}{2}) = \frac{1}{4}$

ab gametes $(\frac{1}{2}) \times (\frac{1}{2}) = \frac{1}{4}$

As the Punnett square in Fig. 16.13 shows, random union of these gametic types produces the expected ratio of 9 yellow round, 3 green round, 3 yellow wrinkled, and 1 green wrinkled. **Fig. 16.14** summarizes how Mendel's experiments led him to formulate his two laws.

Independent assortment reflects the random alignment of chromosomes in meiosis.

Independent assortment of genes on different chromosomes results from the mechanics of meiosis (Chapter 11), in which different pairs of homologous chromosomes align randomly on the metaphase plate. For some pairs of chromosomes, the maternal chromosome goes toward one pole, and the paternal chromosome goes to the other pole, but for other pairs, just the

FIG. 16.14

How are simple traits inherited?

BACKGROUND The experiments of Gregor Mendel, carried out in the years 1856–1863, are among the most important in all of biology.

EXPERIMENT Mendel set out to improve upon previous research in heredity. He writes that "among all the numerous experiments made, not one has been carried out to such an extent and in such a way as to make it possible to determine the number of different forms under which the offspring of the hybrids appear, or to arrange these forms with certainty according to their separate generations, or definitely to ascertain their statistical relations." By studying simple traits across several generations of crosses, Mendel observed how these traits were inherited.

RESULTS The "statistical relations" became very clear. Crosses between plants that were hybrids of a single trait displayed two phenotypes in a ratio of 3:1. Crosses between plants that were hybrids of two traits displayed four different phenotypes in a ratio of 9:3:3:1.

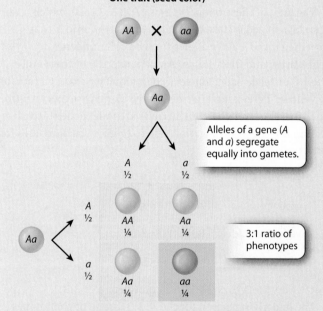

One trait (seed color)

AA × aa

Aa

Alleles of a gene (*A* and *a*) segregate equally into gametes.

A ½   a ½

	A ½	a ½
A ½	AA ¼	Aa ¼
a ½	Aa ¼	aa ¼

(Aa × Aa)

3:1 ratio of phenotypes

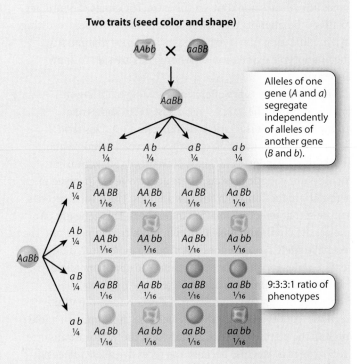

Two traits (seed color and shape)

AAbb × aaBB

AaBb

Alleles of one gene (*A* and *a*) segregate independently of alleles of another gene (*B* and *b*).

	A B ¼	*A b* ¼	*a B* ¼	*a b* ¼
A B ¼	AA BB ¹⁄₁₆	AA Bb ¹⁄₁₆	Aa BB ¹⁄₁₆	Aa Bb ¹⁄₁₆
A b ¼	AA Bb ¹⁄₁₆	AA bb ¹⁄₁₆	Aa Bb ¹⁄₁₆	Aa bb ¹⁄₁₆
a B ¼	Aa BB ¹⁄₁₆	Aa Bb ¹⁄₁₆	aa BB ¹⁄₁₆	aa Bb ¹⁄₁₆
a b ¼	Aa Bb ¹⁄₁₆	Aa bb ¹⁄₁₆	aa Bb ¹⁄₁₆	aa bb ¹⁄₁₆

AaBb

9:3:3:1 ratio of phenotypes

CONCLUSION From observing these ratios among several different traits, Mendel made two key conclusions, now called Mendel's laws:

1. The principle of segregation states that individuals inherit two copies (alleles) of each gene, one from the mother and one from the father, and when the individual forms reproductive cells, the two copies separate (segregate) equally in the eggs or sperm.

2. The principle of independent assortment states that the two copies of each gene segregate into gametes independently of the two copies of another gene.

FOLLOW-UP WORK Mendel's work was ignored during his lifetime, and its importance was not recognized until 1900, 16 years after his death. The rediscovery marks the beginning of the modern science of genetics.

SOURCE Mendel's paper in English is available at http://www.mendelweb.org/Mendel.html.

opposite occurs. Because the alignment is random, gene pairs on different chromosomes assort independently of one another.

Fig. 16.15 illustrates two possible alignments that are equally likely. In one alignment, the *B* allele (dark red) goes to the same pole as the *A* allele (dark blue), and in the other alignment it is the *b* allele (light red) that goes in the same direction as the *A* allele. The first type of alignment results in a 1:1 ratio of *A B* : *a b* gametes, and the second type of alignment results in a 1:1 ratio of *A B* : *a b* gametes. Because the two orientations are equally likely, the overall ratio of *A B* : *a b* : *A B* : *a b* from a large number of cells undergoing meiosis is expected to be 1:1:1:1. This is the principle of independent assortment for genes located in different chromosomes.

Not all genes undergo independent assortment. For example, genes that are sufficiently close together in one chromosome do not assort independently of one another. Genes in the same chromosome that fail to show independent assortment are said to be **linked**. Genes that are genetically linked are discussed in Chapter 17.

FIG. 16.15 Independent assortment of genes in different chromosomes. Chromosomes are sorted into daughter cells randomly during meiosis, resulting in independent assortment of genes.

Independent assortment of genes in different chromosomes reflects the fact that nonhomologous chromosomes can orient in either of two ways that are equally likely.

Anaphase I   Anaphase I

Resulting gametes   Resulting gametes

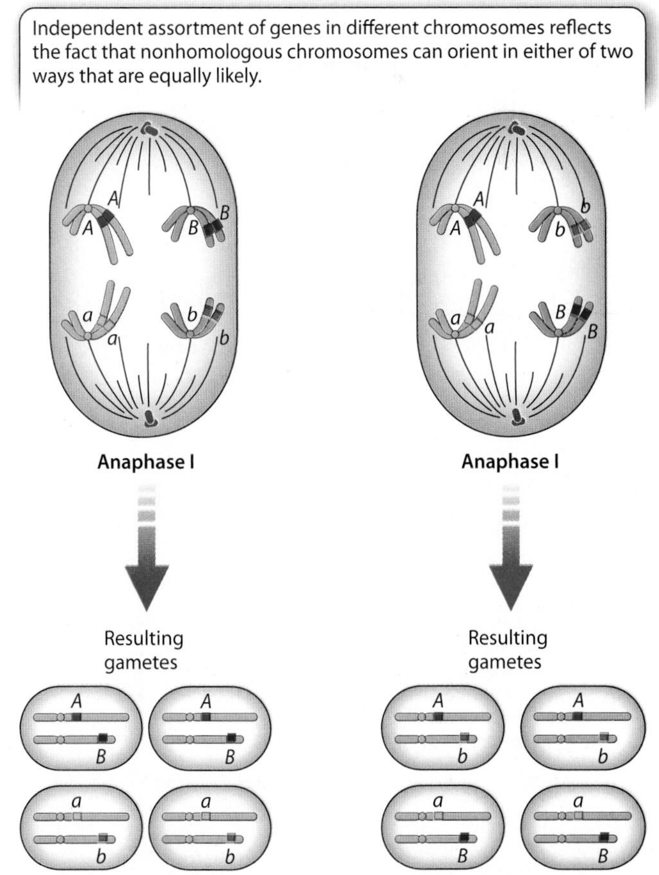

Phenotypic ratios can be modified by interactions between genes.

The 9:3:3:1 ratio results from independent assortment of two genes when one allele of each gene is dominant and when the

FIG. 16.16 **Epistasis, the interaction of genes affecting the same trait.** Epistasis can modify the 9:3:3:1 ratio of phenotypes, in this example to 13:3.

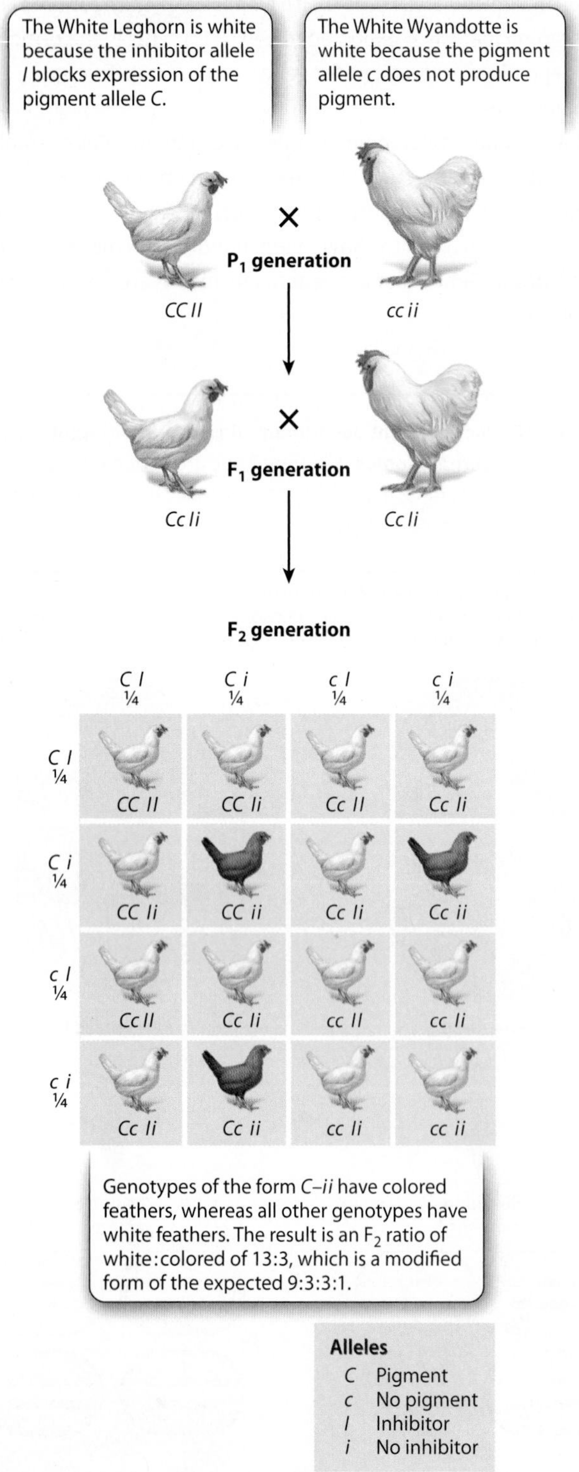

The White Leghorn is white because the inhibitor allele *I* blocks expression of the pigment allele *C*.

The White Wyandotte is white because the pigment allele *c* does not produce pigment.

P₁ generation

CC II   *cc ii*

F₁ generation

Cc Ii   *Cc Ii*

F₂ generation

	$C\,I$ ¼	$C\,i$ ¼	$c\,I$ ¼	$c\,i$ ¼
$C\,I$ ¼	*CC II*	*CC Ii*	*Cc II*	*Cc Ii*
$C\,i$ ¼	*CC Ii*	*CC ii*	*Cc Ii*	*Cc ii*
$c\,I$ ¼	*Cc II*	*Cc Ii*	*cc II*	*cc Ii*
$c\,i$ ¼	*Cc Ii*	*Cc ii*	*cc Ii*	*cc ii*

Genotypes of the form *C–ii* have colored feathers, whereas all other genotypes have white feathers. The result is an F₂ ratio of white:colored of 13:3, which is a modified form of the expected 9:3:3:1.

Alleles

C	Pigment
c	No pigment
I	Inhibitor
i	No inhibitor

two genes affect different traits. However, even with complete dominance, the ratio of phenotypes may be different if the two genes affect the same trait. In this case, the genes can interact to affect the phenotypic expression of the genotypes, resulting in a modification of the expected ratio. Genes that modify the phenotypic expression of other genes are said to show **epistasis.**

There are many types of epistasis leading to different modifications of the 9:3:3:1 ratio. **Fig. 16.16** shows one example, in which the ratio is modified to 13:3. This ratio occurs in the F₂ generation of a cross between White Leghorn and White Wyandotte chickens. Both breeds are white, but for different genetic reasons. There are two genes involved in pigment production, each with two alleles. The *C* gene encodes a protein that affects coloration in feathers. This gene has two alleles, the dominant allele *C*, which produces pigment, and the recessive allele *c*, which does not produce pigment. A different gene, *I*, codes for an inhibitor protein. The dominant allele, *I*, inhibits the expression of *C*, whereas the recessive allele, *i*, does not inhibit the expression of *C*. Therefore, the White Leghorn (genotype *CC II*) is white because the dominant allele *I* inhibits the pigment in the feathers, and the White Wyandotte (genotype *cc ii*) is white because the recessive allele *c* does not produce feather pigment to begin with. The F₁ generation has genotype *Cc Ii* and is also white. With independent assortment, only the three *C–ii* offspring have colored feathers in the F₂ generation (the dash indicates that the second allele could be either *C* or *c*), while the rest have white feathers, and so the ratio of white:colored is 13:3.

→ **Quick Check 5** Why do the F₁ chickens with genotype *Cc Ii* have white feathers?

16.5 PATTERNS OF INHERITANCE OBSERVED IN FAMILY HISTORIES

Segregation of alleles takes place in human meiosis just as it does in peas and most other sexual organisms. The results are not so easily observed as in peas, however, for several reasons. First, humans do not choose their mating partners for the convenience of biologists, and so experimental crosses are not possible. Second, the number of children in human families is relatively small, and so the Mendelian ratios are often obscured by random fluctuations due to chance. Nevertheless, in many cases the occurrence of segregation can be observed even in human families. The patterns are often easiest to spot for inherited traits that are rare because in those cases the mutant alleles occur only in affected individuals and their close relatives.

In studying human families, the record of the ancestral relationships among individuals is summarized in a diagram of

FIG. 16.17 Some conventions used in drawing human pedigrees.

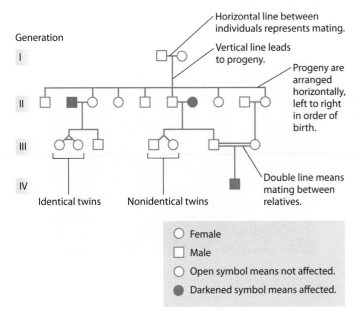

family history called a **pedigree.** Some typical symbols used in pedigrees are shown in **Fig. 16.17.** Females are represented as circles and males as squares. If the pedigree is following the transmission of a disease from one generation to the next, unaffected individuals are indicated by open symbols and affected individuals by darkened symbols. A mating is represented as a horizontal line connecting the partners, and the children of the partners are arranged below them, left to

right in order of birth. The same patterns of dominance and recessiveness that Mendel observed in his pea plants can be seen in some pedigrees. Over the next few sections, we'll see how to recognize telltale features of a pedigree that reveal the genotypic nature of a trait.

Dominant traits appear in every generation.

The pedigree shown in **Fig. 16.18** is for a rare dominant trait, brachydactyly, in which the middle long bone in the fingers fails to grow and therefore the fingers remain very short. This pedigree, published in 1905, was the first demonstration of dominant Mendelian inheritance in humans. This particular form of brachydactyly results from a mutation in a gene whose normal product is a protein involved in cartilage formation, which is necessary for bone growth.

These are the features of the pedigree that immediately suggest dominant inheritance:

1 Affected individuals are equally likely to be females or males.

2 Most matings that produce affected offspring have only one affected parent. This occurs because the brachydactyly trait is rare, and therefore a mating between two affected individuals is extremely unlikely.

3. Among matings in which one parent is affected, approximately half the offspring are affected.

If a dominant trait is rare, then affected individuals will almost always be heterozygous (*Aa*) and not homozygous (*AA*). In a mating in which one parent is heterozygous for the dominant

FIG. 16.18 Pedigree of a trait caused by a dominant allele. This pedigree shows the inheritance of shortened fingers associated with a form of brachydactyly (inset).

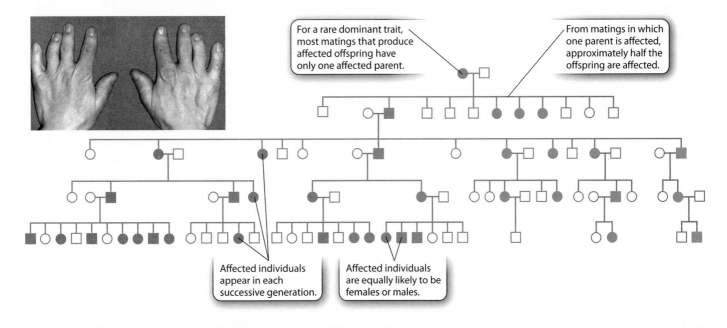

gene (*Aa*) and the other is homozygous recessive (*aa*), half the offspring are expected to be heterozygous (*Aa*) and the other half homozygous recessive (*aa*).

Recessive traits skip generations.

Recessive inheritance shows a pedigree pattern very different from that of dominant inheritance. The pedigree shown in **Fig. 16.19** pertains to albinism, in which the amount of melanin pigment in the skin, hair, and eyes is reduced. In most populations, the frequency of albinism is about 1 in 36,000, but it has a much higher frequency—about 1 in 200—among the Hopi and several other Native American Indian tribes of the Southwest. (It is not unusual for genetic diseases to have elevated frequencies among certain isolated populations.) This type of albinism is due to a mutation in the gene *OCA2*, which encodes a membrane transporter protein. As noted in Chapter 15, another type of mutation affecting expression of this same gene is associated with blue eyes. As shown in this pedigree, double lines represent matings between relatives, and in both cases shown here the mating is between first cousins.

These are the principal pedigree characteristics of recessive traits:

1. The trait may skip one or more generations.

2. Affected individuals are equally likely to be females or males.

3. Affected individuals may have unaffected parents, as in the offspring of the second mating in the second generation in Fig. 16.19. For a recessive trait that is sufficiently rare, virtually all affected individuals have unaffected parents.

4. Affected individuals often result from mating between relatives, typically first cousins.

Recessive inheritance has these characteristics because recessive genes can be transmitted from generation to generation without manifesting the recessive phenotype. In order for an affected individual to occur, the recessive gene must be inherited from both parents. Mating between relatives often allows rare recessive alleles to become homozygous because an ancestor that is shared between the relatives may carry the gene (*Aa*). The recessive gene in the common ancestor can be transmitted to both parents, making them each a carrier of the gene as well. If both parents are unaffected carriers of the allele, they both have the genotype *Aa*, and therefore ¼ of their offspring are expected to be homozygous *aa* and affected.

Many genes have multiple alleles.

The examples discussed so far in this chapter involve genes with only two alleles, such as *A* for yellow seeds and *a* for green seeds, or the allele of human *OCA2* for normal skin pigmentation and the mutant *OCA2* allele for albinism. Because a gene consists

FIG. 16.19   Pedigree of a trait caused by a recessive allele. The photograph is of a group of Hopi males, three with albinism, which is caused by a recessive allele.

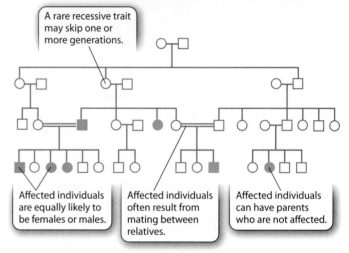

A rare recessive trait may skip one or more generations.

Affected individuals are equally likely to be females or males.

Affected individuals often result from mating between relatives.

Affected individuals can have parents who are not affected.

of a sequence of nucleotides, however, any nucleotide or set of nucleotides in the gene can undergo mutation. Each of the mutant forms that exists in a population constitutes a different allele, and hence a population of organisms may contain many different alleles of the same gene, which are called **multiple alleles.** As noted in Chapter 15, some genes have so many alleles that they can be used for individual identification by means of DNA typing.

In considering genetic diseases, multiple alleles are often grouped into categories such as "mutant" and "normal." But there are often many different "mutant" and many different "normal" alleles in a population. For the "mutant" alleles, the DNA sequences are different from one another, but none of them produces a functional protein product. For the "normal" alleles, the DNA sequences are also different, but they all are able to produce functional protein.

For example, more than 400 different recessive alleles that cause phenylketonuria (PKU) have been discovered across the world. PKU is a moderate to severe form of mental retardation caused by mutations in the gene encoding the enzyme phenylalanine hydroxylase. Children affected with PKU are unable to break down the excess phenylalanine present in a normal diet, and the buildup impairs the development of neurons in the brain. About 1 in 10,000 newborns inherits two mutant alleles, which could be two copies of the same mutant allele or two different mutant alleles, and is affected.

The "normal" form of the gene encoding phenylalanine hydroxylase also exists in the form of multiple alleles, each of which differs from the others, but nevertheless encodes a functional form of the enzyme.

→ **Quick Check 6** How is it possible that there are multiple different alleles in a population and yet any individual can have only two alleles?

Incomplete penetrance and variable expression can obscure inheritance patterns.

Many traits with single-gene inheritance demonstrate complications that can obscure the expected patterns in pedigrees. Chief among these are traits with **incomplete penetrance,** which means that individuals with a genotype corresponding to a trait do not actually show the phenotype, either because of environmental effects or because of interactions with other genes. Penetrance is the proportion of individuals with a particular genotype that show the expected trait. If the penetrance is less than 100%, then the trait shows reduced, or incomplete, penetrance. Familial cancers often show incomplete penetrance. For example, retinoblastoma caused by certain mutations in the *Rb* gene and breast cancer caused by certain mutations in the *BRCA1* and *BRCA2* genes are incompletely penetrant. That is, some people who inherit a mutation in these genes that predisposes to cancer do not in fact develop cancer. Similarly, some mutations in the *apoliprotein E (APOE)* gene increase the risk of developing Alzheimer's disease. However, not everyone who inherits these forms of the gene develops Alzheimer's disease, so these alleles are also incompletely penetrant.

Another common complication in human pedigrees is **variable expressivity,** which means that a particular phenotype is expressed with a different degree of severity in different individuals. Don't confuse variable expressivity with incomplete penetrance. With variable expressivity, the trait is always expressed, though the severity varies; with incomplete penetrance, the trait is either expressed or it is not. Variation among individuals in the expression of a trait can result from the action of other genes, from effects of the environment, or both. An example is provided by deficiency of the enzyme alpha-1 antitrypsin (α1AT) discussed in Chapter 15, which is associated

with loss of lung elasticity and emphysema. Among individuals with emphysema due to α1AT deficiency, the severity of the symptoms varies dramatically from one patient to the next. In this case, tobacco smoking is an environmental factor that increases the severity of the disease.

Incomplete penetrance and variable expressivity both provide examples where a given genotype does not always produce the same phenotype, since the expression of genes is often influenced by other genes, the environment, or a combination of the two.

❓ CASE 3 You, From A To T: Your Personal Genome How do genetic tests identify disease risk factors?

Your personal genome, as well as that of every human being, contains a unique combination of alleles of thousands of different genes. Most of these have no detectable effects on health or longevity, but many are risk factors for genetic diseases. Molecular studies have discovered particular alleles of genes associated with a large number of such conditions, and the presence of these alleles can be tested. More than a thousand genetic tests have already been deployed, and many more are actively being developed. A **genetic test** is a method of identifying the genotype of an individual. The tests may be carried out on entire populations or restricted to high-risk individuals.

The benefits of genetic testing can be appreciated by an example. Screening of newborns for phenylketonuria identifies babies with high blood levels of phenylalanine. In the absence of treatment, 95% of such newborns will progress to moderate or severe mental retardation, whereas virtually all those placed on a special diet with a controlled amount of phenylalanine will have mental function within the normal range. For recessive conditions like phenylketonuria, tests can be carried out on people with affected relatives to identify the heterozygous genotypes. Testing can also identify genetic risk factors for disease, and carriers can take additional precautions. For example, individuals with α1AT deficiency can prolong and improve the quality of their lives by not smoking tobacco, women with genetic risk factors *BRCA1* and *BRCA2* for breast cancer can have frequent mammograms, and those with the *TCF7L2* risk factor for type 2 diabetes can decrease their risk by lifestyle choices that include weight control and exercise.

While there are many potential benefits to genetic testing, there are also some perils. One major concern is maintaining the privacy of those who choose to be tested. With medical records increasingly going online, who will have access to your test results, and how will this information be used? Could your test results be used to deny you health or life insurance because you have a higher than average risk of some medical condition? Or could an employer who got hold of your genetic test results decide to reassign you to another job, or even eliminate your position because of your genetic predispositions? There are some safeguards designed to protect you from such discrimination. The Genetic Information Nondiscrimination Act (GINA) was signed into law in 2008 and forbids the use of genetic information in decisions concerning employment and health insurance. The protection provided by GINA will, it is hoped, allow for the responsible and productive use of genetic information.

There is also increasing concern about the reliability and accuracy of genetic tests, especially direct-to-consumer (DTC) genetic tests. DTC tests can be purchased directly without the intervention of medical professionals. Since the consumer sends a biological sample and DTC tests are carried out by the provider, the tests are not regarded as medical devices and so are unregulated. One problem is that some DTC tests are based on flimsy and unconfirmed evidence connecting a gene with a disease. Another is that the link between genotype and risk may be exaggerated for marketing purposes. Yet another is lack of information on quality control in the DTC laboratories. Finally, consumer misinterpretation may regard genotype as destiny, at one extreme descending into depression and despair, and at the other using a low-risk genotype to justify an unhealthy lifestyle.

Core Concepts Summary

16.1 THE EARLIEST THEORIES OF HEREDITY INCORRECTLY ASSUMED THE INHERITANCE OF ACQUIRED CHARACTERISTICS AND BLENDING OF PARENTAL TRAITS IN THE OFFSPRING.

The inheritance of acquired characteristics suggests that traits that develop during the lifetime of an individual can be passed on to offspring. With rare exceptions, this mode of inheritance does not occur. page 16-1

Blending inheritance is the incorrect hypothesis that characteristics in the parents are averaged in the offspring. This model predicts the blending of genetic material, which does not occur. Different forms of a gene maintain their separate identities even when present together in the same individual. page 16-2

16.2 MODERN TRANSMISSION GENETICS BEGAN WITH GREGOR MENDEL, WHO USED THE GARDEN PEA AS HIS EXPERIMENTAL ORGANISM AND STUDIED TRAITS WITH CONTRASTING CHARACTERISTICS.

Mendel started his experiments with true-breeding plants, ones whose progeny are identical to their parents. He followed just one or two traits at a time, allowing him to discern simple patterns, and he counted all the progeny of his crosses. page 16-3

In crosses of one true-breeding plant with a particular trait and another true-breeding plant with a contrasting trait, just one of the two characteristics appeared in the offspring. The trait that appeared in this generation is dominant, and the trait that is not seen is recessive. page 16-4

Mendel explained this result by hypothesizing that there is a hereditary factor for each trait (now called a gene), that each pea plant carries two copies of the gene for each trait, and that one of two different forms of the gene (alleles) is dominant to the other one. page 16-4

16.3 MENDEL'S FIRST KEY DISCOVERY WAS THE PRINCIPLE OF SEGREGATION, WHICH STATES THAT MEMBERS OF A GENE PAIR SEPARATE EQUALLY INTO GAMETES.

When Mendel allowed the progeny of the first cross to self-fertilize, he observed a 3:1 ratio of the dominant and recessive traits among the progeny. page 16-6

Mendel reasoned that the parent in this generation must have two different forms of the same gene (A and a) and that these alleles segregate from each other to form gametes with each gamete getting A or a but not both. When the gametes combine at random, they produce progeny in the genotypic ratio 1 AA:2 Aa:1 aa, which yields a phenotypic ratio of 3:1 because A is dominant to a. This idea became known as the principle of segregation. page 16-6

The principle of segregation reflects the separation of homologous chromosomes that occurs in anaphase I of meiosis. page 16-8

Some traits show incomplete dominance, in which the phenotype of the heterozygous genotype is intermediate between those of the two homozygous genotypes. page 16-8

The expected frequencies of progeny of crosses can be predicted using the addition rule, which states that when two possibilities are mutually exclusive, the probability of either event occurring is the sum of their individual probabilities, and the multiplication rule, which states that when two possibilities occur independently, the probability of both events occurring is the product of the probabilities of each of the two events. page 16-9

16.4 MENDEL'S SECOND KEY FINDING WAS THE PRINCIPLE OF INDEPENDENT ASSORTMENT, WHICH STATES THAT DIFFERENT GENE PAIRS SEGREGATE INDEPENDENTLY OF ONE ANOTHER.

In a cross with two traits, each with two contrasting characteristics, the two traits behave independently of each other. This idea became known as the principle of independent assortment. For example, in a self-cross of a double heterozygote, the phenotypic ratio of the progeny is 9:3:3:1, reflecting the independent assortment of two 3:1 ratios. page 16-10

Independent assortment results from chromosome behavior during meiosis, specifically from the random orientation of different chromosomes on the meiotic spindle. page 16-12

In some cases, genes interact with each other, modifying the expected ratios in crosses. Epistasis is a form of gene interaction in which one gene affects the expression of another. page 16-14

16.5 THE PATTERNS OF INHERITANCE THAT MENDEL OBSERVED IN PEAS CAN ALSO BE SEEN IN HUMANS.

In a human pedigree, females are represented by circles and males as squares; affected individuals are shown as filled symbols and unaffected individuals as open symbols; and horizontal lines denote matings. page 16-14

Dominant traits appear in every generation and affect males and females equally. page 16-15

Recessive traits skip one or more generations and affect males and females equally. Affected individuals often result from matings between close relatives. page 16-16

Although a given individual has only two alleles of each gene, there can be many alleles of a particular gene in the population as a whole. page 16-16

Interpreting pedigrees can be difficult because of incomplete penetrance and variable expressivity. Penetrance is the percentage of individuals with a particular genotype who show the expected phenotype, and expressivity is the degree to which a genotype is exhibited. page 16-17

Genetic testing enables the genotype of an individual to be determined for one or more genes. Such tests carry both benefits and risks. page 16-17

Self-Assessment

1. Describe two ways in which Mendel's experimental approach differed from others of the time.

2. Distinguish among gene, allele, genotype, and phenotype.

3. Name and describe Mendel's two laws.

4. Explain the relationship between Mendel's two laws and the mechanics of meiosis.

5. Given a set of parental genotypes and phenotypes, predict the progeny of a cross.

6. Describe an instance when a testcross would be useful.

7. Apply the addition and multiplication rules to determine the probability of the offspring of a given cross.

8. Construct a human pedigree for a dominant and a recessive trait and explain the patterns of inheritance.

9. Discuss the benefits and risks of genetic testing and personal genomics.

Do you understand the chapter's Core Concepts? Log into BioPORTAL to check your answers to the Self-Assessment questions, then practice what you've learned and reinforce this chapter's concepts by working through the problems and multimedia tutorials provided there.

📶 http://courses.bfwpub.com/yourbioportal/index.php

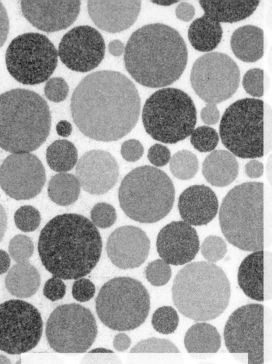

CHAPTER 17

NON-MENDELIAN INHERITANCE

Sex Chromosomes, Linkage, and Organelles

Core Concepts

17.1 The *X* and *Y* chromosomes of some animals, including humans, determine sex and are inherited differently from the autosomes.

17.2 *X*-linked genes, which show a crisscross inheritance pattern, provided the first evidence that genes are present in chromosomes.

17.3 Genetic linkage occurs when two genes are sufficiently close together in the same chromosome that the combination of alleles present in the chromosome tends to remain together in inheritance.

17.4 Most *Y*-linked genes are passed from father to son.

17.5 Mitochondria and chloroplast DNA follow their own inheritance pattern.

Mendel's principles of segregation and independent assortment are the foundation of transmission genetics (Chapter 16). For traits such as pea color and shape, these principles predict simple progeny phenotypic ratios in self-crosses of heterozygous genotypes, such as 3:1 for one gene or 9:3:3:1 for two genes that undergo independent assortment. The principle of segregation also defines the inheritance patterns expected in human pedigrees for traits due to recessive or dominant mutations, as we saw in the case of albinism and brachydactyly.

Some traits, such as color blindness in humans and white eyes in fruit flies, do not show the inheritance patterns predicted by Mendel. In this chapter, we consider some examples in which the expected ratios and pedigree patterns are modified by principles Mendel knew nothing about. One example pertains to genes in the X and Y sex chromosomes, which are transmitted differently from other chromosomes. Although the patterns of inheritance of genes in the sex chromosomes do not follow Mendel's laws, those patterns can easily be understood by following the movement of chromosomes in which they are present.

Another important exception to Mendel's laws has to do with genes that are located close to each other in the same chromosome. Although each gene pair undergoes segregation in the normal manner, independent assortment of different genes does not take place. Finally, the laws of Mendelian segregation and independent assortment do not apply to genes in the DNA molecules in mitochondria and chloroplasts. All of these cases involve genetic transmission with patterns of inheritance beyond those discovered by Mendel.

17.1 THE *X* AND *Y* SEX CHROMOSOMES

Among Mendel's discoveries was that reciprocal crosses, in which the sexes of the parents associated with each genotype are reversed, yield the same types of progeny (Chapter 16). This principle is true of most genes, but an important exception applies to genes located in the X and Y chromosomes, which are associated with the sex of an individual. Mendel did not have to deal with this complication because peas and most other plants do not have sex chromosomes. In organisms that do have them, such as humans, specific rules govern the transmission of their genes.

In many animals, sex is genetically determined and associated with chromosomal differences.

Most chromosomes come in pairs that match in shape and size. The members of each pair are known as homologous chromosomes because they have the same arrangement of genes along their length (Chapter 11). One member of each pair of homologous chromosomes is inherited from the mother and the other from the father. In many animal species, however, the sex of an individual is determined by a special pair of unmatched chromosomes known as the **sex chromosomes,** which are usually designated as the **X chromosome** and the **Y chromosome.** Chromosomes other than the sex chromosomes are known as **autosomes.**

In humans, a normal female has two copies of the *X* chromosome (a sex-chromosome constitution denoted *XX*), and a normal male has one *X* chromosome and one *Y* chromosome (*XY*). The sizes of the human *X* and *Y* chromosomes are very different (**Fig. 17.1**). The *X* chromosome DNA molecule is more than 150 Mb long, while the *Y* chromosome is only about 50 Mb long. Except for a small region near each tip, the gene contents of the *X* and *Y* chromosomes are different from each other. The *X* chromosome, which includes more than 1000 genes, has a gene density similar to that of most autosomes. The vast majority of these genes have no counterpart in the *Y* chromosome. In contrast to the *X* chromosome, the *Y* chromosome contains only about 50 genes.

The regions of homology between the *X* and *Y* chromosomes consist of about 2.7 Mb of DNA near the tip of the short arm and about 0.3 Mb of DNA near the tip of the long arm. These regions of homology allow the chromosomes to pair during meiosis (Chapter 11). In most cells undergoing meiosis, a crossover (physical breakage, exchange of parts, and rejoining of the DNA molecules) occurs in the larger of these regions. The crossover allows the chromosomes to align correctly at metaphase I and to separate from each other at anaphase I.

The relative size and gene content of the *X* and *Y* chromosomes differ greatly among species. In some species of mosquitoes, the *X* and *Y* chromosomes are virtually identical in size and shape, and the regions of homology include almost the entire chromosome. This situation is unusual, however. In most species, the *Y* chromosome contains many fewer genes than the *X* chromosome. Some species, like grasshoppers, have no *Y* chromosome: Females in these species have two *X* chromosomes, and males have only one *X* chromosome. The total number of chromosomes in grasshoppers therefore differs between females and males.

Segregation of the sex chromosomes predicts a 1:1 ratio of females to males.

It is ironic that Mendel did not interpret sex as an inherited trait. If he had, he might have realized that sex itself provides one of the most convincing demonstrations of segregation. In human males, segregation of the *X* chromosome from the *Y* chromosome during anaphase I of meiosis results in half the sperm bearing an *X* chromosome and the other half bearing a *Y* chromosome (**Fig. 17.2**).

FIG. 17.2   Inheritance of the *X* and *Y* chromosomes. Segregation of the sex chromosomes in meiosis and random fertilization result in a 1:1 ratio of female:male embryos.

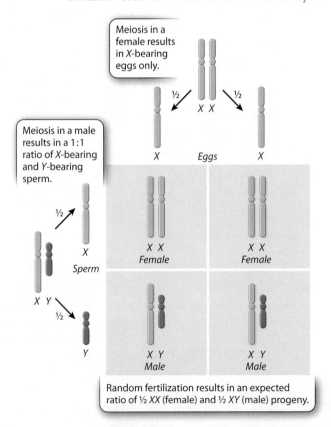

FIG. 17.1   Human sex chromosomes. The human *X* and *Y* sex chromosomes differ in size and number of genes.

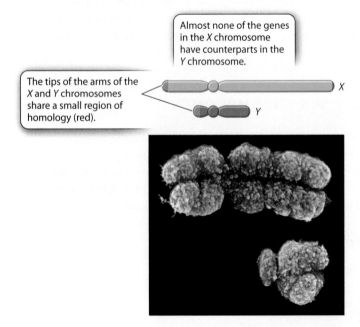

Meiosis in human females results in eggs that each contain one X chromosome. With random fertilization, as shown in Fig. 17.2, half of the fertilized eggs are expected to be chromosomally XX (and therefore female) and half are expected to be chromosomally XY (and therefore male). This 1:1 ratio of female:male is characteristic of Mendelian segregation.

The expected ratio of 1:1 of females:males refers to the sex ratio at the time of conception. This is the primary sex ratio, and it is not easily observed because the earliest stages of fertilization and development are inaccessible to large-scale study. What can be observed is the sex ratio at birth, called the secondary sex ratio, which differs among populations but usually shows a slight excess of males. In the United States, for example, the secondary sex ratio is approximately 100 females:105 males. The explanation seems to be that, for reasons that are not entirely understood, females are slightly less likely to survive from conception to birth. On the other hand, males are slightly less likely to survive from birth to reproductive maturity, and so, at the age of reproductive maturity, the sex ratio is very nearly 1:1. Male mortality continues to be greater than that of females throughout life, so that by age 85 and over, the sex ratio is about 100 females:50 males.

The sex of each birth appears to be random relative to previous births—that is, there do not seem to be tendencies for some families to have boys or for other ones to have girls. Many people are surprised by this, for they know of one or more large families consisting mostly of boys or mostly of girls. But the occasional family with children of predominantly one sex would be expected simply by chance. When one occurs, its unusual sex distribution commands attention out of proportion to the actual numbers of such families. In short, families with unusual sex distributions are not more frequent than would be expected by chance.

17.2 INHERITANCE OF GENES IN THE *X* CHROMOSOME

Genes in the X chromosome are called **X-linked genes**. These genes have a unique pattern of inheritance first discovered by Thomas Hunt Morgan in 1910. Morgan's pioneering studies of genetics of the fruit fly *Drosophila melanogaster* helped bring Mendelian genetics into the modern era. The discovery of X-linked inheritance was not only important in itself, but also provided the first experimental evidence that chromosomes contain genes.

X-linked inheritance was discovered through studies of male fruit flies with white eyes.

Morgan's discovery of X-linked genes began when he noticed a white-eyed male in a bottle of fruit flies in which all the others had normal, or wild-type, red eyes. (The most common phenotype in a population is often called the **wild type**.) This

was the first mutant he discovered, and finding it was a lucky break. As we saw in Chapter 16, most mutations are recessive, which means that when they occur their effect on the organism (the phenotype) is not observed because of the presence of the nonmutant gene in the homologous chromosome. Recall that the nonmutant form of a recessive mutant gene is dominant, and that the different forms of the gene are alleles.

Morgan's initial crosses are outlined in **Fig. 17.3**. In the first generation, he crossed the white-eyed male with a wild-type red-eyed female. All of the progeny fruit flies had red eyes, as you would expect from any recessive mutation. Morgan then carried out brother–sister matings, and he found that the phenotype of white eyes reappeared among the progeny. This result, too, was expected. However, there was a surprise: Morgan observed that the white-eye phenotype was associated with the sex of the fly. In the second generation, all the white-eyed fruit flies were male, and the white-eyed males appeared along with red-eyed males in a ratio of 1:1. No females with white eyes were observed; all the females had red eyes.

FIG. 17.3 Morgan's white-eyed fly. Morgan's discovery of *X*-linked genes derived from his crosses of a white-eyed male in 1910.

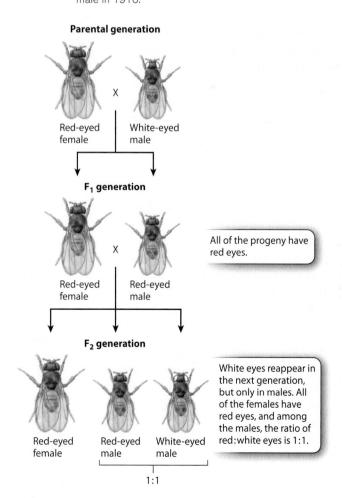

Parental generation

Red-eyed female   X   White-eyed male

F₁ generation

Red-eyed female   X   Red-eyed male

All of the progeny have red eyes.

F₂ generation

Red-eyed female   Red-eyed male   White-eyed male

1:1

White eyes reappear in the next generation, but only in males. All of the females have red eyes, and among the males, the ratio of red:white eyes is 1:1.

Genes in the *X* chromosome exhibit a "crisscross" inheritance pattern.

When Morgan did his crosses with the white-eyed male, the X chromosome had only recently been discovered by microscopic examination of the chromosomes in male and female grasshoppers. Morgan was the first to understand that the pattern of inheritance of the X chromosome would be different from that of the autosomes, and he proposed the hypothesis that the white-eyed phenotype was due to a mutation in a gene in the X chromosome. This hypothesis could explain the pattern of inheritance shown in Fig. 17.3.

The key features of X-linked inheritance are shown in **Fig. 17.4.** In *Drosophila*, as in humans, females are XX and males are XY. Fig. 17.4a shows an XY male in which the X chromosome contains a recessive mutation. Because the Y chromosome does not carry an allele of this gene, the recessive mutation will be reflected in the male's phenotype—in this case, white eyes.

The Punnett square in Fig. 17.4a explains why all the offspring had red eyes when Morgan crossed the white-eyed male with a red-eyed female. During meiosis in the male, the mutant X chromosome segregates from the Y chromosome, and each type of sperm, X or Y, combines with a normal X-bearing egg. The result is that the female progeny are heterozygous. They have only one copy of the mutant allele, and because the mutant allele is recessive, the heterozygous females do not express the white-eye trait. The male progeny are also red-eyed because they receive their X chromosome from their wild-type red-eyed mother.

The Punnett square in Fig. 17.4a illustrates two important principles governing the inheritance of X-linked genes:

1. The XX offspring indicate that a male transmits his X chromosome only to his daughters. In this case, the X chromosome transmitted by the male carries the white-eye mutation.

FIG. 17.4 *X*-linkage. *X*-linked recessive alleles (red) are expressed in males because males have only one *X* chromosome.

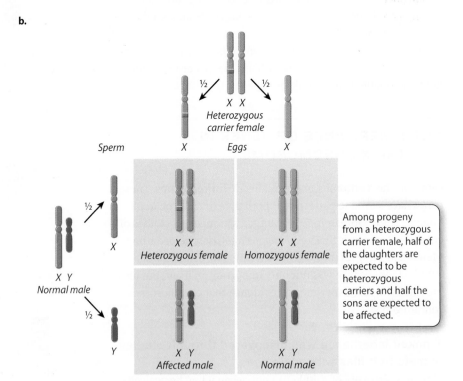

2. The XY offspring indicate that a male inherits his X chromosome from his mother. In this case, the X chromosome transmitted by the mother carries the nonmutant allele of the gene.

These principles underlie a pattern often referred to as **crisscross inheritance:** An X chromosome present in a male in one generation must be transmitted to a female in the next generation, and in the generation after that can be transmitted back to a male. Therefore, an X chromosome can "crisscross," or alternate, between the sexes in successive generations.

The cross illustrated in Fig. 17.4b shows another important feature of X-linked inheritance, one that explains the results of Morgan's F_1 cross. In this case, the mother is a heterozygous female. During meiosis, the mutant allele and the nonmutant allele undergo segregation. Half of the resulting eggs contain an X chromosome with the mutant allele, and half contain an X chromosome with the nonmutant allele. These combine at random with either X-bearing sperm or Y-bearing sperm. Among the female progeny in the next generation, half are heterozygous for the mutant allele and the other half are homozygous for the

normal allele. Thus, none of the females exhibits the white-eye trait because the mutation is recessive. Among the male progeny, half receive the mutant allele and have white eyes, whereas the other half receive the nonmutant allele and have red eyes. The expected progeny from the cross in Fig. 17.4b therefore consist of all red-eyed females, and there is a 1:1 ratio of red-eyed to white-eyed males, which is what Morgan observed in the F_2 generation of his crosses, as shown in Fig. 17.3.

Knowing the patterns revealed by the Punnett squares, we can now assign genotypes to Morgan's original crosses (**Fig. 17.5**). In Fig. 17.5, the white-eyed male that Morgan used in his first crosses are given the genotype of w^-Y, and the red-eyed female has a genotype of w^+w^+. The symbol "w^-" stands for the recessive white-eye mutation in one X chromosome, and the symbol "w^+" stands for the dominant nonmutant allele (red eyes) in the other X chromosome. The symbol "Y" stands for the Y chromosome, and it is important to remember that the Y chromosome does not contain an allele of the white-eye gene.

In the cross between a wild-type red-eyed female and a white-eyed male, illustrated in Fig. 17.5a, the male offspring

FIG. 17.5 Genotypes of Morgan's white-eyed fruit fly crosses.

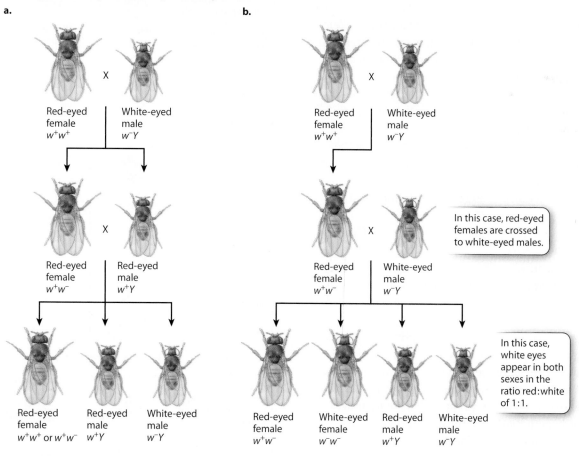

a.

Red-eyed female w^+w^+ X White-eyed male w^-Y

Red-eyed female w^+w^- X Red-eyed male w^+Y

Red-eyed female w^+w^+ or w^+w^- Red-eyed male w^+Y White-eyed male w^-Y

b.

Red-eyed female w^+w^+ X White-eyed male w^-Y

In this case, red-eyed females are crossed to white-eyed males.

Red-eyed female w^+w^- X White-eyed male w^-Y

Red-eyed female w^+w^- White-eyed female w^-w^- Red-eyed male w^+Y White-eyed male w^-Y

In this case, white eyes appear in both sexes in the ratio red:white of 1:1.

have red eyes because they receive their X chromosome from their mother. The female offspring from this cross receive one of their X chromosomes from their father, and hence they are heterozygous, w^+w^-. When the male and female progeny are mated together, their offspring consist of all red-eyed females (half of which are heterozygous) and a 1:1 ratio of red-eyed to white-eyed males, exactly as Morgan had observed.

The hypothesis of X-linkage not only explained the original data, but it also predicted the results of other crosses. One important test is outlined in Fig. 17.5b. Here the original cross is the same as that in Fig. 17.5a, but instead of mating the hybrid females to their brothers, they are mated to white-eyed males. The prediction is that there should be a 1:1 ratio of red-eyed to white-eyed females as well as a 1:1 ratio of red-eyed to white-eyed males. Again, these were the results observed. By the results of these crosses and others, Morgan demonstrated that the pattern of inheritance of the white-eye mutation parallels the pattern of inheritance of the X chromosome.

X-linkage provided the first experimental evidence that genes are in chromosomes.

Morgan's original experiments indicated that the white-eye mutation showed a pattern of inheritance like that expected of the X chromosome. However, it was one of Morgan's students who showed experimentally that the white-eye mutation was actually a physical part of the X chromosome. Today it seems obvious that genes are in chromosomes because we know that genes consist of DNA and that DNA in the nucleus is found in chromosomes. But in 1916, when Calvin B. Bridges, who had joined Morgan's laboratory as a freshman, was working on his PhD research under Morgan's direction, neither the chemical nature of the gene nor the chemical composition of chromosomes was known.

In one set of experiments, Bridges crossed white-eyed females with red-eyed males (**Fig. 17.6**). Usually, the progeny consisted of red-eyed females and white-eyed males (Fig. 17.6a). This is the result expected when the X chromosomes in the mother separate normally at anaphase I in meiosis because all the daughters receive a w^+-bearing X chromosome from their father and all the sons receive a w^--bearing X chromosome from their mother.

But Bridges noted a few rare exceptions. He saw that about 1 offspring in 2000 from the cross was "exceptional"— either a female with white eyes or a male with red eyes. The exceptional females were fertile, and the exceptional males were sterile. To explain these exceptional progeny, Bridges proposed the hypothesis diagrammed in Fig. 17.6b: The X chromosomes in a female occasionally fail to separate in anaphase I in meiosis, and both X chromosomes go to the same spindle pole. Recall from Chapter 15 that chromosomes sometimes fail to separate normally in meiosis, a process

FIG. 17.6 **Nondisjunction as evidence that genes are present in chromosomes.** (a) Normal chromosome segregation yields expected progeny. (b) Nondisjunction yields exceptional progeny.

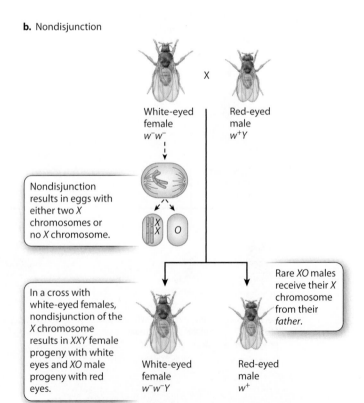

known as **nondisjunction.** Nondisjunction of *X* chromosomes results in eggs containing either two *X* chromosomes or no *X* chromosome. Figure 17.6b shows the implications for eye color in the progeny if the hypothesis is correct. The exceptional white-eyed females would contain two *X* chromosomes plus a *Y* chromosome (genotype $w^-/w^-/Y$), and the exceptional red-eyed males would contain a single *X* chromosome and no *Y* chromosome (genotype w^+).

Bridges's hypothesis for the exceptional progeny in Fig. 17.6b was bold, as it assumed that *Drosophila* males could develop in the absence of a *Y* chromosome (*XO* embryos yielding sterile males, where "*O*" indicates absence of a chromosome), and that females could develop in the presence of a *Y* chromosome (*XXY* embryos yielding fertile females). The hypothesis was accurate as well as bold. Microscopic examination of the chromosomes in the exceptional fruit flies confirmed that the exceptional white-eyed females had *XXY* sex chromosomes and that the exceptional sterile red-eyed males had an *X* but no *Y*. Because fruit flies with three *X* chromosomes (*XXX*) or no *X* chromosome (*OY*) were never observed, Bridges concluded that embryos with these chromosomal constitutions are unable to survive. He also showed that nondisjunction can take place in males as well as in females. From the phenotypes of these exceptional fruit flies and their chromosome constitutions, Bridges concluded that the white-eye gene (and by implication any other *X*-linked gene) is physically present within the *X* chromosome.

Bridges's demonstration that genes are present in chromosomes was also the first experimental evidence of nondisjunction. *Drosophila* differ from humans in that the *Y* chromosome is necessary for male fertility but not for male development. As we will see later in this chapter, a gene in the *Y* chromosome itself is the trigger for male development in humans and other mammals, and so for these organisms, the *Y* chromosome is needed both for male development and male fertility. Nondisjunction occasionally takes place in meiosis in humans as well as in fruit flies. When nondisjunction takes place in the human sex chromosomes, it results in chromosomal constitutions such as 47, *XXY* and 47, *XYY* males as well as 47, *XXX* and 45, *XO* females. Nondisjunction of autosomes can also occur, resulting in fetuses that have extra copies or missing copies of entire chromosomes. The consequences of nondisjunction of human chromosomes were examined in Chapter 15.

Genes in the *X* chromosome show characteristic patterns in human pedigrees.

The features of *X*-linked inheritance can be seen in human pedigrees for traits due to an *X*-linked recessive mutation. These are illustrated in **Fig. 17.7** for red–green color blindness, a condition that affects about 1 in 20 males. An individual with red–green color blindness will have difficulty seeing the number in the colored dots in Fig. 17.7. The key features of *X*-linked inheritance, noted in the pedigree, are listed here:

1. Affected individuals are almost always males because males need only one copy of the mutant gene to be affected, whereas females need two copies to be affected.

2. Affected males have unaffected sons because males transmit their *X* chromosome only to their daughters.

3. A female whose father is affected can have affected sons because such a female must be a heterozygous carrier of the recessive mutant allele.

An additional feature worth mentioning is that the sisters of an affected male each have a 50% chance of being a heterozygous carrier because when a brother is affected the mother must be heterozygous for the recessive allele.

→ **Quick Check 1** Is it possible for an unaffected female to have female offspring with red–green color blindness?

FIG. 17.7   **Inheritance of an *X*-linked recessive mutation.** This pedigree shows the inheritance of red–green color blindness, an *X*-linked recessive mutation.

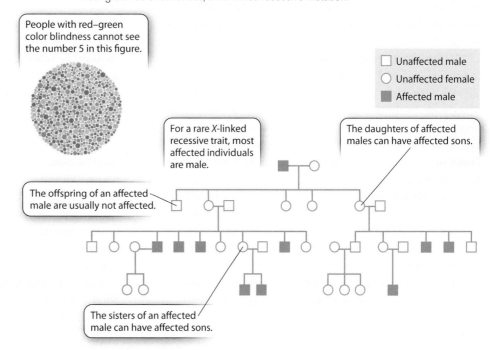

People with red–green color blindness cannot see the number 5 in this figure.

Unaffected male
Unaffected female
Affected male

For a rare *X*-linked recessive trait, most affected individuals are male.

The daughters of affected males can have affected sons.

The offspring of an affected male are usually not affected.

The sisters of an affected male can have affected sons.

FIG. 17.8 *X*-linked hemophilia in European royalty.

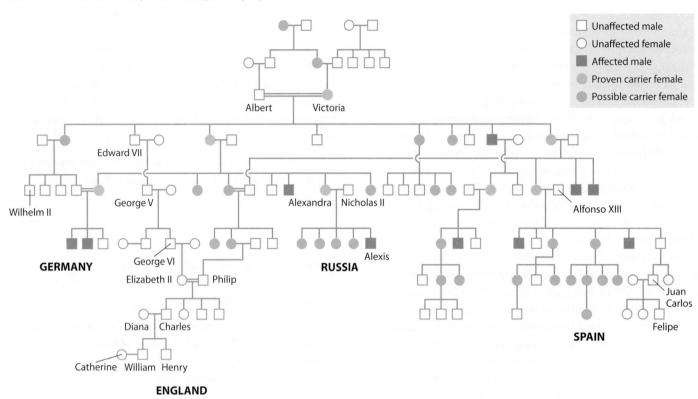

A pedigree for one of the most famous examples of human *X*-linked inheritance is shown in **Fig. 17.8**. The trait is **hemophilia,** which results from a recessive mutation in a gene encoding a protein necessary for blood clotting. Affected individuals bleed excessively from even minor cuts and bruises, and internal bleeding can cause excruciating pain. Affecting about 1 in 7000 males, hemophilia is famous because of its presence in many members of European royalty descended from Queen Victoria of England (1819–1901), who was a heterozygous carrier of the gene. By the marriages of her carrier granddaughters, the gene was introduced into the royal houses of Germany, Russia, and Spain. The mutant allele is not present in the present royal family of England, however, because this family descends from King Edward VII, one of Victoria's four sons, who was not himself affected and therefore passed only a normal X chromosome to his descendants.

The source of Queen Victoria's hemophilia mutation is not known. None of her ancestors is reported to have had a bleeding disorder. Quite possibly the mutation was present for a few generations before Victoria was born but remained hidden because it was passed from heterozygous female to heterozygous female.

17.3 GENETIC LINKAGE AND RECOMBINATION

Mendel was fortunate not only because peas do not possess sex chromosomes, but also because the genes that influenced the traits he studied, such as round/wrinkled and green/yellow seeds, were on separate chromosomes or far apart on the same chromosome. What happens when genes are close to each other in the same chromosome? We explore the answer to this question in this section.

Nearby genes in the same chromosome show linkage.

Genes that are sufficiently close together in the same chromosome are said to be **linked.** That is, they tend to be transmitted together in inheritance and do not assort independently of each other as Mendel observed. Note that *linked genes* refer to two genes that are close together in the same chromosome, which may be an autosome or sex chromosome. This is not to be confused with an *X-linked gene*, which is simply one that is present in the X chromosome.

Linkage was discovered in *Drosophila* by Alfred H. Sturtevant, another of Morgan's students. Once again, genes in the X chromosome played a key role in the discovery, as seen in **Fig. 17.9**. Sturtevant worked with male fruit flies that have an X chromosome carrying two recessive mutations. One is in the *white* gene (*w*) discussed earlier, which when nonmutant results in fruit flies with red eyes and when mutant results in fruit flies with white eyes. The other recessive mutation is in a gene called *crossveinless* (*cv*), which when nonmutant results in fruit flies with tiny crossveins in the wings and when mutant results in the absence of these crossveins.

Sturtevant crossed this doubly mutant male with a female carrying the nonmutant forms of the genes (w^+ and cv^+) in both X chromosomes. He saw that the offspring consist of phenotypically wild-type females that are heterozygous for both genes, and phenotypically wild-type males. When these are crossed with each other, the female F$_2$ progeny do not tell us anything because they are all wild type; each female receives the w^+cv^+ X chromosome from her father and therefore has red eyes and normal crossveins. In the male F$_2$ progeny, the situation is different: Each male progeny receives its X chromosome from the mother and its Y chromosome from the father, and so the phenotype of each male immediately reveals the genetic constitution of the X chromosome that the male inherited from the mother.

As shown in Fig. 17.9, the male F$_2$ progeny consist of four types:

Genotype of F$_2$ progeny	Number of fruit flies
w^+cv^+/Y (red eyes, normal crossveins)	357
w^-cv^-/Y (white eyes, missing crossveins)	341
w^+cv^-/Y (red eyes, missing crossveins)	52
w^-cv^+/Y (white eyes, normal crossveins)	45

Although all four possible classes of maternal gametes are observed in the male progeny, they do not appear in the ratio 1:1:1:1 expected when gametes contain two independently assorting genes (Chapter 16). The lack of independent assortment means that the genes show linkage.

The male progeny fall into two groups. One group, represented by fewer numbers of progeny, consists of w^+cv^- and w^-cv^+ combinations of alleles. These are called **recombinants,**

FIG. 17.9 Linkage of the *white* (*w*) and *crossveinless* (*cv*) genes in the **X** chromosome. Note that genes are written according to their order along the chromosome, with a line between homologous chromosomes, in this case between the *X* and *Y* chromosomes.

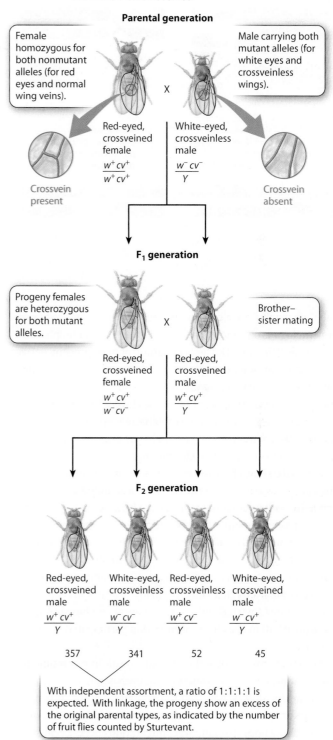

Parental generation

Female homozygous for both nonmutant alleles (for red eyes and normal wing veins).

X

Male carrying both mutant alleles (for white eyes and crossveinless wings).

Red-eyed, crossveined female
$$\frac{w^+\,cv^+}{w^+\,cv^+}$$

White-eyed, crossveinless male
$$\frac{w^-\,cv^-}{Y}$$

Crossvein present

Crossvein absent

F$_1$ generation

Progeny females are heterozygous for both mutant alleles.

X

Brother–sister mating

Red-eyed, crossveined female
$$\frac{w^+\,cv^+}{w^-\,cv^-}$$

Red-eyed, crossveined male
$$\frac{w^+\,cv^+}{Y}$$

F$_2$ generation

Red-eyed, crossveined male
$$\frac{w^+\,cv^+}{Y}$$

White-eyed, crossveinless male
$$\frac{w^-\,cv^-}{Y}$$

Red-eyed, crossveinless male
$$\frac{w^+\,cv^-}{Y}$$

White-eyed, crossveined male
$$\frac{w^-\,cv^+}{Y}$$

357   341   52   45

With independent assortment, a ratio of 1:1:1:1 is expected. With linkage, the progeny show an excess of the original parental types, as indicated by the number of fruit flies counted by Sturtevant.

FIG. 17.10 **Linkage and recombination.** Crossing over during meiosis results in recombination between linked genes.

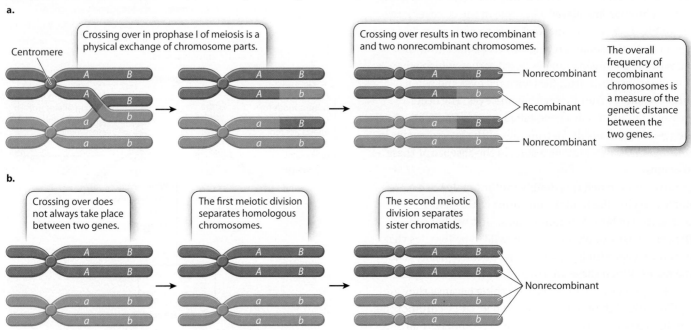

and they result from a **crossover,** the physical exchange of parts of homologous chromosomes, which takes place in prophase I of meiosis (Chapter 11). The other group of male progeny derives from maternal gametes containing either w^+cv^+ or w^-cv^-. These gametes each carry a chromosome that contains the alleles in the same combination as in one of the chromosomes in the mother. The w^+cv^+ and w^-cv^- combinations are therefore called **nonrecombinants** (that is, the alleles are present in the same combination as that seen in the parent).

Fig. 17.10 shows how recombinant and nonrecombinant chromosomes arise, using the hypothetical linked genes A and B. In a cell undergoing meiosis in which a crossover takes place between the linked genes, the allele combinations are broken up in the chromatids involved in the exchange, and the resulting gametes are AB, Ab, aB, and ab. In Fig. 17.10a, the Ab and aB gametes have undergone recombination: The allele combinations that were originally together in each chromosome (A with B and a with b) have recombined (A with b and a with B) in the chromosomes that participated in the crossover.

Note that crossing over does not just result in recombinant chromosomes. Fig. 17.10a shows that, even when a crossover occurs in the interval between the genes, two of the resulting chromosomes contain the nonrecombinant configuration of alleles. These nonrecombinant configurations occur because crossing over occurs at the four-strand stage of meiosis (when

each homologous chromosome is a pair of sister chromatids), but only two of the four strands (one sister chromatid from each homologous chromosome) are included in any crossover.

Fig. 17.10b shows a second way in which nonrecombinant chromosomes originate. When genes are linked, some cells undergoing meiosis do not undergo a crossover in the interval between the genes. In this case, the AB combination of alleles in one chromosome and the ab combination of alleles in the homologous chromosome both remain intact, and the gametes produced are AB and ab.

Recombination frequency is a measure of the distance between linked genes.

When two genes are on separate chromosomes, a ratio of 1:1:1:1 is expected for the nonrecombinant (parental) and recombinant (nonparental) gametic types (Chapter 16). For two genes present in the same chromosome, we can consider two extreme situations. If they are located very far apart from each other, crossing over will certainly occur, and there will be a 1:1:1:1 ratio of nonrecombinant and recombinant gametes (as shown in Fig. 17.10a). At the other extreme, if two genes are so close together that crossing over never takes place between them, we would expect only nonrecombinant chromosomes (Fig. 17.10b).

What happens in between these extremes? In these cases, the nonrecombinant chromosomes in the offspring are more numerous than the recombinant chromosomes, as we saw with *w* and *cv* (see Fig. 17.9). The frequency of recombinants depends on the distance between the genes. The closer, or more tightly linked, that two genes are to each other, the smaller the frequency of recombinants among the progeny. The distance between the genes is important because whether or not a crossover occurs between the genes is a matter of chance, and the closer the genes are along the chromosome, the less likely it is that a crossover will take place in the interval between them. Because the formation of recombinant chromosomes requires a crossover between the genes, genes that are close together show less recombination than genes that are far apart. In fact, the proportion of recombinant chromosomes observed among the total, which is called the **frequency of recombination,** is a convenient measure of distance between the genes along the chromosome.

In the example with the genes *w* and *cv*, the total number of chromosomes observed among the progeny is $357 + 341 + 52 + 45 = 795$, and the number of recombinant chromosomes is $52 + 45 = 97$. The frequency of recombination between *w* and *cv* is therefore $97/795 = 0.122$, or 12.2%, and this serves as a measure of distance between the genes. In studies of genetic linkage, the distance between genes is not measured directly by physical distance between them, but rather by the frequency of recombination.

The frequency of recombination between any two genes ranges from 0% (when crossing over between the genes never takes place) to 50% (when the genes are so far apart that crossing over between the genes always takes place). Genes that are linked have a recombination frequency somewhere between 0% and 50%.

→ **Quick Check 2** Why is the upper limit of recombination 50% rather than 100%?

Recombination plays an important role in creating new combinations of alleles in each generation and in ensuring the genetic uniqueness of each individual. If there were no recombination (that is, if all the alleles in each chromosome were completely linked), any individual human would be able to produce only $2^{23} = 8.4$ million types of reproductive cells. While this is a large number, the average number of sperm per ejaculate is much larger—approximately 350 million. Because recombination does occur, and because the crossovers resulting in recombination can occur at any of thousands of different positions in the genome, each of the 350 million sperm is virtually certain to carry a different combination of alleles.

Genetic mapping assigns a location to each gene along a chromosome.

With the exception of a few regions, such as the area near the centromere, the likelihood of a crossover occurring somewhere between two points on a chromosome is approximately proportional to the length of the interval between the points. Therefore, the frequency of recombination can be used as a measure of the physical distance between genes. These distances are used in the construction of a **genetic map,** which is a diagram showing the relative position of genes along a chromosome. The maps are drawn using a scale in which one unit of distance (called a **map unit**) is the distance between genes resulting in 1% recombination. Thus, in a *Drosophila* genetic map containing the genes *w* and *cv*, the distance between the genes is 12.2 map units.

Genetic maps are built up step by step as new genes are discovered that are genetically linked with known genes, as shown in **Fig. 17.11.** Across distances that are less than about 15 map units, the map distances are approximately additive, which means that the distances between adjacent genes can be added to get the distance between the genes at the ends. For example, in Fig. 17.11, there are two genes between *w* and *cv*. The map distance between *w* and the next gene, *ec*, is 4.0, the distance between *ec* and the next gene, *rb*, is 2.0, and the distance between *rb* and *cv* is 6.2. The map distance between *w* and *cv* is therefore $4.0 + 2.0 + 6.2 = 12.2$ map units, and hence the expected frequency of recombination between these genes is 12.2%, which is the value observed.

However, for two genes that are farther apart than about 15 map units, the observed recombination frequency is somewhat smaller than the sum of the map distances between the genes. The reason is that, with greater distances, two or more crossovers between the genes may occur in the same chromosome, and thus an exchange produced by one crossover may be reversed by another crossover farther along the way.

→ **Quick Check 3** For two genes that show independent assortment, what is the frequency of recombination?

Genetic risk factors for disease can be localized by genetic mapping.

The discovery of abundant genetic variation in DNA sequences in human populations, such as single-nucleotide polymorphisms (Chapter 15), made it possible to study genetic linkage in the human genome. At first, the focus was on finding mutations that cause disease, such as a mutation that causes cystic fibrosis (Chapter 14). The method was to study large families extending over three or more generations in which the disease was present and then to identify the genotypes of each of the individuals for thousands of genetic markers (previously discovered DNA polymorphisms) throughout the genome. The goal was to find genetic markers that showed a statistical association with the disease gene, which would indicate genetic

FIG. 17.11

Can recombination be used to construct a genetic map of a chromosome?

BACKGROUND In 1910, Thomas Hunt Morgan discovered *X*-linkage by studying the white-eye mutation in *Drosophila*. Soon other *X*-linked mutations were found. Alfred H. Sturtevant, Morgan's student, decided to test whether mutant genes in the same *X* chromosome were inherited together, that is, linked. He found that genes in the *X* chromosome were linked, but not completely, and that different pairs of genes showed great differences in their linkage. Some genes showed almost no recombination, whereas others underwent so much recombination that they showed independent assortment.

HYPOTHESIS Sturtevant hypothesized that recombination was due to crossing over between the genes, and that genes farther apart in the chromosome would show more recombination.

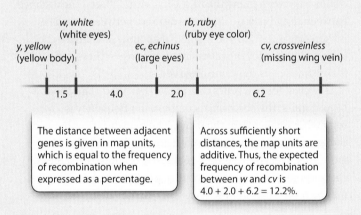

The distance between adjacent genes is given in map units, which is equal to the frequency of recombination when expressed as a percentage.

Across sufficiently short distances, the map units are additive. Thus, the expected frequency of recombination between *w* and *cv* is 4.0 + 2.0 + 6.2 = 12.2%.

EXPERIMENT Taking this idea a step further, Sturtevant reasoned that if one knew the frequency of recombination between genes *a* and *b*, between *b* and *c*, and between *a* and *c*, then one should be able to deduce the order of genes along the chromosome. He also predicted that, if the order of genes were known to be *a–b–c*, then if the genes were close enough, the frequency of recombination between *a* and *c* should equal the sum of the frequencies between *a* and *b* and that between *b* and *c*.

RESULTS Sturtevant studied the frequencies of recombination between many pairs of genes along the *X* chromosome, including some of those shown in the accompanying illustration.

CONCLUSION The results confirmed Sturtevant's hypothesis and showed that genes could be arranged in the form of a genetic map, depicting their linear order along the chromosome, with the distance between any pair of genes proportional to the frequency of recombination between them. Across sufficiently short regions, the frequencies of recombination are additive.

FOLLOW-UP WORK Genetic mapping remains a cornerstone of genetic analysis, showing which chromosome contains a mutant gene and where along the chromosome the gene is located. The method helped to identify the genes responsible for many single-gene inherited disorders, including Huntington's disease, cystic fibrosis, and muscular dystrophy.

SOURCE Sturtevant, A. H. 1913. "The Linear Arrangement of Six Sex-Linked Factors in *Drosophila*, as Shown by Their Mode of Association." *Journal of Experimental Zoology* 14: 43–59.

---

linkage and reveal the approximate location of the disease gene along the chromosome.

Fig. 17.12 illustrates the underlying concept. It assumes 100 chromosomes observed among different individuals in a pedigree, of which 50 carry a mutant allele of a gene and 50 carry a nonmutant allele. These chromosomes are tested for a marker of known location, in this case a single-nucleotide polymorphism (SNP) in which one of the nucleotide pairs in the DNA is a G–C base pair in some chromosomes and A–T in others. In Fig. 17.12a, there is clearly an association between the disease gene and the SNP. Almost all of the chromosomes that carry the mutant allele show the G–C nucleotide pair, whereas almost all of the chromosomes that carry the nonmutant allele show the A–T nucleotide pair. The two chromosomes in which

the mutant and nonmutant genes are associated with the other SNPs can be attributed to recombination.

The association in Fig. 17.12a may be contrasted with the pattern in Fig. 17.12b, in which there is no association. In this case, each of the alleles of the disease gene is equally likely to carry either form of the SNP. The failure to find an association means that the SNP is not closely linked to the disease gene, and may actually be in a different chromosome. In actual studies, an association is almost never observed, but the lucky find of an association helps identify the location of the disease gene in the genetic map. Using such association methods, hundreds of important disease genes have been located by genetic mapping. Once the location of the disease gene is known, the identity and normal function of the gene can be determined.

FIG. 17.12 Genetic mapping. SNPs associated with a mutant gene show where that gene is located in the genetic map.

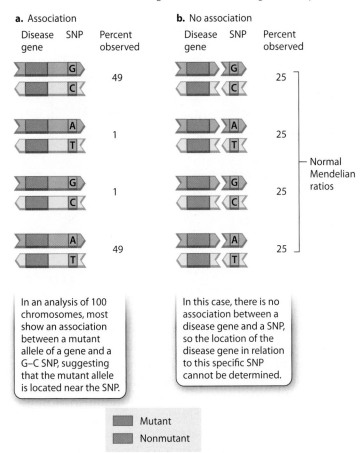

a. Association

b. No association

In an analysis of 100 chromosomes, most show an association between a mutant allele of a gene and a G–C SNP, suggesting that the mutant allele is located near the SNP.

In this case, there is no association between a disease gene and a SNP, so the location of the disease gene in relation to this specific SNP cannot be determined.

Mutant
Nonmutant

17.4 INHERITANCE OF GENES IN THE Y CHROMOSOME

Like the X chromosome, the Y chromosome exhibits a particular pattern of inheritance because of its association with the male sex. In humans and other mammals, all embryos initially develop immature internal sexual structures of both females and males. *SRY*, a gene in the Y chromosome, encodes a protein that is the trigger for male development. ("*SRY*" stands for "sex-determining region in the Y chromosome.") In the presence of *SRY*, male structures complete their development and female structures degenerate. In the absence of *SRY*, male embryonic structures degenerate and female structures complete their

development. The *SRY* gene is therefore the male-determining gene in humans and other mammals.

Because they are linked to *SRY*, most genes in the Y chromosome show a distinctive pattern of inheritance different from that Mendel observed. In this case, they are passed from father to son.

Y-linked genes are transmitted from father to son to grandson.

Genes that are present in the unique region of the Y chromosome (the part that cannot cross over with the X) are known as **Y-linked genes,** of which there are not many. As well as the *SRY* male-determining gene, they include a number of genes in which mutations are associated with impaired fertility and low sperm count.

The pedigree characteristics of Y-linked inheritance are striking (**Fig. 17.13**):

1. Only males are affected with the trait.

2. Females never inherit or transmit the trait, regardless of how many affected male relatives they have.

3. All sons of affected males are also affected.

Because the Y chromosome is always transmitted from father to son (and never transmitted to daughters), a trait determined by a Y-linked gene will occur in fathers, sons, grandsons, and so forth. Traits resulting from Y-linked genes cannot be present in females nor can they be transmitted by females. However, other than maleness itself and some types of impaired fertility, no physical traits are known that follow a strict Y-linked pattern of inheritance. This observation emphasizes the extremely low density of functional genes in the Y chromosome.

FIG. 17.13 Inheritance of Y-linked traits. The pedigree pattern is that of father to son to grandson to great-grandson, and so forth.

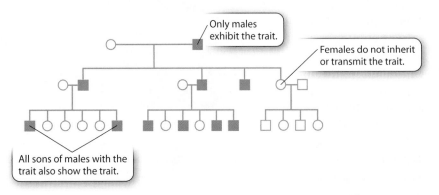

Only males exhibit the trait.

Females do not inherit or transmit the trait.

All sons of males with the trait also show the trait.

? CASE 3 You, From A to T: Your Personal Genome
How can the Y chromosome be used to
trace ancestry?

The example of Claudia Gilmore illustrates how, through tests of her personal genome with regard to the *BRCA1* and *BRCA2* mutations, she became aware of her elevated risk of breast cancer. Your personal genome not only can tell you about your genetic risk factors for disease, but it also contains important information about your genetic ancestry. For example, your male ancestors can be traced through your Y chromosome. The regions at the tips in which the X and Y chromosomes share homology is only about 6% of the entire length of the Y chromosome. This means that 94% of the Y chromosome consists of sequences in which genetic linkage is complete because it does not pair with another chromosome and does not undergo crossing over.

Because of this complete linkage, each hereditary lineage of Y chromosomes is separate from every other lineage. As mutations occur along the Y chromosome, they are completely linked to any past mutations that may be present and also completely linked to any future mutations that may take place. The mutations therefore accumulate, and this allows the evolutionary history of a set of sequences to be reconstructed.

Fig. 17.14 shows an evolutionary tree based on the accumulation of mutations at a set of nucleotide sites along the Y chromosome. Because the nucleotide sites are completely linked, the nucleotides shown need not be adjacent but can be anywhere along the Y. Each unique combination of nucleotides constitutes a Y-chromosome **haplotype,** or haploid genotype. In the figure, the most ancient Y chromosomes are at the top, and the accumulation of new mutations as the generations proceed results in the successive creation of new haplotypes. Each Y-chromosome lineage may leave some nonmutant descendants as well as some mutant descendants, and hence any or all of the sequences shown may coexist in a present-day population.

In human history, the mutations creating new Y-chromosome haplotypes were occurring at the same time as populations were migrating and founding new settlements across the globe, and so each geographically distinct population came to have a somewhat different set of Y-chromosome haplotypes. The differences

FIG. 17.14 *Y*-chromosome haplotypes. Because *Y* chromosomes in a lineage conform to an evolutionary tree, the ancestry of a male's *Y* chromosome can be traced.

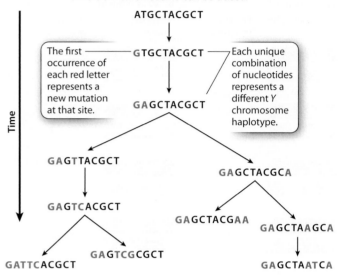

among populations are offset to some extent by migration among populations, which mixes the geographical locations of various haplotypes. Nevertheless, the fact that the mutations accumulate through time and are completely linked allows the evolutionary history of the haplotypes to be reconstructed. It also enables Y chromosomes to be traced to their likely ethnic origin.

The worldwide distribution of real Y-chromosome lineages among human populations is shown in **Fig. 17.15.** The different colors in

FIG. 17.15 Geographical distribution of *Y*-chromosome haplotypes. The evolutionary trees of *Y*-chromosome haplotypes reflect the origin and movement of different *Y* chromosomes over time.

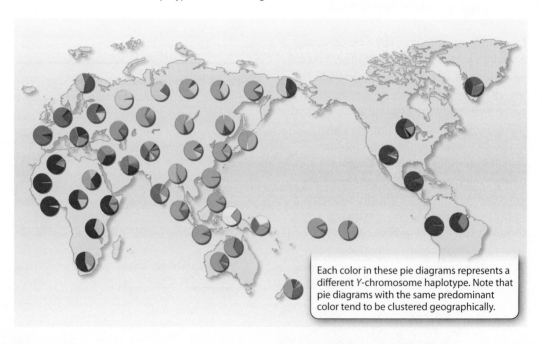

Each color in these pie diagrams represents a different *Y*-chromosome haplotype. Note that pie diagrams with the same predominant color tend to be clustered geographically.

the pie diagrams represent different mutations. Neighboring populations tend to have more closely related Y chromosomes than more distant populations. Four major clusters of Y-chromosome lineages can be recognized in Fig. 17.15. One is concentrated in Africa, another in Southeast Asia and Australia, a third in Europe and central and western Asia, and the fourth in North and South America. These clusters correspond roughly with the spread of human settlements around the globe inferred from archaeological evidence.

The implication of Fig. 17.15 is that the haplotype of your Y chromosome (if you have a Y chromosome) contains genetic information about its origin. And you can learn what this information is from genetic testing companies that sell direct-to-consumer (DTC) services. Their tests are not regarded as medical devices and so are unregulated, and quality control is sometimes uncertain. Nevertheless, you can send saliva or other biological samples to a DTC provider, which will (for a fee) test your Y chromosome and send you a report that details its possible origin. Of course, because of recombination and independent assortment of genes in other chromosomes, the ethnic origin of your Y chromosome may have little or nothing to do with the ethnic origins of genes in any of your other chromosomes.

17.5 INHERITANCE OF MITOCHONDRIAL AND CHLOROPLAST DNA

Sex chromosomes and linked genes are not the only genes that are inherited in ways Mendel did not describe. Genes in mitochondria and chloroplasts also show distinct inheritance patterns. Mitochondria and chloroplasts are ancient organelles of eukaryotic cells originally acquired by the engulfing of prokaryotic cells (Chapter 5). Mitochondria generate most of the ATP that cells use for their chemical energy, and they also function in the cell cycle, programmed cell death, and other important processes. Chloroplasts are found only in plant cells and eukaryotic algae. These organelles contain chlorophyll, a green pigment that absorbs light and, in the process of photosynthesis (Chapter 8), produces the sugars that are essential for growth of the plant or algal cells and of the organisms that eat them. Mitochondria and chloroplasts have their own genomes, so genes present in these genomes move with the organelle during cell division.

Mitochondrial and chloroplast genomes often show uniparental inheritance.

During sexual reproduction, cellular organelles do not show the regular, highly choreographed movements that chromosomes undergo during Mendelian segregation. These organelles are partitioned to the gametes along with other cytoplasmic components, and therefore their mode of inheritance depends on how the gametes are formed, how much cytoplasm is included in the gametes, and the fate of the cytoplasm in each parental gamete after fertilization.

Considering the great diversity in the details of reproduction in different groups of organisms, it is not surprising that there is a diversity of types of inheritance of cytoplasmic organelles. The three most important types are:

- **Maternal inheritance,** in which the organelles in the off-spring cells derive from those in the mother.

- **Paternal inheritance,** in which the organelles in the offspring cells derive from those in the father.

- **Biparental inheritance,** in which the organelles in the offspring cells derive from those in both parents.

In most organisms, either maternal inheritance or paternal inheritance predominates, but sometimes there is variation from one offspring to the next. For example, transmission of the chloroplasts ranges from strictly paternal in the giant redwood *Sequoia,* to strictly maternal in the sunflower *Helianthus,* to either maternal or paternal (or less frequently biparental) in the fern *Scolopendrium,* to mostly maternal but sometimes paternal or biparental in the snapdragon *Antirrhinum.*

There is likewise great diversity among organisms in the inheritance of mitochondrial DNA. Most animals show maternal transmission of the mitochondria, as would be expected from their large, cytoplasm-rich eggs and the small, cytoplasm-poor sperm. Among other organisms, there is again much variation, including maternal transmission of mitochondria in flowering plants and paternal transmission in the green alga *Chlamydomonas.*

Maternal inheritance is characteristic of mitochondrial diseases.

In humans and other mammals, mitochondria show strictly maternal inheritance—the mitochondria in the offspring cells derive from those in the mother. **Fig. 17.16** shows the characteristic pedigree patterns of a trait due to maternal inheritance:

1. Both males and females can show the trait.

2. All offspring from an affected female show the trait.

3. Males never transmit the trait to their offspring.

The pedigree in Fig. 17.16 follows a mitochondrial disease known as MERRF syndrome (the acronym stands for "myoclonic epilepsy with ragged red fibers"). As its name suggests, the syndrome is characterized by epilepsy, a neurological disease characterized by seizures, as well as by the accumulation of abnormal mitochondria in muscle fibers. This extremely rare disease is associated with a single point mutation in a mitochondrial gene involved in protein synthesis that affects oxidative phosphorylation (Chapter 7).

More than 40 different diseases show these pedigree characteristics. They all result from mutations in the mitochondrial DNA, but the tissues and organs affected as well as the severity differs from one to the next. All of the mutations

FIG. 17.16 Maternal inheritance. Human mitochondrial DNA is transmitted from a mother to all of her offspring.

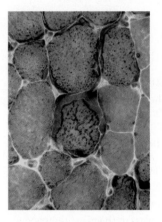

Inherited mitochondrial diseases are often associated with muscle weakness reflecting deficient production of ATP. The red patches in the microscopic image result from clumps of defective mitochondria in muscle fibers observed in one form of epilepsy due to mutation in mitochondrial DNA.

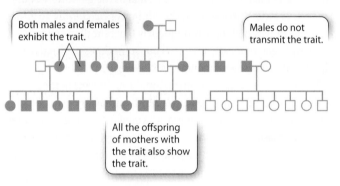

Both males and females exhibit the trait.

Males do not transmit the trait.

All the offspring of mothers with the trait also show the trait.

affect energy production in one way or another. In some cases, disease results directly from lack of adequate amounts of ATP, in other cases from intermediates in energy production that are toxic to the cell or that damage the mitochondrial DNA.

? CASE 3 You, From A to T: Your Personal Genome
How can mitochondrial DNA be used to trace ancestry?
Sequencing of mitochondrial DNA reveals mitochondrial haplotypes analogous to those in the Y chromosome. As in the Y chromosome, mutations in mitochondrial DNA accumulate through time, and each mitochondrial haplotype remains intact through successive generations because recombination between mitochondrial genomes is rare. This means that mitochondrial DNA can be used to trace ancestry and population history, much as described previously for the Y chromosome. The mitochondrial DNA is actually more informative than Y-chromosomal DNA because it shows substantially more genetic variation.

The use of mitochondrial DNA to trace human origins and migration is discussed in greater detail in Chapter 24. As with the Y chromosome, your personal mitochondrial genome includes information about its origin. If you want to learn about your mitochondrial DNA, you can send a tissue sample to any of a number of direct-to-consumer genotyping services that will, for a fee, analyze the DNA and provide you with a report.

Core Concepts Summary

17.1 THE X AND Y CHROMOSOMES OF SOME ANIMALS, INCLUDING HUMANS, DETERMINE SEX AND ARE INHERITED DIFFERENTLY FROM THE AUTOSOMES.

In humans and other mammals, XX individuals are female and XY individuals are male. page 17-2

The human X and Y chromosomes are different lengths and contain different genes, except for small regions of homology that allow the two chromosomes to pair in meiosis. page 17-2

Segregation of the X and Y chromosomes during male meiosis results in half of the sperm receiving an X chromosome and half a Y chromosome so that random union of gametes predicts a 1:1 female:male sex ratio at the time of fertilization. page 17-2

17.2 X-LINKED GENES, WHICH SHOW A CRISSCROSS INHERITANCE PATTERN, PROVIDED THE FIRST EVIDENCE THAT GENES ARE PRESENT IN CHROMOSOMES.

Morgan studied a mutation in the fruit fly *Drosophila melanogaster* that resulted in fruit flies with white eyes rather than normal red eyes. In this species, as in mammals, females are XX and males are XY. page 17-3

In a cross of a normal red-eyed female with a mutant white-eyed male, all of the male and female progeny had red eyes. When brothers and sisters of this cross were mated with each other, all of the females had red eyes, but males were red-eyed and white-eyed in a 1:1 ratio. page 17-3

This pattern of inheritance is observed because the gene Morgan studied, called *white*, is located in the X chromosome. The nonmutant w^+ allele is dominant to the mutant w^- allele, and the gene is present only in the X chromosome and not in the Y chromosome. page 17-4

X-linked genes show a crisscross inheritance pattern, in which the X chromosome with the mutant gene that is present in males in one generation is present in females in the next generation. page 17-5

Bridges observed rare fruit flies that did not follow the usual pattern for X-linked inheritance and inferred that these exceptional fruit flies resulted from nondisjunction, or failure of homologous chromosomes to segregate, in male or female meiosis. His observations provided evidence that genes are carried in chromosomes. page 17-6

In humans, X-linked inheritance shows a pattern in which affected individuals are almost always males, affected males have unaffected sons, and a female whose father is affected can have affected sons. page 17-7

17.3 GENETIC LINKAGE OCCURS WHEN TWO GENES ARE SUFFICIENTLY CLOSE TOGETHER IN THE SAME CHROMOSOME THAT THE COMBINATION OF ALLELES PRESENT IN THE CHROMOSOME TENDS TO REMAIN TOGETHER IN INHERITANCE.

Genes that are close together in the same chromosome are linked and do not undergo independent assortment. page 17-8

Recombinant chromosomes result from crossing over between genes on the same chromosome and show a nonparental combination of alleles. page 17-9

Nonrecombinant chromosomes have the same configuration of alleles as one of the parental chromosomes. page 17-10

In genetic mapping, the observed proportion of recombinant chromosomes is the frequency of recombination and can be used as a measure of distance along a chromosome. A recombination frequency of 1% is one map unit. page 17-10

Gene linkage and mapping are used to identify the locations of disease genes in the human genome. page 17-11

17.4 MOST Y-LINKED GENES ARE PASSED FROM FATHER TO SON.

In humans and other mammals, the Y chromosome contains a gene called SRY that results in male development. page 17-13

In Y-linked inheritance, only males are affected and all sons of an affected male are affected. Females are never affected and do not transmit the trait. page 17-13

Most Y-linked genes show complete linkage, which allows their evolutionary history to be traced. page 17-14

17.5 MITOCHONDRIA AND CHLOROPLAST DNA FOLLOW THEIR OWN INHERITANCE PATTERN.

Mitochondria and chloroplasts have their own genomes, which reflect their evolutionary history as free-living prokaryotes. page 17-15

Mitochondria in humans and other mammals show maternal inheritance, in which individuals inherit their mitochondrial DNA from their mother. page 17-15

Because mitochondrial DNA does not undergo recombination and is maternally inherited, it can be used to trace human ancestry and migration. page 17-16

Self-Assessment

1. Explain how the human X and Y chromosomes can pair during meiosis even though they are of different lengths and most of their genes are different.

2. Describe the biological basis for the 1:1 ratio of males and females at conception in mammals.

3. For a recessive X-linked mutation, such as color blindness, draw and explain its pattern of inheritance through a set of crosses.

4. Explain why linked genes do not exhibit independent assortment.

5. Describe how recombination frequency can be used to build a genetic map.

6. Describe the pattern of inheritance expected from a Y-linked gene in a human pedigree.

7. Describe the pattern of inheritance expected from a gene present in mitochondrial DNA in a human pedigree.

8. Explain how Y-chromosome and mitochondrial DNA data can be used to trace ancestry.

Do you understand the chapter's Core Concepts? Log into BIO PORTAL to check your answers to the Self-Assessment questions, then practice what you've learned and reinforce this chapter's concepts by working through the problems and multimedia tutorials provided there.

🛜 http://courses.bfwpub.com/yourbioportal/index.php

CHAPTER 18

THE GENETIC AND ENVIRONMENTAL BASIS OF COMPLEX TRAITS

Core Concepts

18.1 Complex traits are those influenced both by the action of many genes and by environmental factors.

18.2 Genetic effects on complex traits are reflected in resemblance between relatives.

18.3 Twin studies help separate the effects of genotype and environment on variation in a trait.

18.4 Many common diseases and birth defects are affected by multiple genetic and environmental risk factors.

Biologists initially had a hard time accepting the principles of Mendelian inheritance because they seem so at odds with everyday observations. Common and easily observed traits like height, weight, hair color, and skin color give no evidence of segregation in pedigrees, and simple phenotypic ratios like 3:1 or 9:3:3:1 are not observed for them. The lack of these characteristic ratios raised serious doubt whether Mendel's principles are valid for common traits—some biologists concluded that they apply only to seemingly trivial traits like round and wrinkled seeds in peas.

At about the time that Mendel was studying inheritance in garden peas, the biologist Francis Galton, a friend and cousin of Charles Darwin, was studying common traits including human height. From studies of height and other common traits in parents and their offspring, Galton discovered general principles in the inheritance of such traits. For example, parents who are tall tend to have offspring who are taller than average but not as tall as themselves. Galton's principles for the inheritance of common traits did not invoke genes, segregation, independent assortment, or other features of Mendelian inheritance, but they did describe the observations. Not only were genes—what Mendel called "hereditary factors"—thought to be unnecessary in Galton's theory of inheritance, but also many biologists thought that Galton's theories and Mendel's were incompatible.

This, it turned out, was not the case. The traits that Mendel studied are now called **single-gene traits** because each one is determined by variation at a single gene and the traits are for the most part not influenced by the environment. By focusing on single-gene traits, Mendel was able to infer underlying mechanisms of inheritance based on physical factors we now call genes. By contrast, **complex traits,** such as human height, are influenced by multiple genes as well as by the environment. As a result, their inheritance patterns are more difficult to follow and simple phenotypic ratios are not observed.

In many ways, complex traits are more important than single-gene Mendelian traits. One reason is their prevalence—complex traits are found everywhere and include most of the traits we can see around us. By contrast, there are relatively few examples of single-gene traits. Complex traits are also important in human health and disease. In the most common disorders—among them heart disease, diabetes, and cancer—single-gene Mendelian inheritance is seldom found. It is therefore important to understand the inheritance of complex traits and common disorders, which are the subjects of this chapter. We begin by describing some of the features of complex traits, and then show how these principles are not only compatible with, but in fact predicted by, Mendelian inheritance. Finally, we describe how modern molecular genetics and genomics have allowed the identification of genes affecting complex traits.

18.1 HEREDITY AND ENVIRONMENT

Complex traits are important not only in humans, but also in agricultural plants and animals. We will examine human height in some detail because it has been widely studied, but equally well known complex traits are number of eggs laid by hens, milk production in dairy cows, and yield per acre of grain (**Fig. 18.1**).

Many common human diseases, including high blood pressure, obesity, diabetes, and depression, are complex traits (**Fig. 18.2**). High blood pressure, for example, affects about one-third of the U.S. population, and obesity another third. Type 2 diabetes affects around 8% of the U.S. population, and an estimated 15% will suffer at least one episode of severe depression in the course of a lifetime. Taken together, about 200 million Americans—two-thirds of the entire population—suffer from one or more of these common disorders. None of these traits shows single-gene Mendelian inheritance.

In many complex traits, the phenotype of an individual is determined by measurement: Human height is measured in inches, milk yield by the gallon, grain yield by the bushel, egg production by the number of eggs, blood pressure by millimeters of mercury, and blood sugar by millimoles per liter. Because the phenotype of complex traits such as these is measured along a continuum with only small intervals between similar individuals, complex traits like these are often called **quantitative traits.** By contrast, single-gene traits often appear in one of two or more different phenotypes, such as round versus wrinkled seeds, or green versus yellow seeds.

Complex traits are affected by the environment.

Expression of complex traits is notoriously susceptible to lifestyle choices and other environmental factors. Inadequate nutrition is linked to slow growth rate and short stature in adults. Salt intake is associated with an increased likelihood of high blood pressure and is therefore an **environmental risk factor** for this common disorder. An environmental risk factor is a characteristic in a person's surroundings that increases the likelihood of developing a particular disease. A junk-food diet high in fat and carbohydrates is an environmental risk factor for obesity and diabetes.

Environmental effects are also important in agriculture. Farmers are well aware that adequate nutrition is essential to normal growth of chicks, lambs, piglets, and calves, and that continued high-quality feed is necessary for high egg production and milk yield when the animals reach adulthood. In crop plants like grains, adequate soil moisture and nutrients are necessary for sustained high yields.

Environmental factors not only affect the average phenotype for complex traits, but they also affect the variation in phenotype from one individual to the next. For example, most fields of corn you see planted along the roadside come from seeds that are genetically identical to one another, yet there is phenotypic variation in complex traits like plant height (**Fig. 18.3**). Because the plants are genetically identical, the differences in phenotype result from differences in the environment. Some parts of the field may receive more sunlight than others, and some parts may have better water drainage. No matter how uniform an environment may seem, there are always minor differences from one area to the next, and these differences can result in variation in complex traits.

Environmental effects on complex traits in animals are evident in true-breeding, totally homozygous strains produced by many generations of brother–sister matings, like those used by Mendel in his experiments with pea plants. Such true-breeding, homozygous strains are called **inbred lines,** and they are often used for research. Even though all animals in any inbred line are genetically identical, and are caged in the same facility and fed the same food, there is variation from one animal to the next. In one study of cholesterol levels in an inbred line of mice, for example, average serum cholesterol was 120 mg/dl (milligrams per deciliter), but the range was 60–180 mg/dl. Because the mice are

---

FIG. 18.1 Examples of complex traits. (a) Human height, (b) egg number, (c) milk production, and (d) grain yield.

FIG. 18.2 Examples of human diseases that are complex traits. (a) High blood pressure, (b) obesity, (c) diabetes, and (d) depression.

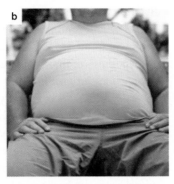
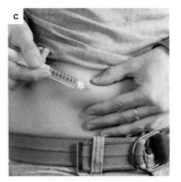

genetically identical, the variation in serum cholesterol resulted from variation in the environment.

Complex traits are affected by multiple genes.

Most complex traits are affected by many genes, in contrast to Mendel's traits, which are primarily affected only by one. Therefore, in complex traits the familiar phenotypic ratios such as 3:1 that Mendel observed when he crossed two true-breeding strains with contrasting characters are not observed. For complex

FIG. 18.3 Phenotypic variation due to variation in the environment. Genetically identical corn plants vary in height because of variation in exposure to sun and in soil composition at different locations in the same field.

traits, the effects of individual genes are obscured by variation in phenotype that is due to multiple genes affecting the trait and also due to the environment. The number of genes affecting complex traits is usually so large that different genotypes can have very similar phenotypes, which also makes it difficult to see the effects of individual genes on a trait.

In a few traits, however, the effects of the environment are minor and the number of genes is small, and in these cases the genetic basis of the trait can be analyzed. A classic example, studied by Herman Nilsson-Ehle about a century ago, concerns the color of seed casing in wheat (the "seed color"), which ranges from nearly white to dark red (**Fig. 18.4**). His experiment demonstrated that complex traits are subject to the same laws that Mendel worked out for single-gene traits, but that the inheritance patterns are more difficult to see because of the number of genes involved.

In studying seed color in true-breeding varieties and their first-generation and second-generation hybrids, Nilsson-Ehle realized that the relative frequencies of different shades of red color could be explained by the effects of three genes that undergo independent assortment, as illustrated by the Punnett square shown in Fig. 18.4. Each of the genes has two alleles, designated by combinations of upper-case and lower-case letters. In the development of seed color, each upper-case allele in a genotype intensifies the red coloration in an additive fashion. Altogether there are seven possible phenotypes, ranging from a phenotype of 0 (nearly colorless, genotype *aa bb cc*) to 6 (dark red, genotype *AA BB CC*).

In the cross shown at the top of Fig. 18.4, the parental genotypes are both *Aa Bb Cc*, and so they each have a phenotype of 3, an intermediate seed color on the 0-to-6 color scale. If the three genes show independent assortment (Chapter 16), then the distribution of phenotypes expected in progeny from the cross *Aa Bb Cc* × *Aa Bb Cc* is as shown in the Punnett square, in which the numbers indicate the number of upper-case alleles in each class of offspring. The bar graph below the Punnett square shows the distribution of the seed-color phenotypes and the probability

FIG. 18.4 Multiple genes contributing to a complex trait. Three unlinked genes, each with two alleles, influence the intensity of red coloration of the seed casing in wheat.

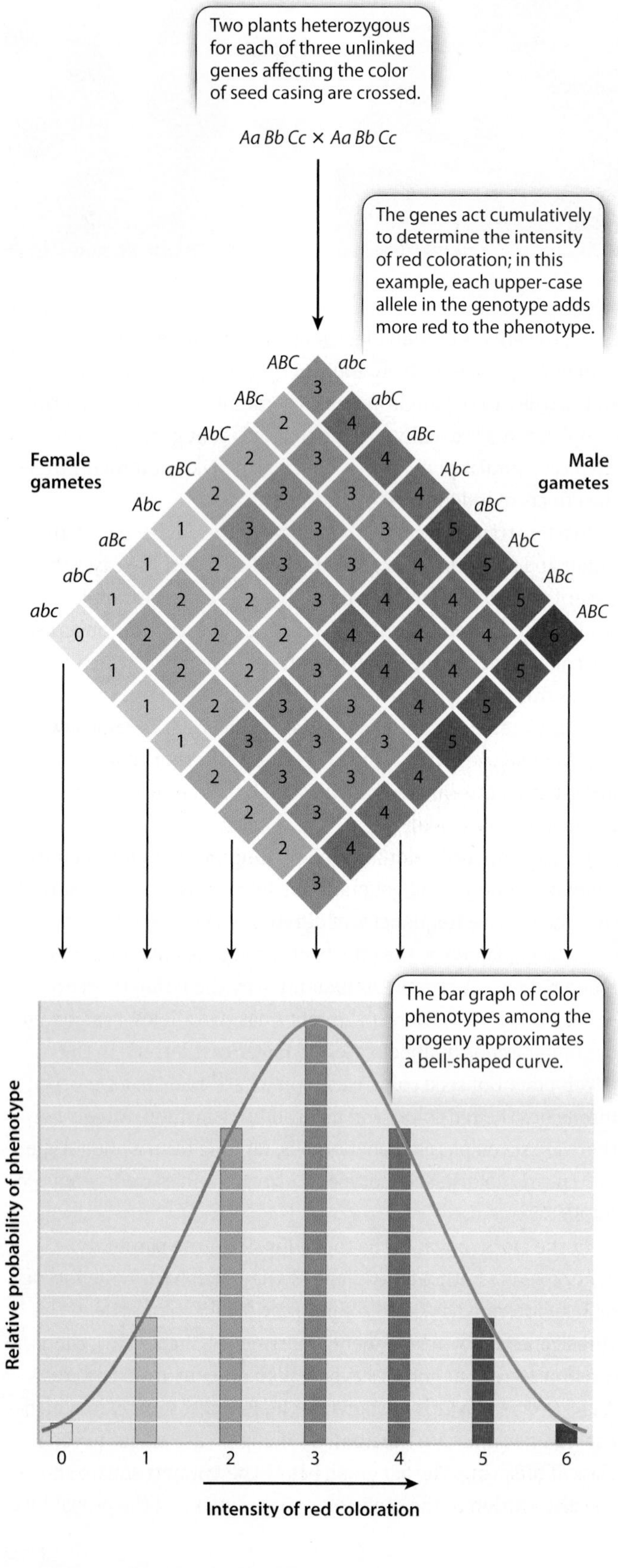

of each of the possible phenotypes, which is approximated reasonably well by the bell-shaped curve known as the **normal distribution.** The phenotypes of many complex traits, including human height, conform to the normal distribution. Nelson-Ehle's results conformed to a normal distribution, consistent with the hypothesis of three unlinked genes each with two alleles influencing seed color in wheat.

When differences in phenotype due to the environment can be ignored, the genetic variation affecting complex traits can be detected more easily. And when studying inbred lines, differences in phenotype due to genotype can be ignored because all individuals have the same genotype, and the effects of environment can be observed. In most cases, however, genetic variation among individuals and environmental variation among individuals are both present, and it is difficult to quantify how much variation in phenotype is due to genetics and how much due to environment.

It's important to point out that complex traits are not really more "complex" than any other biological trait. The term is used merely to imply that both genetic factors and environmental factors contribute to variation in phenotype among individuals. As there are environmental factors that affect complex traits such as height, so there are genetic factors that affect height (as we discuss below). Similarly, just as an environmental risk factor increases the likelihood of a common disease, so does a genetic risk factor predispose an individual to the condition. For example, the human gene *ApoE* encodes a protein that helps transport fat and cholesterol. Certain alleles of *ApoE* are associated with high levels of cholesterol, and one particular allele is a genetic risk factor for Alzheimer's disease, the most common serious form of age-related loss of cognitive ability.

The relative importance of genes and environment can be determined by differences among individuals.

For any one individual, it is impossible to specify the relative roles of genes and environment in the expression of a complex trait. For example, in an individual 66 inches tall, it would be meaningless to attribute 33 inches of height to parentage (genes) and 33 inches of height to nutrition (environment). This kind of partitioning makes no sense because genes and environment act together so intimately in each individual that their effects are inseparable. To attempt to separate them for any individual would be like asking to what extent it is breathing or oxygen that keeps us alive. Both are important, and both must take place together if we are to stay alive.

It is nevertheless possible to separate genes and environment in regard to their effects on the *differences*, or variation, among individuals within a particular population. For some traits, the variation seen among individuals is due largely if not exclusively to differences in the environment. For other traits, the variation is due mainly to genetic differences. In the case of human height, roughly 80% of the variation among individuals of the same sex is due to genetic differences, and the remaining 20% to differences in their environment, primarily differences in nutrition during their years of growth.

Genetic and environmental effects can interact in unpredictable ways.

One of the features of complex traits is that genetic and environmental effects may interact, often in unpredictable ways. Consider the example shown in **Fig. 18.5.** In this experiment, two strains of corn were each grown in a series of soils in which the amount of nitrogen had been enriched by the growth of legumes. The yield of strain 1 varies little across these different environments. The yield of strain 2, however, increases dramatically with soil nitrogen. Each of the lines is known as a **norm of reaction,** which for any genotype graphically depicts how the environment (shown on the x-axis) affects phenotype (shown on the y-axis) across a range of environments. Note that in one case in Fig. 18.5, the environment has little to no effect on the phenotype (the norm of reaction is nearly flat), but in the other it has a very noticeable effect. Therefore, it is impossible to predict the phenotype of a given genotype without knowing what the environmental conditions are and how the phenotype changes in response to variation in the environment.

Such variation in the effects of the environment on different genotypes is known as **genotype-by-environment interaction.** This type of interaction is important because it implies that the effect of a genotype cannot be specified without knowing the environment, and the other way around. A further implication is that there may be no genotype that is the "best" across a broad range of environments, and likewise

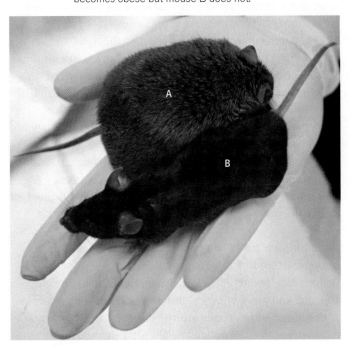

FIG. 18.6 **Genotype-by-environment interaction for obesity in mice.** When fed a normal diet, both inbred lines grow to be about the same size. When fed a high-fat diet, mouse A becomes obese but mouse B does not.

no environment that is "best" for all genotypes. For complex traits, phenotype depends on both genotype *and* environment. For the strains of corn in Fig. 18.5, for example, which strain is "better" depends on the soil nitrogen. With little nitrogen enrichment, strain 1 is better; at intermediate values, both strains yield about the same; and with high nitrogen enrichment, strain 2 is better. In this case, knowing the norms of reaction, and recognizing the magnitude and direction of genotype-by-environment interaction, allows each farmer to use the strains likely to perform best under the available conditions of cultivation.

Genotype-by-environment interaction implies that the interplay between genes and the environment is difficult to predict. An example of genotype-by-environment interaction affecting obesity is shown in **Fig. 18.6.** The animals shown are adults of two inbred lines of mice. When fed a normal diet, both inbred lines grow to be about the same size. When fed a high-fat diet, however, the inbred line A becomes obese, whereas inbred line B does not. Hence, it is not genotype alone that causes obesity in line A because with a normal diet, line A does not become obese. Nor is it a high-fat diet alone that causes obesity because the high-fat diet does not cause obesity in line B. Rather, the obesity in line A results from a genotype-by-environment interaction (which in this case is a genotype-by-diet interaction).

FIG. 18.5 **Genotype-by-environment interaction for grain yield in corn.** The effect of soil nitrogen on grain yield is minimal in strain 1, but dramatic in strain 2.

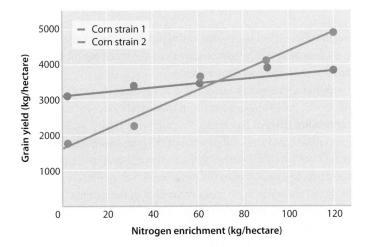

18.2 RESEMBLANCE AMONG RELATIVES

Mendel had many advantages over Galton in his studies of inheritance. Mendel's peas were true breeding, produced a new generation each year, and yielded large numbers of progeny. The environment had a negligible effect on the traits, and the genetic effect on each trait was due to the alleles of a single gene. Mendel's crosses yielded simple ratios such as 3:1 or 1:1, which could be interpreted in terms of segregation of dominant and recessive alleles.

By contrast, Galton studied variation in such traits as height in humans. Humans are obviously not true breeding and have few offspring. Galton had one big advantage, though: Whereas most simple Mendelian traits are relatively uncommon, Galton's traits are readily observed in everyday life. What did Galton discover?

For complex traits, offspring resemble parents but show regression toward the mean.

Galton studied many complex traits, including human height, strength, and various physical characteristics, including number of fingerprint ridges. The discovery he regarded as fundamental resulted from his data on adult height of parents and their progeny (**Fig. 18.7**). Galton noted that each category of parent (tall parents or short parents) produced a range of progeny forming a distribution with its own mean. He also noted that the mean height of the progeny of tall parents was taller than the average height in the entire population but shorter than that of the parents. Finally, he noted that the mean height of the progeny of short parents was shorter than the population average but taller than that of the parents.

The bar graph in Fig. 18.7a shows the distribution of height among the progeny of the tallest parents, whose average height is 72 inches. The mean height of the offspring is 71 inches, which is greater than the mean height of the whole population of the study (68.25 inches) but less than that of the parents. The bar graph in Fig. 18.7b is the distribution of height of progeny of the shortest parents, who averaged 66 inches. In this case, the mean height of the progeny is 67 inches, which is less than the mean height of the population but greater than that of the parents. Note, however, that *some* of the offspring of tall parents are taller than their parents, and likewise *some* of the offspring of short parents are shorter than their parents. It is only *on average* that the height of the offspring is less extreme than that of the parents.

Galton's analysis led him to the trend shown in **Fig. 18.8.** The graph plots the average height of parents and the average height of their progeny across the whole range of heights observed. Consider two cases. If the mean parent height is 72 inches (above the mean height in the population as a whole), the mean offspring height is less than the mean parent height but more than the population average. By contrast, if the mean parent

FIG. 18.7 Galton's data showing distribution of height of offspring of (a) the tallest parents and (b) the shortest parents.

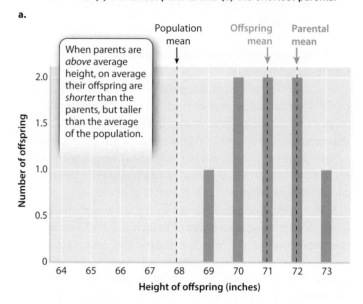

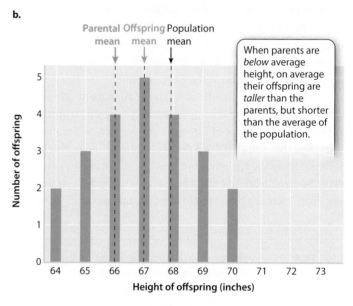

height is 66 inches (below the mean height in the population), the mean offspring height is more than the mean parent height but less than the population average.

Galton regarded this observation as his most important discovery, publishing his results in 1886, and today we call it **regression toward the mean.** The offspring exhibit an average phenotype that is less different from the population mean than that of the parents. In other words, when the average height of the parents is *smaller* than the population mean, then the average height of the offspring is *greater* than that of the parents (but smaller than the population mean). Likewise, when the average height of the parents is *greater* than the population mean, then the average height of the offspring is *smaller* than that of the parents (but greater than the population mean).

FIG. 18.8 **Regression toward the mean.** Galton's data on the average adult height of parents and that of their offspring show that offspring mean height (blue line) falls between the parental mean (dashed red line) and the population mean (dashed black line).

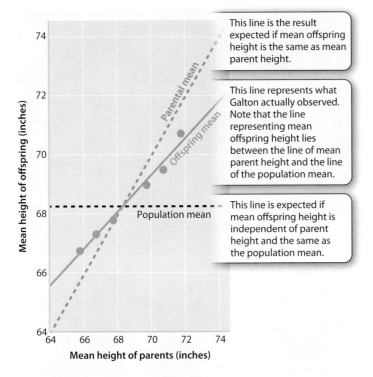

This line is the result expected if mean offspring height is the same as mean parent height.

This line represents what Galton actually observed. Note that the line representing mean offspring height lies between the line of mean parent height and the line of the population mean.

This line is expected if mean offspring height is independent of parent height and the same as the population mean.

Regression toward the mean is observed for two reasons. The first is that during meiotic cell division (Chapter 11), segregation and recombination break up combinations of genes that result in extreme phenotypes, such as very tall or very short, that are present in the parents. The second reason is that the phenotype of the parents results not only from genes but also from the environment. Environmental effects are not inherited, so to the extent the parents' phenotypes result from environmental effects, the same phenotypes will not necessarily appear in the offspring.

→ **Quick Check 1** Does regression toward the mean imply that the human population is getting shorter over time?

Heritability is the proportion of the total variation due to genetic differences among individuals.

How much of the difference in height among individuals is due to genetic differences, and how much is due to environmental differences? The slope of the line that relates the average phenotype of parents to the average phenotype of their offspring (the blue line in the graph in Fig. 18.8) can answer this question because it provides a measure of the **heritability** of the trait. The heritability of a trait in a population of organisms is the proportion of the total variation in the trait that is due to genetic differences among individuals. For a complex trait, the heritability determines how closely the mean of the progeny resembles that of the parents.

When heritability is 100%, all of the variation among individuals in the population is due to differing genotypes, and in this case the mean phenotype of the offspring is identical to that of the parents. If height had a heritability of 100%, then the blue line in Fig. 18.8 would be the same as the line representing the parental mean (the dashed red line). In contrast, when the heritability of a trait is 0%, all of the variation in the trait in a population is due to differences in environment, and in this case the mean phenotype of offspring would have no resemblance to that of their parents. In Fig. 18.8, if the heritability of height were 0%, then the blue line would be superimposed on the horizontal line depicting the population mean (the dashed black line).

The term "heritability" is often misinterpreted. The problem is that, in non-scientific contexts, the word means "the capability of being inherited or being passed by inheritance." This definition suggests that heritability has something to do with the inheritance of a trait. But "heritability" as used for complex traits means no such thing. It refers only to the *variation* in a trait among individuals, and specifically to the proportion of the variation among individuals in a population due to differences in genotype.

Hence, a heritability of 100% does not imply that the environment cannot affect a trait. As emphasized earlier, the environment is always important, just as oxygen is important to life. What a heritability of 100% means is that *variation* in the environment does not contribute to differences among individuals in a specific population. For example, if genetically different strains of corn are grown in a greenhouse and subject to identical environmental conditions, then differences in height have to be due to genetic differences, and the heritability of the trait would be 100% (**Fig. 18.9a**). Similarly, a heritability of 0% does not imply that genotype cannot affect the trait. A heritability of 0% merely means that differences in genotype do not contribute to the *variation* in

FIG. 18.9 **Heritability, the proportion of the total phenotypic variation that is the result of genetic differences.** Heritability can vary, even for a particular trait like corn height, so it is defined only for a particular population in a particular set of environmental conditions.

a. Genetically different strains of corn

All of these corn plants are grown in the same environment, so differences in height are due to genetic differences.

Heritability of height of corn = 100%

b. Genetically identical strains of corn

All of these corn plants are genetically identical, so differences in height are due to environmental differences.

Heritability of height of corn = 0%

the trait among individuals in a specific population. If genetically identical strains of corn are grown in different environments, then differences in height must be due to the environment, and heritability would be 0% (**Fig. 18.9b**).

The magnitude of heritability therefore is not an intrinsic property of a trait. For corn height, as we have seen, the heritability in one case was 100% and in the second 0%. Heritability applies only to the trait in a particular population across the range of environments that exist at a specific time. Similarly, the heritability depicted by the slope of the blue line in Fig. 18.8 applies only to the population studied (205 pairs of British parents and their 930 adult offspring, in the late nineteenth century), and may be larger or smaller in different populations at different times. In particular, the magnitude of the heritability cannot specify how much of the difference in average phenotype *between* two populations is due to genotype and how much due to environment.

If the heritability of a trait can change depending on the population and the conditions being studied, why is it a useful measure? Heritability is important in evolution, particularly in studies of artificial selection, a type of selective breeding in which only certain chosen individuals are allowed to reproduce (Chapter 21). Practiced over many generations, artificial selection can result in considerable changes in morphology or behavior or almost any trait that is selected. The large differences among breeds of pigeons and other domesticated animals prompted Charles Darwin to point to artificial selection as an example of what natural selection could achieve. Heritability is important because this quantity determines how rapidly a population can be changed by artificial selection. A trait with a high heritability responds rapidly to selection, whereas a trait with a low heritability responds slowly or not at all.

→ **Quick Check 2** Many people are surprised to learn that, while each individual's fingerprints are unique, the total number of fingerprint ridges is highly heritable, about 90% heritability in many populations. What does high heritability of this trait mean?

18.3 TWIN STUDIES

Galton pioneered studies of twins as a way to separate the effects of genotype and environment in phenotype differences among individuals. Depending on whether they arise from one or two egg cells, twins can be **identical (monozygotic twins)** or **fraternal (dizygotic twins).** Identical twins arise from a single fertilized egg (the zygote), which, after several rounds of cell division, separates into two distinct but genetically identical embryos. Strikingly similar in overall appearance (**Fig. 18.10a**), identical twins have stimulated the imagination since antiquity, inspiring stories by the Roman playwright Plautus, William Shakespeare (himself the father of twins), Alexander Dumas, Mark Twain, and many others.

FIG. 18.10 **Identical twins.** (a) Identical (monozygotic) twins arise from a single fertilized egg and are genetically identical. (b) Fraternal (dizygotic) twins arise from two different fertilized eggs and are no more closely related than other pairs of siblings.

In contrast, fraternal twins result when two separate eggs, produced by a double ovulation, are fertilized by two different sperm. Whereas identical twins are genetically identical, fraternal twins are only as closely related as any other pair of siblings (**Fig. 18.10b**).

Identical twins share the same genotype.

The utility of twins in the study of complex traits derives from the genetic identity of identical twins. Whereas differences between fraternal twins with regard to any trait may arise because of genetic or environmental factors (or genotype-by-environment interactions), differences between identical twins must be due only to environmental factors because the twins are genetically identical. Consequently, if variation in a trait has an important genetic component, then identical twins will be more similar to each other than fraternal twins are similar to each other. But if the genetic contribution to variation is negligible, then identical twins will not be more similar to each other than fraternal twins are to each other.

One criticism that arises in twin studies—and it is a serious one—is that the environment of identical twins is often more similar than that of fraternal twins. Within the uterus, identical twins frequently share the same embryonic membranes and placenta, whereas fraternal twins rarely do. After birth, the striking resemblance in facial appearance, body shape, and other features between identical twins often leads their parents, teachers, and friends to treat them more similarly than if they were fraternal twins. Resemblances between identical twins due to similarities in their environments will mistakenly be attributed to their genetic identity. This difficulty can be minimized in part by studying identical twins who were separated from each other shortly after birth and reared in different environments, but identical twins reared apart are rare.

Ongoing studies at the University of Minnesota begun about 30 years ago united dozens of twins reared apart and found some astonishing coincidences—separated twins wearing the same color of clothes, sporting the same number of rings on the same fingers, giving their dogs the same name, sending their friends the same birthday cards. But some skepticism of such coincidences may be in order. If you sit down with anybody—even a complete stranger—of your age, sex, ethnic group, and socioeconomic background and compare your life histories, likes, dislikes, hobbies, sports, and personality traits, the two of you are likely to discover many quirky similarities. This observation does not invalidate twin studies but suggests that they should be interpreted with caution.

Twin studies help separate the effects of genes and environment in differences among individuals.

For complex traits, such as depression or diabetes, the extent to which twins are alike is measured according to the **concordance** of the trait, which is defined as the percentage of cases in which both members of a pair of twins show the trait when it is known that at least one member shows it. The relative importance of genetic and environmental factors in causing differences in phenotype can be estimated by comparing the concordance of identical and fraternal twins. A significantly higher concordance rate for a given trait for identical twins compared to that for fraternal twins suggests that the trait has a strong genetic component. Similar concordance rates for identical and fraternal twins suggest that the genetic component is less important.

In the study of concordance, twin pairs in which neither member is affected contribute no information, and these twin pairs must be removed from the analysis. The concordance is based solely on twin pairs in which one or both members express the trait. To take a concrete example, let us symbolize each member of a twin pair as a closed square (■) if the member shows the trait and as an open square (□) if the member does not show the trait. Then, in any sample of identical twins, there are three possibilities, illustrated with data for adult-onset diabetes:

- ■ ■ 36 identical twin pairs, both showing adult-onset diabetes

- ■ □ 40 identical twin pairs, only one showing adult-onset diabetes

- □ □ 336 identical twin pairs, neither showing adult-onset diabetes

In this example, the 336 twin pairs who do not show the trait provide no information. The concordance is based only on the first two types of twin pairs, among which in 36 pairs both members show the trait and in 40 pairs only one shows the trait. In this case the concordance among identical twins is $36/(36 + 40) = 47\%$. Among fraternal twins, by contrast, the concordance for adult-onset diabetes is only 10%. The difference in concordance between identical and fraternal twins (47% for identical twins versus 10% for fraternal twins) implies that differences in the risk of adult-onset diabetes have an important genetic component. Furthermore, the observation that the concordance for identical twins is much less than 100% implies that environmental factors (which we now know to include diet and exercise) are also important in the risk of adult-onset diabetes.

Table 18.1 shows identical and fraternal twin concordance rates for a number of other disorders. Just as with diabetes, the marked difference in concordance rates between identical and fraternal twins for high blood pressure, asthma, rheumatoid arthritis, and epilepsy suggests that all these disorders have an important genetic component. In addition, the fact that the concordance is not 100% even for identical twins implies that both genes and environment—"nature" *and* "nurture"—play important roles in the differences in risk among people.

TABLE 18.1 Concordance Rates for Identical and Fraternal Twins for Several Diseases

DISORDER	CONCORDANCE IN IDENTICAL TWINS (%)	CONCORDANCE IN FRATERNAL TWINS (%)
High blood pressure	25	7
Asthma	47	24
Rheumatoid arthritis	34	7
Epilepsy	37	10
Cancer at any site	16	13
Acute infection leading to death	8	9

FIG. 18.11

What is the relative importance of genes and the environment for complex traits?

BACKGROUND Twin studies remain important for assessing the relative importance of "nature" (genotype) and "nurture" (environment) in determining variation among individuals for complex traits. The idea of using twins to distinguish nature from nurture is usually attributed to Francis Galton because of an article he wrote about twins in 1875. In fact, the modern twin study does not trace to Galton but to Curtis Merriman in the United States and Hermann Siemens in Germany, who independently hit upon the idea in 1924. In Galton's time, it was not even known that there are genetically two kinds of twins.

EXPERIMENT The rationale of a twin study is to compare identical twins with same-sex fraternal twins. In principle, identical twins differ only because of environment, whereas fraternal twins differ because of genotype as well as environment. The extent to which fraternal twins differ more from each other than identical twins differ from each other measures the effects of genotype. Some twin studies focus on twins reared apart in order to compensate for shared environmental influences that may be stronger for identical twins than for fraternal twins.

RESULTS The bar graph shows the results of typical twin studies for various traits. The concordance between twins is the fraction of twin pairs in which both twins show the trait among all those pairs in which at least one twin shows the trait. Roughly speaking, the difference in the concordance between identical twins and fraternal twins is a measure of the relative importance of genotype. In the data shown here, for example, autism and clinical depression both show strong genetic influences, whereas female alcoholism shows almost no genetic influence.

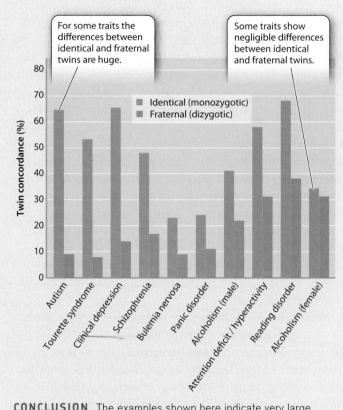

CONCLUSION The examples shown here indicate very large differences in the importance of genotype versus environment among complex traits. These results are typical of most complex traits.

FOLLOW-UP WORK Twin studies must be interpreted in light of other studies comparing complex traits among individuals with various degrees of genetic relatedness. On the whole, twin studies of complex traits have yielded results that are consistent with other available evidence.

SOURCES Rende, R. D., R. Plomin, S. G. Vandenberg. 1990. "Who Discovered the Twin Method?" *Behavior Genetics* 20:277–285; McGue, M., and T. J. Bouchard, Jr. 1998. "Genetic and Environmental Influences on Human Behavioral Differences." *Annual Review of Neuroscience* 21:1–24.

Contrast these results with the data for cancer and death from acute infection in Table 18.1. Note that in these cases the concordance rates for identical twins are very similar to those for fraternal twins—there is no significant genetic component to variation in risk, at least insofar as can be determined from twin studies. For these conditions, the environment plays an important role. (There are some inherited cancer syndromes, but these are so rare relative to the overall incidence of cancer that they have a negligible effect on twin concordance.)

Fig. 18.11 shows the identical and fraternal concordance rates for a number of common behavioral disorders. For some, such as schizophrenia, depression, and autism, the difference between identical and fraternal twins is very great, again implying an

important role for genetic factors. For other traits, such as alcoholism in females, the difference is negligible, suggesting an important role for environmental and social factors. This example also illustrates that complex traits can have quite different risk factors and outcomes in different sexes.

18.4 COMPLEX TRAITS IN HEALTH AND DISEASE

Much evidence beyond twin studies implies an important role for particular alleles as risk factors for diabetes, high blood pressure, asthma, rheumatoid arthritis, epilepsy, schizophrenia, clinical

FIG. 18.12 Incidence of the most common birth anomalies.

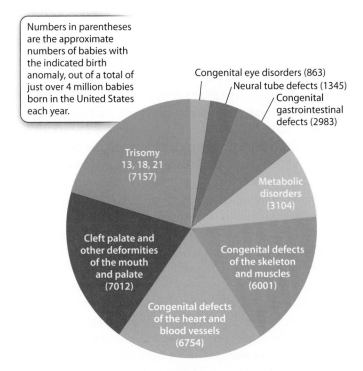

Numbers in parentheses are the approximate numbers of babies with the indicated birth anomaly, out of a total of just over 4 million babies born in the United States each year.

Congenital eye disorders (863)
Neural tube defects (1345)
Congenital gastrointestinal defects (2983)
Trisomy 13, 18, 21 (7157)
Metabolic disorders (3104)
Cleft palate and other deformities of the mouth and palate (7012)
Congenital defects of the skeleton and muscles (6001)
Congenital defects of the heart and blood vessels (6754)

depression, autism, and many other conditions. These are all complex traits, affected by genotype, environment, and genotype-by-environment interactions. Even the most common birth defects are affected by multiple genetic risk factors. The most common birth anomalies and the numbers of affected babies born in the United States each year—collectively more than 35,000—are indicated in **Fig. 18.12.** About 20% of these anomalies are due to an extra chromosome, and trisomy 21 (Down syndrome) is by far the most common. Another roughly 10% are due to defects in metabolism. Many of these—among them diseases such as cystic fibrosis, sickle-cell anemia, and phenylketonuria (the inability to break down the amino acid phenylalanine)—are rare simple Mendelian disorders. But the majority of birth anomalies are affected by both genetic and environmental risk factors.

Most common diseases and birth defects are affected by many genes that each have relatively small effects.
Because the most common birth anomalies as well as childhood and adult disorders are complex traits, biologists are keenly interested in identifying the genes that contribute to differences in risk, understanding what these genes do, and translating this knowledge into prevention or treatment. They have therefore begun to apply modern molecular methods—genome sequencing (Chapter 13), genome annotation (Chapter 14), and genotyping (Chapter 15)—to complex traits.

The identification of genes affecting complex traits is not only a major goal of much current research in human genetics, but also in domesticated animals and plants. Gene identification is

also important in model organisms used in research, especially the laboratory mouse. Much is already known about these model organisms and they are easily manipulated, making it possible to discover the molecular mechanisms by which genes affecting complex traits exert their effects.

The study of complex traits has already reached a stage at which patterns are beginning to emerge. Many of these patterns are exemplified by the chromosome map in **Fig. 18.13,** which shows the location of genes in the human genome that affect cholesterol levels. The first observation is that many genes contribute to cholesterol levels in humans—specifically,

FIG. 18.13 Genes affecting the level of serum cholesterol in the human genome.

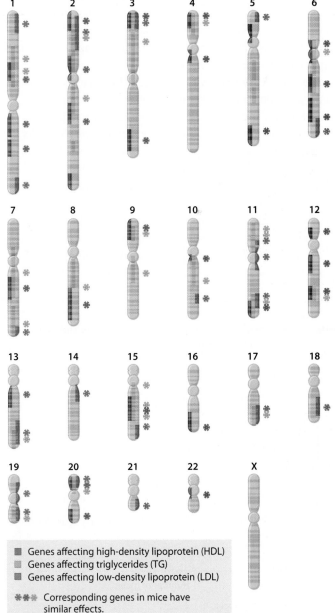

■ Genes affecting high-density lipoprotein (HDL)
■ Genes affecting triglycerides (TG)
■ Genes affecting low-density lipoprotein (LDL)

✳✳✳ Corresponding genes in mice have similar effects.

more than 50 genes contribute to the level of HDL (high-density lipoproteins, or "good cholesterol"), LDL (low-density lipoproteins, or "bad cholesterol"), or triglycerides. A second observation is that many of these genes affect two or even all three of the types of molecule. (A single gene that has multiple effects is said to show **pleiotropy.**) Third, many of the genes show epistasis, that is, they interact with one another (Chapter 16). Fourth, many of the genes occur in clusters, being physically close together in the same chromosome. Clustering of genes reflects the fact that many genes arose through the process of duplication of a single gene followed by divergence over time, generating a family of genes near one another with related functions (Chapter 14). Finally, the functions of all of the genes that contribute to a complex trait are not known. Some of the genes in Fig. 18.13 affect serum cholesterol through known metabolic pathways, but many others work through unknown pathways. Many of the human genes shown have counterparts in the mouse genome that have similar effects on serum cholesterol, so these genes are open to direct experimental investigation.

A principle that is not evident in Fig. 18.13 is that the effects of the genes on cholesterol levels are very unequal. Some have relatively large effects, while others have small ones. The distribution of the magnitude of gene effects for complex traits resembles that shown in **Fig. 18.14.** The axes are labeled only in relative terms, because the actual numbers and effect sizes differ from one trait to the next. However, the main point is that for the majority of genes that contribute to a complex trait, the magnitude of their individual effects is typically quite small. The magnitude of genetic effects also often differs between the sexes, which helps explain why complex traits so often differ in prevalence or severity between males and females.

FIG. 18.14 Relationship between number of genes and their effect on complex traits.

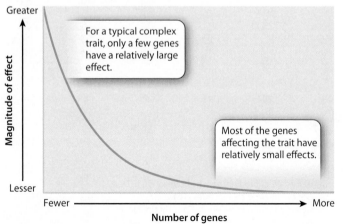

→   **Quick Check 3** When genes for complex traits have effects that are distributed as shown in Fig. 18.14, which are easier to identify: those that are numerous with small effects, or those that are few with large effects?

Human height is affected by hundreds of genes.

For most complex traits, the genes that have been identified to date account for only a relatively small fraction of the total variation in the trait. One extreme example is adult height. An enormous amount of data is available for height, not because height has been studied extensively for its own sake, but because in studies of common diseases the height of each individual is recorded, and hence data on height are available without additional effort or expense.

In one analysis, results from 46 separate studies were combined. These studies included about 185,000 individuals who were genotyped for common nucleotide variants (SNPs) at about 3 million nucleotide sites. The analysis identified at least 180 genes affecting height. Some of these genes are known to affect skeletal development, growth hormones, or other growth factors, but most have no obvious connection to the biology of growth. Some of the genes had previously been identified by studies of rare mutations that have pronounced effects on skeletal growth, either in human families or in laboratory mice. An unexpected finding was that a few genes affecting height are known to be associated with bone mineral density, obesity, and rheumatoid arthritis. These and many other of the genes identified might affect height indirectly.

The 180 genes for height identified among the 185,000 individuals account for only about 12% of the genetic variation in height. The authors calculate that studies of 500,000 individuals would reveal approximately 520 additional genes with effects as large as or larger than those of the 180 genes identified. They also estimate that these 700 genes in total would still account for only 20% of the genetic variation in height, suggesting that many more genes of still smaller effect contribute to variation in height. And this analysis does not address at all the effects of the environment on human height, nor genotype-by-environment interactions, which likely play an important role as well. Complex traits therefore require sophisticated studies to tease apart all the genetic and environmental factors that play a role.

? **CASE 3 You, From A to T: Your Personal Genome Can personalized medicine lead to effective treatments of common diseases?**

The multiple genetic and environmental factors affecting complex traits imply that different people can have the same disease for different reasons. For instance, one person might develop breast cancer because of a mutation in the *BRCA1* or *BRCA2* genes, while another might develop breast cancer because of other genetic risk factors or even environmental ones. Similarly, one person might develop emphysema because of a mutation in the gene that encodes the enzyme alpha-1 antitrypsin (α1AT) (Chapter 15), and another might have emphysema as a result of cigarette smoking. Other examples where the same disease can be the result of different underlying genetic or environmental factors include elevated cholesterol levels, high blood pressure, and depression. Because the underlying genetic basis for the same disease may be different in different patients, some patients respond well to certain drugs and others do not.

The traditional strategy for treating diseases is to use the same medicine for the same disease. However, because we now know that the same disease may have different causes, another possibility has emerged: to identify each patient's genotype for each of the relevant genes, and then to match the treatment to the genetic risk factors in each patient. The approach is known as **personalized medicine.** Personalized medicine matches the treatment to the patient, not the disease.

Personalized medicine not only aims to identify ahead of time medicine that will work effectively, but also to avoid medicines that may lead to harmful side effects, even death. Advertisements and enclosures with prescription drugs enumerate long lists of side effects that you may get if you take a particular medicine. At present, it is difficult to know in advance who will get one or more of these side effects and who won't—that is, the side

effects of taking medicine are themselves complex traits and the result of many underlying genetic and environmental factors. If we could identify ahead of time those patients who will respond negatively to a particular medicine and those who won't, we could minimize potentially harmful effects of medicines on certain individuals.

Someday, it may be possible to determine each patient's genome sequence quickly, reliably, and cheaply. At present, personalized medicine is restricted to studies of a few key genes known to have important effects on treatment outcomes. In the treatment of asthma, for example, some of the differences in response to albuterol inhalation have been traced to genetic variation in the gene *ADRB2*, encoding the β-(beta-)2-adrenergic receptor. Similarly, certain drugs used in the treatment of Alzheimer's disease are less effective in women with a particular *apolipoprotein E* (*APOE*) genotype than in other classes of patients. Also, more than half of the cases of muscle weakness occurring as an adverse effect of drug treatment used to control high cholesterol can be traced to genetic variation in the gene *SLCO1B1*, which encodes a liver transport protein.

Other factors in addition to genes are involved in these disorders, but genes play an important role. Knowledge of a patient's genotype can help guide treatment. These are only a few of many examples, but they demonstrate the substantial potential benefits of personalized medicine.

Core Concepts Summary

18.1 COMPLEX TRAITS ARE THOSE INFLUENCED BOTH BY THE ACTION OF MANY GENES AND BY ENVIRONMENTAL FACTORS.

Complex traits that are measured on a continuous scale, like human height, are called quantitative traits. page 18-2

It is usually difficult to assess the relative roles of genes and the environment ("nature" vs. "nurture") in the production of a given trait in an individual, but it is reasonable to consider the relative roles of genetic and environmental variation in accounting for differences among individuals for a given trait. page 18-2

The relative importance of genes and environment in causing differences in phenotype among individuals differs among traits. For some traits (like height), genetic differences are the more important source of variation, whereas for others (such as cancer), environmental differences can be the more important. page 18-4

Genetic and environmental factors can interact in unpredictable ways, resulting in genotype-by-environment interactions. page 18-5

18.2 GENETIC EFFECTS ON COMPLEX TRAITS ARE REFLECTED IN RESEMBLANCE BETWEEN RELATIVES.

In an analysis of heights of parents and offspring, Galton observed regression toward the mean, in which the offspring exhibit an average phenotype that is less different from the population mean than that of the parents. page 18-6

"Heritability" refers to the proportion of the total variation in a trait that can be attributed to genetic differences among individuals. page 18-7

The heritability of the same trait can differ among populations because of differences in genotype or environment. page 18-8

18.3 TWIN STUDIES HELP SEPARATE THE EFFECTS OF GENO-TYPE AND ENVIRONMENT ON VARIATION IN A TRAIT.

Monozygotic, or identical, twins result from the fertilization of a single egg and are genetically identical. page 18-8

Dizygotic, or fraternal, twins result from the fertilization of two eggs and are genetically related to each other in the same way that other siblings are related to each other. page 18-8

Concordance is the percentage of cases in which both members of a pair of twins show the trait when it is known that at least one member shows it. page 18-9

Comparisons of concordance rates of identical twins and concordance rates of fraternal twins can help to determine to what extent variation in a particular trait has a genetic component. page 18-9

18.4 MANY COMMON DISEASES AND BIRTH DEFECTS ARE AFFECTED BY MULTIPLE GENETIC AND ENVIRONMENTAL RISK FACTORS.

Complex traits are often influenced by many genes with multiple, interacting, and unequal effects. page 18-12

Hundreds of genes affect human height. page 18-12

Personalized medicine tailors treatment to an individual's genetic makeup. page 18-12

Self-Assessment

1. Give three examples of a complex trait.

2. Explain why complex traits are often called quantitative traits.

3. Name several factors that influence variation in complex traits.

4. Explain why it does not make sense to try to separate the effects of genes ("nature") and the environment ("nurture") in a single individual.

5. Explain how you would go about determining the relative importance of genes and the environment for a particular trait.

6. Graph a trait, like human height, with height on the x-axis and number of individuals on the y-axis, and describe the shape of the resulting graph.

7. Explain why the effect of a genotype on a phenotype cannot always be determined without knowing what the environment is, and why the effect of a particular environment on a phenotype cannot always be determined without knowing the underlying genotype.

8. Define what is meant by "regression toward the mean."

9. Define the "heritability" of a trait and explain why it depends on the population being studied.

10. Define "concordance" and explain how twin studies can be used to investigate the importance of genetic and environmental factors in the expression of a trait.

11. For a typical complex trait, describe the relationship between the number of genes affecting the trait and the magnitude of their effects on the trait.

12. Explain what personalized medicine is and how it relates to complex traits such as human diseases.

Do you understand the chapter's Core Concepts? Log into BIO PORTAL to check your answers to the Self-Assessment questions, then practice what you've learned and reinforce this chapter's concepts by working through the problems and multimedia tutorials provided there.

🛜 http://courses.bfwpub.com/yourbioportal/index.php

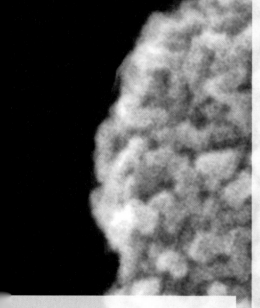

CHAPTER 19

GENETIC AND EPIGENETIC REGULATION

Core Concepts

19.1 The regulation of gene expression in eukaryotes takes place at many levels, including DNA packaging in chromosomes, transcription, and RNA processing.

19.2 After an mRNA is transcribed and exported to the cytoplasm in eukaryotes, gene expression can be regulated at the level of mRNA stability, translation, and posttranslational modification of proteins.

19.3 Transcriptional regulation is illustrated in bacteria by the control of the production of proteins needed for the utilization of lactose, and in viruses by the control of the lytic and lysogenic pathways.

In the discussion of complex traits in Chapter 18, we emphasized the principle that complex traits are not determined by single genes with simple Mendelian inheritance. The traits we usually encounter in ourselves or in others, such as height and weight, diabetes and high blood pressure, are influenced by multiple genes that interact with one another and with environmental factors such as diet and exercise. The number of genes influencing complex traits can be large—for example, hundreds of genes contribute to adult height. The activities of these genes must be coordinated in time (for instance, at a particular point in development) and place (for instance, in a particular type of tissue). For example, growth to normal adult height requires that the production of growth hormone be coordinated in time and place with the production of growth-hormone receptor.

In Chapters 3 and 4, we outlined the basic steps of information flow in a cell, focusing on transcription and translation. In these processes, DNA is a template for the production of messenger RNA (mRNA), which directs the synthesis of a protein. For these processes to work in a living organism to produce the traits that we see, they must be coordinated so that genes are only **expressed,** or turned on, in the right place and time, and in the right amount. In a multicellular organism, for example, certain genes are expressed in some cells but not in others. Muscle actin and myosin are turned on in muscle cells but not in liver or kidney cells. And even for single-celled organisms like bacteria, certain genes are expressed only in response to environmental signals, such as the availability of nutrients, as we discuss in section 19.3.

Gene regulation encompasses the ways in which cells control gene expression. It can be thought of as the *where? when?* and *how much?* of gene expression. Where (in which cells) are genes turned on? When (during development or in response to changes in the environment) are they turned on? How much gene product is made? This chapter provides an overview of the most important ways in which gene expression is regulated.

One of the important principles we discuss is that gene regulation can occur at almost any step in the path from DNA to mRNA to protein—at the level of the chromosome itself, by controlling transcription or translation, and, perhaps surprisingly, even after the protein product is made. Each of these steps or levels of gene expression may be subject to regulation. In other words, each successive event that takes place in the expression of a gene is a potential control point for gene expression.

We begin by discussing gene regulation in eukaryotes, and then turn to regulation in prokaryotes and viruses. All life, from the simplest to the most complex, requires gene regulation. Gene regulation relies on similar processes in all organisms because all life shares common ancestry. Nevertheless, certain features of eukaryotes—the packaging of DNA into chromosomes, mRNA processing, and the separation in space of transcription and translation—provide additional levels of gene regulation in eukaryotes that are not possible in prokaryotes.

19.1 CHROMATIN TO MESSENGER RNA IN EUKARYOTES

Gene regulation in multicellular eukaryotes leads to cell specialization: Different types of cell express different genes. The human body contains about 200 major cell types, and although for the most part they share the same genome, they look and function differently from one another because each type of cell expresses different sets of genes. For example, the insulin needed to regulate sugar levels in the blood is produced only by small patches of cells in the pancreas. Every cell in the body contains the genes that would lead to the production of insulin, but only in these patches of pancreatic cells are they expressed. In this section, we take a look at gene regulation as it occurs in eukaryotic cells, focusing on regulation at the level of DNA, chromatin, and mRNA.

Gene expression can be influenced by chemical modification of DNA or histones.

Fig. 19.1 shows the major places where gene regulation in eukaryotes can take place. The first level of control is at the chromosome, even before transcription takes place. The manner in which DNA is packaged in the nucleus in eukaryotes provides an important opportunity for regulating gene expression.

In many eukaryotic organisms, gene expression is affected by chemical modification of certain bases in the DNA (**Fig. 19.2**), the most common of which is the addition of a methyl group to the base cytosine. Methylation often occurs in cytosine bases that are adjacent to guanosine bases on a DNA strand. Such pairs of nucleotides are abbreviated "CpG" (the "p" represents the phosphate in the backbone of the DNA strand between the two nucleotides). In mammalian protein-coding genes, CpG sites are often clustered in small regions located in or near the promoter of the gene, the region where RNA polymerase and associated proteins bind to the DNA to initiate transcription. Such a cluster of CpG sites is known as a **CpG island.**

Some CpG sites in the genome are methylated and some are not. Methylated CpG sites are rarely seen in CpG islands near active genes (Fig. 19.2a), whereas transcriptional repression of a gene is often accompanied by heavy methylation of a nearby CpG island (Fig. 19.2b). The methylation state of a CpG island can change over time or in response to environmental cues, providing a way to turn genes on or off. Cells sometimes heavily methylate CpG islands of transposable elements or viral DNA sequences that are integrated into the genome, thus preventing the expression of genes in viruses and transposable elements (Chapter 14). In cancer cells, CpG island methylation often takes place, repressing genes that could restrict the cells' growth.

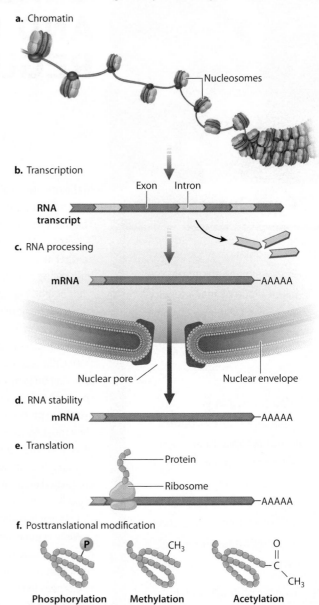

FIG. 19.1 Levels of gene expression regulation.

a. Chromatin

Nucleosomes

b. Transcription

Exon　Intron

RNA transcript

c. RNA processing

mRNA —AAAAA

Nuclear pore　　Nuclear envelope

d. RNA stability

mRNA —AAAAA

e. Translation

Protein

Ribosome

—AAAAA

f. Posttranslational modification

P

CH_3

$\overset{O}{\underset{CH_3}{\overset{\|}{C}}}$

Phosphorylation　　Methylation　　Acetylation

DNA in eukaryotes is packaged as **chromatin,** a complex of DNA, RNA, and proteins that gives chromosomes their structure. Chromatin includes a thread of nucleosome particles in which about 150 base pairs of DNA are wrapped around each octamer of histone proteins. (Greater detail in the structure of chromatin and nucleosomes is depicted in Fig. 3.13.) When chromatin is in its coiled state, the DNA is not accessible to the proteins that carry out transcription. The chromatin must unravel to allow space for transcriptional enzymes and proteins to work. This is accomplished through **chromatin remodeling,** in which the nucleosomes are repositioned to expose different stretches of

FIG. 19.2 Methylation states of CpG islands in or near the promoter of a gene.

a. Undermethylated CpG island

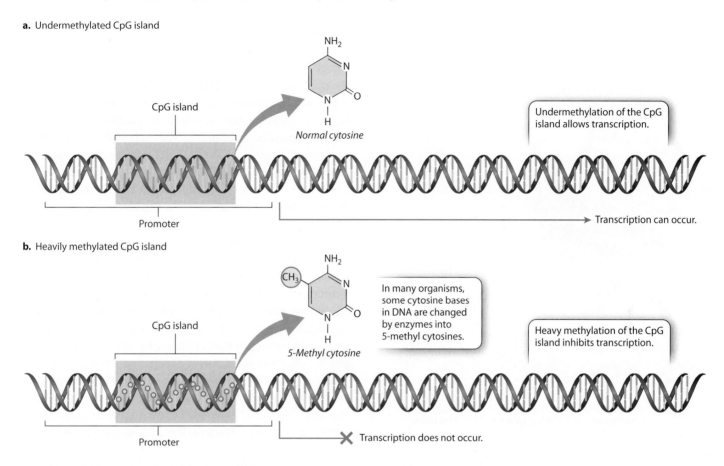

b. Heavily methylated CpG island

DNA to the nuclear environment. Chromatin remodeling is another level at which gene expression can be controlled.

One way in which chromatin is remodeled is by chemical modification of the histones around which DNA is wound (**Fig. 19.3**). Modification usually occurs on **histone tails**, strings of amino acids that protrude from the histone proteins in the nucleosome (Fig. 19.3a). Individual amino acids in the tails can be modified by the addition (or later removal) of different chemical groups, including methyl groups (—CH$_3$) and acetyl groups (—COCH$_3$). Most often, methylation or acetylation occurs on the lysine residues of the histone tails.

The pattern of modifications of the histone tails is thought to constitute a **histone code** that affects chromatin structure and gene transcription (Fig. 19.3b). For example, methylation of lysine with a single methyl group and lysine acetylation are often associated with the activation of transcription (+ in Fig. 19.3b), whereas methylation of lysine with three methyl groups is often associated with repression of transcription (− in Fig. 19.3b). Modification of histones takes place at key times in development to ensure that the proper genes are turned on or off, as well as in response to environmental cues.

Together, these modifications of bases, changes to histones, and alterations in chromatin structure are often termed **epigenetic,** from the Greek *epi-* ("over and above," "in addition to") and *genetic* ("inherited"). That is, epigenetic mechanisms of gene regulation typically involve changes not to the DNA sequence itself but to the manner in which DNA is packaged. Epigenetic modifications can in some cases affect gene expression. They can be inherited through cell divisions, just as genes are, but are often reversible and responsive to changes in the environment.

Gene expression can be regulated at the level of an entire chromosome.

A striking example of an epigenetic form of gene regulation is the manner in which mammals equalize the expression of X-linked genes in *XX* females and *XY* males. For most genes, there is a direct relation between the number of copies of the gene (the gene dosage) and the level of expression of the gene. An increase in gene dosage increases the level of expression because each copy of the gene is regulated independently of

FIG. 19.3   Histone modifications. (a) Typical modifications of the amino acid lysine observed in the histone tails of nucleosomes include addition of a methyl group (Me), addition of three methyl groups (Me₃), and acetylation (Ac). (b) Modification of specific lysine amino acids is associated with increases (+) or decreases (−) in transcription, and constitutes a histone code.

a.

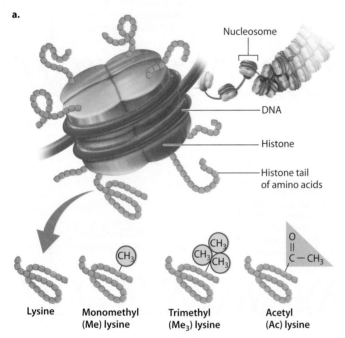

Nucleosome

DNA

Histone

Histone tail of amino acids

Lysine

Monomethyl (Me) lysine

Trimethyl (Me₃) lysine

Acetyl (Ac) lysine

b.

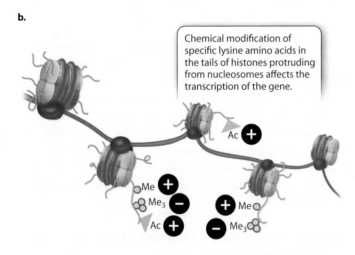

Chemical modification of specific lysine amino acids in the tails of histones protruding from nucleosomes affects the transcription of the gene.

other copies. For example, as we saw in Chapter 15, the presence of an extra copy of most human chromosomes results in spontaneous abortion because of the increase in the expression of the genes in that chromosome.

XX females and XY males have different numbers of X chromosomes. For genes contained in the X chromosome, the dosage of genes is twice as great in females as it is in males. However, the level of expression of X-linked genes is about the same in both sexes. These observations imply that the regulation of X-chromosomal genes is different in females and in males. The differential regulation is called **dosage compensation.**

Different species have evolved different mechanisms of dosage compensation. In *Drosophila* fruit flies, males double the transcription of the single X chromosome to achieve equal expression compared to the two X chromosomes in females. In *Caenorhabditis* nematode worms, females decrease the transcription of both X chromosomes in females to one-half the level of the single X chromosome in males. In mammals, including humans, dosage compensation occurs through the inactivation of one X chromosome in each cell in females. This process, now known as **X-inactivation,** was first proposed by Mary F. Lyon in the early 1960s.

Soon after a fertilized egg with two X chromosomes implants in the mother's uterine wall, one X chromosome is selected at random and inactivated (**Fig. 19.4**). In Fig. 19.4a, the inactive X chromosome is shown in gray. The inactive state persists through cell division, so in each cell lineage, the same X chromosome that was originally inactivated remains inactive. The result is that a normal female is a mosaic, or patchwork, of tissue. In some patches, the genes on the maternal X are expressed (and the paternal X is inactivated), whereas in other patches, the genes on the paternal X are expressed (and the maternal X is inactivated). The term "inactive X" is a slight exaggeration since a substantial number of genes are still transcribed, although usually at a low level.

As one argument for her X-inactivation hypothesis, Lyon called attention to calico cats, which are nearly always female (Fig. 19.4b). In calico cats, the orange or black fur colors are due to different alleles of a single gene in the X chromosome. In a heterozygous female, X-inactivation predicts discrete patches of orange and black, and this is exactly what is observed. (The white patches on a calico cat are due to an autosomal gene.)

How does X-inactivation work? Some of the details are still unknown, but the main features of the process are shown in **Fig. 19.5.** A key player is a small region in the X chromosome called the X-chromosome inactivation center (*XIC*), which contains a gene called *Xist* (X-inactivation specific transcript). The *Xist* gene is normally transcribed at a very low level, and the RNA is unstable, but in an X chromosome about to become inactive, *Xist* transcription markedly increases. The transcript undergoes RNA splicing, but it does not encode a protein. *Xist* RNA is therefore an example of a noncoding RNA, introduced in Chapter 3. Instead of being translated, the processed *Xist* RNA coats the *XIC* region, and as it accumulates, the coating spreads outward from the *XIC* until the entire chromosome is coated with *Xist* RNA. The presence of *Xist* RNA along the chromosome recruits factors that promote DNA methylation, histone modification, and other changes associated with transcriptional silencing.

FIG. 19.4   **X-inactivation in female mammals.** X-inactivation equalizes the expression of most genes in the X chromosome between XX females and XY males.

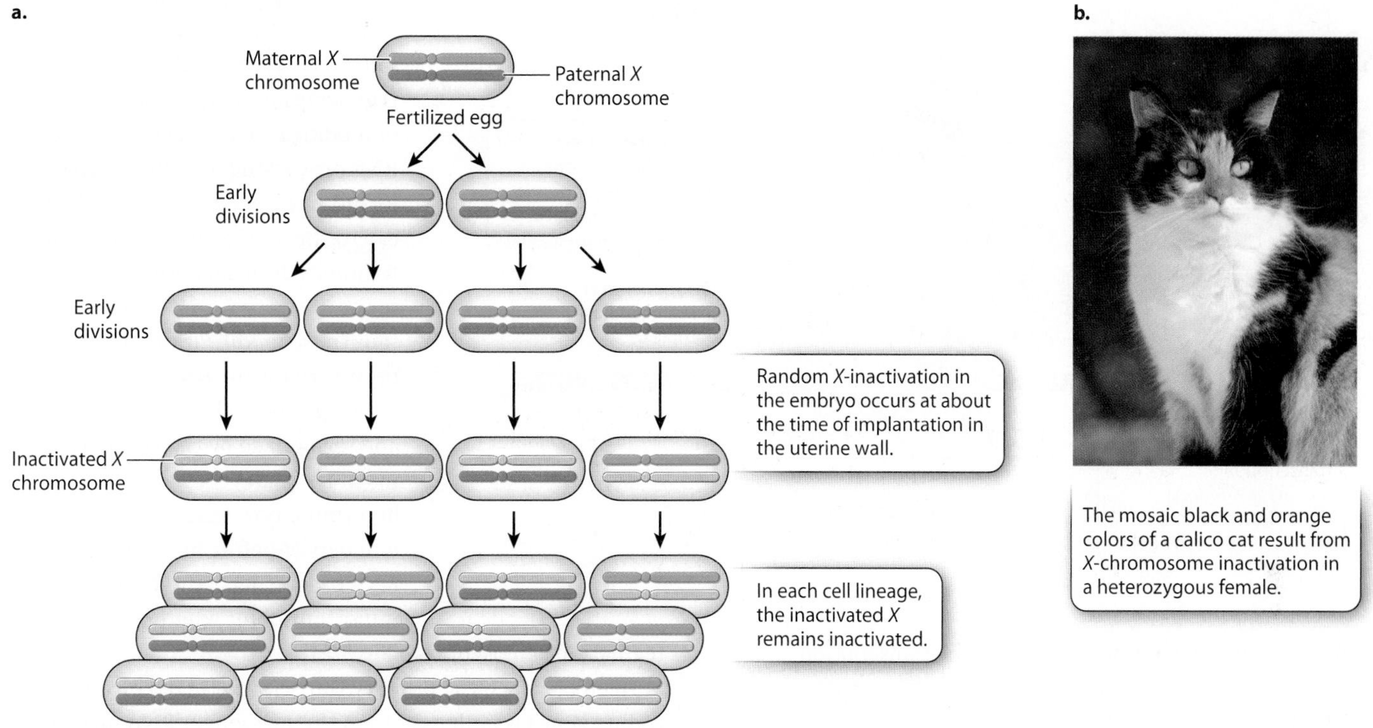

a.

Maternal X chromosome
Paternal X chromosome
Fertilized egg

Early divisions

Early divisions

Random X-inactivation in the embryo occurs at about the time of implantation in the uterine wall.

Inactivated X chromosome

In each cell lineage, the inactivated X remains inactivated.

b.

The mosaic black and orange colors of a calico cat result from X-chromosome inactivation in a heterozygous female.

Transcription is a key control point in gene expression.

While access to DNA and appropriate histone modifications are necessary for transcription, they are not sufficient. The molecular machinery that actually carries out transcription is also required once the template DNA is made accessible through chromatin remodeling and histone modification. The mechanisms that regulate whether or not transcription occurs are known collectively as **transcriptional regulation** (see Fig. 19.1b).

Transcriptional regulation in eukaryotic cells requires the coordinated action of many proteins that interact with one another and with DNA sequences near the gene. Let's first review the basic process of transcription (Chapter 3). An important group of proteins are the **general transcription factors.** These proteins bind to the gene's promoter, which is the region of a gene that recruits factors necessary to start transcription. The transcription factors are brought there by one of the proteins that binds to a short sequence called the TATA box, which is usually situated 25–30 nucleotides upstream of the nucleotide site where transcription begins. Once bound to the promoter, the transcription factors recruit the components of the **RNA polymerase complex,** which synthesizes the RNA transcript complementary to the template strand of DNA.

Where in the many steps of transcription initiation does regulation occur? The first place where transcription can be

FIG. 19.5   **The role of *Xist* in *X*-inactivation.** *Xist* is noncoding RNA that is expressed from the inactive X chromosome and coats the entire chromosome, leading to inactivation of most of the genes on the chromosome.

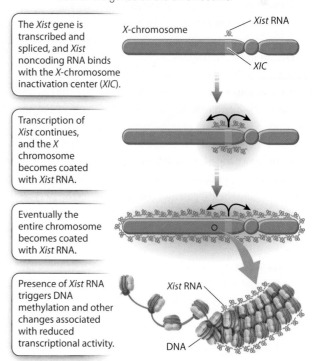

The *Xist* gene is transcribed and spliced, and *Xist* noncoding RNA binds with the X-chromosome inactivation center (*XIC*).

X-chromosome
Xist RNA
XIC

Transcription of *Xist* continues, and the X chromosome becomes coated with *Xist* RNA.

Eventually the entire chromosome becomes coated with *Xist* RNA.

Presence of *Xist* RNA triggers DNA methylation and other changes associated with reduced transcriptional activity.

Xist RNA

DNA

FIG. 19.6 Protein–DNA and protein–protein interactions in the eukaryotic transcription complex.

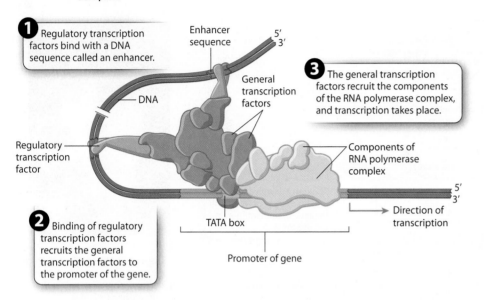

1 Regulatory transcription factors bind with a DNA sequence called an enhancer.

Enhancer sequence

5′
3′

DNA

General transcription factors

3 The general transcription factors recruit the components of the RNA polymerase complex, and transcription takes place.

Regulatory transcription factor

Components of RNA polymerase complex

5′
3′

2 Binding of regulatory transcription factors recruits the general transcription factors to the promoter of the gene.

TATA box

Promoter of gene

Direction of transcription

RNA processing is also important in gene regulation. A great deal happens in the nucleus after transcription takes place. The initial transcript, called the **primary transcript,** undergoes several types of modification, collectively called **RNA processing** (Chapter 3), that includes the addition of a nucleotide cap to the 5′ end and a string of tens to hundreds of adenosine nucleotides to the 3′ end to form the poly(A) tail. These modifications are necessary for the RNA molecule to be transported to the cytoplasm and recognized by the translational machinery, and they also help to determine how long the RNA will persist before being degraded. RNA processing is therefore an important point where gene regulation can occur (see Fig. 19.1c).

regulated is in the recruitment of the general transcription factors and components of the RNA polymerase complex (**Fig. 19.6**). Recruitment of these elements is controlled by proteins called **regulatory transcription factors.** Transcription does not occur if the regulatory transcription factors do not recruit the components of the transcription complex to the gene. Each regulatory transcription factor has two binding sites, one of which binds with a particular sequence in the DNA in or near a gene known as an **enhancer** (Fig. 19.6). A second binding site on the regulatory transcription factor recruits one or more general transcription factors to the promoter region. The general transcription factors then recruit the RNA polymerase complex, and transcription can begin (Chapter 3).

Hundreds of different regulatory transcription factors control the transcription of thousands of genes. A typical gene has several different types of enhancer sequence, each with its own regulatory transcription factor or set of transcription factors. Transcription takes place only when all the regulatory transcription factors are present and work together, as shown in Fig. 19.6. Transcription of a gene therefore depends on the presence of a particular combination of enhancers and their regulatory transcription factors, a type of regulation called combinatorial control.

→ **Quick Check 1** The idea that the expression of some genes is controlled by the products of other genes was originally criticized on the ground that, if *n* genes were to be controlled, then another *n* genes would be needed to control them, and then another *n* genes would be needed to control the controllers, and so on and on. How does combinatorial control help refute this criticism?

In eukaryotes, the primary transcript of many protein-coding genes is far longer than the messenger RNA ultimately used in protein synthesis. The long primary transcript consists of regions that are retained in the messenger RNA (the **exons**) interspersed with regions that are excised and degraded (the **introns**). The introns are excised during **RNA splicing** (Chapter 3). The exons are joined together in their original linear order to form the processed messenger RNA.

RNA splicing provides an opportunity for regulating gene expression because the same primary transcript can be spliced in different ways to yield different proteins in a process called **alternative splicing.** This process takes place because what the spliceosome—the splicing machinery—recognizes as an exon in some primary transcripts it recognizes as part of an intron in other primary transcripts. The alternative-splice forms may be produced in the same cells or in different types of cell. Alternative splicing accounts in part for the observation that we produce many more proteins than our total number of genes. By some estimates, over 90% of human genes undergo alternative splicing.

Fig. 19.7 shows the primary transcript of a gene encoding an insulin receptor found in humans and other mammals. During RNA splicing in liver cells, exon 11 is included in the messenger RNA, and the insulin receptor produced from this messenger RNA has low affinity for insulin. In contrast, in cells of skeletal muscle, the 36 nucleotides of exon 11 are spliced out of the primary transcript along with the flanking introns. The resulting protein is 12 amino acids shorter, and

FIG. 19.7 **Alternative splicing of a mammalian insulin-receptor transcript.** Alternative splicing generates different processed mRNAs and different proteins from the same primary transcript.

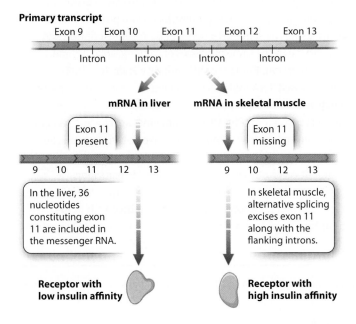

this form of the insulin receptor has high affinity for insulin. The different forms of the protein are important: The higher sensitivity of muscle cells to insulin enables them to absorb enough glucose to fulfill their energy needs.

Some RNA molecules can become a substrate for enzymes that modify particular bases in the RNA, thereby changing its

FIG. 19.8 **RNA editing.** RNA editing results in chemical modifications to the bases in mRNA, which can lead to changes in the amino acid sequence of the protein.

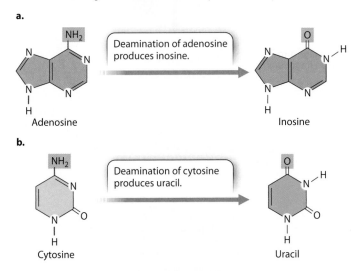

sequence and what it codes for. This process is known as **RNA editing** (**Fig. 19.8**). One type of editing enzyme (Fig. 19.8a) removes the amino group (—NH$_2$) from adenosine and converts it to inosine, a base that in translation functions like guanosine. Another enzyme (Fig. 19.8b) removes the amino group from cytosine and converts it to uracil. In the human genome, hundreds if not thousands of transcripts undergo RNA editing. In many cases, not all copies of the transcript are edited, and some copies may be edited more extensively than others. The result is that transcripts from the same gene can produce multiple types of proteins even in a single cell.

Transcripts from the same gene may undergo different editing in different cell types. An example of tissue-specific RNA editing is shown in **Fig. 19.9.** The mRNA fragments show part of the coding sequence for apolipoprotein B. The unedited mRNA in the liver (Fig. 19.9a) is translated into a protein that transports cholesterol in the blood. In contrast, RNA editing of the message occurs in the intestine (Fig. 19.9b). The cytosine nucleotide in codon 2153 is edited to uracil. The edited codon is UAA, which is a stop codon. Translation therefore terminates at this point, releasing a protein only about half as long as the liver form. This shorter form of the protein helps the cells of the intestine absorb lipids from the foods we eat.

FIG. 19.9 **Tissue-specific RNA editing of the human apolipoprotein B transcript.** Different RNA editing in the (a) liver and (b) intestine result in proteins with different functions.

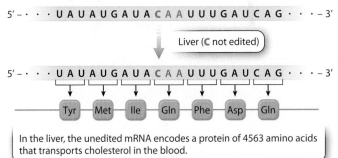

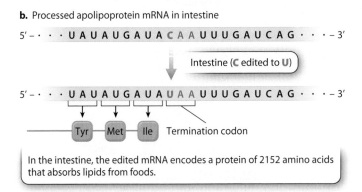

19.2 MESSENGER RNA TO PHENOTYPE IN EUKARYOTES

In eukaryotes, a processed mRNA must exit the nucleus before the translation step of gene expression can occur. The mRNA migrates to the cytoplasm through one of a few thousand nuclear pores, large protein complexes that traverse the nuclear envelope and regulate the inflow and outflow of macromolecules. Once the mRNA is in the cytoplasm, there are multiple opportunities for gene regulation at the levels of mRNA stability, translation, and protein activity (see Figs. 19.1d–19.1f).

Small regulatory RNAs inhibit translation or promote RNA degradation.

Regulatory RNA molecules known as **small regulatory RNAs** are among the most exciting recent discoveries in gene regulation. They often work by binding to transcripts and blocking translation. Small regulatory RNAs are of exceptional interest to biologists and drug researchers because their small size allows easy synthesis in the laboratory, and researchers can design their sequences to target transcripts of interest.

One type of small regulatory RNA, **microRNA (miRNA),** starts out just like the RNA transcribed from protein-coding genes, using the same RNA polymerase for transcription and going through the same processes of capping, splicing, and polyadenylation. But there the similarity ends. In miRNA, the processed RNA folds back upon itself to form one or more **hairpin** structures, or stems-and-loops, stabilized by base pairing in the stem (**Fig. 19.10a**). Enzymes specifically recognize processed and folded miRNAs and cleave the stems from the hairpin, then further cleave the stem into small double-stranded fragments typically about 20–25 nucleotide pairs long.

One strand from each RNA fragment is incorporated into a protein complex known as **RISC (RNA-induced silencing complex).** The small, single-stranded RNA (the miRNA) targets

FIG. 19.10 MicroRNA (miRNA) and small interfering RNA (siRNA). (a) miRNAs are small noncoding RNAs that inhibit translation. (b) siRNAs are small noncoding RNAs that degrade mRNA.

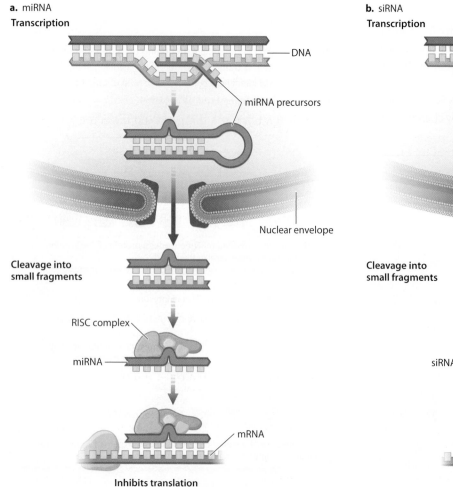

a. miRNA
Transcription

DNA

miRNA precursors

Nuclear envelope

Cleavage into small fragments

RISC complex

miRNA

mRNA

Inhibits translation

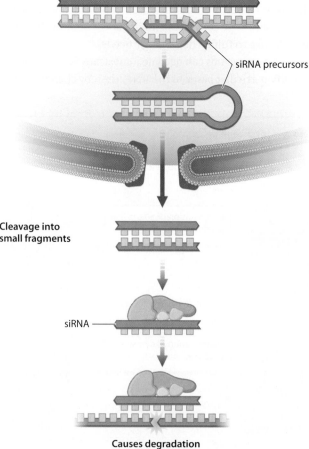

b. siRNA
Transcription

siRNA precursors

Cleavage into small fragments

siRNA

Causes degradation

the RISC complex to specific mRNA molecules by base pairing with short regions on the target mRNA (Fig. 19.10a). The miRNA in the RISC complex does not base pair exactly with the target mRNA, but has enough sequence in common that the two strands anneal. Once bound to the target mRNA, the RISC complex inhibits translation. Human chromosomes are thought to encode about 1000 miRNAs, each of which can inhibit translation of tens or hundreds of mRNA molecules. Half or more of human proteins may have their synthesis regulated in part by miRNA.

A second type of small regulatory RNA is known as **small interfering RNA (siRNA).** Transcription and processing of siRNA and miRNA are virtually identical, including incorporation into a RISC complex. But unlike miRNAs, which have a few mismatches in their double-stranded region, siRNA molecules have strands that match exactly. RISC complexes containing siRNA cleave the targeted RNA, instead of just binding to the target mRNA (**Fig. 19.10b**). The cleavage exposes unprotected 5′ and 3′ ends of the single-stranded RNA, which are vulnerable to attack by other nucleases. RISC complexes containing siRNA can lead to degradation of RNA transcripts in the nucleus at any stage during transcription, RNA processing, or export from the nucleus. Regulation by siRNA is widespread in eukaryotes, and is thought to have evolved originally as a defense against viruses and transposable elements.

→ **Quick Check 2** How do small regulatory RNAs differ from messenger RNA?

Translational regulation controls the rate, timing, and location of protein synthesis.

Translation of mRNA into protein provides another level of control of gene expression. **Fig. 19.11** shows the structure of a hypothetical mRNA molecule in a eukaryotic cell and highlights some of the features that help regulate its translation (Chapter 4). Not all mRNA molecules have all the features shown, but all mRNA molecules have a 5′ cap, a 5′ untranslated region (5′ UTR), an open reading frame (ORF) containing the codons that determine the amino acid sequence of the protein, a 3′ untranslated region (3′ UTR), and a poly(A) tail. The 5′ UTR and the 3′ UTR may contain regions that bind with proteins.

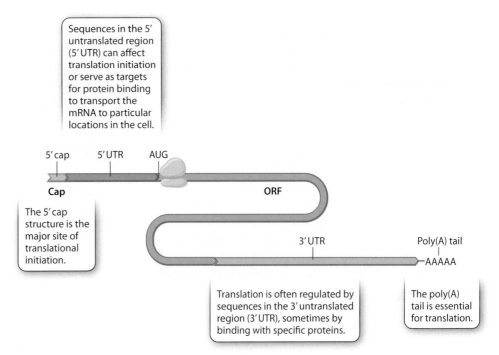

FIG. 19.11 Some features of mRNA that affect gene expression, including the 5′ cap, 5′ UTR, 3′ UTR, and poly(A) tail.

Sequences in the 5′ untranslated region (5′ UTR) can affect translation initiation or serve as targets for protein binding to transport the mRNA to particular locations in the cell.

The 5′ cap structure is the major site of translational initiation.

Translation is often regulated by sequences in the 3′ untranslated region (3′ UTR), sometimes by binding with specific proteins.

The poly(A) tail is essential for translation.

In some cases, these proteins interact with molecular motors that transport the mRNA to particular regions of the cell. In other cases, the proteins are localized in the cell and repress translation of the mRNAs to which they are bound. By either transport or repression, these proteins cause the mRNA to be translated only in certain places in the cell.

The cap structure is one of the main recognition signals for translation initiation, which requires the coordinated action of about 25 proteins. These are present in most cells in limiting amounts, and so at any one time while some mRNAs from a gene are being translated, other mRNAs transcribed from the same gene may not have a translation initiation complex assembled. Upon formation, the initiation complex moves along the 5′ UTR, scanning for an AUG codon (the initiation codon) to allow the complete ribosome to assemble and begin translation. Although translation initiation is the principal mode of translational regulation, not all mRNA molecules are equally accessible to translation. Among the key variables are the secondary (folded) structure of the 5′ UTR, the distance from the 5′ cap to the AUG initiation codon, and the sequences flanking the AUG initiation codon.

The 3′ UTR and the poly(A) tail are also important in translation initiation. The mRNA forms a loop during initiation and the 3′ end is brought into proximity with the 5′ end. Because of their proximity to the start site for translation, sequences at the 3′ end help regulate translation. In fact, most mRNA sequences that regulate translation are present in the 3′ UTR.

Protein structure and chemical modification modulate protein effects on phenotype.

Once translation is completed, the resulting protein can alter the phenotype of the cell or organism by affecting metabolism, signaling, or cell structure. After translation, proteins are modified in multiple ways that regulate their structure and function. Collectively, these processes are called **posttranslational modification** (see Fig. 19.1e). Regulation at this level is essential because some proteins are downright dangerous. For example, proteases such as the digestive enzyme trypsin must be kept inactive until secreted out of the cell. If they were not, their activity would kill the cell itself. These types of protein are often controlled by being translated in inactive forms that are made active by modification after secretion.

Folding and acquiring stability are key control points for some proteins (Chapter 4). While many proteins fold properly as they come off the ribosome, others require help from other proteins, called chaperones, which act as folding facilitators. Correct folding is important because improperly folded proteins may form aggregates that are destructive to cell function. Many diseases are associated with protein aggregates, including Alzheimer's disease, Huntington's disease, and mad cow disease.

Posttranslational modification also helps regulate protein activity. Many proteins are modified by the addition of one or more sugar molecules to the side chains of some amino acids. This modification can alter the protein's folding and stability, or target the molecule to particular cellular compartments. Reversible addition of a phosphate group to the side groups of amino acids such as serine, threonine, or tyrosine is a key regulator of protein activity (Chapter 9). Introduction of the negatively charged phosphate group alters the conformation of the protein, in some cases switching it from an inactive state to an active state and in other cases the reverse. Because the function of a protein molecule results from its shape and charge (Chapter 4), a change in protein conformation affects protein function.

Marking proteins for enzymatic destruction by the addition of chemical groups after translation is also important in controlling their activity. We have already seen how the destruction of successive waves of cyclin proteins helps move the cell through its division cycle (Chapter 11).

? CASE 3 You, From A to T: Your Personal Genome How do lifestyle choices affect expression of your personal genome?

What does gene regulation have to do with *you*? If you examine Fig. 19.1 as a whole and consider the DNA sequence shown as your personal genome, the situation looks pretty grim. You might be led to believe that genes dictate everything, and that biology is destiny. But if you focus on the lower levels of regulation in Fig. 19.1, a different picture emerges. The picture is different because much of the regulation that occurs after transcription (posttranslational modifications, regulation of translation, regulation of RNA

stability) is determined by the physiological state of your cells, which in turn is strongly influenced by your lifestyle choices. For example, your cells can synthesize 12 of the amino acids, but if any of these is present in sufficient amounts in your diet, it is absorbed during digestion and not synthesized. The essential amino acid you ingest blocks the synthetic pathway through feedback effects.

The effect of an intervention—genetic or environmental—at any given level can affect regulatory processes at both higher and lower levels. This cascade of regulatory effects in both directions can occur because the expression of any gene is regulated at multiple levels, and because there is much feedback and signaling back and forth between nucleus and cytoplasm. It is because of these feedback and signaling mechanisms that the effects of lifestyle choices can be propagated *up* the regulatory hierarchy. For example, it has been shown that dietary intake of fats and cholesterol affects not only the activity of enzymes directly involved in the metabolism of fats and cholesterol, but also the levels of transcription of the genes encoding these enzymes by affecting the activity of their regulatory transcription factors. Similarly, lifestyles that combine balanced diets with exercise and stress relief have been shown to increase transcription of genes whose products prevent cellular dysfunction and to decrease transcription of genes whose products promote disease, including cancer.

So far, we have been talking primarily about complex traits of the type discussed in Chapter 18, which are affected by multiple genes and by multiple environmental factors as well as by genotype-by-environment interaction. For example, there are both genetic and environmental risk factors for breast and ovarian cancers, as we have seen. Simple Mendelian traits caused by mutations in single genes, such as cystic fibrosis and alpha-1 antitrypsin (α1AT) deficiency (Chapter 17), are less responsive to lifestyle choices. But even in these cases, lifestyle does matter—for example, people with α1AT deficiency should not smoke tobacco and should avoid environments with low air quality.

19.3 TRANSCRIPTIONAL REGULATION IN PROKARYOTES

The central message of Fig. 19.1 is that the regulation of gene expression occurs by means of a hierarchy of regulatory mechanisms acting at different levels (and usually at multiple levels) from DNA to protein. Gene regulation in prokaryotes is simpler than gene regulation in eukaryotes since DNA is not packaged into chromosomes, mRNA is not processed, and transcription and translation are not separated by a nuclear envelope. In prokaryotes, expression of a protein-coding gene entails transcription of the gene into messenger RNA and translation of the messenger RNA into protein. Each of these levels of gene expression is subject to regulation.

Because gene regulation is simpler in prokaryotes than gene regulation in eukaryotes, prokaryotes have served as model organisms for understanding how genes are turned on and off. In this section, we consider in more detail how gene expression is regulated at the level of transcription in bacteria and in viruses that infect bacteria. We focus on two well-studied systems: (1) the regulation of genes in the intestinal bacterium *Escherichia coli* that allows proteins needed to utilize the sugar lactose to be produced only when lactose is present in the environment and only when it is the best nutrient available, and (2) the regulation of genes in a virus that infects *E. coli* that control whether the virus integrates its DNA into the bacterial host or lyses (breaks open) the cell. In both cases, specific genes are turned on and off in response to environmental conditions.

Transcriptional regulation can be positive or negative.

Transcription can be positively or negatively regulated. In **positive regulation,** a regulatory molecule (usually a protein) must bind to the DNA at a site near the gene in order for transcription to take place. In **negative regulation,** a regulatory molecule (again, usually a protein) must bind to the DNA at a site near the gene in order for transcription to be prevented.

Fig. 19.12 illustrates positive regulation. The main players are DNA, the RNA polymerase complex, and a regulatory protein called a transcriptional **activator.** As shown in Fig. 19.12a, when the activator protein is present in a state that can interact with its binding site in the DNA, the RNA polymerase complex is recruited to the promoter of the gene and transcription takes place. When the activator is not present, or not able to bind with the DNA (Fig. 19.12b), transcription does not occur. The binding site for the activator may be upstream of the promoter, as shown in the figure, downstream of the promoter, or even overlap the promoter.

Sometimes, the activator protein combines with a small molecule in the cell and undergoes a change in shape that alters its binding affinity for DNA. The change in shape is an example of an **allosteric effect** (Chapter 6). In some cases, combining with the small molecule allows the activator to bind with DNA, and the presence of the small molecule in the cell results in transcription of the gene. Genes subject to this type of positive control typically encode proteins needed only when the small molecule is present in the cell. For example, in *E. coli*, the genes for degradation of the sugar arabinose are regulated by an activator that binds to the sugar. When arabinose is present, the genes are transcribed, but when arabinose is absent, the genes are not transcribed. For some other genes, activator proteins can bind DNA only when a small molecule is absent from the cell. These genes typically encode proteins needed for synthesis of the small molecule. In *E. coli,* the genes for synthesis of the amino acid cysteine are regulated in this fashion.

Fig. 19.13 illustrates negative regulation. In this case, the DNA in its native state can recruit the RNA polymerase complex, and

---

FIG. 19.12 Role of the activator in positive transcriptional regulation in prokaryotes. When an activator protein binds to DNA, it promotes transcription of a gene.

a.

In positive transcriptional regulation, RNA polymerase can bind to the promoter only if an activator protein binds to a site near the promoter.

Activator protein

RNA polymerase complex

Activator binding site

Polymerase binding site (promoter)

→ Transcription can occur.

b.

→ Transcription does not occur.

If the activator does not bind to the DNA, the RNA polymerase cannot bind and transcription does not occur.

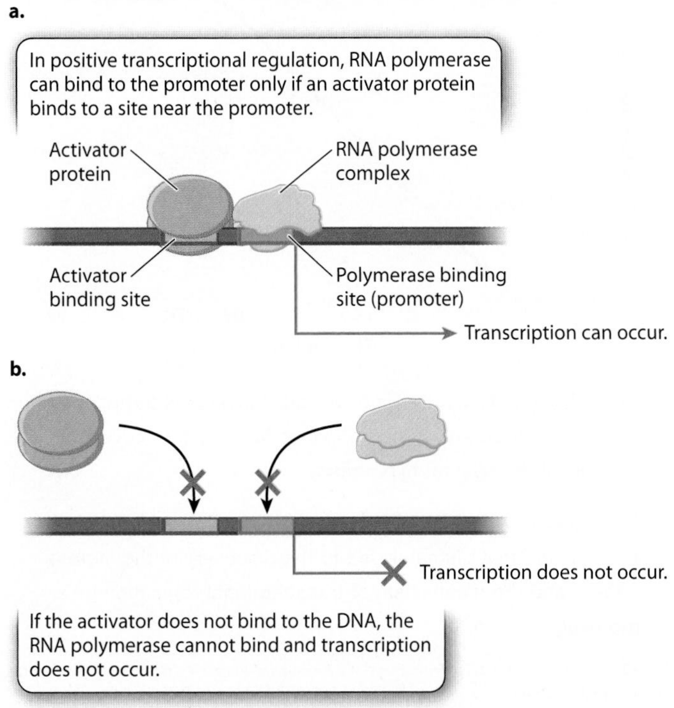

FIG. 19.13 Role of the repressor in negative transcriptional regulation in prokaryotes. When a repressor protein binds to DNA, it prevents transcription of a gene.

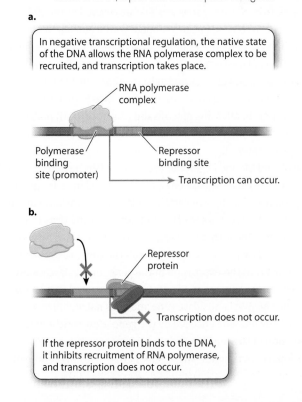

a.

In negative transcriptional regulation, the native state of the DNA allows the RNA polymerase complex to be recruited, and transcription takes place.

RNA polymerase complex

Polymerase binding site (promoter)

Repressor binding site

→ Transcription can occur.

b.

Repressor protein

→ Transcription does not occur.

If the repressor protein binds to the DNA, it inhibits recruitment of RNA polymerase, and transcription does not occur.

transcription takes place at a constant rate unless something turns it off (Fig. 19.13a). What turns it off is binding with a protein called a **repressor** (Fig. 19.13b). Again, the binding site for the repressor can be upstream from the promoter, downstream, or overlapping.

As with positive control, the active state of the repressor is often determined by an allosteric interaction with a small molecule. A small molecule that prevents binding by the repressor is called an **inducer.** In the next section, we will look closely at the regulation of genes for the breakdown of the sugar lactose in E. coli, and we will see that lactose binds to and inhibits the repressor and is therefore an inducer of these genes. In other cases, the small molecule changes the conformation of the repressor so that it can bind with the repressor binding site. Genes regulated in this way are often needed for synthesis of the small molecule. In E. coli, for example, the genes for the synthesis of the amino acid tryptophan are negatively regulated by tryptophan. When tryptophan is present in sufficient amounts, it binds with a regulatory protein to form the functional repressor, and transcription of the genes does not occur. When the level of tryptophan drops too low to form the repressor, transcription of the genes is initiated.

→ **Quick Check 3** An activator and inducer both activate gene expression. What's the difference between an activator and an inducer?

Lactose utilization in *E. coli* is the pioneering example of transcriptional regulation.

The principle that the product of one gene can regulate transcription of other genes was first discovered in the 1960s by François Jacob and Jacques Monod, who studied how the bacterium E. coli regulates production of the proteins needed for utilization of the sugar lactose. Lactose consists of one molecule each of the sugars glucose and galactose covalently joined by a β- (beta-) galactoside bond. An enzyme called β-galactosidase cleaves lactose, releasing glucose and galactose. Both molecules can then be broken down and used as a source of carbon and energy (Chapter 7).

Jacob and Monod began their research with the observation that active β-galactosidase enzyme is observed in cells only in the presence of lactose or certain molecules chemically similar to lactose. Why is this so? **Fig. 19.14** describes and tests two hypotheses. One is that lactose stabilizes an unstable form of β-galactosidase produced by all cells all the time. The other is that lactose leads to the expression of the gene for β-galactosidase. The experiment shown in Fig. 19.14 demonstrated that lactose turns on the β-galactosidase gene and does not stabilize or activate the enzyme encoded by the gene. How lactose activates expression of the β-galactosidase gene was the subject of additional experiments. These Nobel Prize–winning follow-up

FIG. 19.14

How does lactose lead to the production of active β-galactosidase enzyme?

BACKGROUND Active β-galactosidase enzyme is observed only in *E. coli* cells that are growing in the presence of lactose.

HYPOTHESES One hypothesis is that the enzyme is always being produced, but is produced in an unstable form that breaks down rapidly in the absence of lactose. A second hypothesis is that the enzyme is stable, but is produced only in the presence of lactose.

EXPERIMENT François Jacob and Jacques Monod exposed a culture of growing cells to lactose and later removed it. They measured the amount of β-galactosidase present in the culture during the experiment.

RESULTS Almost immediately upon addition of lactose, β-galactosidase began to accumulate, and its amount steadily increased. When lactose was removed, the enzyme did not disappear immediately (as would be the case if it were unstable). Instead, the amount of enzyme remained the same as when lactose was present. This result is expected only if β-galactosidase is a stable enzyme that is synthesized when lactose is added and stops being synthesized when lactose is removed.

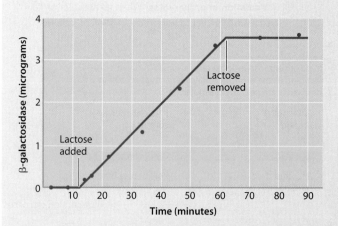

CONCLUSION Synthesis of β-galactosidase is turned on when lactose is added and turned off when lactose is removed, in support of the second hypothesis.

FOLLOW-UP WORK These results stimulated pioneering experiments that ultimately led to the discovery of the lactose operon and the mechanism of transcriptional regulation by a repressor protein.

SOURCE Monod, J. 1965. "From Enzymatic Adaption to Allosteric Transitions." Nobel Prize lecture. http://nobelprize.org/nobel_prizes/medicine/laureates/1965/monod-lecture.htm.

FIG. 19.15 **Structural and regulatory elements of the lactose operon.** The *lac* operon consists of the promoter, the operator, and all the structural genes that are transcribed into a single mRNA called a polycistronic mRNA.

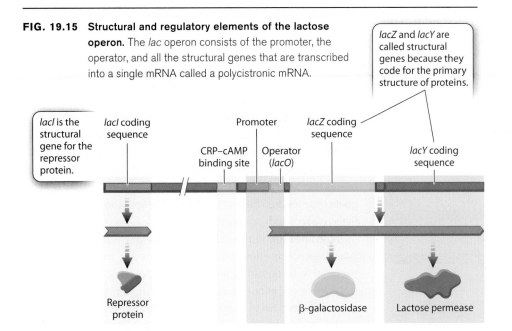

lacZ and *lacY* are called structural genes because they code for the primary structure of proteins.

lacI is the structural gene for the repressor protein.

lacI coding sequence

Promoter

CRP–cAMP binding site

Operator (*lacO*)

lacZ coding sequence

lacY coding sequence

Repressor protein

β-galactosidase

Lactose permease

studies of Jacob and Monod gave the first demonstrated example of transcriptional gene regulation.

To understand how the genes for lactose utilization are regulated, you need to know the main players, and these are shown in **Fig. 19.15.** The overall situation looks quite complicated, but when you take it apart and look at the individual pieces, it is in fact quite simple. Let us start with the two coding sequences on the right:

- *lacZ* is the gene (coding sequence) for β-galactosidase, which cleaves the lactose molecule into its glucose and galactose constituents.

- *lacY* is the gene (coding sequence) for lactose permease, which transports lactose from the external medium into the cell.

These genes are called **structural genes** because they code for the sequence of amino acids making up the primary structure of each protein. Bacteria that contain mutations in the *lacZ* gene or the *lacY* gene or both cannot utilize lactose as a source of energy. Without a functional product from *lacY*, lactose cannot enter the cell, and without a functional product from *lacZ*, lactose cannot be cleaved into its component sugars. Thus, β-galactosidase and permease are essential for the utilization of lactose for cell growth.

Regulation of the *lacZ* and *lacY* structural genes is controlled by the product of another structural gene, called *lacI*, which encodes a repressor protein. Located between *lacI* and *lacZ* are a series of regulatory sequences in the DNA that include a promoter, whose function is to recruit the RNA polymerase complex and initiate transcription, and an **operator** (*lacO*), which is the binding site for the repressor protein. Another regulatory region is a binding site for a protein called CRP, which is discussed later.

The kind of gene organization depicted in Fig. 19.15 is common in bacteria. Typically, a group of functionally related genes are located next to one another along the bacterial DNA, and when they are transcribed they are transcribed together into a single molecule of messenger RNA. Such an mRNA is called a **polycistronic RNA** ("cistron" is an old term for "coding sequence"). In Fig. 19.15, the polycistronic RNA includes the coding sequences for β-galactosidase and lactose permease. The region of DNA consisting of the promoter, the operator, and the coding sequence for the structural genes is called an **operon.**

Operons are found in bacteria and archaeons, whose cells can translate polycistronic mRNA molecules correctly because their ribosomes can initiate translation anywhere along an mRNA that contains a proper ribosome-binding site (Chapter 4). In a polycistronic mRNA, each of the coding sequences is preceded by a ribosome-binding site, so translation can be initiated there.

The repressor protein binds with the operator and prevents transcription, but not in the presence of lactose.

The lactose operon is negatively regulated by the repressor protein—that is, the structural genes of the lactose operon are always expressed unless the operon is turned off by a regulatory molecule, in this case the repressor. What the operon looks like in the absence of lactose is shown in **Fig. 19.16.** The *lacI* gene,

FIG. 19.16 **The lactose operon in the repressed state in the absence of lactose.**

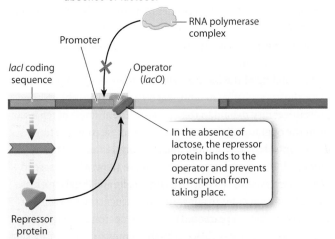

RNA polymerase complex

Promoter

lacI coding sequence

Operator (*lacO*)

In the absence of lactose, the repressor protein binds to the operator and prevents transcription from taking place.

Repressor protein

FIG. 19.17 The lactose operon in the induced state in the presence of lactose.

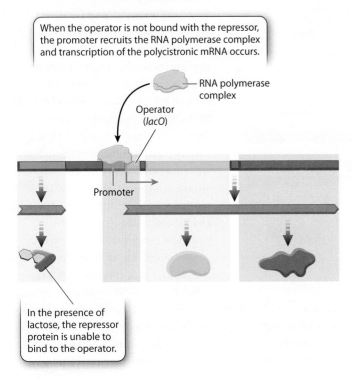

When the operator is not bound with the repressor, the promoter recruits the RNA polymerase complex and transcription of the polycistronic mRNA occurs.

RNA polymerase complex

Operator (*lacO*)

Promoter

In the presence of lactose, the repressor protein is unable to bind to the operator.

encoding the repressor protein, is expressed constantly at a low level. The repressor protein binds with the operator (*lacO*), the RNA polymerase complex is not recruited, and transcription does not take place.

The configuration of the lactose operon in the presence of lactose is shown in **Fig. 19.17**. When lactose is present in the external medium, the repressor protein is unable to bind to the operator, RNA polymerase is recruited, and transcription occurs. In other words, lactose acts as an inducer since it prevents binding of the repressor protein. The inducer is not actually lactose itself, but rather an isomer of lactose called allolactose, which differs in the way the sugars are linked with each other. Allolactose is produced in small amounts whenever lactose is present in the cell.

The binding of the inducer with the repressor protein results in an allosteric change in repressor structure that inhibits the protein's ability to bind to the operator. The absence of repressor from the operator allows the RNA polymerase complex to be recruited to the promoter, and the polycistronic mRNA is produced. The resulting lactose permease allows the lactose to be transported into the cell on a large scale, and β-galactosidase cleaves the molecules to allow the constituents to be used as a source of energy and carbon. The lactose operon is therefore an example of negative regulation by the repressor, whose function is modulated by an inducer.

The function of the lactose operon was revealed by genetic studies.

Although the interactions shown in Fig. 19.16 and Fig. 19.17 have since been confirmed by direct biochemical studies, the inferences about how the repressor and operator work were originally drawn from studies of mutations (**Fig. 19.18**). As part of their investigation, Jacob and Monod identified bacterial mutants that expressed β-galactosidase and permease in the absence of lactose. The phenotype of a cell carrying such a mutation is said to be **constitutive** for production of the proteins. Constitutive expression means that it occurs continuously. The most common constitutive phenotype resulted from a mutation in the *lacI* gene that produced a defective repressor protein (Fig. 19.18a).

Jacob and Monod also did experiments in which *E. coli* contained not one but two lactose operons (Fig. 19.18b). In bacterial cells containing one mutant and one normal copy of *lacI* (repressor), gene expression was no longer constitutive but instead showed normal regulation. This finding is consistent with the idea that the *lacI* gene produces a diffusible protein since the normal repressor is able to bind to and repress transcription from both operons, not just the one that it is physically linked to.

A much less common class of constitutive mutants identified the operator (Fig. 19.18c). Genetic studies of the mutations in these cells showed that they were not located in the *lacI* gene that encodes the repressor but, rather, closer to the coding sequence of *lacZ*. The genetic element in which the mutations occurred was called the lactose *operator* (*lacO*), and the constitutive mutations were designated *lacO*^{c} ("*c*" for "constitutive"). When two different lactose operons, one normal and one with *lacO*^{c}, were in the same cell, the operon carrying *lacO*^{c} was transcribed constitutively, even in the presence of normal repressor, because the repressor was unable to bind to the mutant operator site (Fig. 19.18d). "To explain this effect," Jacob and Monod wrote, "it seems necessary to invoke a new type of genetic entity, called an 'operator,' which would be: (a) adjacent to the group of genes and would control their activity; and (b) would be sensitive to the repressor produced by a particular regulatory gene."

→ **Quick Check 4** Predict the consequence of a mutation in *lacI* (repressor gene) that produces repressor protein that is able to bind to the operator, but not able to bind allolactose.

The lactose operon is also positively regulated by CRP–cAMP.

Fig. 19.16 and Fig. 19.17 show how the ability of the repressor to bind with either the operator (in the absence of lactose) or with the inducer (in the presence of lactose) provides a simple and elegant way for the bacterial cell to transcribe the genes needed for lactose utilization only in the presence of lactose. The elucidation of these interactions was as far as the research tools used by Jacob and Monod could take them. Since the original

FIG. 19.18 Lactose operon regulatory mutants. Jacob and Monod found two classes of constitutive mutants, one affecting the repressor (a) and the other the operator (c). In cells containing both a mutant and a nonmutant lactose operon, those with the repressor mutant became regulated (b), and those with the operator mutant remained constitutive (d).

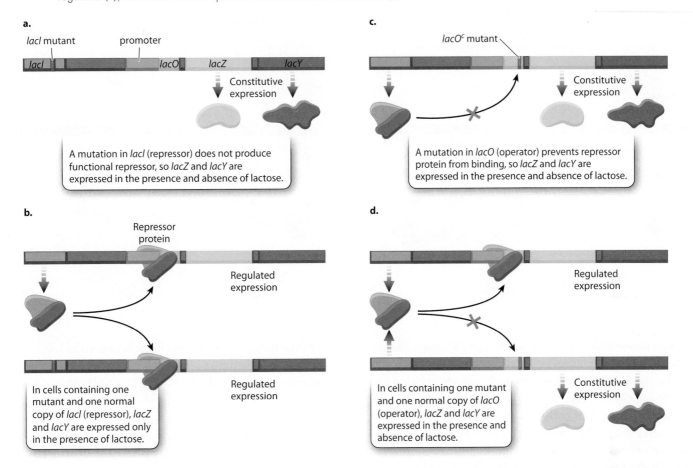

experiments, the lactose operon has been studied in much greater detail and additional levels of regulation have been discovered.

One of these additional levels involves the CRP binding site shown in Fig. 19.15, which in **Fig. 19.19** is occupied by a protein called the CRP–cAMP complex. The CRP–cAMP complex is a positive regulator of the lactose operon, which you will recall is a protein that activates gene expression upon binding to DNA. "CRP" stands for "cAMP receptor protein." The role of CRP–cAMP is to provide another level of control of transcription that is more sensitive to the nutritional needs of the cell than the level of control provided by the presence or absence of lactose. *E. coli* can utilize many kinds of molecules as sources of energy. When more than one type of energy source is available in the environment, certain sources are used before others. For example, glucose is preferred to lactose, and lactose is preferred to glycerol. The CRP–cAMP complex helps regulate which compounds are utilized.

The concentration of the small molecule cAMP in the cell is a signal about the nutritional state of the cell. In the absence of glucose, cAMP levels are high, and cAMP binds to CRP, changing the shape of CRP so that it can bind DNA and activate

transcription. In this way, cAMP is an allosteric activator of CRP, acting as described earlier. If lactose is present, the repressor can't bind and the lactose operon is induced (Fig. 19.19a). If lactose is not present, the repressor is bound and the lactose operon is not transcribed even in the presence of the cAMP–CRP complex.

In the presence of glucose, cAMP levels are low, and the cAMP–CRP complex does not bind the lactose operon. As a result, even in the presence of lactose, the lactose operon is not transcribed to high levels (Fig. 19.19b). In this way, *E. coli* preferentially utilizes glucose when both glucose and lactose are present, and utilizes lactose only when glucose is depleted.

Transcriptional regulation determines the outcome of infection by a bacterial virus.

Transcriptional regulation has also been well studied in viruses. Bacterial cells are susceptible to infection by a variety of viruses known as **bacteriophages** ("bacteriophage" literally means "bacteria-eater," and is often shortened to just "phage"). Among bacteriophages is a type that can undergo either of two fates when infecting a cell. The best known example is bacteriophage λ (lambda), which infects cells of *E. coli*. The possible fates of

FIG. 19.19 The CRP–cAMP complex, a positive regulator of the lactose operon. (a) In the absence of glucose, cAMP levels are high and the CRP–cAMP complex binds to a site near the promoter, where it activates transcription. (b) In the presence of glucose, cAMP levels are low and the CRP–cAMP complex does not bind, so transcription is not induced to high levels, even in the presence of lactose.

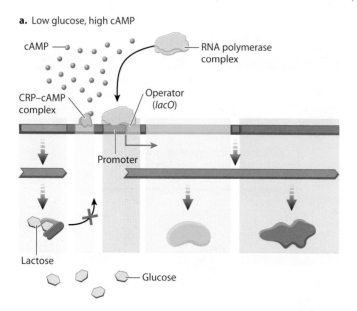

a. Low glucose, high cAMP

b. High glucose, low cAMP

λ infection are illustrated in **Fig. 19.20.** Upon infection, the linear DNA of the phage genome is injected into the bacterial cell, and almost immediately the ends of the molecule join to form a circle. In normal cells growing in nutrient medium, the usual outcome of infection is the **lytic pathway,** shown at the left in Fig. 19.20. In the lytic pathway, the virus hijacks the cellular machinery to replicate the viral genome and produce viral proteins. After about an hour, the infected cell undergoes **lysis** and the cell bursts open to release a hundred or more progeny phage capable of infecting other bacterial cells.

The alternative to the lytic pathway is **lysogeny,** shown at the right in Fig. 19.20. In lysogeny, the bacteriophage DNA and the bacterial DNA undergo a process of recombination at a specific site in both molecules, which results in a slightly enlarged bacterial DNA molecule that now includes the bacteriophage DNA. Lysogeny often takes place in cells growing in poor conditions. The relative sizes of the DNA molecules in Fig. 19.20 are not to scale. In reality, the length of the bacteriophage DNA is only about 1% of that of the bacterial DNA. When the bacteriophage genome is integrated in lysogeny, the only bacteriophage gene transcribed and translated is one that represses the transcription of other phage genes, preventing entry into the lytic pathway. The bacteriophage DNA is replicated along with the bacterial DNA and transmitted to the bacterial progeny when the cell divides. Under stress, such as exposure to ultraviolet light, recombination is reversed, freeing the bacterial genome and initiating the lytic pathway.

At the molecular level, the choice between the lytic and lysogenic pathways is determined by the positive and negative regulatory effects of a small number of bacteriophage

FIG. 19.20 Alternative outcomes of infection by bacteriophage λ. The bacteriophage can enter either the lytic or the lysogenic pathway.

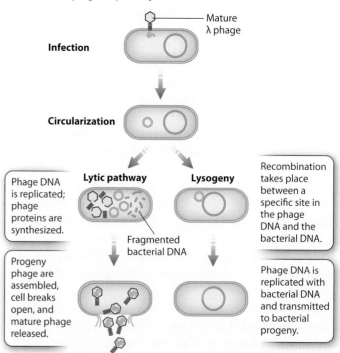

FIG. 19.21 Transcriptional regulation of *cl* and *cro* genes, which determine the lytic pathway versus lysogeny.

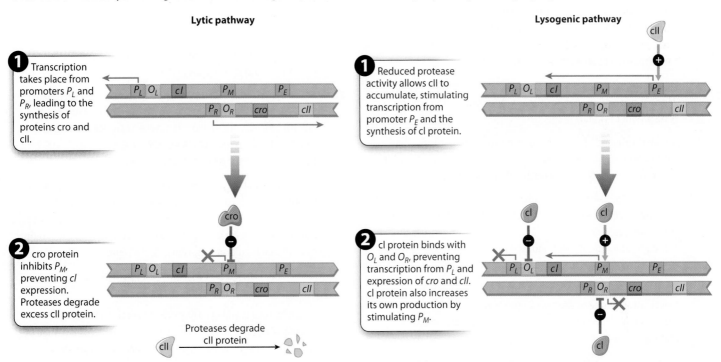

proteins produced soon after infection. **Fig. 19.21** shows the small region of the bacteriophage DNA in which the key interactions take place. Almost immediately after infection and circularization of the bacteriophage DNA, transcription takes place from the promoters P_L and P_R. The transcript from P_R encodes the proteins cro and cII. The cro protein represses transcription from another promoter P_M, which prevents transcription and synthesis of the protein cI. In normal cells growing in nutrient medium, proteases present in the bacterial cell degrade cII and prevent its accumulation. With cro protein preventing *cI* expression and cII protein unable to accumulate, transcription of bacteriophage genes in the lytic pathway takes place, including those genes needed for bacteriophage DNA replication, those encoding proteins in the bacteriophage head and tail, and, finally, those needed for lysis.

Alternatively, in bacterial cells growing in poor conditions, reduced protease activity allows cII protein to accumulate. When cII protein reaches a high enough level, it stimulates transcription from the promoter P_E. The transcript from P_E includes the coding sequence for cI protein, and the cI protein has three functions:

- It binds with the operator O_R and prevents further expression of *cro* and *cII*.

- It stimulates transcription of its own coding sequence from the

promoter P_M, establishing a positive feedback loop that keeps the level of cI protein high.

- It binds with the operator O_L and prevents further transcription from P_L.

The result is that cI production shuts down transcription of all bacteriophage genes except its own gene, and this is the regulatory state that produces lysogeny. (The protein needed for recombination between the bacteriophage DNA and the bacterial DNA is produced by transcription from the P_L promoter before it is shut down by cI.) When cells that have undergone lysogeny are exposed to ultraviolet light or certain other stresses, the cI protein is degraded. In this case, cro and cII are produced again, and the lytic pathway follows.

Regulation of the lytic pathway and lysogeny works to the advantage of bacteriophage λ, but the process is not as simple and elegant as something an engineer might design. That is because biological systems are not engineered, they evolve. Regulatory mechanisms are built up over time by the selection of successive mutations. Each evolutionary step refines the regulation in such a way as to be better adapted to the environment than it was before. Each successive step occurs only because it increases survival and reproduction.

Core Concepts Summary

19.1 THE REGULATION OF GENE EXPRESSION IN EUKARYOTES TAKES PLACE AT MANY LEVELS, INCLUDING DNA PACKAGING IN CHROMOSOMES, TRANSCRIPTION, AND RNA PROCESSING.

Gene expression involves the turning on or turning off of a gene. Gene regulation determines where, when, and how much gene product is made. page 19-1

Regulation at the level of chromatin involves chemical modifications of DNA and histones that make a gene accessible or inaccessible to the transcriptional machinery. page 19-2

Dosage compensation is the process by which the expression of X-linked genes is equalized in XX individuals (who have two copies of each X chromosome and hence two copies of each X-linked gene) and XY individuals (who have only one copy of each X chromosome and X-linked gene). page 19-4

One mechanism of dosage compensation involves the inactivation of one of the two X chromosomes in females; this mechanism, known as X-inactivation, is observed in mammals. page 19-4

X-inactivation occurs by the transcription of a noncoding RNA known as Xist, which binds to the X-chromosome inactivation center (XIC) and coats the entire X chromosome, leading to DNA and histone modifications and transcriptional repression. page 19-4

Transcriptional regulation controls whether or not transcription of a gene occurs. page 19-5

Transcription can be regulated by regulatory transcription factors that bind to specific DNA sequences near genes known as enhancers. page 19-6

Further levels of regulation after a gene is transcribed to mRNA include RNA processing, splicing, and editing. page 19-6

19.2 AFTER AN mRNA IS TRANSCRIBED AND EXPORTED TO THE CYTOPLASM IN EUKARYOTES, GENE EXPRESSION CAN BE REGULATED AT THE LEVEL OF mRNA STABILITY, TRANSLATION, AND POSTTRANSLATIONAL MODIFICATION OF PROTEINS.

Small regulatory RNAs, especially microRNA (miRNA) and small interfering RNA (siRNA), affect gene expression through their effects on translation (miRNA) or RNA stability (siRNA). page 19-8

Translational regulation controls the rate, timing, and location of protein synthesis. page 19-9

Translational regulation is determined by many features of an mRNA molecule, including the 5' and 3' UTR, the cap, and the poly(A) tail. page 19-9

Posttranslational modification comes into play after a protein is synthesized, and includes chemical modification of side groups of amino acids, affecting the structure and activity of a protein. page 19-10

Gene regulation is influenced by both genetic and environmental factors. page 19-10

19.3 TRANSCRIPTIONAL REGULATION IS ILLUSTRATED IN BACTERIA BY THE CONTROL OF THE PRODUCTION OF PROTEINS NEEDED FOR THE UTILIZATION OF LACTOSE, AND IN VIRUSES BY THE CONTROL OF THE LYTIC AND LYSOGENIC PATHWAYS.

Transcriptional regulation can be positive, in which a gene is usually off and is turned on in response to the binding to DNA of a regulatory protein called an activator, or negative, in which a gene is usually on and is turned off in response to the binding to DNA of a regulatory protein called a repressor. page 19-11

Jacob and Monod studied the lactose operon in E. coli as a model for bacterial gene regulation. page 19-12

When lactose is added to culture of bacteria, the genes for the uptake of lactose (permease, encoded by lacY) and cleavage of lactose (β-galactosidase, encoded by lacZ) are expressed. page 19-12

The lactose operon is negatively regulated by the repressor protein (encoded by lacI), which binds to DNA sequences known as the operator. page 19-13

When lactose is added to the medium, it induces an allosteric change in the repressor protein, preventing it from binding to the operator and allowing transcription of lacY and lacZ. In this way, lactose acts as an inducer of the lactose operon. page 19-14

An additional level of regulation of the lactose operon is provided by the CRP–cAMP complex, a positive activator of transcription. page 19-14

In infection of E. coli cells by bacteriophage λ, predominance of cro protein results in the lytic pathway, whereas predominance of the cI protein results in the lysogenic pathway. page 19-15

Self-Assessment

1. Distinguish between gene expression and gene regulation.

2. Explain what is meant by "different levels" of gene regulation and give some examples.

3. Give a few examples of how DNA bases or chromatin can be modified to regulate gene expression.

4. Explain how X-inactivation in female mammals results in patchy coat color in calico cats.

5. Explain how one protein-coding gene can code for more than one polypeptide chain.

6. Name and describe three ways in which gene expression can be influenced after mRNA is processed and leaves the nucleus.

7. Diagram the lactose operon in *E. coli* with the proper order of the elements *lacI, lacO, lacY,* and *lacZ,* and explain how expression is controlled in the presence and absence of lactose.

8. Describe the role of the CRP–cAMP complex in positive regulation of the lactose operon in *E. coli.*

9. Describe what is meant by lysis and lysogeny, and explain how gene regulation controls these two pathways.

Do you understand the chapter's Core Concepts? Log into BIO *PORTAL* to check your answers to the Self-Assessment questions, then practice what you've learned and reinforce this chapter's concepts by working through the problems and multimedia tutorials provided there.

📶 **http://courses.bfwpub.com/yourbioportal/index.php**

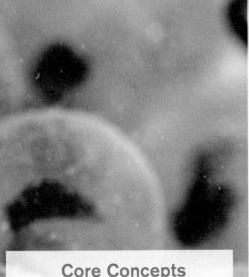

CHAPTER 20

GENES AND DEVELOPMENT

Core Concepts

20.1 In the development of humans and other animals, stem cells become progressively more restricted in their possible pathways of cellular differentiation.

20.2 The genetic control of development is a hierarchy in which genes are deployed in groups that in turn regulate the next set of genes.

20.3 Many proteins that play key roles in development are evolutionarily conserved but can have dramatically different effects in different organisms.

20.4 Combinatorial control is a developmental strategy in which cellular differentiation depends on the particular combination of transcription factors present in a cell.

20.5 Ligand–receptor interactions activate signal transduction pathways that converge on transcription factors and other genes that determine cell fate.

Altogether, the human body contains about 200 different types of cell, all of which derive from a single cell, the zygote. In animals, some cells become muscle cells, others nerve cells, and still others connective tissue. Almost all of these cells have exactly the same genome: They differ not in their content of genes, but instead in the groups of genes that are expressed or repressed. In other words, these cell types differ as a result of gene regulation, discussed in the previous chapter.

Gene regulation is especially important in multicellular organisms because it underlies **development,** the process in which a fertilized egg undergoes multiple rounds of cell division to become an embryo with specialized tissues and organs. During development, cells undergo changes in gene expression as genes are turned on and off at specific times and places. Gene regulation causes cells to become progressively more specialized, a process known as **differentiation.**

In this chapter, we focus on the general principles by which genes control development. We will see that, as cells differentiate along one pathway, they progressively lose their ability to differentiate along other pathways. Yet gene expression can sometimes be reprogrammed to reopen pathways of differentiation that had previously been shut off, a process that has important implications for therapeutic replacement of diseased or damaged tissue. We will also see that, while some of the key molecular mechanisms of development are used over and over again in different organisms, they have evolved to yield such differences in shape and form as to conceal the underlying similarity in mechanism.

20.1 GENETIC PROGRAMS OF DEVELOPMENT

Genetic programs and computer programs have a lot in common. Computer code is written as a linear string of letters, which corresponds to the sequence of nucleotides in genomic DNA. Once a computer program is initiated, it automatically runs and performs its coded task. Small mistakes in the code, analogous to mutations, can have big consequences and even cause the program to crash.

The analogy between genetic programs and computer programs has an important limitation. Computer programs, designed by humans, are consciously written, whereas genetic programs evolve. The genetically encoded developmental programs of all living organisms emerged over hundreds of millions of years through mutation and natural selection. These developmental programs changed gradually through time, persisting only if they produced organisms that could successfully survive and reproduce in the existing environment. Here, we explore the genetic program of development— that is, the genetic instructions that lead from a single fertilized egg to a complex multicellular organism.

The fertilized egg is a totipotent cell.

In all sexually reproducing organisms, the fertilized egg is special because of its developmental potential. The fertilized egg is said to be **totipotent,** which means that it can give rise to a complete organism. In mammals, the egg also forms the membranes that surround and support the developing embryo (Chapter 42).

Development begins with **fertilization,** which in human females normally occurs in one of the two fallopian tubes stretching from the upper corners of the uterus to the ovaries on either side, where the tubes flare out with tiny fingerlike projections to catch the egg released at ovulation. The fertilized egg, or **zygote,** travels down the fallopian tube toward the uterus, undergoing mitotic cell division as it moves along. One cell becomes two, two become four, four become eight, eight become sixteen, and so on, with all the cells contained within the egg's outer membrane (**Fig. 20.1**). This clump of cells,

called the **morula,** reaches the uterus about 4 or 5 days after fertilization.

These early cell divisions are different from mitotic cell division later in life because the cells do not grow between divisions; they merely replicate their chromosomes and divide again. The result is that the cytoplasm of the egg is partitioned into smaller and smaller packages, the new cells all bunched together inside the gelatinous envelope that covers the developing embryo.

Cell division continues in the morula until there are a few thousand cells. The cells then begin to move in relation to one another, pushing against and expanding the membrane that encloses them and rearranging themselves to form a hollow sphere called a **blastocyst** (Fig. 20.1). In one region of the inner wall of the blastocyst, there is a group of cells known as the **inner cell mass,** from which the body of the embryo develops. The wall of the blastocyst forms several membranes that envelop and support the developing embryo. Once the blastocyst forms, 5 or 6 days after fertilization, it implants in the uterine wall. From implantation onward, the cells in the blastocyst approximately double their size with each cell division. This is the first great trial of the embryo, which can no longer draw on the cytoplasm in the egg produced by the mother. To survive, the cells of the embryo must now manufacture their own cytoplasm.

Once implanted in the uterine wall, the multiplying cells of the inner cell mass reorganize to form a **gastrula.** It is at this stage that the three **germ layers** are established (Fig. 20.1). Germ layers are sheets of cells that include the ectoderm, mesoderm, and endoderm and that differentiate further into specialized cells. Those formed from the **ectoderm** include epithelial cells and pigment cells in the skin and nerve cells in the brain; cells from the **mesoderm** include cells that make up the inner layer of the skin, muscle cells, and red blood cells; and cells formed from the **endoderm** include cells of the lining of the digestive tract and lung, as well as liver cells and pancreas cells.

Cellular differentiation increasingly restricts alternative fates.

At each successive stage in development, as the cells become differentiated they lose the potential to develop into any kind of cell. The fertilized egg is totipotent because it can differentiate into both the inner cell mass and supporting membranes, and eventually into an entire organism. The cells of the inner cell mass, called embryonic stem cells, are **pluripotent** because they are able to give rise to any of the three germ layers, and therefore to any cell of the body. However, pluripotent cells cannot on their own give rise to an entire organism, as a totipotent cell can. Cells further along in differentiation are **multipotent;** these cells can form a limited number of types of specialized cell. Totipotent, pluripotent, and multipotent cells are all considered **stem cells,** cells that are capable of differentiating into different cell types.

FIG. 20.1   Early development of a human embryo. The zygote is a totipotent cell because its daughter cells can develop into any cell type and eventually into a complete organism.

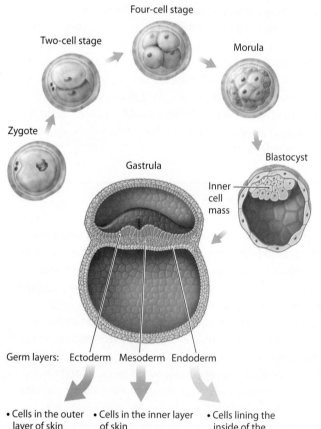

Two-cell stage

Four-cell stage

Morula

Zygote

Gastrula

Blastocyst

Inner cell mass

Germ layers: Ectoderm   Mesoderm   Endoderm

- Cells in the outer layer of skin
- Pigment cells
- Nerve cells in the brain

- Cells in the inner layer of skin
- Muscle cells
- Bone cells
- Red blood cells

- Cells lining the inside of the digestive tract
- Cells lining the inside of the lung
- Liver cells
- Pancreas cells

→ **Quick Check 1** From what you know about embryonic development, do you think that a cell from the inner cell mass or one from the ectoderm has more developmental potential?

Why do differentiating cells increasingly lose their developmental potential? One hypothesis focuses on gene regulation. When cells become committed to a particular developmental pathway, genes no longer needed are turned off (that is, repressed) and are difficult to turn on again. Another hypothesis is genome reduction: As cells become differentiated, they delete the DNA for genes they no longer need.

These hypotheses can be distinguished by an experiment in which differentiated cells are reprogrammed to mimic earlier states. If loss of developmental potential is due to gene regulation, then cells could be reprogrammed to become pluripotent or multipotent. If loss of developmental potential is due to genome reduction, then differentiated cells could not be reprogrammed to become pluripotent or multipotent.

British developmental biologist John Gurdon carried out such experiments in the early 1960s (**Fig. 20.2**). Gurdon used a procedure called **nuclear transfer,** in which a hollow glass needle is used to insert the nucleus of a cell into the cytoplasm

HOW DO WE KNOW?

FIG. 20.2

How do stem cells lose their ability to differentiate into any cell type?

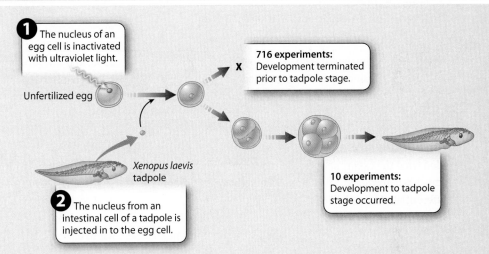

① The nucleus of an egg cell is inactivated with ultraviolet light.

Unfertilized egg

Xenopus laevis tadpole

② The nucleus from an intestinal cell of a tadpole is injected in to the egg cell.

716 experiments: Development terminated prior to tadpole stage.

10 experiments: Development to tadpole stage occurred.

BACKGROUND During differentiation, cells become progressively more specialized and restricted in their fates. Early studies left it unclear whether cell differentiation occurs because of changes in gene expression, or whether cell differentiation results from loss of genes.

HYPOTHESES One hypothesis is that differentiation occurs as a result of changes in gene expression. A second hypothesis is that differentiation occurs as a result of genome reduction, in which genes that are not needed are deleted.

EXPERIMENT John Gurdon carried out experiments in the amphibian *Xenopus laevis* to test these hypotheses. He transferred nuclei from differentiated cells into unfertilized eggs whose nuclei had been inactivated with ultraviolet light. If differentiation is due to changes in gene expression, then the differentiated nucleus should be able to reprogram itself in the egg cytoplasm and differentiate again into all the cells of a tadpole. If differentiation is accompanied by loss of genes, then differentiation is irreversible and development will not proceed.

RESULTS The experiment was carried out 726 times. In 716 cases, development did not occur; in 10, development proceeded normally.

CONCLUSION Although the experiment succeeded in only 10 of 726 attempts, it showed that the nucleus of an intestinal cell and the cytoplasm of the unfertilized egg are able to support complete development of a normal animal. This result allows us to reject the hypothesis that differentiation occurs by the loss of genes. Differentiated cells must contain a complete genome. The first hypothesis—that cells become differentiated as a result of changes in gene expression—was supported. But, because of the small number of successes in reprogramming, additional experiments were needed to validate the conclusions.

FOLLOW-UP WORK This work was controversial. Some critics argued that the successful experiments resulted from a small number of undifferentiated cells present in intestinal epithelium. Others accepted the conclusion but expressed misgivings about possible applications to humans. Later experiments that succeeded in cloning mammals from fully differentiated cells confirmed the original conclusion.

SOURCE Gurdon, J. B. 1962. "The Developmental Capacity of Nuclei Taken from Intestinal Epithelium Cells of Feeding tadpoles." *Journal of Embryology & Experimental Morphology* 10: 622–640.

FIG. 20.3　Results of nuclear transfer of differentiated cells.

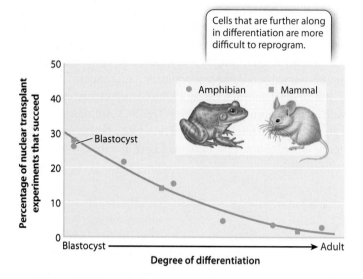

> Cells that are further along in differentiation are more difficult to reprogram.

of an egg whose own nucleus has been destroyed or removed. Previous nuclear transfer experiments had been carried out in the leopard frog, *Rana pipiens*. Whereas nuclei from pluripotent or multipotent cells could often be reprogrammed to develop into normal tadpoles, attempts with nuclei from fully differentiated cells failed.

Gurdon tried the experiments in a different organism, the clawed toad *Xenopus laevis*, and demonstrated that nuclei from fully differentiated intestinal cells could be reprogrammed to support normal development of the tadpole (Fig. 20.2). Only 10 of 726 experiments succeeded, but this was sufficient

to show that intestinal cell nuclei still contained a complete *Xenopus* genome. In other words, his findings supported the first hypothesis—all of the same genes are present in intestinal cells as in early embryonic cells, but some of the genes are turned off, or repressed, during development.

Fig. 20.3 summarizes the results of many nuclear transfer experiments carried out in mammals and amphibians. The percentage of reprogramming experiments that fail increases as cells differentiate. The best chance of success is to use pluripotent nuclei from cells in the blastocyst (or its amphibian equivalent, the blastula). However, even some experiments using nuclei from fully differentiated cells have been successful.

When nuclear transfer succeeds, the result is a **clone**—an individual that carries an exact copy of the nuclear genome of another individual. In this case, the new individual shares the same genome as that of the individual from which the donor nucleus was obtained. (The mitochondrial DNA is not from the nuclear donor, but from the donor of the egg cytoplasm.) The first mammalian clone was a lamb called Dolly (**Fig. 20.4a**), born in 1996. She was produced from the transfer of the nucleus of a cell in the mammary gland of a sheep, and was the only successful birth among 277 nuclear transfers. Successful cloning in sheep soon led to cloning in cattle, pigs, and goats.

The first household pet to be cloned was a kitten named CopyCat (**Fig. 20.4b**), born in 2001 and derived from a differentiated ovarian cell. CopyCat was the only success among 87 tries. As shown in Fig. 20.4b, the cat from which the donor nucleus was obtained was a calico, but CopyCat herself was not, even though the two cats are clones of each other. The reason for their different appearance has to do with X-inactivation, discussed in Chapter 19. Recall

FIG. 20.4　Celebrity clones and their genetic mothers. (a) Dolly. (b) CopyCat.

that the mottled orange and black calico pattern results from random inactivation of one of the two X chromosomes during development. The lack of a calico pattern in CopyCat implies that the X chromosomes in the transferred nucleus did not "reset" as they do in normal embryos. Instead, the inactive X in the donor nucleus remained inactive in all the cells in the clone. Hence, while CopyCat and her mother share the same nuclear genome, the genes were not expressed in the same way because of irreversible epigenetic regulation in the donor nucleus.

→ **Quick Check 2** *X*-inactivation results in two clones of cells differing in the genes expressed. Can you think of other reasons why two genetically identical individuals might look different from each other?

? CASE 3 You, From A to T: Your Personal Genome
Can cells with your personal genome be reprogrammed for new therapies?
Stem cells play a prominent role in **regenerative medicine,** which aims to use the natural processes of cell growth and development to replace diseased or damaged tissues. Stem cells are already used in bone marrow transplantation and may someday be used to treat Parkinson's disease, Alzheimer's disease, heart failure, certain types of diabetes, severe burns and wounds, and spinal cord injury.

At first it seemed as though the use of embryonic stem cells gave the greatest promise for regenerative medicine because of their pluripotency. This approach proved ethically controversial because obtaining embryonic stem cells requires the destruction of human blastocysts. A major breakthrough took place in 2006 when Japanese scientists demonstrated that adult cells can be reprogrammed by activation of just a handful of genes, most of them encoding transcription factors or chromatin proteins. The reprogrammed cells were pluripotent and were therefore called **induced pluripotent cells (iPS cells).**

The success rate was only about one iPS cell per thousand, and the genetic engineering technique required the use of viruses that can sometimes cause cancer. Nevertheless, the result was regarded as spectacular. Other researchers soon found other genes that could be used for reprogramming adult cells into pluripotent or multipotent stem cells, and still other investigators developed virus-free methods for delivering the genes. In recent years, researchers have even discovered small organic molecules that can reprogram adult cells.

This kind of reprogramming opens the door to personalized stem cell therapies. The goal is to create stem cells derived from the adult cells of the individual patient. Since these cells contain the patient's own genome, problems with tissue rejection are minimized or eliminated (Chapter 43). There remains much to learn before therapeutic use of induced stem cells becomes

routine. Researchers will face challenges such as increasing the efficiency of reprogramming, verifying that reprogramming is complete, making sure that the reprogrammed cells are not prone to cancer, and demonstrating that the reprogrammed cells differentiate as they should. Nevertheless, researchers hope that someday soon your own cells containing your personal genome could be reprogrammed to restore cells or organs damaged by disease or accident.

20.2 HIERARCHICAL CONTROL OF DEVELOPMENT

During development of a complex multicellular organism, many genes are activated and repressed at different times, thus restricting cell fates. One of the key principles of development is that genes expressed early in an organism's development control the activation of other groups of genes that act later in development. Gene regulation during development is therefore **hierarchical** in the sense that genes expressed at each stage in the process control the expression of genes that act later.

Drosophila development proceeds through egg, larval, and adult stages.

The fruit fly *Drosophila melanogaster* has played a prominent role in our understanding of the genetic control of early development, and in particular the hierarchical control of development. Researchers have isolated and analyzed a large number of mutant genes that lead to a variety of defects at different stages in development. These studies have revealed many of the key genes and processes in development, which are the focus of the following sections.

The major events in *Drosophila* development are illustrated in **Fig. 20.5**. DNA replication and nuclear division begin soon after the egg and sperm nuclei fuse (Fig. 20.5a). Unlike in mammalian development, the early nuclear divisions in the *Drosophila* embryo occur without cell division, and therefore the embryo consists of a single cell with many nuclei in the center (Fig. 20.5b). When there are roughly 5000 nuclei, they migrate to the periphery (Fig. 20.5c), where each nucleus becomes enclosed in its own cell membrane, and together they form the **cellular blastoderm** (Fig. 20.5d).

Then begins the process of **gastrulation,** in which the cells of the blastoderm migrate inward, creating layers of cells within the embryo. As in humans and most other animals (section 20.1 and Chapter 42), gastrulation forms the three germ layers (ectoderm, mesoderm, and endoderm) that differentiate into different types of cell. A *Drosophila* embryo during gastrulation is shown in Fig. 20.5e. At this stage, the embryo already shows an organization into discrete parts or segments, the formation of which is known

FIG. 20.5 **Life cycle of the fruit fly *Drosophila melanogaster*.** The life cycle begins with (a) a fertilized egg, followed by (b–e) a developing embryo, (f–h) larval stages, (i) pupa, and (j) adult.

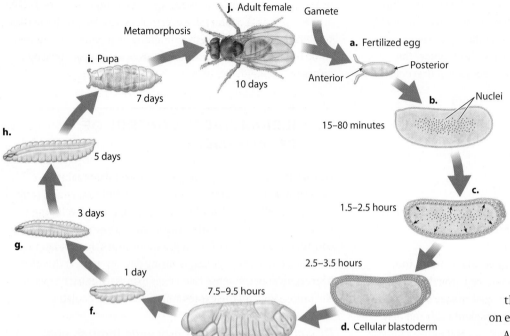

j. Adult female
Gamete

Metamorphosis

i. Pupa

10 days

7 days

h.

5 days

3 days

g.

1 day

7.5–9.5 hours

f.

e. Gastrulating embryo

*Images not drawn to scale.

a. Fertilized egg

Posterior

Anterior

b.

Nuclei

15–80 minutes

c.

1.5–2.5 hours

2.5–3.5 hours

d. Cellular blastoderm

early development (**Fig. 20.6**). These defects in very early development can be easily seen by the time the mutants reach the larval stage. In one class of mutants, called *bicoid*, larvae are missing segments at the anterior end. In another class of mutants, called *nanos*, larvae are missing segments at the posterior end. The mutant larvae are grossly abnormal and do not survive. Nusslein-Volhard and Wieschaus were able to identify each segment that was missing based on each segment's distinctive pattern of hairlike projections. In Fig. 20.6, the patterns are shown as dark shapes on each segment.

A distinguishing feature of *bicoid* and *nanos* mutants is that the abnormalities in the embryo depend on the genotype of the mother, not the genotype of the embryo. The reason the genotype of the mother can affect the phenotype of the developing embryo is that successful development requires a functioning oocyte. In

as **segmentation.** There are three cephalic segments, C1–C3 (the term "cephalic" refers to the head); three thoracic segments, T1–T3 (the thorax is the middle region of an insect); and eight abdominal segments (A1–A8). Each of these segments has a different fate in development.

About one day after fertilization, the embryo hatches from the egg as a larva (Fig. 20.5f). Over the next eight days, the larva grows and replaces its rigid outer shell, or cuticle, twice (Fig. 20.5g and h). After a week of further growth, the cuticle forms a casing—called the pupa—in which the larva is immobilized (Fig. 20.5i), and where it undergoes dramatic developmental changes known as metamorphosis that give rise to the adult fruit fly.

The egg is a highly polarized cell.

How genes control development in *Drosophila* was inferred from systematic studies of mutants by Christiane Nusslein-Volhard and Eric F. Wieschaus, work for which they were awarded the 1995 Nobel Prize in Physiology or Medicine. One of their findings was that development starts even before a zygote is formed, in the maturation of the **oocyte,** the unfertilized egg cell produced by the mother. The oocyte, which matures under control of the mother's genes, is nonetheless important for normal embryonic development. This finding applies not only to insects like *Drosophila*, but also to many multicellular animals.

Among the striking mutants Nusslein-Volhard and Wieschaus generated and investigated were ones that significantly affected

FIG. 20.6 **Normal and mutant *Drosophila* larvae.** (a) Nonmutant larva have anterior, middle, and posterior segments. (b) *Bicoid* mutant larva lack anterior segments. (c) *Nanos* mutant larva lack posterior structures.

a. Nonmutant larva

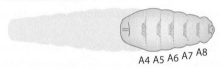

Anterior

Posterior

C1
C2
C3

T1 T2 T3 A1 A2 A3 A4 A5 A6 A7 A8

b. Larva from *bicoid* mutant

A4 A5 A6 A7 A8

c. Larva from *nanos* mutant

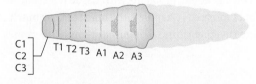

C1
C2
C3

T1 T2 T3 A1 A2 A3

FIG. 20.7 **Gradients of *bicoid* and *nanos* mRNA and protein in the developing embryo.** (a) The mRNA and protein for *bicoid* are localized in the anterior end of the egg. (b) The mRNA and protein for *nanos* are localized in the posterior end of the egg.

a. Distribution of *bicoid* mRNA and protein in the egg

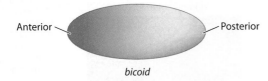

Anterior — Posterior

bicoid

b. Distribution of *nanos* mRNA and protein in the egg

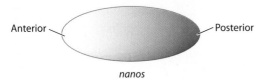

Anterior — Posterior

nanos

Drosophila and many other organisms, the composition of the egg includes macromolecules (such as RNA and protein) synthesized by cells in the mother and transported into the egg. If the mother carries mutations in genes involved in the development of the oocyte, the offspring can be abnormal. Genes such as *bicoid* and *nanos* that are expressed by the mother but affect the phenotype of the offspring (in this case the developing embryo and larvae) are called **maternal-effect genes.**

A normal *Drosophila* oocyte is highly polarized, meaning that one end is distinctly different from the other. For example, there are gradients of macromolecules that define the anterior–posterior axis of the embryo as well as the dorsal–ventral axis. The best known of these gradients are those of messenger RNAs that correspond to the maternal-effect genes *bicoid* and *nanos*. **Fig. 20.7a** shows the gradient of *bicoid* mRNA across the oocyte. The bulk of *bicoid* mRNA comes from the mother, not from the oocyte, and is localized in the anterior of the egg by proteins that attach them to the cytoskeleton.

The mRNA corresponding to the maternal-effect gene *nanos* is also present in a gradient, but its maximum is at the posterior end (**Fig. 20.7b**). Like *bicoid*, mRNA for *nanos* is synthesized by the mother's cells and then imported into the oocyte. After fertilization, the zygote produces Bicoid and Nanos proteins,

and they have concentration gradients resembling those of the mRNAs in the oocyte (Fig. 20.7).

The anterior–posterior axis set up by the gradients of Bicoid and Nanos proteins is reinforced by gradients of two transcription factors called Caudal and Hunchback (**Fig. 20.8**). Like the mRNAs for Bicoid and Nanos, the mRNAs for Caudal and Hunchback are transcribed from the mother's genome and transported into the egg. As shown in Fig. 20.8a, the mRNAs for *caudal* and *hunchback* are spread uniformly in the cytoplasm of the fertilized egg. However, the mRNAs are not translated uniformly in the egg. Bicoid protein represses translation of *caudal*, and Nanos protein represses translation of *hunchback* (Fig. 20.8b). Caudal protein is therefore concentrated at the posterior end and Hunchback protein is concentrated at the anterior end. The expression of Caudal and Hunchback illustrates gene regulation at the level of translation, discussed in Chapter 19. Bicoid protein is also a transcription factor that promotes transcription of the *hunchback* gene from zygotic nuclei, which reinforces the localization of Hunchback protein at the anterior end.

The Hunchback and Caudal gradients set the stage for the subsequent steps in development. The Hunchback transcription factor targets genes needed for the development of anterior structures like eyes and antennae, and Caudal

FIG. 20.8 **Caudal and Hunchback gradients in the developing embryo.** (a) mRNA levels of *hunchback* and *caudal* are uniform across the embryo. (b) Hunchback and Caudal protein levels are localized to the anterior and posterior ends of the embryo, respectively, because Bicoid and Nanos control the translation of *hunchback* and *caudal* mRNA.

a.

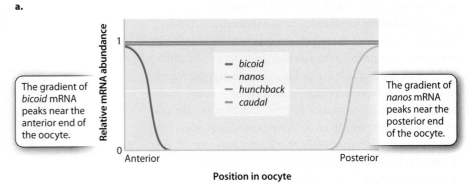

The gradient of *bicoid* mRNA peaks near the anterior end of the oocyte.

The gradient of *nanos* mRNA peaks near the posterior end of the oocyte.

Relative mRNA abundance

— *bicoid*
— *nanos*
— *hunchback*
— *caudal*

Anterior — Posterior

Position in oocyte

b.

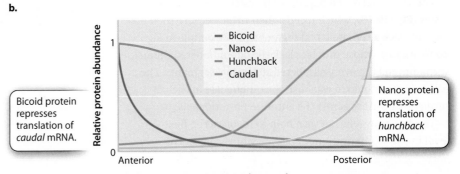

Bicoid protein represses translation of *caudal* mRNA.

Nanos protein represses translation of *hunchback* mRNA.

Relative protein abundance

— Bicoid
— Nanos
— Hunchback
— Caudal

Anterior — Posterior

Position in 2.5-hour embryo

targets genes needed for the development of posterior structures like legs. In this way, genes expressed early in development influence the expression of genes important in later development. Because the products of the *bicoid* and *nanos* mRNA are the ones initially responsible for organizing the anterior and posterior ends of the embryo, respectively, mothers that are mutant for *bicoid* have larvae that lack anterior structures, and mothers that are mutant for *nanos* have larvae that lack posterior structures.

→ **Quick Check 3** Do you think development would happen normally if the mother has normal *bicoid* function, but the embryo does not?

Development proceeds by progressive regionalization and specification.

Nusslein-Volhard and Wieschaus also discovered mutants in three other classes of developmental genes. Analysis of these mutants showed that genes controlling development are turned on in groups, and that each successive group acts to refine and narrow the pattern of differentiation generated by previous groups. This, too, is a general principle of development in many multicellular organisms.

The anterior–posterior gradient set up by the maternal-effect genes is first narrowed by genes called gap genes (**Fig. 20.9**), each of which is expressed in a broad region of the embryo. The name "gap gene" derives from the phenotype of mutant embryos, which are missing groups of adjoining segments, leaving a gap in the pattern of segments. Fig. 20.9 shows the expression pattern of the gap gene *Krüppel*, which is expressed in the middle region of the embryo. Mutants of *Krüppel* lack some larval thoracic and abdominal segments. *Krüppel* is expressed in the pattern shown in Fig. 20.9 because it is under the control of the transcription factor Hunchback, which in this embryo is stained in green. High concentrations of Hunchback repress *Krüppel* transcription entirely, and low concentrations fail to induce *Krüppel* transcription. Because Hunchback is present in an anterior–posterior gradient (see Fig. 20.8), the pattern of Hunchback expression means that *Krüppel* is transcribed only in the middle region of the embryo where Hunchback is present but not too abundant.

The next level of the regulatory hierarchy is that of pair-rule genes (**Fig. 20.10**), which receive their name because their mutants lack alternate larval segments. The example in Fig. 20.10 is *hairy*, whose mutants lack the odd-numbered thoracic segments and the even-numbered abdominal segments. The pair-rule genes help to establish the uniqueness of each of seven broad stripes across the anterior–posterior axis.

The pair-rule genes in turn help to regulate the next level in the segmentation hierarchy, which consists of

FIG. 20.9 Normal gap-gene expression pattern and mutant phenotype.

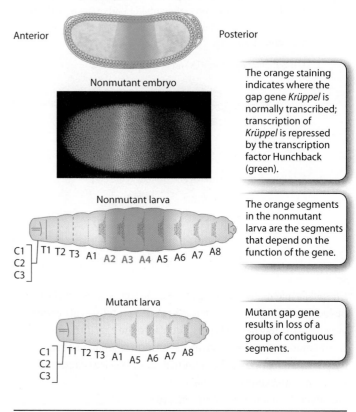

Anterior   Posterior

Nonmutant embryo

The orange staining indicates where the gap gene *Krüppel* is normally transcribed; transcription of *Krüppel* is repressed by the transcription factor Hunchback (green).

Nonmutant larva

C1
C2   T1 T2 T3 A1 A2 A3 A4 A5 A6 A7 A8
C3

The orange segments in the nonmutant larva are the segments that depend on the function of the gene.

Mutant larva

C1
C2   T1 T2 T3 A1 A5 A6 A7 A8
C3

Mutant gap gene results in loss of a group of contiguous segments.

FIG. 20.10 Normal pair-rule gene expression pattern and mutant phenotype.

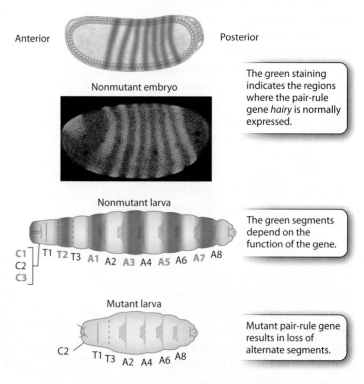

Anterior   Posterior

Nonmutant embryo

The green staining indicates the regions where the pair-rule gene *hairy* is normally expressed.

Nonmutant larva

C1
C2   T1 T2 T3 A1 A2 A3 A4 A5 A6 A7 A8
C3

The green segments depend on the function of the gene.

Mutant larva

C2   T1 T3 A2 A4 A6 A8

Mutant pair-rule gene results in loss of alternate segments.

FIG. 20.11 Normal segment-polarity gene expression pattern and mutant phenotype.

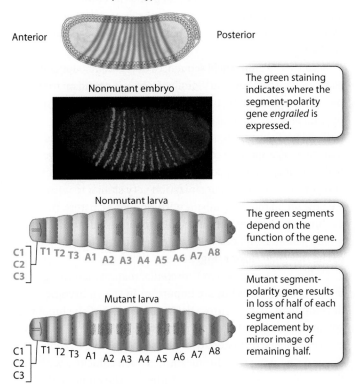

The green staining indicates where the segment-polarity gene *engrailed* is expressed.

The green segments depend on the function of the gene.

Mutant segment-polarity gene results in loss of half of each segment and replacement by mirror image of remaining half.

segment-polarity genes (**Fig. 20.11**). The segment-polarity genes refine the 7-striped pattern still further into a 14-striped pattern. Each of the 14 stripes has distinct anterior and posterior ends determined by the segment-polarity genes. Embryos with mutations in segment-polarity genes lose this anterior–posterior differentiation, with the result that the anterior and the posterior halves of each segment are mirror images. The example in Fig. 20.11 is *engrailed,* which eliminates the posterior pattern element in each stripe and replaces it with a mirror image of the anterior pattern element.

→ **Quick Check 4** Do you think that the pattern of segment-polarity gene expression would be normal if one or more gap genes are not expressed properly?

Homeotic genes determine where different body parts develop in the organism.

Together, the segment-polarity genes and certain genes expressed earlier in the hierarchy control the pattern of expression of another set of genes called **homeotic genes**. Originally discovered in *Drosophila*, homeotic genes encode some of the most important transcription factors in animal development. A homeotic gene is a gene that specifies the identity of a body part or segment during embryonic development. For example, homeotic genes instruct the three thoracic segments (T1, T2, and T3) to each develop a set of legs, and the second thoracic segment (T2) to develop wings.

Two classic examples of the consequences of mutations in homeotic genes in *Drosophila* are shown in **Fig. 20.12**. Fig. 20.12a shows what happens when the homeotic gene *Antennapedia*, which specifies the development of the leg, is inappropriately expressed in anterior segments. The mutation causes legs to grow where antennae usually would. Similarly, a mutation in the homeotic gene *Bithorax* results in the transformation of thoracic segment 3 (T3) into thoracic

FIG. 20.12 **Homeotic genes and segment identity.** (a) Normal antennae are transformed into legs in an *Antennapedia* mutant. (b) Normal structures in the third thoracic segment are transformed into wings in a *Bithorax* mutant.

Normal | Mutant

a. *Antennapedia*

b. *Bithorax*

Haltere

FIG. 20.13 Tissues controlled by homeotic genes. Homeotic genes specify the fate of clumps of tissue in the *Drosophila* larva.

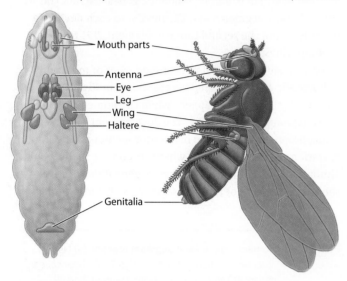

- Mouth parts
- Antenna
- Eye
- Leg
- Wing
- Haltere
- Genitalia

segment 2 (T2), so that the fruit fly has two T2 segments in a row. As shown in the Fig. 20.12b, the result is a fruit fly with two complete sets of wings.

In *Drosophila*, the adult body parts like legs, antennae, and wings are formed from organized collections of tissue located throughout the larval body (**Fig. 20.13**). The development of these tissues and their metamorphosis into the adult body parts are regulated by the homeotic genes. First expressed at about the same time as the segment-polarity genes (see Fig. 20.11), the homeotic genes continue to be expressed even after the genes that regulate early development have shut down. Their continuing activity is due to the presence of chromatin remodeling proteins that keep the chromatin physically accessible to the transcription complex (Chapter 19).

Homeotic genes encode transcription factors. The DNA-binding domain in the homeotic proteins is a sequence of 60 amino acids called a **homeodomain,** whose sequences are very similar from one homeotic protein to the next. The homeodomain is specified by a DNA sequence within the homeotic genes called the **homeobox** (the name is the origin of the term **Hox gene,** which is often used as a synonym for "homeotic gene").

The *Drosophila* genome contains eight *Hox* genes comprising two distinct clusters, the *Antennapedia* complex and the *Bithorax* complex (**Fig. 20.14**). The genes are arranged along the chromosome in the same order as their products function in anterior–posterior segments along the embryo. In addition, the timing of their expression corresponds to their order along the chromosome and location of expression, with genes that

are expressed closer to the anterior end turned on earlier than genes that are expressed closer to the posterior end. The correlation among linear order along the chromosome, anterior–posterior position in the embryo, and timing of expression is observed in *Hox* clusters in almost all organisms studied.

Because the amino acid sequences of the homeodomains of *Hox* gene products are very similar from one organism to the next, *Hox* gene clusters have been identified in a wide variety of animals with bilateral symmetry (organisms in which both sides of the midline are mirror images), from insects to mammals. Comparison of the number and types of *Hox* genes in different species supports the hypothesis that the ancestral *Hox* gene cluster had an organization very similar to what we now see in most organisms with *Hox* gene clusters. In its evolutionary history, the vertebrate genome underwent two whole-genome duplications; hence, vertebrates have four copies of the *Hox* gene cluster (**Fig. 20.15**).

Unlike the *Hox* genes in *Drosophila*, mammalian *Hox* genes do not specify limbs but are important in the embryonic development of structures that become parts of the hindbrain, spinal cord, and vertebral column (Fig. 20.15). As in *Drosophila*, the genes in each cluster are expressed according to their linear order along the chromosome, which coincides with the linear order of regions the genes affect in the embryo. Each gene helps to specify the identity of the region in which it is expressed. Many of the genes in the mammalian *Hox* clusters

FIG. 20.14 Organization of the *Hox* gene clusters in *Drosophila* and the body parts that they affect. The order of genes along the chromosome corresponds to their position along the anterior–posterior axis in the developing embryo.

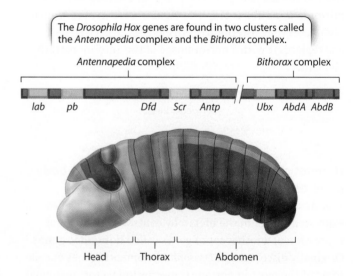

The *Drosophila Hox* genes are found in two clusters called the *Antennapedia* complex and the *Bithorax* complex.

Antennapedia complex | *Bithorax* complex

lab   pb   Dfd   Scr   Antp   Ubx   AbdA   AbdB

Head   Thorax   Abdomen

FIG. 20.15 Organization and content of *Hox* gene clusters in the mouse and the regions of the embryo in which they are expressed.

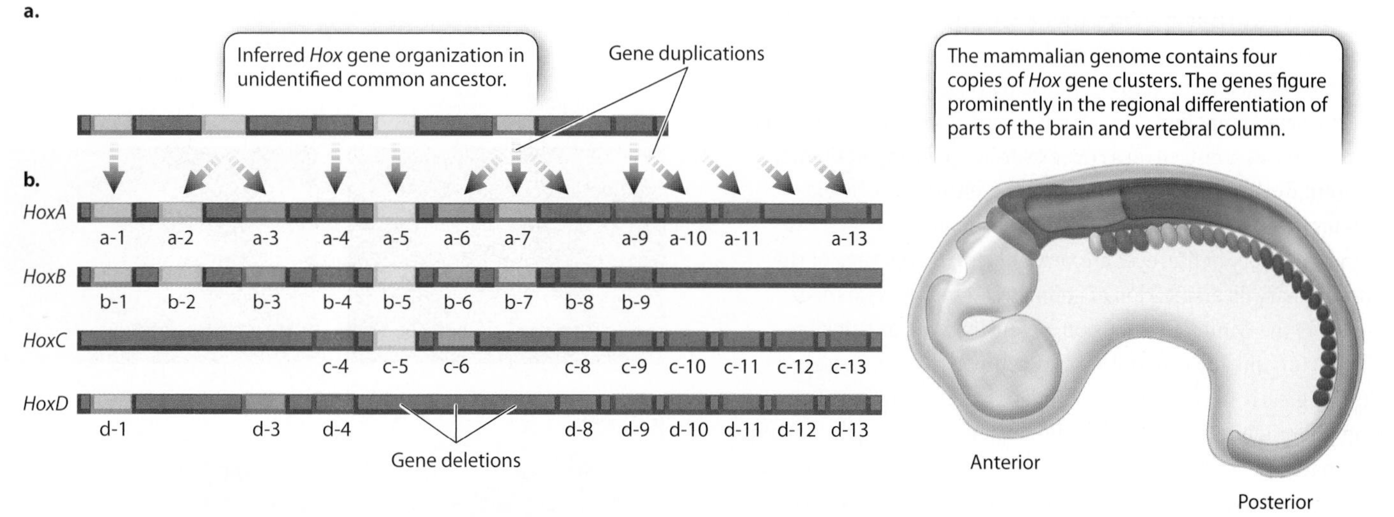

a.

Inferred *Hox* gene organization in unidentified common ancestor.

Gene duplications

The mammalian genome contains four copies of *Hox* gene clusters. The genes figure prominently in the regional differentiation of parts of the brain and vertebral column.

b.

HoxA a-1 a-2 a-3 a-4 a-5 a-6 a-7 a-9 a-10 a-11 a-13

HoxB b-1 b-2 b-3 b-4 b-5 b-6 b-7 b-8 b-9

HoxC c-4 c-5 c-6 c-8 c-9 c-10 c-11 c-12 c-13

HoxD d-1 d-3 d-4 d-8 d-9 d-10 d-11 d-12 d-13

Gene deletions

Anterior

Posterior

have redundant or overlapping functions so that learning exactly what each gene does continues to be a research challenge.

20.3 EVOLUTIONARY CONSERVATION OF KEY TRANSCRIPTION FACTORS IN DEVELOPMENT

As we have seen, *Hox* genes and the proteins they encode are very similar in a wide range of organisms. As a result, they can be identified by their similarity in DNA or amino acid sequence. Molecules that are similar in sequence among distantly related organisms are said to be evolutionarily conserved. Their similarity in sequence suggests that they were present in the most recent common ancestor and have changed very little over time because they carry out a vital function. Many transcription factors important in development are evolutionarily conserved. An impressive example is found in the development of animal eyes.

Animals have evolved a wide variety of eyes.

Animal eyes show an amazing diversity in their development and anatomy (**Fig. 20.16**). Among the simplest eyes are those of the planarian flatworm (Fig. 20.16a), which are only pit-shaped cells containing light-sensitive photoreceptors. The planarian eye has no lens to focus the light, but the animal can perceive differences in light intensity. The incorporation of a spherical lens, as in some jellyfish (Fig. 20.16b), improves the image.

Among the most complex eyes are the camera-type eyes of the squid (Fig. 20.16c) and human (Fig. 20.16d), which have a single

FIG. 20.16 Diversity of animal eyes.

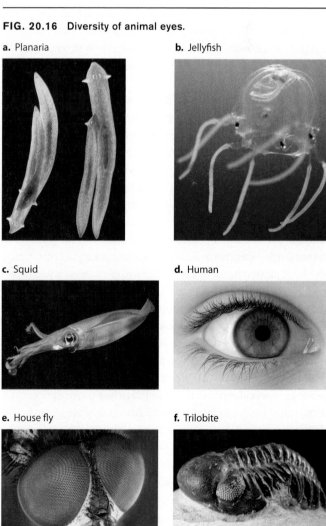

a. Planaria

b. Jellyfish

c. Squid

d. Human

e. House fly

f. Trilobite

lens to focus light onto a light-sensitive tissue, the retina (Chapter 36). Though the single-lens eyes of squids and vertebrates are similar in external appearance, they are vastly different in their development, anatomy, and physiology.

Some organisms, such as the house fly (Fig. 20.16e) and other insects, have compound eyes, that is, eyes consisting of hundreds of small lenses arranged on a convex surface pointing in slightly different directions. This arrangement of lenses allows a wide viewing angle and detection of rapid movement.

In the history of life, eyes are very ancient. By the time of the extraordinary diversification of animals 542 million years ago known as the Cambrian explosion, organisms such as trilobites (Fig. 20.16f) already had well-formed compound eyes. These differed greatly from the eyes in modern insects, however. For example, trilobite eyes had hard mineral lenses composed of calcium carbonate (the world's first safety glasses, so to speak). Altogether, about 96% of living animal species have true eyes that produce an image, as opposed to simply being able to detect differences in light intensity. Despite this common feature, the extensive diversity among the eyes of different organisms encouraged evolutionary biologists in the belief that the ability to perceive light may have evolved independently about 40 to 60 times.

Pax6 is a master regulator of eye development.

The diversity of animal eyes suggests that they may have evolved independently in different organisms. However, more recent evidence suggests an alternative hypothesis—that they evolved once, very early in evolution and subsequently diverged over time. One argument against the idea of multiple independent origins for light perception is the observation that the light-sensitive molecule in all light-detecting cells is the same, a derivative of vitamin A complexed with a protein called opsin (Chapter 36). The presence of the same light-sensitive molecule in diverse eyes argues that it may have been present in the common ancestor of all animals with eyes and has been retained over time.

Another argument against multiple independent origins of eyes came from studies of eye development. Researchers identified *eyeless,* a gene in the fruit fly *Drosophila.* As its name implies, the phenotype of *eyeless* mutants is abnormal eye development (**Fig. 20.17a**). When the protein product of the *eyeless* gene was identified, it was found to be a transcription factor called Pax6. Mutant forms of a *Pax6* gene were already known to cause small eyes in the mouse (**Fig. 20.17b**) and aniridia (absence of the iris) in humans.

The mutations in the *Pax6* gene that cause the development defects in the eye in fruit flies, mice, and humans are **loss-of-function mutations.** A loss-of-function mutation is just that: a mutation that inactivates the normal function of a gene. In this case, loss-of-function mutations in *Pax6* make a defective version of the Pax6 transcription factor that is not able to carry out its function.

The strong conservation of Pax6 in *Drosophila* and mouse and the similarity in their mutant phenotypes led Swiss developmental

FIG. 20.17   Effect of Pax6 mutations on eye development.
(a) Normal and *eyeless* mutant in *Drosophila;* (b) normal and *small eye* mutant in mouse.

Normal	Mutant

a. *Drosophila*

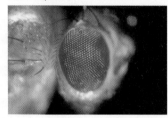 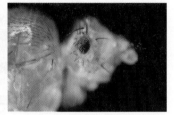

b. Mouse

biologist Walter Gehring to hypothesize that Pax6 might be a master regulator of eye development. In other words, he hypothesized that Pax6 binds to regulatory regions of a set of genes that turns on a developmental program that induces eye development. In theory, this means that Pax6 can induce the development of an eye in any tissue in which it is expressed.

To test this hypothesis, Gehring and collaborators genetically engineered fruit flies that would produce the normal Pax6 transcription factor in the antenna, where it is not normally expressed (**Fig. 20.18a**). Any mutation in which a gene is expressed in the wrong place or at the wrong time is known as a **gain-of-function mutation.** (We saw an example of gain-of-function mutations when the *Hox* genes were expressed in the wrong segments of the fruit fly, producing legs where antennae normally develop and thus resulting in four-winged fruit flies.) For genes that control a developmental pathway, loss-of-function mutations and gain-of-function mutations often have opposite effects on phenotype.

→   **Quick Check 5** For genes that control pathways of development, loss-of-function mutations are usually recessive whereas gain-of-function mutations are usually dominant. Can you suggest a reason why?

Since loss-of-function mutations in *Pax6* result in an eyeless phenotype, a gain-of-function mutation should result in eyes developing in whatever tissue *Pax6* is expressed. The result is shown in **Fig. 20.18b**. In the gain-of-function mutation, the antenna developed into a miniature compound eye, and electrical recordings demonstrated that some of these antennal eyes were

FIG. 20.18 Pax6, a master switch controlling eye development.
(a) Normal fly antenna; (b) eye tissue induced by expression of fruit fly *Pax6* in the antenna; (c) eye tissue induced by expression of mouse *Pax6* in the antenna.

 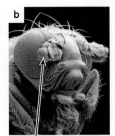 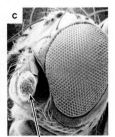

Normal antenna

Antennal eye induced by *Drosophila Pax6* gene

Antennal eye induced by mouse *Pax6* gene

functional. The researchers also created other gain-of-function mutations that led to eyes on the legs, wings, and other tissues, which the *New York Times* publicized in an article headlined "With New Fly, Science Outdoes Hollywood."

Gehring and his group then went one step further. They took the *Pax6* gene from mice and expressed it in fruit flies to see whether the mouse *Pax6* gene is similar enough to the fruit fly version of the gene that it could induce eye development in the fruit fly. Specifically, they created transgenic fruit flies that expressed the *Pax6* gene from mice in the fruit fly antenna. The result is shown in **Fig. 20.18c**. The mouse gene induced a miniature eye in the fly. Note, however, that the *Pax6* gene from mice induced the development of a compound eye of *Drosophila*, not the single-lens eye of mouse.

The ability of mouse Pax6 to make an eye in fruit flies suggests that mouse and fruit fly *Pax6* are not only similar in DNA and amino acid sequence, but also similar in function, and indeed act as a master switch that can turn on a developmental program leading to the formation of an eye. But these observations lead to another question: Why did the mouse *Pax6* gene produce fruit fly eyes instead of mouse eyes? The answer is that the fruit fly genome does not include the genes needed to make mouse eyes. Mouse Pax6 protein induces fly eyes because of the **downstream genes** affected by Pax6, those that function later in the process of eye development. Transcription factors like Pax6 interact with their target genes by binding with short DNA sequences adjacent to the gene, usually at the 5′ end, called **cis-regulatory elements.** Some transcription factors act as repressors that prevent transcription of the target gene, and others serve as activators by recruiting the transcriptional machinery to the target gene (Chapter 19). A transcription factor can even repress some of its target genes and activate others.

In the fruit fly, Pax6 binds to cis-regulatory elements in many genes, turning some genes on and others off. The products

of these downstream genes in turn affect the expression of further downstream genes. The total number of genes that are downstream of Pax6 and that are needed for eye development is estimated at about 2000. Most are not direct targets of Pax6 but are activated indirectly through other transcription factors downstream of Pax6. When mouse Pax6 is expressed in fruit flies, it is similar enough in sequence to activate the genes involved in fruit fly eye development, so it makes sense that mouse Pax6 leads to the development of a fruit fly eye, not a mouse eye.

One scenario of how Pax6 became a master switch for eye development in a wide range of organisms, but produces a diversity of eyes in these organisms, is that Pax6 evolved early in the history of life as a transcription factor able to bind to and regulate genes involved in early eye development. Over time, different genes in different organisms acquired new Pax6-binding cis-regulatory elements by mutation, and if these were beneficial they persisted. The downstream genes that are targets of Pax6 therefore are different in different organisms, but they share two features—they are regulated by Pax6 and they are involved in eye development. So, the early steps are conserved, but the later ones are not.

These studies of Pax6 argue that the genetic pathway for eye development evolved early and is shared among a wide range of animals, even though the eyes that are produced are quite diverse.

20.4 COMBINATORIAL CONTROL IN DEVELOPMENT

Most cis-regulatory elements are located near one or more binding sites for transcription factors, some of which are activators of transcription and others repressors of transcription. The rate of transcription of any gene in any type of cell is therefore determined by the combination of transcription factors that are present in the cell and by the relative balance of activators and repressors. Regulation of gene transcription according to the mix of transcription factors in the cell is known as **combinatorial control.** Combinatorial control of transcription is another general principle often seen in all multicellular organisms at many stages of development. Here, we discuss flower development as an example of this general principle.

Floral differentiation is a model for plant development.

The plant *Arabidopsis thaliana*, a weed commonly called mouse-ear cress, is a model organism for developmental studies and presents a clear case of combinatorial control. As in all plants, *Arabidopsis* has regions of undifferentiated cells, called meristems, where growth can take place (Chapter 31). Meristem cells are similar to stem cells in animals. They are the growing points where shoots, roots, and flowers are formed. In floral meristems of *Arabidopsis*, the flowers develop from a pattern of four concentric circles, or whorls, of cells.

FIG. 20.19 Development of the *Arabidopsis* floral organs from concentric whorls of cells in the floral meristem.

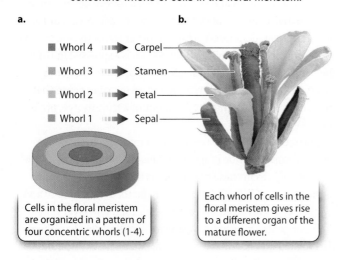

Cells in the floral meristem are organized in a pattern of four concentric whorls (1-4).

Each whorl of cells in the floral meristem gives rise to a different organ of the mature flower.

From the outermost whorl (whorl 1) of cells to the innermost whorl (whorl 4), the floral organs are formed as shown in **Fig. 20.19**:

- Cells in whorl 1 form the green sepals, which are modified leaves forming a protective sheath around the petals in the flower bud that unfold like petals when the flower opens.

- Cells in whorl 2 form the petals.

- Cells in whorl 3 form the stamens, the male sexual structures in which pollen is produced. (The small yellow granules in Fig. 20.19b are pollen grains.)

- Cells in whorl 4 form the carpels, the female reproductive structures that receive pollen and contain the ovaries.

The identity of the floral organs is determined by combinatorial control.

The genetic control of flower development in *Arabidopsis* was discovered by the analysis of mutant plants, an investigation similar in principle to the way that genetic control of development in fruit flies was determined. The plant mutants fell into three classes showing characteristic floral abnormalities (**Fig. 20.20**). Mutations in the gene *APETALA-2* inactivate the gene's function and affect whorls 1 and 2 (Fig. 20.20b), those in *APETALA-3* or *PISTILLATA* affect whorls 2 and 3 (Fig. 20.20c), and those in *AGAMOUS* affect whorls 3 and 4 (Fig. 20.20d). (There are different standards for naming genes and proteins in different organisms. In *Arabidopsis*, wild-type alleles are written in capital letters with italics, and wild-type proteins in capital letters without italics. Mutant alleles and proteins follow the same rules, but are written in lower-case letters.)

The observation that the mutant phenotypes affect development of pairs of adjacent whorls already hints at combinatorial control, which researchers incorporated into a model of floral development called the **ABC model.** The model invokes three activities arbitrarily called A, B, and C. These activities represent the function of a protein or proteins that is hypothesized to be present in cells of each whorl as shown in **Fig. 20.21**. The A activity is present in whorls 1 and 2, B in whorls 2 and 3, and C in whorls 3 and 4. According to the ABC model, activity of A alone results in the formation of sepals, A and B together result in petals, B and C together result in stamens, and C alone results in carpels. Like any good hypothesis (Chapter 1), this one makes specific predictions. Mutants lacking A will have defects

FIG. 20.20 Phenotypes of the normal and floral mutants of *Arabidopsis*.

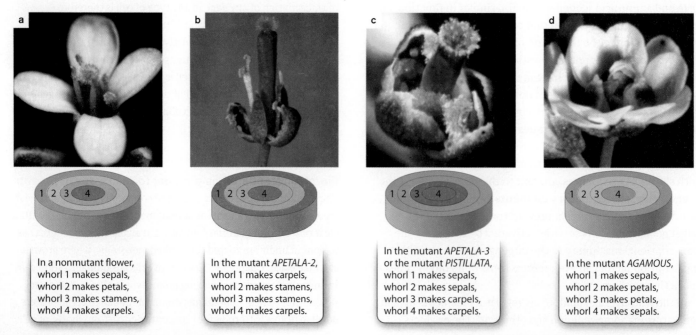

In a nonmutant flower, whorl 1 makes sepals, whorl 2 makes petals, whorl 3 makes stamens, whorl 4 makes carpels.

In the mutant *APETALA-2*, whorl 1 makes carpels, whorl 2 makes stamens, whorl 3 makes stamens, whorl 4 makes carpels.

In the mutant *APETALA-3* or the mutant *PISTILLATA*, whorl 1 makes sepals, whorl 2 makes sepals, whorl 3 makes carpels, whorl 4 makes carpels.

In the mutant *AGAMOUS*, whorl 1 makes sepals, whorl 2 makes petals, whorl 3 makes petals, whorl 4 makes sepals.

FIG. 20.21 The ABC model for flower development in *Arabidopsis*.

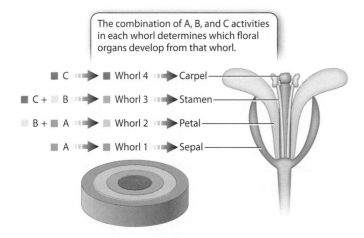

The combination of A, B, and C activities in each whorl determines which floral organs develop from that whorl.

C ➡ Whorl 4 ➡ Carpel

C + B ➡ Whorl 3 ➡ Stamen

B + A ➡ Whorl 2 ➡ Petal

A ➡ Whorl 1 ➡ Sepal

in whorls 1 and 2, mutants lacking B will have defects in whorls 2 and 3, and mutants lacking C will have defects in whorls 3 and 4.

Matching these predictions with the mutants in Fig. 20.20 yields the following correspondence:

- The A activity is encoded by the gene *APETALA-2*.

- The B activity is encoded jointly by the genes *APETALA-3* and *PISTILLATA*.

- The C activity is encoded by the gene *AGAMOUS*.

To account for the mutant phenotypes in Fig. 20.20, you need only to postulate that when A is absent, C is expressed in whorls 1 and 2 in addition to its normal expression in whorls 3 and 4; and when C is absent, A expression expands into whorls 3 and 4 in addition to its normal expression in whorls 1 and 2. The domains of expression expand in this way because, in addition to its role in activating certain downstream genes, the product of *APETALA-2* represses the expression of *AGAMOUS* in whorls 1 and 2. As a result, *AGAMOUS* is normally not expressed in whorls 1 and 2. Similarly, in addition to its role in activating other genes, the product of *AGAMOUS* represses the expression of *APETALA-2* in whorls 3 and 4, so *APETALA-2* is normally not expressed in whorls 3 and 4.

→ **Quick Check 6** Predict the phenotype of a flower in which *APETALA-2* (activity A) and *AGAMOUS* (activity C) are expressed normally, but *APETALA-3* and *PISTILLATA* (activity B) are expressed in all four whorls.

The identification of the products of these genes demonstrates combinatorial control and explains the mutant phenotypes. All of the genes encode transcription factors, which are called AP2, AP3, PI, and AG, corresponding to the four genes. The transcription factors bind to cis-regulatory elements of genes that encode proteins necessary for each whorl's development, similar to what we saw earlier for Pax6 and eye development. AP3 and PI are both necessary for the B activity

because the proteins form a heterodimer, a protein made up of two different subunits.

Although other transcription factors associated with activities D and E that also contribute to flower development were discovered later, the original ABC model is still valid and serves as an elegant example of combinatorial control. As in the case of the *Pax6* gene in the development of animals' eyes, evolution of the cis-regulatory sequences in downstream genes has resulted in a wide variety of floral morphologies in different plant lineages, some of which are shown in **Fig. 20.22**.

20.5 CELL SIGNALING IN DEVELOPMENT

As we have seen in the discussion of stem cells, differentiated cells can be reprogrammed by the action of only a few key genes or small organic molecules. In some cases, the processes that push differentiation in a forward direction are also quite simple. An important example is **signal transduction,** in which an extracellular molecule acts as a signal to activate a membrane protein that in turn activates molecules inside the cell that control differentiation (Chapter 9). The signaling molecule is called the **ligand** and the membrane protein that it activates is called the **receptor.** The following example shows how a simple receptor–ligand pair can

FIG. 20.22 Floral diversity. (a) Colorado blue columbine (*Aquilegia coaerulea*); (b) slipper orchid (*Paphiopedilum holdenii*); (c) ginger flower (*Smithatris supraneanae*); (d) garden rose (hybrid).

have profound effects not only on the differentiation of the cell that carries the receptor but also on its neighbors.

A signaling molecule can cause multiple responses in the cell.

Pioneering experiments on signal transduction in development were carried out in the soil nematode *Caenorhabditis elegans* (**Fig. 20.23**). This worm is a favored model organism for developmental studies because of its small size (the adult is about 1 millimeter long), short generation time (2½ days from egg to sexually mature adult), and stereotyped process of development. (A stereotyped process is one that is always the same.) The adult animal consists of exactly 959 somatic (body) cells, and the cells' patterns of division, migration, differentiation, and morphogenesis are identical in each individual *C. elegans*. The adult is typically a hermaphrodite that produces both male and female reproductive cells. The eggs are fertilized internally by sperm, and, after undergoing five or six cell divisions, the eggs are laid through an organ known as the vulva (Fig. 20.23).

Vulva development is relatively simple and therefore amenable to experimental studies. The entire structure arises from only three cells that undergo either of two types of differentiation and divide to produce a vulva consisting of exactly 22 cells. Cells resulting from type 1 differentiation form the opening of the vulva, and cells resulting from type 2 differentiation form a supporting structure around the vulval opening. In each of the two types of differentiation, different genes are activated or repressed, resulting in differentiated cells with different functions.

How each of the three original cells, called progenitor cells, differentiates is determined by its position in the developing worm (**Fig. 20.24**). The fate of the progenitor cells is determined by their proximity to another cell, called the anchor cell (AC in Fig. 20.24a), which secretes a protein called epidermal growth factor (EGF) that binds to and activates a transmembrane EGF

receptor (Chapter 9). The progenitor cell closest to the anchor cell receives the most amount of signal, and upon activation of its EGF receptor the progenitor cell carries out three functions:

- It activates the genes for differentiation into a type 1 cell (Fig. 20.24a)

- It prevents the adjacent cells from differentiating as type 1 (a process called **lateral inhibition**).

- It induces the adjacent cells to differentiate as type 2 cells.

Developmental signals are amplified and expanded.

How can a single ligand–receptor pair cause so many changes in gene expression that it determines the pathway of differentiation not only of the cell itself but also of its neighbors? **Fig. 20.25** shows the mechanisms in simplified form. On the left is the progenitor cell nearest the anchor cell, which receives the strongest EGF signal. Activation of the EGF receptor by the ligand initiates a process of signal transduction in the cytoplasm, in which the signal is transmitted from one protein to the next by means of phosphorylation, which amplifies the signal at each

---

FIG. 20.24 Vulval development in *Caenorhabditis elegans*. The cells of the vulva differentiate in response to molecular signals from other cells.

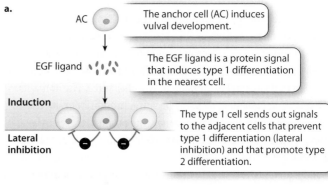
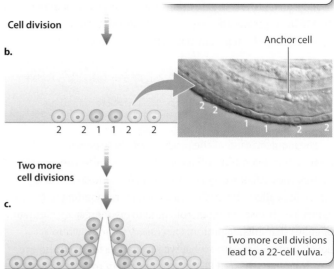

a.

AC — The anchor cell (AC) induces vulval development.

EGF ligand — The EGF ligand is a protein signal that induces type 1 differentiation in the nearest cell.

Induction

Lateral inhibition — The type 1 cell sends out signals to the adjacent cells that prevent type 1 differentiation (lateral inhibition) and that promote type 2 differentiation.

Cell division

b.

2   2   1   1   2   2

Anchor cell

Two more cell divisions

c.

Two more cell divisions lead to a 22-cell vulva.

FIG. 20.23 The nematode worm *Caenorhabditis elegans*.

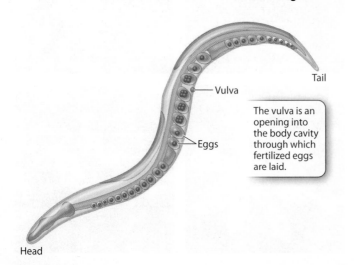

Tail

Vulva

The vulva is an opening into the body cavity through which fertilized eggs are laid.

Eggs

Head

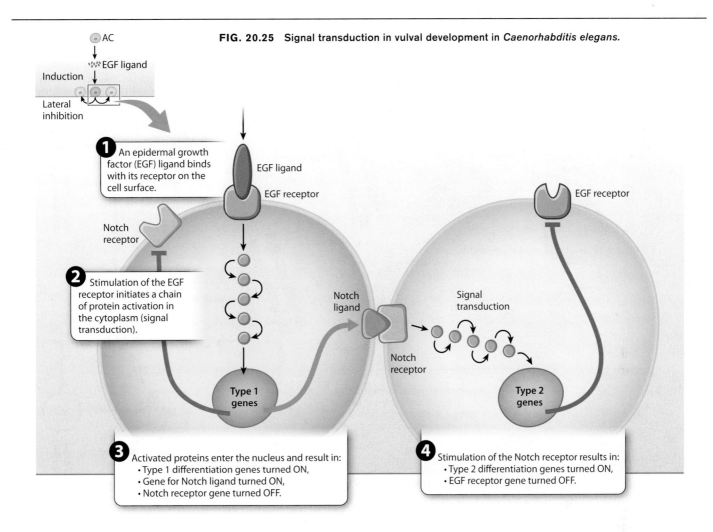

FIG. 20.25 Signal transduction in vulval development in *Caenorhabditis elegans*.

AC

EGF ligand

Induction

Lateral inhibition

1 An epidermal growth factor (EGF) ligand binds with its receptor on the cell surface.

EGF ligand

EGF receptor

Notch receptor

2 Stimulation of the EGF receptor initiates a chain of protein activation in the cytoplasm (signal transduction).

Notch ligand

Notch receptor

EGF receptor

Signal transduction

Type 1 genes

Type 2 genes

3 Activated proteins enter the nucleus and result in:
• Type 1 differentiation genes turned ON,
• Gene for Notch ligand turned ON,
• Notch receptor gene turned OFF.

4 Stimulation of the Notch receptor results in:
• Type 2 differentiation genes turned ON,
• EGF receptor gene turned OFF.

stage (Chapter 9). The result of signal transduction is that a set of transcription factors is activated.

In the nucleus, the transcription factors activate transcription of genes for type 1 differentiation. The transcription factors also activate transcription of genes that produce another type of protein ligand, called Notch. The Notch ligand is a transmembrane protein that activates Notch receptors in the neighboring cells. Activation of the Notch receptor in these cells activates another signal transduction cascade, which results in transcription of the genes for type 2 differentiation. The cascade started by the binding of Notch also activates transcription of other genes whose products inhibit the EGF receptor. Inhibiting the EGF receptor in type 2 cells prevents EGF from eliciting a type 1 response in the type 2 cell. In addition, at the same time that the Type 1 cell produces the Notch ligand, it produces proteins that inhibit its own Notch receptors, and this prevents Notch from initiating a type 2 response in the type 1 cell.

While vulva development in nematodes is a fairly simple example of the importance of ligand–receptor signaling in development, EGF and Notch ligands and their receptors are found in virtually all animals. They are among dozens of ligand–receptor pairs that have evolved as signaling mechanisms to regulate processes in cellular metabolism and development.

Humans have several distinct but related gene families of EGF and Notch ligands and receptors. Human EGF is important in cell survival, proliferation, and differentiation. EGF functions in the differentiation and repair of multiple types of cells in the skin; it is present in all body fluids and helps regulate rapid metabolic responses to changing conditions. Human Notch ligands are involved in development of the nervous and immune systems as well as heart, pancreas, and bone. Abnormalities in EGF or Notch signaling are associated with many different types of cancer.

Therefore, just as we saw in our discussion of eye and flower development, the molecular players involved in development are often evolutionarily conserved across a wide range of organisms. This is true even of genes that we typically associate with disease, such as *BRCA1* and *BRCA2* and their link with cancer. These genes not only play a role in cell cycle control in the adult, but also in early development in many organisms. In fact, although heterozygous mutations in these genes predispose to breast and ovarian cancers in humans, homozygous mutations are lethal in early embryonic stages. We focus on the *BRCA1* gene to summarize key concepts about DNA replication, mutation, genetic variation, inheritance, gene regulation, and development in **Fig. 20.26**.

Gene expression

FIG. 20.26

BRCA1 Genetics

The *BRCA1* gene on chromosome 17 encodes a protein that repairs double-strand breaks in DNA that result from DNA replication or environmental agents. The *BRCA1* gene is present in all cells, but is expressed, or turned on, in rapidly dividing cells, including breast and ovarian cells. If *BRCA1* does not function properly due to a mutation, damaged DNA is not repaired, which in turn increases the risk for certain kinds of cancers, particularly breast and ovarian cancers in women.

Genetic variation:
Everyone carries two copies of the *BRCA1* gene on chromosome 17. Some individuals have an allele of the gene that increases the risk of breast and ovarian cancer. In some populations, such as Ashkenazi Jews, the frequency of specific mutations in the gene is high.

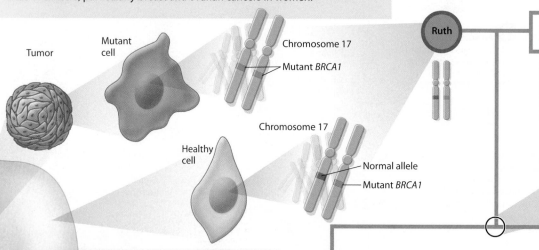

Tumor

Mutant cell

Chromosome 17

Mutant *BRCA1*

Chromosome 17

Healthy cell

Normal allele

Mutant *BRCA1*

Ruth

Isaac

Mutation:
This individual inherits one mutation in the *BRCA1* and is heterozygous. In one cell or a few of her cells, a new mutation is acquired in the normal *BRCA1* gene, and these cells go on to be cancerous.

Genotype and phenotype:
For a woman with a mutation in *BRCA1*, the risk of breast cancer by age 40 is 37%; by age 55, 66%; and by age 80, 85%.

Susan

Ben

Sarah

Testing and Ethical issues

DNA testing can be used to determine whether or not a person carries an allele of a gene that increases the risk of a disease, but it also raises questions and ethical issues. In 2008, the Genetic Information Nondiscrimination Act (GINA) was passed to protect individuals from discrimination by insurance companies or employers based on genetic profile.

DNA testing can be used to determine whether any of these individuals carry a mutation in the *BRCA1* gene.
If any individual in this family gets a positive result, everyone else can figure out their risk of carrying the mutation.
If an individual tests positive, what should he or she do?
What happens if an individual finds a mutation in the *BRCA1* gene which is not known to be associated with cancer?

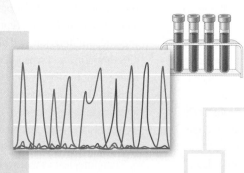

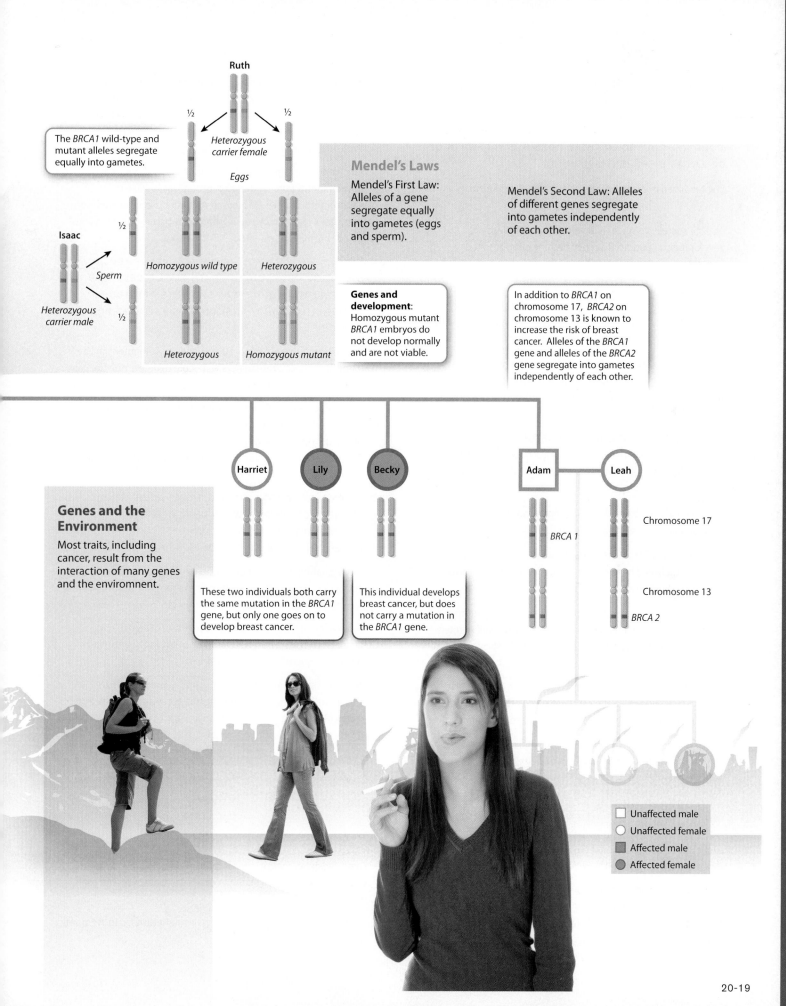

Ruth

½ ½

Heterozygous carrier female

The *BRCA1* wild-type and mutant alleles segregate equally into gametes.

Eggs

Isaac

½

Sperm

½

Heterozygous carrier male

Homozygous wild type

Heterozygous

Heterozygous

Homozygous mutant

Mendel's Laws

Mendel's First Law: Alleles of a gene segregate equally into gametes (eggs and sperm).

Mendel's Second Law: Alleles of different genes segregate into gametes independently of each other.

Genes and development: Homozygous mutant *BRCA1* embryos do not develop normally and are not viable.

In addition to *BRCA1* on chromosome 17, *BRCA2* on chromosome 13 is known to increase the risk of breast cancer. Alleles of the *BRCA1* gene and alleles of the *BRCA2* gene segregate into gametes independently of each other.

Genes and the Environment

Most traits, including cancer, result from the interaction of many genes and the enviromnent.

Harriet | Lily | Becky | Adam | Leah

Chromosome 17

BRCA 1

These two individuals both carry the same mutation in the *BRCA1* gene, but only one goes on to develop breast cancer.

This individual develops breast cancer, but does not carry a mutation in the *BRCA1* gene.

Chromosome 13

BRCA 2

☐ Unaffected male
◯ Unaffected female
▣ Affected male
⬤ Affected female

Core Concepts Summary

20.1 IN THE DEVELOPMENT OF HUMANS AND OTHER ANIMALS, STEM CELLS BECOME PROGRESSIVELY MORE RESTRICTED IN THEIR POSSIBLE PATHWAYS OF CELLULAR DIFFERENTIATION.

The fertilized egg can give rise to a complete organism. page 20-2

At each successive stage in development, cells lose developmental potential as they become differentiated. page 20-2

Embryonic stem cells can give rise to any of the three germ layers, those further along in differentiation can form only a limited number of specialized cell types, and those still further along can form only one cell type. page 20-2

Stem cells play a prominent role in regenerative medicine, which uses stem cells—in some cases reprogrammed cells from the patient's own body—to replace diseased or damaged tissues. page 20-5

20.2 THE GENETIC CONTROL OF DEVELOPMENT IS A HIERARCHY IN WHICH GENES ARE DEPLOYED IN GROUPS THAT IN TURN REGULATE THE NEXT SET OF GENES.

Hierarchical gene control can be seen in fruit fly (*Drosophila*) development. page 20-5

The oocyte of a fruit fly is highly polarized, with gradients of mRNA established by the mother that set up anterior–posterior and dorsal–ventral axes. page 20-6

These gradients in turn affect the expression of segmentation genes in the zygote, including the gap, pair-rule, and segment-polarity genes, which define specific regions in the developing embryo. page 20-8

The segmentation genes direct the expression of homeotic genes, key transcription factors that specify the identity of each segment of the fly and that are conserved in animal development. page 20-9

20.3 MANY PROTEINS THAT PLAY KEY ROLES IN DEVELOPMENT ARE EVOLUTIONARILY CONSERVED BUT CAN HAVE DRAMATICALLY DIFFERENT EFFECTS IN DIFFERENT ORGANISMS.

Many proteins important in development are similar in sequence from one organism to the next. They are said to be evolutionarily conserved. page 20-11

The downstream targets, or cis-regulatory elements, of homeotic genes are different in different animals, allowing homeotic genes to activate different developmental pathways in different organisms. page 20-12

Although animals exhibit an enormous diversity in eye morphology, the observation that the proteins involved in light perception are evolutionarily conserved suggests that the ability to perceive light may have evolved once, early in the evolution of animals. page 20-12

The Pax6 transcription factor is a master regulator of eye development. Loss-of-function mutations in *Pax6* result in abnormalities in eye development, whereas gain-of-function mutations result in eye development in tissues in which eyes do not normally form. page 20-12

20.4 COMBINATORIAL CONTROL IS A DEVELOPMENTAL STRATEGY IN WHICH THE PATHWAY OF CELLULAR DIFFERENTIATION DEPENDS ON THE PARTICULAR COMBINATION OF TRANSCRIPTION FACTORS PRESENT IN A CELL.

By analyzing mutants that affect flower development in the plant *Arabidopsis*, researchers were able to determine the genes involved in normal flower development. page 20-13

The ABC model of flower development invokes three activities (A, B, and C) present in circular regions (whorls) of the developing flower, with the specific combination of factors determining the developmental pathway in each whorl. page 20-14

20.5 LIGAND–RECEPTOR INTERACTIONS ACTIVATE SIGNAL TRANSDUCTION PATHWAYS THAT CONVERGE ON TRANSCRIPTION FACTORS AND OTHER GENES THAT DETERMINE CELL FATE.

Cell signaling involves a ligand, an extracellular molecule that acts as a signal to activate a membrane receptor protein, which in turn activates molecules inside the cell. page 20-15

Activation of a receptor sets off a pathway of signal transduction, in which a series of proteins in the cytoplasm become sequentially activated. page 20-16

Because signal transduction can amplify and expand a developmental signal, a single ligand–receptor pair can cause major changes in gene expression and ultimately determine the pathway of differentiation. page 20-16

An example of signal transduction in development is differentiation of the nematode vulva, which is determined by means of an EGF ligand and receptor. page 20-16

Self-Assessment

1. Distinguish among totipotent, pluripotent, and multipotent stem cells, and give an example of where you would find each type of cell.

2. Explain how an individual's own cells might be used in stem cell therapy.

3. Draw a diagram to illustrate how overlapping domains of gap-gene expression along the anterior–posterior axis of a *Drosophila* embryo can create a series of segments, each expressing a unique combination of gap genes.

4. Explain the role of homeotic genes in *Drosophila* development, and describe one phenotype in *Drosophila* resulting from a mutation in a homeotic gene that leads to development of a body part in an inappropriate segment.

5. Explain why some genes, particularly those involved in the early stages of development, are evolutionarily conserved.

6. Define combinatorial control in the context of the ABC model of floral development.

7. Diagram a pathway of signal transduction including a ligand, receptor, and ultimately a transcription factor that activates a gene that inhibits the receptor.

Do you understand the chapter's Core Concepts? Log into BIO*PORTAL* to check your answers to the Self-Assessment questions, then practice what you've learned and reinforce this chapter's concepts by working through the problems and multimedia tutorials provided there.

📶 **http://courses.bfwpub.com/yourbioportal/index.php**

QUICK CHECK ANSWERS

Chapter 1

1. One hypothesis is that their tan fur protects the mice from predators by allowing them to blend in with their surroundings. To test this idea, you could devise an experiment in which dark and tan mice (or, to be more humane, artificial mice) are exposed to a predator, such as a hawk, on a variety of backgrounds. Do hawks preferentially attack dark mice on light sands and light mice on dark backgrounds?

2. One test would be to take two large populations of laboratory mice and introduce cigarette smoke into the cages of one population but not the other. Do mice subjected to smoke develop cancer at rates that are significantly higher than those of the control group? We can also make observations of human populations: Do smokers develop lung cancer at rates significantly higher than nonsmokers?

3. DNA directs the formation of proteins that do the cell's work. Mutations can result in proteins with altered structure and, therefore, different functions. Changes in protein function can cause the cell to work improperly, or fail altogether, resulting in some cases in disease.

4. The use of antibiotics selects for antibiotic resistance among bacteria. Bacteria do not become antibiotic resistant out of "need" or because resistance would be advantageous for them. Instead, before the application of antibiotics, bacteria with antibiotic resistance exist in low numbers. The application of antibiotics allows these bacteria to grow and reproduce more successfully than those that are susceptible to antibiotics. Mutations, such as those responsible for antibiotic resistance, are not influenced by whether or not the organism is in an environment in which that mutation would be advantageous.

Chapter 2

1. One conclusion is that atoms consist mainly of empty space, and hence most negatively charged particles passing through the gold foil do not come close enough to any positive charge to be deflected. Another conclusion is that the positively charged protons in the nucleus must be small and densely packed.

2. Hydrogen and lithium are in the same column, or group, in the periodic table. They both have one valence electron in their outer orbital. As a result, one atom of lithium combines with one atom of hydrogen to make lithium hydride, with a full complement of two electrons in the single molecular orbital.

3. Ice is less dense than liquid water. As a result, when water freezes it expands in volume and can burst closed containers, such as cans of soda or water pipes in houses. This property is unusual. For most substances, the solid phase is more dense than the liquid phase.

4. Glucose and galactose differ only in the orientation of the –OH and –H groups attached to carbon number 4.

Chapter 3

1. Because R = A or G, then %R = %A + %G; and because %A = %T and %G = %C, we can write %R = %A + %G = %T + %C. But T or C = Y, and so %T + %C = %Y. It follows that %R = %Y.

2. The RNA transcript has the sequence 5'–AUCGCUGAAAGU–3'.

3. The incorporation of a nucleotide with a 3' H rather than a 3' OH will stop subsequent elongation because the 3' OH is necessary to attack the high energy phosphate bond of the incoming nucleoside triphosphate. The incorporation of a nucleotide with a 2' H rather than a 2' OH will have no effect on elongation, as this group is not involved in the polymerization reaction.

4. The eukaryotic DNA sequence contains introns, which the bacterial cell cannot splice out properly, and so the correct protein is not produced from the information in the bacterial RNA transcript.

Chapter 4

1. The sequence of amino acids in a protein determines how a protein folds, so a change in even a single amino acid can affect the way the protein folds and can disrupt its function.

2. The three reading frames are

   UUU GGG UUU GGG…, which codes for repeating Phe–Gly–Phe–Gly…

   UUG GGU UUG GGU…, which codes for repeating Leu–Gly–Leu–Gly…

   UGG GUU UGG GUU…, which codes for repeating Trp–Val–Trp–Val…

3. With proper eukaryotic processing, the RNA transcript from the bacterial DNA will be capped at the 5' end. The initiation complex will form at the 5' cap and move along the mRNA until the first AUG codon is encountered, and then translation begins. When one of the termination codons is encountered, the polypeptide is released. Translation of the downstream polypeptides cannot take place because the Shine–Dalgarno sequences preceding them are not recognized by the eukaryotic translational machinery.

4. The eukaryotic DNA sequence contains introns, which the bacterial cell cannot splice out properly, and so the correct protein is not produced from the information in the bacterial RNA transcript.

Chapter 5

1. Saturated fatty acids have reduced membrane mobility compared to that of unsaturated fatty acids. As a result, fatty acids tend to be solid at room temperature, while unsaturated fatty acids tend to be liquid. Margarine and animal fats contain saturated fatty acids and are solid, while many plant and fish oils, containing unsaturated fatty acids, are liquid at room temperature.

2. Water molecules move in both directions, but the *net* movement of water molecules is from side A to side B. This process is called

osmosis: Water moves from regions of higher water concentration to regions of lower water concentration. Likewise, sodium and chloride ions move in both directions, but the *net* movement of sodium and chloride ions is from side B to side A. Movement of water and ions results from diffusion, the random motion of substances. Even when the concentration of all molecules is the same on the two sides, diffusion still occurs, but there is no net movement of water molecules or ions.

3. If the sodium-potassium pump is poisoned, cells tend to swell and even burst, as the extracellular fluid becomes hypotonic relative to the inside of the cell and water moves into the cell by osmosis.

Chapter 6

1. No, because the second law of thermodynamics applies to the universe as a whole. This means that we have to consider not just the air in the room but the heat released to the outdoors as well. An air conditioner produces more hot air than cold air, and therefore total entropy increases, as expected from the second law of thermodynamics.

2. Increasing the temperature increases the value of $T\Delta S$, which decreases ΔG, since $\Delta G = \Delta H - T\Delta S$. As a result, an increase in temperature makes it more likely that a reaction will proceed without a net input of energy.

3. Enzymes increase the reaction rate and decrease the activation energy. The other parameters are not changed by enzymes.

Chapter 7

1. The higher-energy forms are ATP, NADH, $FADH_2$, $C_6H_{12}O_6$, and reduced molecules; the lower-energy forms are ADP, NAD^+, FAD, CO_2, and corresponding oxidized molecules.

2. At the end of glycolysis, the energy in the original glucose molecule is contained in pyruvate, ATP, and NADH.

3. At the end of the citric acid cycle, the energy in the original glucose molecule is held in ATP, NADH, and $FADH_2$.

4. Oxygen is consumed in cellular respiration. Oxygen is the final electron acceptor and is converted to water in the electron transport chain.

5. Uncoupling agents decrease the proton gradient and therefore decrease the levels of ATP. The energy of the proton gradient is not used for oxidative phosphorylation, but instead is dissipated as heat. Uncoupling agents are found naturally in certain tissues, such as fat, for heat generation. They can also act as poisons.

6. Yeast cells are eukaryotes. In breadmaking, yeast use sugar as a food source for ethanol fermentation. The carbon dioxide produced in the process causes the bread to rise. The ethanol is removed in the baking process.

Chapter 8

1. You should label the oxygen in CO_2 (that is, inject $C^{18}O_2$) because the entire CO_2 molecule is combined with RuBP by rubisco, whereas H_2O is the electron donor needed for the reduction step of the Calvin cycle. The extraction of electrons from water releases O_2 as a by-product.

2. NADPH supplies the major input of energy that is used to synthesize carbohydrates in the Calvin cycle.

3. Antenna chlorophylls transfer absorbed light energy from one antenna chlorophyll molecule to another, and ultimately to the reaction center. Reaction center chlorophylls transfer absorbed light energy and a high-energy electron to an electron acceptor, resulting in the oxidation of the reaction center chlorophyll molecule.

4. The energy difference between the oxidation of water and the reduction of $NADP^+$ is greater than the amount of energy that can be harvested when a single photosystem absorbs light energy.

5. Rubisco faces a fundamental trade-off between selectivity and speed because it can use both CO_2 and O_2 as substrates. High selectivity of CO_2 over O_2 requires that the reaction have a high energy barrier, leading to a lower catalytic rate.

6. Like cellular respiration, photorespiration releases CO_2. Unlike photorespiration, it consumes rather than produces ATP.

Chapter 9

1. Only cells that have receptors for the hormone respond to the signal. Therefore, signaling can be specific for particular cells.

2. No. A G protein-coupled receptor is a transmembrane receptor protein, which interacts with another protein called a G protein located inside the cell on the cytoplasmic side of the plasma membrane.

3. The signal to increase heart rate carried by adrenaline can be reversed in at least four ways: (1) Decreasing the amounts of the signaling molecule available to bind and activate the G protein-coupled receptor; (2) inactivating the G protein; (3) decreasing the amount of second messenger cAMP; and (4) dephosphorylating the target proteins that caused the increased rate of contraction of the muscle cells.

Chapter 10

1. A defect in dynein would cause the melanin granules to remain dispersed since dynein transports the granules back toward the minus end of the microtubule during granule aggregation.

2. Adherens junctions form a belt around cells, whereas desmosomes are button-like attachments. In addition, adherens junctions connect to actin microfilaments, whereas desmosomes connect to intermediate filaments.

3. Tight junctions prevent the passage of materials through the space between cells. Gap junctions in animal cells and plasmodesmata in plant cells permit the exchange of materials between the cytoplasm

of adjacent cells.

4. Integrins are responsible for the production of milk proteins by mammary cells in response to the extracellular matrix because integrins bind extracellular matrix proteins. By contrast, cadherins bind to other cadherins when cells adhere to other cells.

Chapter 11

1. A mutation that disrupts the function of the FtsZ protein will block cell division.

2. Sister chromatids are the result of DNA replication during S phase, and so they have identical DNA sequences (with the exception of a few changes due to rare mutations). The two homologous chromosomes are inherited from two different parents. The DNA sequences of these chromosomes are therefore similar, but not identical.

3. A cell that undergoes mitosis but not cytokinesis will become a single cell with two nuclei (and therefore twice the normal amount of DNA); this type of cell is called a multinucleate cell.

4. In human cells at the end of prophase I, there are 92 chromatids, 46 centromeres, and 23 bivalents.

5. In meiosis I, homologous chromosomes pair, undergo crossing over, and segregate from each other. These events do not occur in mitosis. In mitosis, centromeres divide and sister chromatids separate, events that do not take place in meiosis I.

6. The products of meiosis are different from each other as a result of two key processes: (1) crossing over, which occurs at essentially random positions along the chromosomes and creates unique combinations of genetic differences that may be present in the maternal and paternal chromosomes, and (2) random orientation of the homologous chromosomes on the spindle in metaphase I, so each nucleus receives a random combination of maternal and paternal homologs.

7. The function of the p53 protein can be disrupted by a mutation in the *p53* gene. Alternatively, certain viral proteins, such as the E6 protein of HPV discussed in Case 2: Cancer, can interfere with the function of p53.

8. An oncogene causes cancer by producing an excess of protein activity that pushes the cell to divide. A tumor suppressor like p53 functions oppositely. Its normal function is to prevent cell division and its absence is what allows the cell to divide uncontrollably.

Chapter 12

1. After one round of replication, you would predict only $^{14}N/^{15}N$ hybrid DNA, which has a density of 1.708 gm/cm³. After two rounds of replication, you would predict half the molecules to be $^{14}N/^{15}N$ hybrid (density 1.708 gm/cm³) and half to be $^{15}N/^{15}N$ heavy (density 1.722 gm/cm³).

2. There are many possible reasons that might explain the absence of a band following PCR and gel electrophoresis. The DNA

polymerase might be defective or have low activity, or you may have inadvertently left out one of the components of the reaction, or the primer sequences might have been incorrect so that there was not a complementary sequence for them to anneal to, or you may have connected the positive and negative leads to the wrong ends of the gel box so that the products ran off the top of the gel.

3. The sequence of the template strand is antiparallel to the synthesized strand and inferred from complementary base pairing as 5'-ACTCGGTAGT-3'.

4. The value of sticky ends is that they give the researcher greater control over which restriction fragments can come together and be attached. Sticky ends can pair only with other sticky ends that have complementary 3' and 5' overhangs. Hence, restriction fragments produced by *Bam*HI can combine only with other fragments produced by *Bam*HI, and not with fragments produced by *Hind*III, for example. However, any blunt end can be attached to any other blunt end, for example, a *Hpa*I end to a *Sma*I end.

Chapter 13

1. DNA sequencing technology is limited to DNA molecules that are less than about 1000 nucleotides, so the challenge of genome sequencing is the size of many genomes, which can far exceed 1000 nucleotides. Sequencing whole genomes required a method of piecing together smaller sequenced DNA fragments.

2. Even when short repeated sequences can be sequenced, there is an assembly problem similar to that for longer repeats in which the researcher has no way of knowing where in the repeat any particular sequenced fragment should be assigned. The result is that the total number of repeats remains unresolved. It could be in the hundreds, thousands, tens of thousands, hundreds of thousands, or even millions.

3. The observation that closely related lentiviruses have closely related host organisms suggests that each type of lentivirus can infect only one or a small number of closely related organisms.

4. You can't tell. The C-value paradox means that you cannot predict genome size from the complexity of the organism. In fact, the genome of an amoeba is much larger than the genome of a human.

Chapter 14

1. Mutant genes that are harmful or neutral are much less likely to persist in a population than ones that result in increased survival and reproduction because of greater fitness.

2. The number of nucleotides that are inserted or deleted is almost always an exact multiple of 3 because each codon in the genetic code consists of three nucleotides. Any insertion or deletion that includes a number of nucleotides that is not an exact multiple of 3 shifts the reading frame, and the resulting sequencing will most likely code for a nonfunctional protein.

3. Mutations are random; they are not directed by the environment. This does not mean that the environment cannot affect the *rate*

of mutation. Mutagens increase the rate of the mutation, but they cannot induce specific mutations that would be beneficial to the organism in response to the environment.

Chapter 15

1. Mutations that cause antibiotic resistance are clearly beneficial to bacteria when antibiotic is present, but are neutral or even harmful in the absence of antibiotic. The effect of a mutation on phenotype often depends on the environment.

2. Only a small fraction of the human genome codes for proteins or other functional elements (Chapter 13), so most mutations are neutral.

3. If the suspect is the actual source of a sample, then the DNA "fingerprints" must match exactly, and any mismatch rules out the suspect as the source of the sample. When there is a match, however, there is always a small chance (typically very small) that the sample came from another person with the same DNA "fingerprint."

4. In a VNTR, the restriction fragments are different lengths because of a variable number of repeats between restriction sites (one, two, three, four, or more). In a RFLP, the restriction fragments are different lengths because a restriction site is removed in one DNA sequence and not in another, making the distances between flanking sites different.

5. A point mutation is a change in a single nucleotide in an individual cell, such as C to G. A SNP results from a point mutation that occurred at some time in the past, so that now in the population there are two or more different single nucleotides at a given position. For example, some people might have C at a certain position and others might have G at that position.

6. Both Y chromosomes in the XYY baby must come from the father, so nondisjunction took place in the father. Consider now normal meiosis, shown in Fig. 15.12a, and suppose we let dark blue represent the X chromosome and light blue the Y chromosome. The first meiotic division separates the X chromosome from the Y chromosome, and the second meiotic division separates the sister chromatids of the X chromosome and the sister chromatids of the Y chromosome. For the Y chromosomes to remain together and be included in the same sperm, nondisjunction must take place in the second meiotic division (Fig. 15.12c).

Chapter 16

1. For the true-breeding plants with yellow seeds, the phenotype is yellow seeds, and the genotype is AA. For the true-breeding plants with green seeds, the phenotype is green seeds, and the genotype is aa.

2. Yes in both cases. When an allele is recessive, the homozygous dominant and heterozygous individuals have the same phenotype but different genotypes, as in AA and Aa plants. When a trait is influenced by the environment, individuals with the same genotype can have different phenotypes because of the environment. An example discussed in Chapter 15 is how smoking tobacco increases the severity of emphysema resulting from the PiZ allele of alpha-1 antitrypsin.

3. Half the progeny will have the AA genotype and half will have the Aa genotype. All the plants will have yellow seeds.

4. The probability that the first pea is green is ¼; the probability that the second pea is green is also ¼; the probability that the third pea is yellow is ¾; and the probability that the fourth pea is yellow is ¾. We use the multiplication rule (because these are mutually exclusive events) to figure out that the probability of this configuration is ¼ × ¼ × ¾ × ¾ = 9/256. There are six different ways that a pod of four seeds can have two green seeds and two yellow seeds (the green seeds can be in positions 1 and 2; 1 and 3; 1 and 4; 2 and 3; 2 and 4; or 3 and 4). Each of these configurations occurs with a probability of 9/256 (as previously described). The probability of *any* of these occurring (*either* one configuration *or* another *or* another) is given by the addition rule, or 9/256 + 9/256 + 9/256 + 9/256 + 9/256 + 9/256 = (9/256) × 6 = 54/256, or about 21%.

5. The F₁ chickens have white feathers because the dominant inhibitor allele I inhibits expression of the pigment allele C.

6. In the population as a whole, there are many copies of each chromosome, so any gene can have multiple alleles present in the different copies. Any one individual can have only two copies of any chromosome, and so any individual can have no more than two different alleles.

Chapter 17

1. A woman whose father is color blind must be heterozygous for the mutant allele. If she has children with a man who is color blind, then half of the female offspring are expected to be homozygous mutant and therefore color blind.

2. Even when one (or more) crossovers occurs between the genes, only two of the four products of meiosis are recombinant because crossing over takes place at the four-strand stage of meiosis (Fig. 17.10a). With two strands that are recombinant and two that are nonrecombinant, the frequency of recombination is 2/4 = 50%, and so this is the maximum.

3. Independent assortment means that a doubly heterozygous genotype like AB ab produces gametes in the ratio 1/4 AB, 1/4 Ab, 1/4 aB, 1/4 ab. The first and last are nonrecombinant gametes, and the second and third are recombinant gametes. The frequency of recombination is therefore 1/4 + 1/4 = 1/2, or 50%. This means that independent assortment is observed for genes that are far apart in the same chromosome as well as for genes in different chromosomes.

Chapter 18

1. No. Regression toward the mean simply indicates that, in any

population, parents with extreme phenotypes (very tall or very short, for example) will tend to have offspring that are closer to the average height of the population.

2. Let's consider some possibilities, some true, some false.

   a. In the development of fingerprint ridges in the embryo, genes play a predominant role.

   b. In the development of fingerprint ridges in the embryo, the environment plays only a minor role.

   c. Differences in the number of fingerprint ridges among individuals are determined largely by differences in genotype.

   d. Differences in the number of fingerprint ridges among individuals are almost unaffected by differences in the environment.

   e. The average number of fingerprint ridges in the offspring is not much different from the average number of fingerprint ridges in the parents.

   f. The average number of fingerprint ridges in the offspring is almost unrelated to the average number of fingerprint ridges in the parents.

   Statements a and b are false no matter what the heritability because heritability refers to differences (variation) among individuals and not to the phenotype of any one individual. High heritability implies that statements c, d, and e are all correct. Statement f is false because such a trait would have a low heritability.

3. The easier genes to detect are the few genes with large effects. The magnitude of gene effects that can be detected depends on the number of individuals studied. The larger the number, the smaller the effects that can be detected. Whatever the size of the study, however, the genes with the largest effects are always easier to detect, even though there may be few of them.

Chapter 19

1. Combinatorial control requires far fewer genes because there is not a one-to-one correspondence between the genes that are regulated and those that do the regulating. The products of a relatively small number of regulatory genes can be used in combination to control the expression of a far larger number of target genes. As an analogy, consider the virtually limitless combinations of sounds that can be played on a standard piano that has only 88 keys (36 black and 52 white).

2. Small regulatory RNAs are not translated into proteins (Chapter 3). As a result, they are often called noncoding RNAs since they do not encode for proteins. Their function is often to regulate the expression of other genes. By contrast, mRNAs are translated into proteins.

3. An activator turns on the expression of a gene directly by binding to DNA. An inducer binds a repressor, preventing the repressor from turning off the expression of a gene.

4. A mutation in the repressor gene that does not allow the repressor protein to bind allactose will lead to a cell that is not able to produce β-galactosidase, in the presence or absence of lactose. In other words, the lactose operon would not be inducible.

Chapter 20

1. A cell from the inner cell mass of a blastocyst has more developmental potential than a cell from the ectoderm, which is one of the three germ layers, because the blastocyst occurs earlier in development than the formation of the three germ layers.

2. In Chapter 19, we saw that many common traits result from an interaction of genes and the environment, and so even clones can look different from each other because of environmental influences. Furthermore, if the clone is produced by nuclear transplantation, as in the cases of Dolly and CopyCat, the nuclear genomes of clone and parent are identical, but their mitochondrial genomes are different.

3. Yes. The embryo would develop normally, even though the embryo does not have normal *bicoid* function, because *bicoid* is a maternal-effect gene, in which the mother's genotype affects the phenotype of the offspring.

4. The gap genes control the expression of the pair-rule genes, which in turn control the expression of segment-polarity genes. Therefore, if gap-gene expression is not normal, you would predict that segment-polarity gene expression would also not be normal.

5. Sexually reproducing organisms carry two copies of most genes, one from the mother and the other from the father. If either of these is knocked out by a loss-of-function mutation, the other is still present and compensates for the mutant. Hence, a loss-of-function mutation is expected to be recessive. In a gain-of-function mutation, one of the gene copies is expressed in the wrong amount, or the wrong tissue, or at the wrong time, and if such a gene turns on a developmental pathway, expression of only one copy of the gene is sufficient to turn the pathway on. Hence, a gain-of-function mutation in a gene that controls a developmental pathway is expected to be dominant.

6. Because A and B together result in petals, and B and C together result in stamens, a flower expressing B activity in all four whorls would have, from outside to inside, petals, petals, stamens, and stamens.

GLOSSARY

ABC model   A model of floral development that invokes three activities, A, B, and C, each of which represents the function of a protein or proteins hypothesized to be present in the cells of each whorl.

absolute temperature (T)   Temperature measured on the Kelvin scale.

accessory pigments   Pigments other than chlorophyll in the thylakoid membrane; carotenoids are important accessory pigments.

acidic   Describes a solution in which the concentration of protons is higher than that of hydroxide ions (the pH is lower than 7).

actin   A motor protein that make up microfilaments.

activated   The state of the receptor after binding the signaling molecule; the activated receptor transmits the information through the cytoplasm of the cell.

activation energy (E_A)   The energy input necessary to reach the transition state.

activators   Synthesized compounds that increase the activity of enzymes.

active site   The portion of the enzyme that binds substrate and converts it to product.

active transport   The "uphill" movement of substances against a concentration gradient.

addition rule   The principle that the probability of either of two mutually exclusive outcomes occurring is given by the sum of their individual probabilities.

adenine (A)   A purine base.

adenosine triphosphate (ATP)   The molecule that provides energy in a form that all cells can readily use to perform the work of the cell. ATP is the universal energy currency for all cells.

adherens junction   A beltlike junctional complex composed of cadherins that attaches a band of actin to the plasma membrane.

aldoses   Monosaccharides with an aldehyde group.

alleles   The different forms of a gene, corresponding to different DNA sequences in each different form.

allosteric effect   A change in shape, altering the binding affinity for DNA, that may occur when the activator protein combines with a small molecule in the cell.

allosteric enzymes   Enzymes that change their conformation on binding to a substrate, activator, or inhibitor. This change in shape influences the activity of the enzyme, either activating or inhibiting it.

alpha (α) carbon   The central carbon atom of each amino acid.

alpha (α) helix   One of the two principal types of secondary structure found in proteins.

alternative splicing   A process in which primary transcripts from the same gene can be spliced in different ways to yield different mRNAs and therefore different protein products.

amino acid replacement   A change in the identity of an amino acid at a particular site in a protein resulting from a mutation in the gene.

amino acids   Organic molecules containing a central carbon atom, a carboxyl group, an amino group, a hydrogen atom, and a side chain. Amino acids are the building blocks of proteins.

amino end   The end of a polypeptide chain that has a free amino group.

amino group NH_2; a nitrogen atom bonded to two hydrogen atoms, covalently linked to the central carbon atom of an amino acid.

aminoacyl (A) site   One of three binding sites for tRNA on the large subunit of a ribosome.

aminoacyl tRNA synthetases   Enzymes that attach specific amino acids to specific tRNA molecules.

amphipathic   Having both hydrophilic and hydrophobic regions.

amplified   In PCR technology, an alternative term for "replicated."

anabolism   The set of chemical reactions that build molecules from smaller units utilizing an input of energy, usually in the form of ATP.

anaphase   The stage of mitosis in which the sister chromatids separate.

anaphase I   The stage of meiosis I in which the two homologous chromosomes of each bivalent separate as they are pulled in opposite directions, but the sister chromatids remained joined at the centromere.

anaphase II   The stage of meiosis II in which the centromere of each chromosome splits and the separated chromatids are pulled toward opposite poles of the spindle.

anchors   Membrane proteins that attach to other proteins that help to maintain cell structure and shape.

annealing   The coming together of complementary strands of single-stranded nucleic acids by base pairing.

antiparallel   Oriented in opposite directions; the strands in a DNA duplex are antiparallel.

aquaporins   Protein channels that allow water to flow through the plasma membrane more readily by facilitated diffusion.

aqueous   Watery.

Archaea   One of the three domains of life, consisting of single-celled organisms without true chromosomes or a nucleus that divides by binary fission, differing from bacteria in many aspects of their cell and molecular biology.

asexual reproduction   The reproduction of cells or single-celled organisms by cell division.

atom   The basic unit of matter.

atomic mass   The mass of the atom determined by the number of protons and neutrons.

ATP synthase An enzyme that couples the movement of protons through the enzyme with the synthesis of ATP.

autocrine signaling Signaling between different parts of a cell; the signaling cell and the responding cell are one and the same.

autosomes Chromosomes other than the sex chromosomes.

autotrophs Organisms that are able to convert carbon dioxide into glucose, thus making their own organic sources of carbon.

Bacteria One of the three domains of life, consisting of single-celled organisms without true chromosomes or a nucleus that divide by binary fission, differing from archaeons in many aspects of their cell and molecular biology.

bacteriophages Viruses that attack bacterial cells.

bands Crosswise striations in chromosomes, or horizontal stripes in an electrophoresis gel.

basal lamina A specialized form of extracellular matrix that underlies and supports all epithelial tissues.

base A nitrogen-containing compound that makes up part of a nucleotide.

base excision pair A specialized repair system in which an improper DNA base and its sugar are both removed and the resulting gap is repaired.

base stacking Stabilizing interactions between bases in the same strand of DNA.

basic Describes a solution in which the concentration of protons is lower than that of hydroxide ions (the pH is higher than 7).

beta (β) sheet One of the two principal types of secondary structure found in proteins.

beta-(β-)oxidation The process of shortening fatty acids by a series of reactions that sequentially remove two carbon units from their ends.

bilayer A two-layered structure of the cell membrane with hydrophilic "heads" pointing outward toward the aqueous environment and hydrophobic "tails" oriented inward, away from water.

binary fission The process by which cells of bacteria or archaeons divide.

binding affinity The tightness of the binding between the receptor and the signaling molecule.

biologists Scientists who study life.

biology The science of life and how it works.

biparental inheritance A type of inheritance in which the organelles in the offspring cells derive from those in both parents.

bivalent The four-stranded structure consisting of two pairs of sister chromatids aligned along their length and held together by chiasmata.

blastocyst A hollow sphere produced by cells in the morula that move in relation to one another, pushing against and expanding the membrane that encloses them.

blending inheritance The now-discredited model in which heredity factors transmitted by the parents become intermingled in the offspring instead of retaining their individual genetic identities.

cadherins Calcium-dependent adherence proteins, important in the adhesion of cells to other cells.

Calvin cycle The process in which carbon dioxide is reduced to synthesize carbohydrates, with ATP and NADPH as the energy sources.

cancer A group of diseases characterized by uncontrolled cell division.

carbohydrates Organic molecules containing C, H, and O atoms that provide a source of energy for metabolism and that make up the cell wall in bacteria, plants, and algae.

carboxyl end The end of a polypeptide chain that has a free carboxyl group.

carboxyl group COOH; a carbon atom with a double bond to oxygen and a single bond to a hydroxyl group.

carboxylation The first step of the Calvin cycle, in which carbon dioxide absorbed from the air is added to a 5-carbon molecule.

carriers Transporters that facilitate movement of molecules.

catabolism The set of chemical reactions that break down molecules into smaller units and, in the process, produces ATP.

cell The simplest self-replicating entity that can exist as an independent unit of life.

cell adhesion molecules Cell-surface proteins that attach cells to one another and to the extracellular matrix.

cell cycle The collective name for the steps that make up eukaryotic cell division.

cell division The process by which cells make more cells.

cell plate In dividing plant cells, a new cell wall formed in the middle of the cell from the fusing of vesicles during late anaphase and telophase.

cell theory The theory that the cell is the fundamental unit of life in all organisms and that cells come only from preexisting cells.

cell wall A defining boundary in many organism, external to the cell membrane, that helps maintain the shape and internal composition of the cell.

cellular blastoderm In *Drosophila* development, the structure formed by the nuclei in the single-cell embryo when they migrate to the periphery of the embryo and each nucleus becomes enclosed in its own cell membrane.

cellular junctions Regions in the plasma membrane, consisting of cell adhesion molecules and other cytosolic proteins, where cells make contact with and adhere to other cells or the extracellular matrix.

cellular respiration A series of chemical reactions that convert the energy stored in nutrients into a chemical form that can be readily used by cells.

central dogma The theory that information transfer in a cell usually goes from DNA to RNA to protein.

centromere   A constriction that physically holds sister chromatids together; the site of the attachment of the spindle fibers that move the chromosome in cell division.

centrosome   A compact structure that is the microtubule organizing center for animal cells.

chain terminator   A term for a dideoxynucleotide, which if incorporated into a growing daughter strand stops strand growth because there is no hydroxyl group to attack the incoming nucleotide.

channels   Transporters with passages that allow the movement of molecules through them.

chaperones   Proteins that help shield slow-folding proteins until they can attain their proper three-dimensional structure.

checkpoint   One of multiple regulatory mechanism that coordinate the temporal sequence of events in the cell cycle.

chemical bond   Any form of attraction between atoms that holds them together.

chemical reaction   The process by which molecules are transformed into different molecules.

chemotrophs   Organisms that derive their energy directly from organic molecules such as glucose.

chiasmata   Crosslike structures within bivalents constituting physical manifestations of crossing over.

chlorophyll   The major photosynthetic pigment contained in the thylakoid membrane; it plays a key role in the chloroplast's ability to capture energy from sunlight. Chlorophyll appears green because it is poor at absorbing green wavelengths.

chloroplast genome   In plant eykaryotic cells, the genome of the chloroplast.

chloroplasts   Organelles that convert energy of sunlight into chemical energy by synthesizing simple sugars.

cholesterol   An amphipathic lipid that is a major component of animal cell membranes.

chromatin   A complex of DNA, RNA, and proteins that gives chromosomes their structure; chromatin fibers are either 30 nm in diameter or, in a relaxed state, 10 nm.

chromatin remodeling   The process in which the nucleosomes are repositioned to expose different stretches of DNA to the nuclear environment.

chromosome   In eukaryotes, the physical structure in which DNA in the nucleus is packaged; used more loosely to refer to the DNA in bacterial cells or archaeons.

chromosome condensation   The progressive coiling of the chromatin fiber, an active, energy-consuming process requiring the participation of several types of proteins.

cilia   Organelles that propel the movement of cells or of substances within cells; shorter than flagella.

cis-regulatory elements   Short DNA sequences adjacent to the gene, usually at the 5′ end, that interact with transcription factors.

cisternae   The series of flattened membrane sacs that make up the Golgi apparatus.

citric acid cycle   The third stage of cellular respiration, in which acetyl-CoA is broken down and more carbon dioxide is released.

clone   An individual that carries an exact copy of the nuclear genome of another individual.

codon   A group of three adjacent nucleotides that specifies an amino acid in a protein or that terminates polypeptide synthesis.

coenzyme Q   The final electron acceptor from both complexes I and II in the electron transport chain.

cofactor   A substance that associates with an enzyme and plays a key role in its function.

combinatorial control   Regulation of gene transcription by means of multiple transcription factors acting together.

comparative genomics   The analysis of the similarities and differences in protein-coding genes and other types of sequence in the genomes of different species.

competitive inhibitors   Reversible inhibitors that bind to the active site of the enzyme and prevent the binding of the substrate.

complementary   Describes the relationship of purine and pyrimidine bases, in which the base A pairs only with T, and G pairs only with C.

complex carbohydrates   Long, branched chains of monosaccharides.

complex traits   Traits that are influenced by multiple genes as well as by the environment.

concordance   The percentage of cases in which both members of a pair of twins show the trait when it is known that at least one member shows it.

connective tissue   A type of tissue characterized by a few cells and substantial amounts of extracellular matrix; a major component of the dermis.

conserved   Describes sequences that are similar in different organisms.

constitutive   Describes expression of a gene that occurs continuously.

contractile ring   In animal cells, a ring of actin filaments that forms at the equator of the cell perpendicular to the axis of what was the spindle at the beginning of cytokinesis.

contractile vacuoles   Compartments that take up excess water from inside the cell and expel it into the external environment.

copy-number variation (CNV)   Differences among individuals in the number of copies of a region of the genome.

covalent bond   A chemical bond formed by a shared pair of electrons holding two different atoms together.

CpG island   A cluster of CpG sites on a DNA strand where cytosine (C) is adjacent to guanosine (G); the "p" represents the phosphate in the backbone.

crisscross inheritance   A pattern in which an X chromosome present in a male in one generation is transmitted to a female in the next generation, and in the generation after that can be transmitted back to a male.

crossover   The physical breakage, exchange of parts, and reunion between non-sister chromatids.

C-value paradox   The disconnect between genome size and organismal complexity (the C-value is the amount of DNA in a reproductive cell).

cyclic electron transport   An alternative pathway for electrons during the Calvin cycle that increases the production of ATP.

cyclin-dependent kinases (CDKs)   Kinases that are always present within the cell but active only when bound to the appropriate cyclin.

cyclins   Regulatory proteins whose levels rise and fall with each round of the cell cycle.

cytochrome b_6f complex   Part of the photosynthetic electron transport chain, through which electrons pass between photosystem II and photosystem I.

cytochrome c   The enzyme to which electrons are transferred in complex III of the electron transport chain.

cytokinesis   In eukaryotic cells, the division of the cytoplasm into two separate cells.

cytoplasm   The contents of the cell other than the nucleus.

cytosine (C)   A pyrimidine base.

cytoskeleton   In animals, a protein scaffold that helps cells to maintain their shape and serves as a network of tracks for the movement of substances within cells.

cytosol   The region of the cell inside the plasma membrane but outside the organelles; the jelly-like internal environment that surrounds the organelles.

daughter strand   In DNA replication, the strand synthesized from a parental template strand.

deletion   A missing region of a gene or chromosome.

denaturation   The unfolding of proteins by chemical treatment or high temperature; the separation of paired, complementary strands of nucleid acid.

deoxyribonucleic acid (DNA)   A linear polymer of four subunits, the information archive in all organisms.

deoxyribose   The sugar in DNA.

dermis   The layer of skin beneath the epidermis, which supports the epidermis both physically and by supplying it with nutrients. It also provides a cushion surrounding the body.

desmosomes   Buttonlike points of adhesion that hold the plasma membranes of adjacent cells together.

development   The process in which a fertilized egg undergoes multiple rounds of cell division to become an embryo with specialized tissues and organs.

dideoxynucleotides   Nucleotides lacking the 3' hydroxyl group on the sugar ring.

differentiation   The process in which cells become progressively more specialized as a result of gene regulation.

diffusion   The random movement of molecules.

dimerization   The mutual attraction of two similar or dissimilar folded polypetide chains that brings them together to form a single molecule.

diploid   A cell with two complete sets of chromosomes.

DNA ligase   An enzyme that uses the energy in ATP to close a nick in a DNA strand, joining the 3' hydroxyl of one end to the 5' phosphate of the other end.

DNA microarray   A waferlike supporting surface to which are attached millions of different oligonucleotides of known sequence; used in genotyping DNA and measuring levels of gene expression.

DNA polymerase   An enzyme that is a critical component of a large protein complex that carries out DNA replication.

DNA replication   The process of duplicating a DNA molecule, during which the parental strands separate and new partner strands are made.

DNA transposable elements (DNA TEs)   Sequences that replicate and can move from one location to another in the genome.

DNA typing   The analysis of a small quantity of DNA to uniquely identify an individual.

dominant   The trait that appears in the heterozygous offspring of a cross between homozygous genotypes.

donor   In recombinant DNA technology, the source of the DNA fragment that is inserted into a cell of another organism.

dosage   The number of copies of each gene in a chromosome.

dosage compensation   The differential regulation of X-chromosomal genes in females and in males.

double bond   A covalent bond in which covalently joined atoms share two pairs of electrons.

double helix   The structure formed by two strands of complementary nucleotides that coil around each other.

Down syndrome   A condition resulting from the presence of an extra copy of chromosome 21; also known as trisomy 21.

downstream genes   Genes that function later than another in development.

duplex DNA   Double-stranded DNA.

duplication   A region of a chromosome that is present twice instead of once.

duplication and divergence   The process of creating new genes by duplication followed by progressive change in sequence through evolutionary time.

dynamic instability   Cycles of shrinkage and growth in microtubules.

dynein   A motor protein that carries cargo away from the plasma membrane toward the minus ends of microtubules.

ecology   The study of how organisms interact with one another and with their physical environment in nature.

ectoderm   The germ layer that differentiates into epithelial cells, pigment cells in the skin, and nerve cells in the brain.

electrochemical gradient   A gradient that combines the charge gradient and the chemical gradient of protons and other ions.

electron acceptor   A molecule that gains electrons.

electron carriers   Molecules that store and transfer energy in the form of "high-energy" or "excited" electrons.

electron donor   A molecule that loses electrons.

electron transport chain   The transfer of electrons along a series of membrane-associated proteins to a final electron acceptor, releasing the energy of the electrons to produce ATP.

electronegativity   The ability of atoms to attract electrons.

electrons   Negatively charged particles that move around the atomic nucleus.

elements   Pure substances, such as oxygen, copper, gold, and sodium, that cannot be further broken down by the methods of chemistry.

elongation   The process in protein translation in which successive amino acids are added one by one to the growing polypeptide chain.

elongation factors   Proteins that break the high-energy bonds of the molecule GTP to provide energy for ribosome movement and elongation of a growing polypeptide chain.

endergonic   Describes reactions with a positive ΔG that are not spontaneous and so require an input of energy.

endocrine signaling   Signaling by molecules that travel through the bloodstream.

endocytosis   The process in which a vesicle buds off from the plasma membrane, bringing material from outside the cell into that vesicle, which can then fuse with other organelles.

endoderm   The germ layer that differentiates into cells of the lining of the digestive tract and lung, liver cells, and pancreas cells.

endomembrane system   A cellular system that includes the nuclear envelope, the endoplasmic reticulum, the Golgi apparatus, lysosomes, the plasma membrane, and the vesicles that move between them.

endoplasmic reticulum (ER)   The organelle involved in the synthesis of proteins and lipids.

energetic coupling   The driving of a non-spontaneous reaction by a spontaneous reaction.

enhancer   A specific DNA sequence necessary for transcription.

enthalpy (H)   The total amount of energy in a system.

entropy (S)   The degree of disorder in a system.

environmental risk factor   A characteristic in a person's surroundings that increases the likelihood of developing a particular disease.

environmental variation   Variation among individuals that is due to differences in the environment.

enzymes   Proteins that function as catalysts to accelerate the rates of chemical reactions; enzymes are critical in determining which chemical reactions take place in a cell.

epidermis   The outer layer of skin, which serves as a water-resistant, protective barrier.

epigenetic   Describes effects on gene expression due to differences in DNA packaging, such as modifications in histones or chromatin structure.

epistasis   Interaction between genes that modifies the phenotypic expression of genotypes.

epithelial tissue   A type of animal tissue, made up of epithelial cells, that covers the outside of the body and lines many internal structures.

equational division   Another name for meiosis II because cells in meiosis II have the same number of chromosomes at the beginning and at the end of the process.

ethanol fermentation   The fermentation pathway in plants and fungi during which pyruvate releases carbon dioxide to form acetaldehyde, and electrons from NADH are transferred to acetaldehyde to produce ethanol and NAD+.

Eukarya   One of the three domains of life consisting of cells with a true nucleus containing chromosomes that divide by mitosis; cells of Eukarya are eukaryotes.

eukaryotes   Cells with a true nucleus containing chromosomes that divide by mitosis.

evolution   Changes in populations of organisms over generations resulting in progressive adaptation to the environment and the origin of new species.

evolutionarily conserved   Little changed through evolution and therefore similar from one organism to the next.

exergonic   Describes reactions with a negative ΔG that release energy and proceed spontaneously.

exit (E) site   One of three binding sites for tRNA on the large subunit of a ribosome.

exocytosis   The process in which a vesicle fuses with the plasma membrane and empties its contents into the extracellular space or delivers proteins to the plasma membrane.

exons   Sequences that are left intact in mRNA after RNA splicing.

experimentation   A disciplined and controlled way of learning about the world and testing hypotheses in an unbiased manner.

expressed   Turned on or activated, as a gene or protein.

extension   A step in the polymerase chain reaction (PCR) for producing new DNA fragments in which the reaction mixture is heated to the optimal temperature for DNA polymerase, and each primer is elongated by means of deoxynucleoside triphophosphates.

extracellular matrix   A meshwork of proteins and polysaccharides outside the cell.

F_1 generation   The first filial, or offspring, generation.

F_2 generation   The second filial generation; the offspring of the F_1 generation.

facilitated diffusion   Diffusion through a membrane protein, bypassing the lipid bilayer.

fatty acids   A long chain of carbons attached to a carboxyl group; three fatty acid chains attached to glycerol form a triacylglycerol, a lipid used for energy storage.

fermentation A process of breaking down pyruvate through a wide variety of metabolic pathways that extract energy from fuel molecules such as glucose.

fertilization The union of gametes to produce a zygote.

first law of thermodynamics The law of conservation of energy: Energy can neither be created nor destroyed—it can only be transformed from one form into another.

first-division nondisjunction Failure of chromosome separation in meiosis I.

5′ cap The modification of the 5′ end of the primary transcript by the addition of a special nucleotide attached in an unusual chemical linkage.

5′ end The end of a nucleic acid strand containing a free 5′ phosphate group.

flagella Organelles that propel the movement of cells or of substances within cells; longer than cilia.

fluid mosaic model A model that proposes that the lipid bilayer is a fluid structure that allows molecules to move laterally within the membrane and is a mosaic of two types of molecules, lipids and proteins.

fluid Describes lipids that are able to move in the plane of the cell membrane.

folding domain A region of a protein that folds in a similar way across a protein family relatively independently of the rest of the protein.

frameshift mutation A mutation in which the insertion or deletion of a single nucleotide causes a one-nucleotide shift in the reading frame of the mRNA, changing all following codons.

fraternal (dizygotic) twins Twins that arise when two separate eggs, produced by double ovulation, are fertilized by two different sperm.

frequency of recombination The proportion of recombinant chromosomes among the total number of chromosomes observed.

G proteins Proteins that bind to the guanine nucleotides GTP and GDP.

G protein-coupled receptor A receptor that couples to G proteins, which bind to the guanine nucleotides GTP and GDP.

G$_0$ phase The gap phase in which cells pause in the cell cycle between M phase and S phase; may last for periods ranging from days to more than a year.

G$_1$ phase The gap phase in which the size and protein content of the cell increase and specific regulatory proteins are made and activated in preparation for S-phase DNA synthesis.

G$_2$ phase The gap phase in which the size and protein content of the cell increase in preparation for M-phase mitosis and cytokinesis.

gain-of-function mutation Any mutation in which a gene is expressed in the wrong place or at the wrong time.

gametes Specialized reproductive cells: eggs in females, sperm in males.

gap junctions Connections in animal cells between the plasma membranes of adjacent cells that permit materials to pass directly from the cytoplasm of one cell to the cytoplasm of another.

gastrula The reorganized, multiplying cells of the inner cell mass in the uterine wall.

gastrulation The process in which the cells of the blastoderm migrate inward, creating germ layers of cells within the embryo.

gel electrophoresis A procedure to determine the size of a DNA fragment, in which DNA samples are inserted into slots or wells in a gel and a current passed through. Fragments move toward the positive pole according to size.

gene The unit of heredity; the stretch of DNA that affects one or more traits in an organism, usually through an encoded protein or noncoding RNA.

gene expression The production of a functional gene product.

gene family A group of genes with related functions, usually resulting from multiple rounds of duplication and divergence.

gene regulation The various ways in which cells control gene expression.

general transcription factors A set of proteins that bind to the promoter of a gene whose combined action is necessary for transcription.

genetic code The correspondence between codons and amino acids, in which 20 amino acids are specified by 64 codons.

genetic information Information carried in DNA, organized in the form of genes.

genetic map A diagram showing the relative positions of genes along a chromosome.

genetic risk factor Any mutation that increases the risk of a given disease in an individual.

genetic test A method of identifying the genotype of an individual.

genetic variation Differences in genotype among individuals in a population.

genetically modified organisms (GMOs) Organisms that have been genetically engineered, such as modified viruses and bacteria, laboratory organisms, agricultural crops, and domestic animals. Also known as transgenic organisms.

genome The genetic material transmitted from a parental cell or organism to its offspring.

genome annotation The process by which researchers identify the various types of sequence present in genomes.

genotype The genetic makeup of a cell or organism; the particular combination of alleles present in an individual.

genotype-by-environment interaction Variation in the effects of the environment on different genotypes, resulting in different phenotypes.

germ cells The reproductive cells that produce sperm or eggs and the cells that give rise to them.

germ layers   Three sheets of cells, the ectoderm, mesoderm, and endoderm, established from the gastrula; these layers differentiate further into specialized cells.

germ-line mutations   Mutations that occur in eggs and sperm or in the cells that give rise to these reproductive cells.

Gibbs free energy (G)   The amount of energy available to do work.

glycerol   A 3-carbon molecule with OH groups attached to each carbon.

glycogen   The form in which glucose is stored in animals.

glycolysis   The breakdown of glucose to pyruvate; the first stage of cellular respiration. (The second of the four stages is the conversion of pyruvate to acetyl-CoA and the release of CO_2.)

glycosidic bonds   Covalent bonds that attach monosaccharides to each other.

Golgi apparatus   The organelle that modifies proteins and lipids produced by the ER and acts as a sorting station as they move to their final destinations.

grana   Interlinked structures that form the thylakoid membrane.

growth factors   Small, soluble molecules, usually the signal in paracrine signaling, which affect cell growth, cell division, and changes in gene expression.

guanine (G)   A purine base.

hairpin (structures)   Stems-and-loops formed in self-complementary, single-stranded nucleic acid molecules, stabilized by base pairing in the stem.

haploid   A cell with one complete set of chromosomes.

haplotype   A haploid genotype, as the particular combination of alleles present in any particular region of a chromosome.

helicase   A protein that unwinds the parental double helix at the replication fork.

hemidesmosome   A type of desmosome in which integrins are the prominent cell adhesion molecules.

hemophilia   A trait characterized by excessive bleeding that results from a recessive mutation in a gene encoding a protein necessary for blood clotting.

heterotrophs   Organisms that obtain their carbon from organic molecules synthesized by other organisms.

heterozygous   Describes an individual who inherits different types of alleles from the parents, or genotypes in which the two alleles for a given gene are different.

hierarchical   Describes gene regulation during development, in which the genes expressed at each stage in the process control the expression of genes that act later.

high-energy phosphate bond   In nucleic acid polymerization, the bond connecting the innermost phosphate to the next. The cleaved bond provides the energy to drive the reaction that creates the phosphodiester bond attaching the incoming nucleotide to the 3′ end of the growing chain.

highly repetitive DNA   A type of noncoding DNA consting of sequences present in many thousands of copies per genome.

histone   A protein found in all eukaryotes that interacts with DNA to form chromatin.

histone code   The pattern of modifications of the histone tails that affects the chromatin structure and gene transcription.

histone tails   Strings of amino acids that protrude from the histone proteins in the nucleosome.

homeobox   A DNA sequence within homeotic genes, which function in development, that specifies the homeodomain.

homeodomain   The DNA-binding domain in homeotic proteins, a sequence of 60 amino acids whose sequences are very similar from one homeotic protein to the next.

homeostasis   The active maintenance of a constant environment.

homeotic gene   A gene that specifies the identity of a body part or segment during embryonic development; also known as a *Hox* gene.

homologous chromosomes   Pairs of chromosomes, matching in size and appearance, that carry the same set of genes; one of each pair was received from the mother, the other from the father.

homozygous   Describes an individual who inherits an allele of the same type from each parent, or a genotype in which both alleles for a given gene are the same.

horizontal gene transfer   The transfer of genetic material between organisms that are not parent and offspring.

hotspots   Sites in the genome that are especially mutable.

housekeeping genes   Genes that are transcribed continually because their products are needed at all times and in all cells.

Hox gene   A gene that species the identity of a body part or segment during embryonic development; also known as a homeotic gene.

hybridization   Interbreeding between two different varieties or species of an organism.

hydrogen bond   A weak bond between a hydrogen atom in one molecule and an electronegative atom in another molecule.

hydrophilic   "Water loving"; describes a class of molecules with which water can undergo hydrogen bonding.

hydrophobic   "Water fearing"; describes a class of molecules poorly able to undergo hydrogen bonding with water.

hydrophobic effect   The exclusion of nonpolar molecules by polar molecules, which drives biological processes such as the formation of cell membranes and the folding of proteins.

hypothesis   A tentative explanation for one or more observations that makes predictions that can be tested by experiments or additional observations.

identical (monozygotic) twins   Twins that arise from a single fertilized egg, which after several rounds of cell division separates into two distinct but genetically identical embryos.

inbred lines   True-breeding, homozygous strains.

incomplete dominance   Describes inheritance in which the phenotype of the heterozygous genotype is intermediate between those of homozygous genotypes.

incomplete penetrance   The phenomenon in which some individuals with a genotype corresponding to a trait do not show the phenotype, either because of environmental effects or because of interactions with other genes.

induced pluripotent cells (iPS cells)   Cells that have been reprogrammed to become pluripotent by activation of certain genes, most of them encoding transcription factors or chromatin proteins.

inducer   A small molecule that elicits gene expression.

inhibitors   Synthesized compounds that decrease the activity of enzymes.

initiation   The stage of translation in which methionine is established as the first amino acid in a new polypeptide chain.

initiation factors   Proteins that bind to mRNA to initiate translation.

inner cell mass   A mass of cells in one region of the inner wall of the blastocyst, from which the body of the embryo develops.

integral membrane proteins   Proteins that are permanently associated with cell membranes and cannot be separated from the membrane experimentally without destroying the membrane itself.

integrins   Transmembrane proteins, present on the surface of virtually every animal cell, that enable cells to adhere to the extracellular matrix.

intermediate filaments   Polymers of proteins, which vary according to cell type, that combine to form strong, cable-like filaments that provide animal cells with mechanical strength.

intermembrane space   The space between the inner and outer mitochondrial membranes.

interphase   The time between two successive M phases.

introns   Sequences that are excised from the primary transcript and degraded during RNA splicing.

inversion   The reversal of the normal order of a block of genes.

ionic bond   The association of two atoms resulting from the attraction of opposite charges.

ions   Electrically charged atoms.

irreversible inhibitors   The class of inhibitors that usually forms covalent bonds with enzymes and irreversibly inactivates them.

isomers   Molecules that have the same chemical formula but different structures.

isotopes   Atoms of the same element that have different numbers of neutrons.

juxtacrine signaling   Signaling by direct physical contact of one cell with another, with no chemical signal that diffuses or circulates through an external medium.

karyotype   A standard arrangement of chromosomes, showing the number and shapes of the chromosomes representative of a species.

ketoses   Monosaccharides with a ketone group.

kinesin   A motor protein, similar in structure to myosin, that transports cargo toward the plus end of microtubules.

kinetic energy   The energy of motion.

kinetochore   The protein complexes on a chromatid where spindle fibers attach.

Klinefelter syndrome   A sex-chromosomal abnormality in which an individual has 47 chromosomes, including two X chromosomes and one Y chromosome.

lactic acid fermentation   The fermentation pathway in animals and bacteria during which electrons from NADH are transferred to pyruvate to produce lactic acid and NAD^+.

lagging strand   A daughter strand that has its 5′ end pointed toward the replication fork, so as the parental double helix unwinds, a new DNA piece is initiated at intervals, and each new piece is elongated at its 3′ end until it reaches the piece in front of it.

lariat   A loop and tail of RNA formed after RNA splicing.

lateral inhibition   Inhibition of a process in cells adjacent to the cell receiving a signal inducing that process.

leading strand   A daughter strand that has its 3′ end pointed toward the replication fork, so as the parental double helix unwinds, this daughter strand can be synthesized as one long, continuous polymer.

ligand   Alternative term for a signaling molecule that binds with a receptor, usually a protein.

ligand-binding site   The specific location on the receptor protein where a signaling molecule binds.

ligand-gated ion channels   Receptors that alter the flow of ions across the plasma membrane when bound by their ligand.

LINEs   Long interspersed nuclear elements of about 1000 base pairs present in multiple copies in a genome owing to transposition.

linked   Describes genes that are sufficiently close together in the same chromosome that they do not assort independently.

lipid rafts   Lipids assembled in defined patches in the cell membrane.

lipids   Organic molecules that make up cell membranes, store energy, and act as signaling molecules.

liposomes   Enclosed bilayer structures spontaneously formed by phospholipids in environments with neutral pH, like water.

loss-of-function mutation   A mutation that inactivates the normal function of a gene.

LTR elements   Transposable elements characterized by long repeated sequences, called long terminal repeats, at their ends, and which transpose by means of an RNA intermediate.

lumen   In eukaryotes, the continuous interior of the endoplasmic reticulum; in plants, a fluid-filled compartment enclosed by the thylakoid membrane.

lysogeny   The alternative to the lytic pathway; in lysogeny the bacterial DNA and bacteriophage DNA recombine, resulting in bacterial DNA that includes the bacteriophage DNA, which is transmitted to offspring cells.

lysosomes   Vesicles derived from the Golgi apparatus that contain enzymes that break down macromolecules such as proteins, nucleic acids, lipids, and complex carbohydrates.

lytic pathway   The usual outcome of bacteriophage infection in normal cells, in which the virus hijacks the cellular machinery to replicate the viral genome.

M phase   The stage of the cell cycle consisting of mitosis and cytokinesis, in which the parent cell divides into two daughter cells.

major groove   The larger of two uneven grooves on the outside of a DNA duplex.

MAP kinase pathway   A series of kinases that are triggered by activated GTP-bound Ras; the final kinase enters the nucleus, where it phosphorylates its target proteins.

map unit   A unit of distance in a genetic map equal to the distance between genes resulting in 1% recombination.

maternal inheritance   A type of inheritance in which the organelles in the offspring cells derive from those in the mother.

maternal-effect genes   Genes that are expressed by the mother that affect the phenotype of the offspring, typically through the composition or organization of the oocyte.

mediator complex   A complex of proteins that interacts with the Pol II complex and allows transcription to begin.

meiosis I   Reductional division, the first stage of meiotic cell division, in which the number of chromosomes is halved.

meiosis II   Equational division, the second stage of meotic cell division, in which the number of chromosomes is unchanged.

meiotic cell division   A form of cell division that includes only one round of DNA replication but two rounds of nuclear division; meiotic cell division makes sexual reproduction possible.

membrane potential   A difference in electrical charge across the plasma membrane.

mesoderm   The germ layer that differentiates into cells that make up the inner layer of skin, muscle cells, and red blood cells.

messenger RNA (mRNA)   The RNA molecule that combines with a ribosome to direct protein synthesis; it carries the genetic "message" from the DNA to the ribosome.

metabolism   The chemical reactions that convert molecules into other molecules and transfer energy in living organisms.

metaphase   The stage of mitosis in which the chromosomes are aligned in the middle of the dividing cell.

metaphase I   The stage of meiosis I in which the meiotic spindle is completed and the bivalents move to lie on an imaginary plane cutting transverely across the spindle.

metaphase II   The stage of meiosis II in which the chromosomes line up so that their centromeres lie on an imaginary plane cutting across the spindle.

micelles   Spherical structures in which lipids with bulky heads and a single hydrophobic tail are packed.

microfilaments   Helical polymers of actin monomers, present in various locations in the cytoplasm, that help make up the cytoskeleton.

microRNA   Small, regulatory RNA molecules that can inhibit translation; also called miRNA.

microtubules   Hollow, tubelike polymers of tubulin dimers that help make up the cytoskeleton.

minor groov   The smaller of two unequal grooves on the outside of a DNA duplex.

mismatch repair   The correction of a mismatched base in a DNA strand by cleaving one of the strand backbones, degrading the sequence with the mismatch, and resynthesizing from the intact DNA strand.

mitochondria   Specialized organelles that harness energy for the cell from chemical compounds like sugars and convert it into ATP.

mitochondrial genome   In eukaryotic cells, the DNA in the mitochondria.

mitochondrial matrix   The space enclosed by the inner membrane of the mitochondria

mitosis   In eukaryotic cells, the division of the nucleus, in which the chromosomes are separated into two nuclei.

mitotic spindle   A structure in the cytosol made up predominantly of microtubules that pull the chromosomes into separate daughter cells.

moderately repetitive DNA   A type of noncoding DNA consisting of repeated sequences present in hundreds of copies per genome.

molecular clock   The relative constancy of rates of evolutionary change in a DNA nucleotide sequence or a protein amino acid sequence.

molecular orbital   A merged orbital traversed by a pair of shared electrons.

molecules   Substances made up of two or more atoms.

monosaccharide   A simple sugar.

morula   The clump of cells resulting from early cell divisions of the fertilized egg.

motor proteins   Small accessory proteins that cause muscle contraction by moving the actin microfilaments inside muscle cells.

multiple alleles   Two or more different alleles of the same gene, occurring in a population of organisms.

multiplication rule   The principle that the probability of two independent events occurring together is the product of their respective probabilities.

multipotent   Describes cells that can form a limited number of types of specialized cell.

mutagens   Agents that increase the probability of mutation.

mutation   Any heritable change in the genetic material, usually a change the nuelcotide sequence of a gene.

myosin   A motor protein found in muscle cells that carries cargo to the plus ends of microfilaments.

natural selection   The process in which, when there is inherited variation in a population of organisms, the inherited variants best suited for growth and reproduction contribute disproportionately to future generations.

negative feedback   Describes the effect in which the final product of a biochemical pathway inhibits the first step.

negative regulation   The process in which a regulatory molecule must bind to the DNA at a site near the gene to prevent transcription.

neutral   Describes mutations that have no effect or negligible effects on the organism, or whose effects are not associated with differences in survival or reproduction.

neutrons   Electrically neutral particles in the atomic nucleus.

nicotinamide adenine dinucleotide phosphate (NADPH)   An important cofactor in many biosynthetic reactions; the reducing agent used in the Calvin cycle.

non-competitve inhibitors   Reversible inhibitors that usually have a structure very different from that of the substrate and bind to the enzyme at a site different from the active site.

nondisjunction   The failure of a pair of chromosomes to separate normally during anaphase of cell division.

nonrecombinants   Progeny in which the alleles are present in the same combination as that present in a parent.

nonsense mutation   A mutation that creates a stop codon, terminating translation.

non-sister chromatids   Chromatids of differerent members of a pair of homologous chromosomes; although they carry the same complement of genes, they are not genetically identical.

nonsynonymous (missense) mutations   Point mutations (nucleotide substitutions) that cause amino acid replacements.

nontemplate strand   The untranscribed partner of the template strand of DNA used in transcription.

norm of reaction   A graphical depiction of the change in phenotype across a range of environments.

normal distribution   A distribution whose plot is a bell-shaped curve.

nuclear envelope   The cell structure, composed of two membranes, inner and outer, that defines the boundary of the nucleus.

nuclear genome   In eukaryotic cells, the DNA in the chromosomes.

nuclear localization signal   The signal sequence for the nucleus that enables proteins to move through pores in the nuclear envelope.

nuclear pores   Protein channels in the nuclear envelope that act as gateways that allow molecules to move into and out of the nucleus and are thus essential for the nucleus to communicate with the rest of the cell.

nuclear transfer   A procedure in which a hollow glass needle is used to insert the nucleus of a cell into the cytoplasm of an egg whose own nucleus has been destroyed or removed.

nucleic acids   Polymers of nucleotides that encode and transmit genetic information.

nucleoid   In prokaryotes, a cell structure with multiple loops formed from supercoils of DNA.

nucleoside   A molecule consisting of a 5-carbon sugar and a base.

nucleosome   A beadlike repeating unit of histone proteins wrapped with DNA making up the 10-nm chromatin fiber.

nucleotide excision repair   The repair of multiple mismatched or damaged bases across a region; a process similar to mismatch repair, but over a much longer piece of DNA, sometimes thousands of nucleotides.

nucleotide substitution   A mutation in which a base pair is replaced by a different base pair; this is the most frequent type of mutation. Also known as a point mutation.

nucleotides   The subunits of nucleic acids, each consisting of a 5-carbon sugar, a nitrogen-containing base, and one or more phosphate groups.

nucleus (of an atom)   The dense central part of an atom containing protons and neutrons.

nucleus (of a cell)   The compartment of the cell that houses the DNA in chromosomes.

observation   The act of viewing the world around us.

Okazaki fragments   The short DNA pieces in the lagging strand.

oligonucleotides   Short (typically 20 to 30 nucleotides), single-stranded molecules of known sequence produced by chemical synthesis; used as primer sequences in the polymerase chain reaction.

oncogene   A cancer-causing gene.

oocyte   The unfertilized egg cell produced by the mother.

open reading frame (ORF)   A stretch of DNA or RNA consisting of codons for amino acids uninterrupted by a stop codon. In genome annotation, this sequence motif identifies the region as potentially protein coding.

operator   The binding site for a repressor protein.

operon   A group of functionally related genes located in tandem along the DNA and transcribed as a single unit from one promoter; the region of DNA consisting of the promoter, the operator, and the coding sequence for the structural genes.

orbital   A region in space where an electron is present most of the time.

organ   Two or more tissues that combine and function together.

organelles   Compartments in eukaryotes that divide the cell contents into smaller spaces specialized for different functions.

organic molecules   Carbon-containing molecules.

origin of replication   Each point on a DNA molecule at which DNA synthesis is initiated.

osmosis   The diffusion of water.

oxidation reactions   Reactions in which a molecule loses electrons and releases energy.

oxidation–reduction reactions   Reactions involving the loss and gain of electrons between reactants. In biological systems, these reactions are often used to store or release chemical energy.

oxidative phosphorylation   The fourth stage of cellular respiration, in which electron carriers generated in stages 1–3 donate their high-energy electrons to an electron transport chain.

oxidizing agent   An electron acceptor.

P$_1$ generation   The parental generation in a series of crosses.

palindromic   Describes sequence identity in the paired strands of a duplex DNA molecule; a symmetry typical of restriction sites.

paracrine signaling   Signaling by a molecule that travels a short distance to the nearest neighboring cell to bind its receptor and deliver its message.

paternal inheritance   A type of inheritance in which the organelles in the offspring cells derive from those in the father.

pedigree   A diagram of family history that summarizes the record of the ancestral relationships among individuals.

peptide bond   A covalent bond that links the carbon atom in the carboxyl group of one amino acid to the nitrogen atom in the amino group of another amino acid.

peptidyl (P) site   One of three binding sites for tRNA on the large subunit of a ribosome.

periodic table of the elements   The arangement of the chemical elements in tabular form, organized by their chemical properties.

peripheral membrane proteins   Proteins that are temporarily associated with the lipid bilayer or with integral membrane proteins through weak noncovalent interactions.

personalized medicine   An approach in which the treatment is matched to the patient, not the disease; examination of an individual's genome sequence, by revealing his or her disease susceptibilities and drug sensitivities, allows treatments to be tailored to that individual.

phenotype   The expression of a physical, behavioral, or biochemical trait; an individual's observable phenotypes include height, weight, eye color, and so forth.

phosphatase   An enzyme that removes a phosphate group from another molecule.

phosphate group   A chemical group consisting of a phosphorus atom bonded to four oxygen atoms.

phosphodiester bond   A bond that forms when a phosphate group in one nucleotide is covalently joined to the sugar unit in another nucleotide. Phosophodiester bonds are relatively stable and form the backbone of a DNA strand.

phospholipids   A type of lipid and a major component of the cell membrane.

photic zone   The surface layer of the ocean through which enough sunlight penetrates to enable photosynthesis.

photorespiration   The process in which ATP is used to drive the reactions that convert a portion of the carbon atoms in 2-phosphoglycolate into 3-phosphoglyceric acid, which can reenter the Calvin cycle.

photosynthesis   The biochemical process in which carbohydrates are built from carbon dioxide and the energy of sunlight; oxygen is released as a waste product.

photosynthetic electron transport chain   A series of redox reactions in which electrons are passed from one compound to another.

photosystem I   The photosystem that energizes electrons with a second input of light energy so they have enough energy to reduce NADP$^+$.

photosystem II   The photosystem that supplies electrons to the beginning of the electron transport chain. When photosystem II loses an electron it can pull electrons from water.

photosystems   Protein–pigment complexes that absorb light energy to drive redox reactions and thereby set the photosynthetic electron transport chain in motion.

phototrophs   Organisms that capture energy from sunlight.

phragmoplast   In dividing plant cells, a structure formed by overlapping microtubules that guide vesicles containing cell wall components to the middle of the cell.

pili   Threadlike, hollow structures through which plasmids are transferred between bacteria.

plasma membrane   The membrane that defines the space of the cell, separating the living material within the cell from the nonliving environment around it.

plasmids   In bacteria, small, usually circular molecules of DNA carrying a small number of genes that can replicate when the bacterial genomic DNA replicates.

plasmodesmata   Connections in plant cells between the plasma membranes of adjacent cells that permit materials to pass directly from the cytoplasm of one cell to the cytoplasm of another.

pleiotropy   The phenomenon in which a single gene has multiple effects on seemingly unrelated traits.

pluripotent   Describes embryonic stem cells (cells of the inner mass), which can give rise to any of the three germ layers and therefore to any cell of the body.

point mutation   A mutation in which a base pair is replaced by a different base pair; this is the most frequent type of mutation. Also known as a nucleotide substitution.

Pol II   The RNA polymerase complex responsible for transcription of protein-coding genes.

polar (molecule)   A molecule that has regions of positive and negative charge.

polar bodies   The smaller cells produced in meiosis II that later disintegrate, leaving one larger functional egg cell.

polar covalent bond   Bonds that do not share electrons equally.

polarity   An asymmetry such that one end of a structure differs from the other.

poly(A) tail   The nucleotides added to the 3' end of the primary transcript by polyadenylation.

polyadenylation   The addition of a long string of consecutive A-bearing ribonucelotideas to the 3' end of the primary transcript.

polycistronic mRNA   In prokaryotes, molecules of mRNA that code for multiple proteins.

polycistronic RNA   A single molecule of messenger RNA that is formed by the transcription of a group of functionally related genes located next to one another along the bacterial DNA.

polymerase chain reaction (PCR)   A selective and highly sensitive method for making copies of a piece of DNA, which allows a targeted region of a DNA molecule to be replicated into as many copies as desired.

polymers   Complex organic molecules made up of repeated simpler units connected by covalent bonds.

polymorphism   Any genetic difference among individuals sufficiently common that it is likely to be present in a group of 50 randomly chosen individuals.

polypeptide   A polymer of amino acids connected by peptide bonds.

polyploidy   The condition of having more than two complete sets of chromosomes in the genome.

polysaccharides   Simple sugars combined to form polymers. Polysaccharides provide long-term energy storage or structural support.

positive regulation   The process in which a regulatory molecule must bind to the DNA at a site near the gene in order for transcription to take place.

posttranslational modification   The modification, after translation, of proteins in ways that regulate their structure and function.

potential energy   Stored energy that is released by a change in an object's structure or position.

prediction   An informed guess about the outcomeof an experiment or observation based on a hypothesis.

primary active transport   Active transport that uses the energy of ATP directly.

primary structure   The sequence of amino acids in a protein.

primary transcript   The initial RNA transcript that comes off the template DNA strand.

primer   A short stretch of RNA at the beginning of each new DNA strand that serves as a starter for DNA synthesis; an oligonucleotide that serves as a starter in the polymerase chain reaction.

principle of independent assortment   The principle that segregation of one set of alleles of a gene pair is independent of the segregation of another set of alleles of a different gene pair.

principle of segregation   The principle by which half the gametes receive one allele of a gene and half receive the other allele.

probability   Among a very large number of observations, the expected proportion of observations that are of a specified type.

probe   A labeled DNA fragment that can be tracked in a procedure such as a Southern blot.

products   The transformed molecules that result from a chemical reaction.

prokaryotes   Unicellular organisms without a nucleus. Often used to refer collectively to archaeons and bacteria.

prometaphase   The mitosis in which the nuclear envelope breaks down and the microtubules of the mitotic spindle attach to chromosomes.

promoters   Regions where RNA polymerase and associated proteins bind to the DNA duplex.

proofreading   The process in which DNA polymerases correct their own errors by excising and replacing a mismatched base.

prophase   The stage of mitosis characterized by the appearance of visible chromosomes.

prophase I   The beginning of meiosis I, marked by the visible manifestation of chromosome condensation.

prophase II   The stage of meiosis II in which the chromosomes in the now-haploid nuclei recondense to their maximum extent.

protein families   Groups of proteins that are structurally and functionally related.

protein sorting   The process by which proteins end up where they need to be in the cell to perform their function.

proteins   The key structural and functional molecules that do the work of the cell, providing structural support and catalyzing chemical reactions. The term "protein" is often used as a synonym for "polypeptide."

protons   Positively charged particles in the atomic nucleus.

proto-oncogenes   Normal cellullar gene counterparts to oncogenes, which are similar to viral oncogenes but can cause cancer only when mutated.

Punnett square   A worksheet in the form of a checkerboard used to predict the consequences of a random union of gametes.

purine   In nucleic acids, the bases adenine and gunanine, which have a double-ring structure.

pyrimidine   In nucleic acids, the bases thymine, cytosine, and uracil, which have a single-ring structure.

quantitative traits   Complex traits in which the phenotype is measured along a continuum with only small intervals between similar individuals.

quaternary structure   The structure that results from the interactions of several polypeptide chains.

R group   A chemical group attached to the central carbon atom of an amino acid, whose structure and composition determine the identity of the amino acid; also known as a "residue" or side chain.

Ras   A cytoplasmic signaling protein, very similar to the α subunit of G proteins.

reactants   The starting molecules in a chemical reaction.

reaction center   Two specially configured chlorophyll molecules where light energy is converted into electron transport.

reactive oxygen species   Highly reactive forms of oxygen produced when NADP$^+$ is in short supply.

reading frame   Following a start codon, a consecutive sequence of codons for amino acids.

receptor kinase   A receptor that is an enzyme that adds a phosphate group to another molecule.

receptor molecule   The molecule on the responding cell that binds to the signaling molecule.

receptors   Membrane proteins that allow the cell to receive signals from the environment.

recessive   The trait that fails to appear in heterozygous genotypes from a cross between the corresponding homozygous genotypes.

reciprocal crosses   Crosses in which the female and male parents are interchanged.

reciprocal translocation   Interchange of parts between nonhomologous chromosomes.

recombinant DNA   The joining of DNA molecules from two (or more) different sources into a single molecule.

recombinants   Progeny with a different combination of alleles from that of either parent, resulting from one or more crossovers in prophase I of meiosis.

reducing agent   An electron donor.

reduction reactions   Reactions in which a molecule acquires electrons and gains energy.

reduction   Gain of electrons by a molecule in a reaction; in the second step of the Calvin cycle, energy and electrons are transferred to the molecules formed from carboxylation.

reductional division   An alternative name for meiosis I since this division reduces the number of chromosomes by half.

redundant   Describes the genetic code, in which many amino acids are specified by more than one codon.

regeneration   The third step of the Calvin cycle, in which the 5-carbon molecule needed for carboxylation is produced.

regenerative medicine   A discipline that aims to use the natural processes of cell growth and development to replace diseased or damaged tissues.

regression toward the mean   With regard to complex traits, the principle that offspring exhibit an average phenotype that is intermediate between that of the parents and that of the population as a whole.

regulatory transcription factors   Proteins that recruit the components of the transcription complex to the gene.

release factor   A protein that causes the bond connecting the polypeptide to the tRNA to break.

renaturation   The base pairing of complementary single-stranded nucleic acids to form a duplex; also known as hybridization, it is the opposite of denaturation.

replication bubble   A region formed by the opening of a DNA duplex at an origin of replication, which has a replication fork at each end.

replication fork   The site where the parental DNA strands separate as the DNA duplex unwinds.

replication   The exact copying of DNA so genetic information can be passed from cell to cell or from an organism to its progeny.

repressor   A protein that, when bound with the RNA polymerase complex, can turn off transcription.

residues   Amino acids that are incorporated into a protein.

responding cell   The cell that receives information from the signaling molecule.

response   A change in cellular behavior, such as activation of enzymes or genes, following a signal.

restriction enzymes   A class of enzyme that recognizes specific, short nucleotide sequences in double-stranded DNA and cleaves DNA at these sites.

restriction fragment length polymorphism (RFLP)   A polymorphism in which the length of the restriction fragments is different in the two alleles.

restriction sites   Recognition sequences in DNA cutting, which are typically four or six base pairs long. Most enzymes cleave double-stranded DNA at or near these sequences.

reversible inhibitors   The class of inhibitors that form weak bonds with enzymes and easily dissociate from them.

ribonucleic acid (RNA)   A molecule closely related to DNA that is synthesized by proteins from a DNA template.

ribose   The sugar in RNA.

ribosomal RNA (rRNA)   Noncoding RNA found in all ribosomes that aid in translation.

ribosomes   Complex structures of RNA and protein, bound to the cytosolic face of the RER in the cytoplasm, on which proteins are synthesized.

ribulose bisphosphate carboxylase oxygenase (rubisco)   The enzyme that catalyzes a carboxylation reaction.

ribulose-1,5-bisphosphate (RuBP)   The 5-carbon sugar to which carbon dioxide is added in carboxylation.

RISC (RNA-induced silencing complex)   A protein complex that is targeted to specific mRNA molecules by base pairing with short regions on the target mRNA, inhibiting translation or degrading the RNA.

RNA editing   The process in which some RNA molecules become a substrate for enzymes that modify particular bases in the RNA, thereby changing its sequence and what it codes for.

RNA polymerase   The enzyme that carries out polymerization of ribonucleoside triphosphates from a DNA template to produce an RNA transcript.

RNA polymerase complex   Aggregate of proteins that synthesize the RNA transcript complementary to the template strand of DNA.

RNA primase   An RNA polymerase that synthesizes a short piece of RNA complementary to the DNA template and does not require a primer.

RNA processing   Chemical modification that converts the primary transcript into finished mRNA, enabling the RNA molecule to be transported to the cytoplasm and recognized by the translational machinery.

RNA splicing   The process of intron removal from the primary transcript.

RNA transcript   The RNA sequence synthesized from a DNA template.

RNA world hypothesis   The belief that RNA, not DNA, was the original information-storage molecule in the earliest forms of life on Earth.

rough endoplasmic reticulum (RER)   The part of the endoplasmic reticulum with attached ribosomes.

S phase   The phase of interphase in which the entire DNA content of the nucleus is replicated.

saccharides   The simplest carbohydrates, also called sugars; saccharides store energy in their bonds.

Sanger sequencing   A procedure in which the terminated daughter strands help in determining the DNA sequence.

saturated   Describes fatty acids that do not contain double bonds; the maximum number of hydrogen atoms is attached to each carbon atom, "saturating" the carbons with hydrogen atoms.

scaffold   A supporting protein structure in a metaphase chromosome.

scientific method   A deliberate, careful, and unbiased way of learning about the natural world.

second law of thermodynamics   The principle that the transformation of energy is associated with an increase in the degree of disorder in the universe.

second messengers   Intermediate cytosolic signaling molecules that transmit signals from a receptor to a target within the cell. (First messengers transmit signals from outside the cell to a receptor.)

secondary active transport   Active transport that uses the energy of an electrochemical gradient to drive the movement of molecules.

secondary structures   Structures formed by interactions between stretches of amino acids in a protein.

second-division nondisjunction   Disjunction in the second meiotic division.

segmentation   The formation of discrete parts or segments in the insect embryo.

segregate   Separate; applies to chromosomes or members of a gene pair moving into different gametes.

selection   The retention or elimination of random mutations in a population of organisms.

selective barrier   Describes the plasma membrane, which lets some molecules in and out freely, lets others in and out only under certain conditions, and prevents other molecules from passing through at all.

semiconservative replication   The mechanism of DNA replication in which each strand of a parental DNA duplex serves as a template for the synthesis of a new daughter strand.

sequence assembly   The process in which short nucleotide sequences of a long DNA molecule are arranged in the correct order to generate the complete sequence.

sequence motif   Any of a number of sequences or sequence arrangements that indicate the likely function of a segment of DNA.

sex chromosomes   The chromosomes associated with sex, in most animals denoted the X and Y chromosomes.

sexual reproduction   The process of producing offspring that receive genetic material from two parents; in eukaryotes, the process occurs through meiosis and fertilization.

shell (of an atom)   An energy level.

shotgun sequencing   DNA sequencing method in which the sequenced fragments do not originate from a particular gene or region but from sites scattered randomly across the molecule.

sickle-cell anemia   A condition in which hemoglobin molecules tend to crystallize when exposed to lower-than-normal levels of oxygen, causing the red blood cells to collapse and block capillary blood vessels.

side chain   A chemical group attached to the central carbon atom of an amino acid, whose structure and composition determine the identity of the amino acid; also known as an R group.

sigma factor   A protein that associates with RNA polymerase that facilitates its binding to specific promoters.

signal sequences   Amino acid sequences that direct proteins to their proper cellular compartments.

signal transduction   The process in which an extracellular molecule acts as a signal to activate a receptor, which transmits information through the cytoplasm.

signaling cell   The source of the signaling molecule.

signaling molecule   The carrier of information transmitted when the signaling molecule binds to a receptor; also referred to as a ligand.

signal-recognition particle (SRP)   An RNA–protein complex binds with part of a polypeptide chain and marks the molecule for incorporation into the endoplasmic reticulum (eukaryotes) or the plasma membrane (prokaryotes).

SINEs   Short interspersed nuclear elements of about 300 base pairs present in multiple copies in a genome owing to transposition.

single-gene traits   Traits determined by Mendelian alleles of a single gene without much influence of the environment.

single-nucleotide polymorphism (SNP)   A site in the genome where a base pair differs among individuals in a population.

single-stranded binding protein   A protein that binds single-stranded nucleic acids.

sister chromatids   The two identical copies of chromosomes produced by DNA replication.

small interfering RNA (siRNA)   A type of small regulatory RNA that becomes part of a complex able to cleave a target RNA.

small nuclear RNA (snRNA)   Noncoding RNA found in eukaryotes and involved in splicing, polyadenylation, and other processes in the nucleus.

small regulatory RNAs   Short RNA molecules that work primarily by blocking transcription or translation.

smooth endoplasmic reticulum (SER)   The portion of the endoplasmic reticulum that lacks ribosomes.

solvent   A liquid capable of dissolving a substance.

somatic cells   Nonreproductive cells, the most common type of cell in body.

somatic mutations   Mutations that occur in somatic cells.

Southern blot   A method for determining the size and number of copies of a DNA sequence of interest by means of a labeled probe.

spindle apparatus   The organelle formed by microtubules that separates replicated chromosomes during eukaryotic cell division.

spliceosome   A complex of RNA and protein that catalyzes RNA splicing.

spontaneous   Occurring in the absence of any assignable cause; most mutations are spontaneous.

starch   The form in which glucose is stored in plants.

stem cells   Undifferentiated cells that can undergo an unlimited number of mitotic divisions and differentiate into any of a large number of specialized cell types.

steroid   A type of lipid.

stroma   The region surrounding the thylakoid, where carbohydrate synthesis takes place.

structural gene   A genes that code for the sequence of amino acids in a polypeptide chain.

substrate (S)   A molecule acted upon by an enzyme.

substrate-level phosphorylation   A way of generating ATP in which a phosphate group is transferred to ADP from an organic molecule, which acts as a phosphate donor or substrate.

sugars   The simplest carbohydrates; also called saccharides.

supercoils   Coils of coils; a circular molecule of DNA can coil upon itself to form a supercoil.

synapsis   The gene-for-gene pairing of homologous chromosomes in prophase I of meiosis.

synonymous (silent) mutation   A mutation in a codon that does not alter the corresponding amino acid in the polypeptide.

TATA box   A DNA sequence present in many promoters in eukaryotes and archaeons that serves as a protein-binding site for a key general transcription factor.

telomerase   An enzyme that synthesizes telomere repeats.

telomere   A repeating sequence at each end of a eukaryotic chromosome.

telophase   The stage of mitosis in which the nuclei of the daughter cells are formed and the chromosomes uncoil to their original state.

telophase I   The stage of meiosis I in which the chromosomes uncoil slightly, a nuclear envelope briefly reappears, and in many species the cytoplasm divides, producing two separate cells.

telophase II   The stage of meiosis II in which the chromosomes uncoil and become diffuse, a nuclear envelope forms around each set of chromosomes, and the cytoplasm divides by cytokinesis.

template   A strand of DNA or RNA whose squence of nucleotides is used to sythesis a compementary strand.

template strand   In DNA replication, the parental strand whose sequence is used to synthesize a complementary daughter strand.

10-nm chromatin fiber   A relaxed 30-nm chromatin fiber, the state of the chromatin fiber in regions of the nucleus where transcription is currently taking place.

termination   In protein translation, the stage in which the addition of amino acids stops and the completed polypeptide chain is released from the ribosome. In cell communication, the stopping of a signal.

terminator   A DNA sequence at which transcription stops and the transcript is released.

tertiary structure   The overall three-dimensional shape of a protein, formed by interactions between secondary structures.

test (of a hypothesis)   An experiment or observation to determine whether a prediction made by the hypothesis holds true.

testcross   Any cross of an unknown genotype with a homozygous recessive genotype.

tetraploid   A cell or organism with four complete sets of chromosomes.

theory   A general explanation of a natural phenomenon supported by a large body of experiments and observations.

30-nm chromatin fiber   A chromosomal conformation created by the folding of the nucleosome fiber of DNA and histones.

3' end   The end of a nucleic acid strand that carries a free 3' hydroxyl.

3-phosphoglycerate (3-PGA)   A 3-carbon molecule; two molecules of 3-PGA are the first stable products of the Calvin cycle.

thylakoid   The internal membrane-bound compartment in the center of chloroplasts, consisting of the highly folded thylakoid membrane, which contains light-collecting pigments and is the site of the photosynthetic electron transport chain and the interior lumen.

thylakoid membrane   A highly folded membrane in the center of the chloroplast that contains light-collecting pigments and that is the site of the photosynthetic electron transport chain.

thymine (T)   A pyrimidine base.

tight junctions   Junctional complexes that establish a seal between cells so that the only way a substance can travel from one side of a sheet of epithelial cells to the other is by moving through the cells by a cellular transport mechanism.

tissue   A collection of cells that work together to perform a specific function.

topoisomerase II   An enzyme that breaks a DNA double helix, rotates the ends, and seals the break.

topoisomerases   Enzymes that regulate supercoiling by cleaving, partially unwinding, and reattaching one of the strands in a DNA duplex.

totipotent   Describes the ability of a fertilized egg to give rise to a complete organism.

trait   A characteristic of an individual.

transcription   The synthesis of RNA from a DNA template.

transcriptional activator protein   A protein that binds to an enhancer to enable transcription to begin.

transcriptional regulation   The mechanisms that collectively regulate whether or not transcription occurs.

transfer RNA (tRNA)   Noncoding RNA that carries individual amino acids for use in translation.

transformation   The conversion of cells from one state to another, as from nonvirulent to virulent. In recombinant DNA technology, the introduction of recombinant DNA into a recipient cell.

transgenic organisms   An alternative term for genetically modified organisms.

transition state   The brief time in a chemical reaction in which chemical bonds in the reactants are broken and new bonds in the product are formed.

translation   Synthesis of a polypeptide chain corresponding to the coding sequence present in a molecule of messanger RNA.

transmembrane proteins   Proteins that span the entire lipid bilayer; most integral membrane proteins are transmembrane proteins.

transmission genetics   The discipline that deals with the manner in which genetic differences among individuals are passed from generation to generation.

transporters   Membrane proteins that move ions or other molecules across the cell membrane.

transposable element   A DNA sequence that can replicate and move from one location to another in a DNA molecule.

transposition   The movement of a transposable element.

tree of life   The full set of evolutionary relationships among all organisms.

triacylglycerol   A lipid that stores energy.

triose phosphate   A 3-carbon carbohydrate molecule; triose phosphates are the true products of the Calvin cycle because they are the molecules exported from the chloroplast.

triploid   A cell or organism with three complete sets of chromosomes.

trisomy 21   A condition resulting from the presence of three, rather than two, copies of chromosome 21; also known as Down syndrome.

true breeding   Describes a trait whose physical appearance in each successive generation is identical to that in the previous one.

tubulin   Dimers (composed of an α tubulin and a β tubulin) that assemble into microfilaments.

tumor suppressors   A family of genes that encode proteins whose normal activities inhibit cell division.

turgor pressure   The pressure exerted by water against an object, which provides structural support for many plants, fungi, and bacteria.

Turner syndrome   A sex-chromosomal abnormality in which an individual has 45 chromosomes, including only one X chromosome.

unbalanced translocation   Tranlocation in which only part of a reciprocal translocation (and one of the nontranslocated chromosomes) is inherited from one of the parents.

unsaturated   Describes fatty acids that contain carbon–carbon double bonds.

uracil (U)   A pyrimidine base in RNA, where it replaces the thymine found in DNA.

vacuole   A cell structure that absorbs water and contributes to turgor pressure.

valence electrons   The electrons farthest from the nucleus, which are at the highest energy level.

van der Waals forces   The binding of temporarily polarized molecules because of the attraction of opposite charges.

variable   The feature of an experiment that is changed by the experimenter from one treatment to the next.

variable expressivity   The phenomenon in which a particular phenotype is expressed with a different degree of severity in different individuals.

variable number tandem repeat (VNTR)   A genetic difference in which the number of short repeated sequences of DNA differs from one chromosome to the next.

vector   In recombinant DNA, a carrier of the donor fragment, usually a plasmid.

vesicles   Small membrane-enclosed sacs that transport substances within the cell.

virus   A small infectious agent that contains a nucleic acid genome packaged inside a protein coat called a capsid.

visible light   The portion of the electromagnetic spectrum apparent to our eyes.

wild type   The most common allele, genotype, or phenotype present in a population; nonmutant.

X **chromosome**   One of the two sex chromosomes; a normal human female has two copies of the X chromosome, and a normal male has one X and one Y chromosome.

xanthophylls   Yellow-orange pigments that slow the formation of reactive oxygen species by reducing excess light energy; these pigments accept absorbed light energy directly from chlorophyll and convert this energy to heat.

X-**inactivation**   The process in mammals in which dosage compensation occurs through the inactivation of one X chromosome in each cell in females.

X-**linked genes**   Genes in the X chromosome.

Y **chromosome**   One of the two sex chromosomes; a normal human male has one X and one Y chromosome.

Y-**linked genes**   Genes that are present in the region of the Y chromosome that shares no homology with the X chromosome.

Z **scheme**   Another name for the photosynthetic electron transport chain, so called because the overall energy trajectory resembles a "Z."

zygote   The fertilized egg cell formed by the fusion of gametes.

PHOTO CREDITS

Chapter 1

p. 1-1: Frans Lanting Photography. **p. 1-2:** *Fig. 1.1* All Canada Photo/Alamy. **p. 1-4:** *Fig. 1.3 (T)* Kirk Johnson, Denver Museum of Nature & Science. *(B, L)* Dr. David Kring/Photo Researchers, Inc., *(B, R)* Image courtesy of V. L. Sharpton/Lunar and Planetary Institute. **p. 1-5:** *Fig. 1.4* Scott Hailstone/iStockphoto. **p. 1-9:** *Fig. 1.10 (a)* Steve Gschmeissner/Photo Researchers, Inc., *(b)* Steve Gschmeissner/Photo Researchers, Inc., *(c)* Arthur Morris/Visuals Unlimited, *(d)* Sven-Olof Lindblad/Photo Researchers, Inc., *(e)* Megapress/Alamy. **p. 1-10:** *Fig. 1.11 (a)* Biophoto Associates/Photo Researchers, Inc., *(b)* Dr. Jonathan Clarke. Wellcome Images, (c) Hemis/Alamy. **p. 1-11:** *Fig. 1.14* Dr. Gopal Murti/Visuals Unlimited. **p. 1-13:** *Fig. 1.15* © Rob Brodman 2011. **p. 1-14:** *Fig. 1.16* John Giustina/Photoshot. **p. 1-15:** *Fig. 1.18* Neerja Hajela, Michigan State University. **p. 1-16:** *Fig. 1.19* Donald Specker/Animals Animals–Earth Scenes. **p. 1-17:** *Fig. 1.20 (a)* Frans Lanting Photography, *(b)* Ken Lucas/Visuals Unlimited. **p. 1-18:** *Fig. 1.21 (a)* Fred Dimmick/iStockphoto, *(b)* Arndt Sven-Erik/age fotostock, *(c)* Nigel Cattlin/Visuals Unlimited. **p. 1-19:** *Fig. 1.22 (a)* Photo Researchers, Inc., *(b)* G. I. Bernard/Photo Researchers. Inc., *(c)* Look and Learn/The Bridgeman Art Library, *(d)* P.W. Sykes/U.S. Fish and Wildlife Service, *(e)* James Warwick/Photo Researchers, Inc.

Chapter 2

p. 2-1: Science Photo Library/Alamy. **p. 2-19:** *Fig. 2.30* Ray L Frost, Professor of Physical Chemistry, Queensland University of Technology. Australia.

Chapter 3

p. 3-1: Comstock/Getty Images.

Chapter 4

p. 4-1: Pasieka/SPL/Getty Images. **p. 4-5:** *Fig. 4.5* Courtesy of William E. Royer, University of Massachusetts Medical School and Vukica Srajer, BioCARS, Center for Advanced Radiation Sources, The University of Chicago.

Chapter 5

p. 5-1: Dr. George Chapman/Visuals Unlimited. **p. 5-2:** *Fig. 5.1 (L)* Science Museum/SSPL/The Image Works, *(R)* Ted Kinsman/Photo Researchers, Inc. **p. 5-7:** *Fig. 5.8* FRAP of cytoplasmic EGFP in living HeLa cells, performed using an UltraVIEW® spinning disk confocal system (PerkinElmer Inc.). HeLa cells were transfected with pEGFP-C1 (Clontech Laboratories, Inc.) using GeneJuice® transfection reagent (Novagen®). A region of interest in the cytoplasm was photobleached using the UltraVIEW® photokinesis unit, and the recovery of fluorescence in this region was observed. (Fluorescence Recovery After Photobleaching (FRAP) using the UltraVIEW PhotoKinesis accessory, PerkinElmer Technical Note). **p. 5-12:** *Fig. 5.15* Biophoto Associates/Photo Researchers, Inc. **p. 5-16:** *Fig. 5.19* Don W. Fawcett/Photo Researchers, Inc. **p. 5-17:** *Fig.5.20 (T)* David M. Phillips/Photo Researchers, *(B)* Dr. Donald Fawcett/Visuals Unlimited, Inc. **p. 5-18:** *Fig. 5.21* Biophoto Associates/Photo Researchers, Inc. **p. 5-19:** *Fig. 5.22* Dr. Donald Fawcett/Visuals Unlimited, Inc. **p. 5-22:** *Fig. 5.27* Dr. Donald Fawcett, K. Porter/Visuals Unlimited, Inc. **p. 5-23:** *Fig. 5.28* Dr. Jeremy Burgess/Photo Researchers, Inc.

Chapter 6

p. 6-1: Purestock/Getty Images. **p. 6-2:** *Fig. 6.1 (T, L-R)* Dr. Tony Brain/Photo Researchers, Inc., Science PR/Getty Images, Copyright 1997 Microbial Diversity, Rolf Schauder, Dr. Martin Oeggerli/Visuals Unlimited, Inc., *(B, L-R)* DNY59/iStockphoto, Science VU/Visuals Unlimited, Inc., EM image by Manfred Rohde, Helmholtz Centre for Infection Research, Braunschweig, Germany, Anna Omelchenko/Dreamstime.com.

Chapter 7

p. 7-1: David Madison/Getty Images.

Chapter 8

p. 8-1: Japan/Getty Images. **p. 8-2:** *Fig. 8.2* Sinclair Stammers/Photo Researchers. **p. 8-3:** *Fig. 8.3 (a)* Photo by Zoe G. Cardon from cover of Plant, Cell, & Environment (Volume 30, Number 10), Wiley-Blackwell Publishers, *(b)* Oliver Grunewald *(c)* Shattil & Rozinski/Naturepl.com **p. 8-5:** *Fig. 8.5* Manfred Kage/Peter Arnold Inc. **p. 8-9:** *Fig. 8.8* Dr. Howard Berg/Visuals Unlimited, Inc.

Chapter 9

p. 9-1: Steve Gschmeissner/Photo Researchers, Inc. **p. 9-12:** *Fig. 9.12 (T, L)* Mark Boulton/Photo Researchers, Inc., *(T, R)* Mark Smith/Photo Researchers, Inc., *(B, L)* Werner Bollmann/Oxford Scientific/Getty Images, *(B, R)* Phillip Colla

Chapter 10

p. 10-1: Dr. Torsten Wittmann/Photo Researchers, Inc. **p. 10-2:** *Fig. 10.1 (a)* Cheryl Power/Photo Researchers, Inc., *(b)* Professors P. Motta & T. Naguro/Photo Researchers, Inc., *(c)* Innerspace Imaging/Photo Researchers, Inc. *(d)* Biophoto Associates/Photo Researchers, Inc., *(e)* Don W. Fawcett/Photo Researchers, Inc. Colorization by: Mary Martin. **p. 10-3:** *Fig. 10.2* Jose Luis Pelaez Inc./Blend Images/Getty Images. **p. 10-4:** *Fig. 10.4 (L-R)* Dennis Kunkel Microscopy, Inc., Eye of Science/Photo Researchers, Inc., Andrew Syred/Photo Researchers, Inc., Dennis Kunkel Microscopy, Inc./Visuals Unlimited, Inc. **p. 10-5:** *Fig. 10.5* Organization of actin, myosin, and intermediate filaments in the brush border of intestinal epithelial cells. Hirokawa, N. et al. JCB 94:425-443, 1982. **p. 10-6:** *Fig. 10.6* Courtesy of R. D. Goldman; *Fig. 10.7* Helen Osler/Northscot/Rex USA. **p. 10-9:** *Fig. 10.12 (T)* Maryann Haldi, Adam Amsterdam, and Nancy Hopkins, *(B)* Courtesy Darren Logan. **p. 10-10:** *Fig. 10.13 (L-R)* Dennis Kunkel Microscopy, Inc., Dennis Kunkel Microsopy, Inc./Visuals Unlimited, Inc., Gopal Murti/Science Photo Library. **p. 10-11:** *Fig. 10.14* Rachel Fink, Mount Holyoke College. **p. 10-12:** *Fig. 10.15 (T)* Borut Furlan/WaterFrame/age fotostock, *(B)* Franco Banfi/WaterFrame/age fotostock. **p. 10-16:** *Fig. 10.18* Biophoto Associates/Photo Researchers, Inc. **p. 10-17:** *Fig. 10.19* Biophoto Associates/Photo Researchers, Inc.; *Fig. 10.20 (T)* Tom Grundy/Alamy. *(M)* Egon Bümsch/age fotostock, *(B)* Eye of Science/Photo Researchers, Inc. **p. 10-18:** *Fig. 10.21* Dr. Alvin Telser/Visuals Unlimited, Inc. **p. 10-19:** *Fig. 10.23* F. Tao, S. Chaudry, B. Tolloczko, J. G. Martin, and S. M. Kelly "Modulation of smooth muscle phenotype in vitro by homologous cell substrate" Am J Physiol Cell Physiol June 1, 2003 284:(6) C1531-C1541; published ahead of print March 5, 2003, doi:10.1152/ajp.; *Fig. 10.24* Courtesy Motoyoshi Nomizu. **p. 10-20:** *Fig. 10.25* Eye of Science/Photo Researchers, Inc.

Chapter 11

p. 11-1: Jennifer C. Waters/Photo Researchers, Inc. **p. 11-4:** *Fig. 11.3* ISM/Phototake. **p. 11-5:** *Fig. 11.5* Conly Rieder and Alexey Khodjakov/Visuals Unlimited, Inc. **p. 11-7:** *Fig. 11.7 (a)* Dr. Paul Andrews, University of Dundee/Photo Researchers, Inc., *(b)* Dr. Robert Calentine/Visuals Unlimited, Inc. **p. 11-15:** *Fig. 11.14* SeaPics.com, Biology Pics/Photo Researchers, Inc. **p. 11-22:** *Fig. 11.21* Jose Luis Pelaez Inc/Blend Images/Getty Images.

Chapter 12

p. 12-1: Dr. Gopal Murti/Photo Researchers, Inc. **p. 12-3:** *Fig. 12.3* Daniel Hartl. **p. 12-13:** *Fig. 12.14 (b)* Guy Tear/Wellcome Images. **p. 12-15:** *Fig. 12.16* Da'dara, A. A., Walter, R. D. Molecular and biochemical characterization of S-adenosylmethionine decarboxylase from the free-living nematode Caenorhabditis elegans. *Biochem J.* 1998 December 15; 336(Pt 3): 545–550. **p. 12-19:** *Fig.12.20 (a)* Adam Hart-Davis/Photo Researchers, Inc., *(b)* Steve Percival/Photo Researchers, Inc., *(c)* RIA Novosti/Photo Researchers, Inc., *(d)* Murdo Macleod/Polaris, *(e)* Barrett & MacKay Photo, *(f)* Steven Morse/University of Missouri/Polaris.

Chapter 13

p. 13-1: SSPL/Getty Images. **p. 13-10:** *Fig. 13.9* M. Ørgaard, N. Jacobsen, and J.S. Heslop-Harrison. Annals of Botany 76 (1995). **p. 13-11:** *Fig. 13.11* Dr. Klaus Boller/Photo Researchers, Inc. **p. 13-13:** *Fig. 13.13* Courtesy Ulrich Laemmli. **p. 13-14:** *Fig. 13.14* Garini, Y., Macville, M., du Manoir, S., Buckwald, R. A., Lavi, M., Katzir, N., Wine, D., Bar-Am, I., Schröck, E., Cabib, D. and Ried, T. (1996), Spectral karyotyping. Bioimaging, 4: 65–72. doi: 10.1002/1361-6374(199606)4:2<65::AID-BIO4>3.0.CO;2-D; *Fig. 13.15* National Institutes of Health. National Human Genome Research Institute.

Chapter 14

p. 14-1: Tetra Images/Getty Images. **p. 14-3:** *Fig. 14.3* Courtesy Atsushi Hoshino, National Institute for Basic Biology, Japan. **p. 14-4:** *Fig. 14.4* Kathleen R. Cho, University of Michigan Medical School. **p. 14-10:** *Fig. 14.11. (a)* B. Runk/S. Schoenberger/Grant Heilman Photography, *(b)* Rob Martienssen, Cold Spring Harbor Laboratory.

Chapter 15

p. 15-1: Tastyart Ltd/Rob White/Getty Images. **p. 15-8:** *Fig. 15.7* Photodisc, Stockbroker xtra/age fotostock. **p. 15-13:** *Fig. 15.14* Rex Features via AP Images, Biophoto Associates/Photo Researchers, Inc. Colorization by: Mary Martin.

Chapter 16

p. 16-1: Koichi Saito/A. collection/Getty Images. **p. 16-3:** *Fig. 16.2 (inset)* Photo by Authenticated News/Getty Images, Juliette Wade/Getty Images. **p. 16-15:** *Fig. 16.18 (inset)* Reprinted by permission from Macmillan Publishers Ltd: Nature Genetics 28, 386–388 (2001), copyright (2012). Image Courtesy Bo Gao. **p. 16-16:** *Fig. 16.19* National Anthropological Archives, Smithsonian Institution (NAA INV 06404400).

Chapter 17

p. 17-1: SSPL/Getty Images. **p. 17-2:** *Fig. 17.1* Science Photo Library/Photo Researchers, Inc. **p. 17-7:** *Fig. 17.7* Dorling Kindersley/Getty Images. **p. 17-16:** *Fig. 17.16* Courtesy of Dr. Kurenai Tanji, Columbia University Medical Center, New York, NY.

Chapter 18

p. 18-1: Ed Honowitz/Getty Images. **p. 18-2:** *Fig. 18.1 (a)* Randy Faris/Corbis, *(b)* Ashley Cooper/Visuals Unlimited, Inc./Getty Images, *(c)* Heidi & Hans-Juergen Koch/Minden Pictures, *(d)* Radius Images/Getty Images. **p. 18-3:** *Fig. 18.2 (a)* Burwell and Burwell Photography/iStockphoto, *(b)* Ocean/Corbis, *(c)* Junophoto/Getty Images, *(d)* Imago/ZUMApress.com; *Fig. 18.3* Bruce Leighty/Getty Images. **p. 18-5:** *Fig. 18.6* Phil Jones/GHSU. **p. 18-8:** *Fig. 18.10 (a)* AP Photo/Macomb Daily, Craig Gaffield, *(b)* Bruce Roberts/Photo Researchers, Inc.

Chapter 19

p. 19-1: Science Photo Library/Photo Researchers, Inc. **p. 19-5:** *Fig. 19.4* Eyal Nahmias/Alamy.

Chapter 20

p. 20-1: Stephen Dalton/Minden Pictures. **p. 20-4:** *Fig. 20.4 (a)* AP Photo/John Chadwick, *(b)* AP Photo/Pat Sullivan. **p. 20-8:** *Fig. 20.9* James Langeland, Steve Paddock and Sean Carroll, HHMI, Univ. Wisconsin–Madison; *Fig. 20.10* James Langeland, Steve Paddock and Sean Carroll, HHMI, Univ. Wisconsin–Madison. **p. 20-9:** *Fig. 20.11* James Langeland, Steve Paddock and Sean Carroll, HHMI, Univ. Wisconsin–Madison; *Fig. 20.12 (a) (L)* F. Rudolf Turner, Ph.D., Indiana University, *(R)* F. Rudolf Turner, Ph.D., Indiana University, *(b) (L)* Thomas Deerinck, NCMIR/Science Photo Library/Photo Researchers, Inc., *(R)* David Scharf/Science Faction/Getty Images. **p. 20-11:** *Fig. 20.16 (a)* Tom Adams/Visuals Unlimited, Inc., *(b)* Norbert Wu/Science Faction, *(c)* Reinhard Dirscherl/age fotostock, *(d)* Andrey Armyagov/iStockphoto, *(e)* Julian Brooks/age fotostock, *(f)* Walter Geiersperger/age fotostock. **p. 20-12:** *Fig. 20.17 (a) (L)* Carolina Biological Supply, Co/Visuals Unlimited, Inc., *(R)* Carolina Biological Supply, Co/Visuals Unlimited, Inc., *(b) (L)* INSADCO Photography/Alamy, *(R)* Jennifer L. Torrance, Photographer, The Jackson Laboratory. **p. 20-13:** *Fig. 20.18 (a)* Cheryl Power/Photo Researchers, Inc., *(b)* Eye of Science/Photo Researchers, Inc., *(c)* W. J. GEHRING Journal of Heredity 2005:96(3):17–184 doi:10.1093/jhered/esi027. Image Courtesy Walter J. Gehring. **p. 20-14:** *Fig. 20.19* Juergen Berger/Max Planck Institute for Developmental Biology, Tuebingen, Germany, *Fig. 20.20 (a-d)* Courtesy Elliot M. Meyerowitz. **p. 20-15:** *Fig. 20.22 (a)* Tim Fitzharris/ Minden Pictures, *(b)* Cesar Chavez Photography/Big Stock, *(c)* Nonn Panitwong, *(d)* VisionsPictures/Minden Pictures. **p. 20-16:** *Fig. 20.24* © Paul Sternberg. **p. 20-18:** *Fig. 20.26* LWA/Larry Williams/Getty Images, Michael Poehlman/Getty Images. **p. 20-19:** *Fig. 20.26 (L-R)* Digital Vision/Getty Images, Fabrice Lerouge/age fotostock, Piotr Marcinsk/Dreamstime.com.

INDEX

Note: **Bold face** indicates a definition, *italics* indicate a figure, and *t* indicates a table.

A

A (aminoacyl) sites, **4-9**, *4-9*, 4-13
ABC model, **20-14**–20-15, *20-15*
Abortions, spontaneous, 15-13, *15-15*, 15-15–15-16, 19-4
Absolute temperature (*T*), **6-7**
Accessory pigments, **8-9**
Acetyl-CoA
   in the citric acid cycle, 7-9, *7-9*
   synthesis of, 7-7–7-8, *7-8*
Acidic amino acids, 4-2, *4-3*
Acidic solutions, **2-7**
Actin, **10-4**
   and mitosis, 11-7, *11-7*
   and muscle contraction, *10-8*
   polymerization of, and cell movement, 10-10–10-11, *10-11*
Activation energy (*E*$_A$), **6-10**, *6-10*
Activation [of receptors], **9-2**, *9-2*
Activators, 6-13–6-14, **19-11**, *19-11*
Active sites, **6-11**, *6-11*
Active transport, **5-10**
   primary, 5-9–5-10, *5-10*
   secondary, 5-10–5-11, *5-11*
Addition rule, **16-9**–16-10, *16-10*
Adenine (A), **2-12**, *2-12*, **3-5**, *3-5*
   pairing of, *3-7*
Adenosine triphosphate (ATP), **1-12**, **6-1**, **7-1**
   and ATP synthase, 7-12, *7-12*–*7-13*
   and Calvin cycle, 8-7
   as energy currency, 6-4–6-5
   hydrolysis of, 6-8, *6-8*–*6-9*, *6-9*
   and regulation of cellular respiration, 7-19, *7-19*–*7-20*
   structure of, *6-5*
   synthesis of, in cellular respiration, 7-4–7-5, *7-5*, 7-7*t*
   synthesis of, in citric acid cycle, 7-8–7-10, *7-9*
   synthesis of, in organelles, 5-22–5-23
   synthesis of, in photosynthesis, *8-13*
Adherens junctions, 10-12–**10-13**, *10-14*, 10-15*t*
Adipose tissue, 7-18
Adrenaline, and cell signaling, 9-9, 9-9–9-11, *9-10*, *9-11*
Aging, and telomeres, 12-9
Agriculture. *See also* Animal husbandry

and complex traits, 18-2, *18-2*, *18-3*
   and evolution, 1-18
   and genetically modified organisms, 12-19–12-20–*12-19*
   and inheritance, 16-1
   and polyploidy, 13-9–13-10, *13-10*
Albinism, 16-16, *16-16*
Albumin, expression of, 10-20, *10-20*
Aldoses, **2-14**, *2-14*
Algae
   and Calvin cycle, 8-7–8-8
   as cellular organisms, 1-9
   and chlorophyll, 8-11
Alleles, **15-2**, *15-2*, **16-5**
   multiple, 16-16–16-17
   segregation of, 16-8, *16-8*
Allosteric effects, **19-11**–19-12
Allosteric enzymes, **6-14**–6-15
   in cellular respiration, 7-20
α carbons, **2-11**, *2-11*, **4-2**, *4-2*
α helices, **4-5**–4-6, *4-6*
Alternative RNA splicing, **3-17**, *3-17*, **19-6**–19-7, *19-7*
Alvarez, Walter, 1-5
Alzheimer's, 16-17, 19-10
Amide groups, 4-3
Amino acids, **2-11**, *2-11*
   composition of, 4-2, *4-3*
   experimental generation of, 2-18
   structure of, 4-2, *4-2*
Amino ends, **4-4**, *4-4*
Amino groups, **2-11**, *2-11*, **4-2**, *4-2*
Aminoacyl tRNA synthetases, **4-10**, *4-10*
Ammonia, as alternative medium for life, 2-8
Amoebas, movement of, 10-10–10-11, *10-11*
Amphibians
   and cell adhesion, 10-11, *10-12*
   differentiation in, 20-3, *20-3*, *20-4*
Amphipathic molecules, **5-2**, *5-2*
Amplification, **12-11**, *12-12*
Anabolism, **6-3**, *6-3*
   and entropy, 6-6, 6-7–6-8, *6-8*
Anaerobic metabolism, 7-14–7-17, *7-15*
Anaerobic processes, 7-5
Anaphase [mitosis], *11-5*, **11-6**

Anaphase I [meiosis], *11-9*, **11-10**
   and independent assortment of alleles, 16-12–16-13, *16-13*
   and segregation of alleles, 16-8, *16-8*
Anaphase II [meiosis], *11-10*, **11-11**
Ancestry
   and mitochondrial DNA, 17-15–17-16, *17-16*
   and X-linked inheritance, *17-7*, 17-7–17-8, *17-8*
   and Y-linked inheritance, 17-13–17-15, *17-14*
Anchor cells, 20-16, *20-16*
Anchor proteins, **5-5**, *5-5*
Animal husbandry. *See also* Agriculture
   and complex traits, 18-2, *18-2*
   and genetically modified organisms, 12-19, 12-19–12-20
   and inheritance, 16-1
Annealing, PCR, **12-11**, *12-12*
Antenna chlorophylls, 8-10, *8-11*
Anthers, 16-4, *16-4*
Antibiotics. *See* Drugs
Antiparallel strands, **3-7**, *3-7*
Antiporters, 5-10
Ants, leaf-cutter, *1-17*
Apical membranes, 10-14, 10-15
Apolipoprotein B, 19-7, *19-7*
Aquaporins, **5-9**
Aqueous solutions, **2-7**
   acidic *vs.* basic, 2-7
Arabidopsis thaliana [mouse-ear cress], 20-13–20-15, *20-14*, *20-15*
Archaea, **1-12**
   binary fusion in, 11-2, *11-2*
   gene regulation in, 19-13
   genomes of, 13-8–13-9
Aristotle, 2-1, 16-2
Arnold, William, 8-10–8-11
Artificial selection, 1-12–1-13, *1-13*
   and heritability, 18-8
Asexual reproduction, **11-1**
Atomic mass, **2-2**
Atoms, **2-1**–2-4, *2-2*
   components of, 2-1–2-3
   energy levels of, 2-2, 2-3–2-4, *2-4*
   orbitals of, *2-2*, 2-3
   periodic table of, 2-3, *2-3*–*2-4*

ATP. *See* Adenosine triphosphate (ATP)
ATP synthase, 7-12, 7-12–**7-13**
Autocrine signaling, 9-3, **9-4**–9-5
Autosomes, **17-2**
Autotrophs, **6-2**, *6-2*
Avery, Oswald, 3-2–3-3, 3-4

B

Bacillus amyloliquefaciens [bacterium], restriction enzymes from, 12-14
Bacteria, **1-12**. *See also specific bacterium*
   as cellular organisms, 1-9
   chemical composition of, 1-6
   extremophile, C1-2–C1-3
   gene regulation in, 19-10–19-17
   genomes of, 13-8–13-9, 13-11, *13-11*, 13-13
   as prokaryotes, 1-11
   replication of chromosomes of, 12-8, *12-8*
   transcription in, 3-12–3-13
Bacteriophages, **19-15**
   infection by, 19-15–19-17, *19-16*, *19-17*
Bands, 13-14, *13-14*
Basal lamina, **10-3**, *10-3*, 10-14
   as extracellular matrix, 10-18, *10-18*
Base exclusion repairs, **14-14**–14-15, *14-15*
Base stacking, **3-8**, *3-8*
Bases, **2-12**, **3-4**, *3-5*
   complementary, 2-13, *2-13*
Bases pairing, 3-7, *3-7*
   and protein synthesis, 4-10, *4-10*
Basic amino acids, 4-2, *4-3*
Basic solutions, **2-7**
Basolateral membranes, 10-14, 10-15
Behavior, 1-1
Bell-shaped curves. *See* Normal distributions
Benson, Andrew, 8-8
β barrels, 4-15, *4-15*
β-galactosidase, 19-12, 19-12–19-13
β-globin proteins. *See* Hemoglobin
β-oxidation, 7-18, **7-19**
β sheets, **4-5**–4-6, *4-6*